BETROCK'S
Reference Guide to
FLORIDA LANDSCAPE PLANTS

Timothy K. Broschat
Alan W. Meerow
University of Florida - IFAS

BETROCK
Information Systems, Inc.

Library of Congress Catalog Card Number 90-085258
International Standard Book Number 0-9629761-0-5

Every effort has been made to present reliable information in this book, but the authors and the publisher cannot assume responsibility for the validity of material, or for the consequences of their use.

First Printing, 1991
Second Printing, 1992
Third Printing, 1994
Fourth Printing, 1999
Fifth Printing, 2001
Printed in the United States of America

Cover photography by Cornelia Bularca and Derek Burch
Cover Design by Lissie Allen
Book Production and Design by William and April Hutchinson

Table of Contents

Preface

After serving the horticulture industry for more than fifteen years as president of Betrock Information Systems, I understand the importance of providing our subscribers with the latest and finest source of horticultural information.

The data contained in this book was originally gathered for the purpose of displaying scientific details regarding the plants offered for sale and listed in the monthly magazine PlantFinder®. However, it soon became evident that a more comprehensive source of technical information on Florida landscape plants was needed by a much larger population in the horticultural industry.

My intention is to offer a quick reference guide destined for use by students and homeowners as well as horticultural professionals.

Betrock Information Systems gratefully acknowledges the expertise and initiative of the authors, Dr. Timothy Broschat and Dr. Alan Meerow.

I want also to express my deepest appreciation to my office staff and in particular Denis Bedu (M.I.S. Director) and my daughter and son-in-law April and Bill Hutchinson for their total dedication to this project.

Irv Betrock
1991

Introduction

Florida's size and climate allow a diversity of ornamental landscape plants unrivaled anywhere else in the mainland United States. In the panhandle and northern Florida, southern temperate plants are well adapted, whereas subtropical plants generally flourish south of Lake Okeechobee. Strictly tropical plants can usually be grown in the lower Florida Keys. In between north Florida and Lake Okeechobee is a transitional area in which some southern temperate plants and some subtropical species can be grown.

Unfortunately, a truly comprehensive reference source for Florida's extraordinary horticultural flora has been lacking. The purpose of this book is to bring together in one volume most of the essential landscape characteristics of over 1200 ornamental plants that can be successfully grown in the various climatic regions of the state. To conserve space and facilitate rapid access to information, simple key words are used whenever possible to describe each plant's physical appearance, growth and flowering characteristics, environmental requirements and tolerances, propagation methods, and potential environmental or human health problems. Ornamental plants covered in this book include trees, shrubs, vines, some epiphytes, and herbaceous perennials, including aquatics. We have not included annuals, since they are only temporary residents of the landscape and other information sources on these plants are readily available.

The cold hardiness zones discussed in this book follow those of the 1990 USDA Plant Hardiness Zone Map adapted for use in the state of Florida. Of course, during unusually cold weather, some species that are normally well adapted to a particular region may be injured or even killed.

As the population of Florida continues to increase at a rapid rate, the demand for high quality water is sometimes greater than the supply. Thus, there is considerable merit in planting ornamental plants that either require less irrigation or can utilize lower quality brackish water. Similarly, the rapid loss of natural vegetation in some parts of the state has resulted in an increased demand for native plants for landscaping and revegetation of disturbed sites. Plants that are moderately or highly drought tolerant, moderately or highly salt tolerant, or are native to Florida are therefore listed in Appendices in the back of this book to facilitate their selection.

We have decided not to treat several species that are now considered major plant pests by law in several areas of the state. Brazilian pepper (Schinus terebinthifolius), Punk Tree or Cajeput (Melaleuca quinquenervia), Cat's Claw Vine (Macfadyena unguis-cati), and Downy Myrtle (Rhodomyrtus tomentosa) are no longer propagated and offered for sale by reputable nurseries. We have also opted to eliminate all Australian Pines (Casuarina spp.) from the listings, as the use of these plants in the landscape is increasingly controversial and may soon be prohibited by law. While some other species in the book (for example, Bischofia javanica, Ficus benjamina, F. retusa, Acacia auriculiformis) have serious shortcomings as landscape trees, we have decided to include them but have noted their associated problems. We strongly suggest that users of this landscape guide avoid selecting plants with negative environmental attributes. We also encourage wider use of appropriate native species in the Florida landscape.

Although this book is intended to serve as a reference for students and professional horticulturists, scientific terminology has been kept to a minimum to make it understandable to a broader audience. Scientific names generally follow those given in *Hortus Third*, except in cases where the authors are aware of taxonomic revisions subsequent to the publication of *Hortus*. Scientific names are continually being corrected by taxonomists as they obtain new information regarding the identity of various plants, and it should be expected that some of the names used in this book will also be changed as a result of further taxonomic study.

Information in the text was compiled from a wide variety of references, as well as the personal experiences of the authors and their colleagues at the University of Florida. However, plants growing under different environmental conditions often vary considerably in some characteristics and there is no guarantee that a given plant will always conform to the description provided in this book.

Glossary

Scientific Name: The scientific name of the plant.

Common Name: The common name(s) of the plant.

Family: The taxonomic family to which the plant belongs.

Origin: The geographic origin of the plant. Plants of hybrid origin will not have a locality.

Typical Height: The typical maximum height under cultivation in feet for the plant. Actual heights attained will probably vary from that given due to differences in environment.

Growth Rate: The relative growth rate of the plant under cultivation. **Slow** refers to plants that typically grow less than 6 inches per year; **medium** refers to plants that typically grow 6 inches to 3 feet per year; **fast** refers to plants that typically grow more than 3 feet per year.
   Again, actual growth rate will vary depending on the environment in which the plant is growing.

Hardiness Zones: The range of USDA plant hardiness zones (1-11) in which the plant will normally grow. Consult the plant hardiness zone map to determine the zone for your locality.

Salt Tolerance: The plant's relative tolerance of salt, both from saltspray and brackish irrigation water. **Low** refers to plants intolerant of any salt on the foliage or roots; **medium** refers to plants that will tolerate moderate amounts of salt; **high** refers to plants that will tolerate exposed coastal sites.

Drought Tolerance: The plant's relative tolerance of drought conditions in Florida. Recently installed plants will usually be much less tolerant of drought than established plants. **Low** refers to plants that will die if not irrigated regularly; **medium** refers to plants that will require some irrigation under drought conditions; **high** refers to plants that can survive drought conditions without supplemental irrigation.

Soil Requirements: The soil characteristics required by the plant. **Acid** refers to soils with a pH of less than 7.0; **well-drained** refers to soils with good aeration; **wet** or **moist** refer to soils that never completely dry out; **wide** refers to a wide range of soil types that are suitable for plant growth.

Light Requirements: The relative light intensities under which the plant will grow. **Low** refers to deep shade or typical interiorscape conditions (under 500 foot candles); **medium** refers to light shade (500-5000 foot candles); **high** refers to light intensities of 5000 foot candles to full sunlight.

Nutritional Requirements: The relative nutrient requirements of the plant. **Low** refers to plants requiring no supplemental fertilization under most landscape situations; **medium** refers to plants that need light fertilization to grow well; **high** refers to plants that require regular fertilization to survive.

Plant Type: Refers to the general characteristics of the plant. **Deciduous** refers to plants that drop their leaves during the winter; **evergreen** refers to plants that retain their leaves year round; **tree** refers to large woody plants that typically have one or a few trunks and a larger crown; **shrub** refers to plants that are woody, multi-stemmed, and do not usually have exposed trunks; **palm** refers to woody or herbaceous plants in the family Palmae. They may be either single- or multi-stemmed. **Epiphyte** refers to plants that naturally grow on other plants rather than in the soil; **herbaceous** refers to plants that do not have woody stems; **succulent** refers to plants that have thick fleshy leaves and are usually very drought-tolerant; **vine** refers to plants that require some kind of support for their flexible stems; **perennial** refers to plants that live for several to many years; **biennial** refers to plants that usually live for only two years.

Leaf Type: Refers to the leaf form. **Simple** refers to leaves having a single blade; **compound** refers to leaves divided into several distinct leaflets; **pinnately** describes compound leaves having leaflets arising from either side of a central rachis or stem (like a feather); **bipinnately** describes compound leaves that are twice pinnate; **palmately** describes leaves that have leaflets attached at a single point; **linear** refers to leaves that are long and narrow; **needle** refers to leaves that are extremely narrow; **scale-like** refers to leaves that resemble scales on a twig.

Foliage Color: Refers to the color of the leaves. Colors separated by "&" indicate two distinct colors on the same leaf; those separated by "-" are intermediate in color; those separated by ";" occur on different varieties or on the same variety at different times of the year.

Texture: Refers to the relative size of the leaves or leaflets. **Fine** refers to plants having very small leaves or finely divided leaflets; **medium** refers to plants having leaves or leaflets up to four inches long; **coarse** refers to plants having leaves or leaflets up to 1 foot across; **very coarse** refers to plants having leaves or leaflets larger than 1 foot across.

Flower Color: Refers to the color of the flowers, including bracts. Colors separated by "&" indicate two distinct colors on the same flower; those separated by "-" are intermediate in color; those separated by ";" occur on different varieties or on the same variety, but different flowers on the same plant.

Flower Characteristics: Refers to other characteristics of the flowers. **Showy** refers to flowers that are attractive; **insignificant** refers to flowers that are not showy; **fragrant** refers to flowers that have fragrance.

Flowering Season: Refers to the season that the plant usually flowers.

Uses: Refers to typical horticultural uses for the plant. **Specimen plant** refers to use as a single specimen in a garden; **small tree** refers to trees usually under 30 feet tall; **tree** or **shade tree** refers to trees planted for their canopy; **flowering** refers to plants grown primarily for their showy flowers; **shrub** refers to plants with a bushy form; **large shrub** refers to a shrub that often exceeds 10 feet in height; **rock gardens** refers to sites that are open, generally not irrigated, and may be rocky; **beds** refers to mass plantings of a single or multiple species; **groundcover** refers to low-growing plants that rapidly cover the ground; **aquatic** refers to plants which normally grow in standing water; **edible** indicates that parts of the plant are edible; **hedge** refers to shrubs that withstand shearing; **vine** refers to trailing or climbing plants that need some support; **cut flower** indicates that the flowers are long lasting when cut; **flowering pot plant** refers to plants that are grown commercially as flowering potted plants; **foliage plant** indicates a plant that withstands interiorscape conditions; **cut foliage** indicates that the leaves are long lasting when cut; **hanging basket** indicates the plant can be grown in a hanging basket; **annual** indicates the plant is normally grown for only a single season; **seasides** indicates the plant is tolerant of exposed seashore conditions.

Propagation: Refers to common methods of propagation for the plant. These include: **cuttings, seeds, air layering, tissue culture, division,** and **grafting.**

Human Hazards: Refers to possible dangers to people. **Poisonous** indicates that some part of the plant is poisonous if eaten; **irritant** indicates that some parts of the plant may cause skin irritations or respiratory problems if contacted; **spiny** indicates that some part of the plant has sharp spines or thorns.

Environmental Problems: Refers to possible environmental problems associated with the plant; **weak** refers to weak-wooded trees that are subject to toppling or breakage in high winds; **invasive** refers to plants that are weedy or have aggressive root systems; **weedy** refers to plants that readily reproduce themselves in the landscape; **messy** refers to plants which often litter the ground with large leaves, flowers, fruits, or branches.

Major Problems: Refers to insects, diseases, or physiological disorders commonly associated with the plant.

Notes: Miscellaneous information about the plant.

Cultivars: Popular or recommended cultivars for the species are listed along with a brief statement about their characteristics.

Hardiness Zone Map

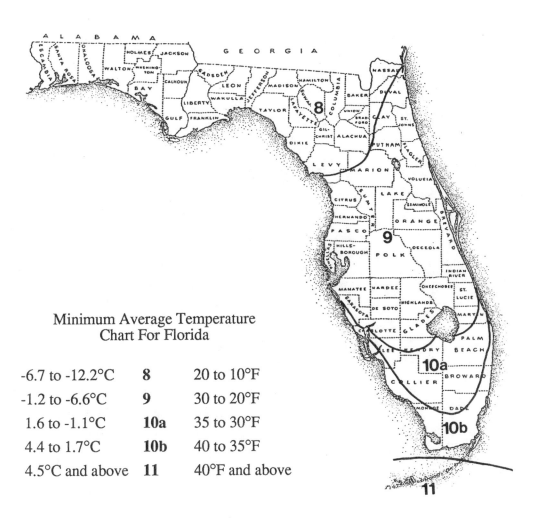

Minimum Average Temperature
Chart For Florida

-6.7 to -12.2°C	**8**	20 to 10°F
-1.2 to -6.6°C	**9**	30 to 20°F
1.6 to -1.1°C	**10a**	35 to 30°F
4.4 to 1.7°C	**10b**	40 to 35°F
4.5°C and above	**11**	40°F and above

Florida Landscape Plant Technical Data

Abelia X grandiflora

Common Name(s) : Glossy Abelia
Origin : Hybrid
Growth Rate : Medium
Salt Tolerance : Low
Soil Requirements : Wide
Plant Type : Evergreen shrub
Foliage Color : Green
Flowering Season : Summer
Flower Color : Pink-white
Propagation : Cuttings
Human Hazards : None
Common Uses : Flowering shrub
Major Problems : None
Additional Notes : A. X grandiflora is a cross between A. chinensis and A. uniflora.
Cultivars
'PROSTRATA' is a prostrate form with white flowers; 'EDWARD GOUCHER' is smaller with pink flowers; 'SHERWOODII' is a dwarf variety with white flowers; 'FRANCIS MASON' has yellow variegated foliage.

Family : Caprifoliaceae **Zone** : 5-9

Typical Height : 6 Ft.
Drought Tolerance : Medium
Nutritional Requirements : Medium
Light Requirements : High
Leaf Type : Simple
Texture : Medium
Flower Characteristics : Showy

Environmental Problems : None

Abutilon megapotamicum

Common Name(s) : Trailing Abutilon
Origin : Southern Brazil
Growth Rate : Fast
Salt Tolerance : Low
Soil Requirements : Wide
Plant Type : Evergreen shrub
Foliage Color : Green
Flowering Season : Year-round
Flower Color : Red-yellow
Propagation : Cuttings
Human Hazards : None
Common Uses : Flowering shrub; foliage plant; hanging baskets
Major Problems : Whiteflies
Additional Notes : A rambling shrub; good for hanging baskets.
Cultivars
'VARIEGATA' has mottled leaves.

Family : Malvaceae **Zone** : 10B-11

Typical Height : 4 Ft.
Drought Tolerance : Low
Nutritional Requirements : Medium
Light Requirements : Medium; high
Leaf Type : Simple
Texture : Medium
Flower Characteristics : Showy

Environmental Problems : None

Abutilon pictum

Common Name(s) : Flowering Maple
Origin : Brazil
Growth Rate : Fast
Salt Tolerance : Low
Soil Requirements : Wide
Plant Type : Evergreen shrub
Foliage Color : Green; variegated
Flowering Season : Spring; summer; fall
Flower Color : Orange-yellow; pink; white; yellow
Propagation : Cuttings
Human Hazards : None
Common Uses : Flowering shrub
Major Problems : Whiteflies
Additional Notes : Has maple-shaped leaves and bell-shaped flowers.
Cultivars
'THOMPSONII' has variegated foliage; 'AURORA' has orange flowers; 'RAINBOW' has pink flowers; 'SUNBEAM' has white flowers; 'POT-O-GOLD' has yellow flowers; 'PLENIFLORUM' has double flowers and green or variegated foliage; 'MOON CHIMES' is compact and has yellow flowers.

Family : Malvaceae **Zone** : 10A-11

Typical Height : 15 Ft.
Drought Tolerance : Low
Nutritional Requirements : Medium
Light Requirements : High
Leaf Type : Simple; palmately lobed
Texture : Medium
Flower Characteristics : Showy

Environmental Problems : None

Acacia auriculiformis

Common Name(s) : Earleaf Acacia
Origin : Australia
Growth Rate : Fast
Salt Tolerance : High
Soil Requirements : Wide
Plant Type : Evergreen tree
Foliage Color : Green
Flowering Season : Spring; summer; fall
Flower Color : Yellow
Propagation : Seed
Human Hazards : None
Common Uses : Shade tree; flowering tree
Major Problems : Thorn bugs
Additional Notes : Brittle, poorly shaped tree with messy flowers, seeds, and pods.

Family : Leguminosae **Zone** : 9-11

Typical Height : 40 Ft.
Drought Tolerance : High
Nutritional Requirements : Low
Light Requirements : High
Leaf Type : Simple
Texture : Medium
Flower Characteristics : Showy

Environmental Problems : Messy; weak

Acacia choriophylla

Common Name(s) : Thornless Acacia
Origin : South Florida and West Indies
Growth Rate : Medium
Salt Tolerance : High
Soil Requirements : Wide
Plant Type : Evergreen tree
Foliage Color : Green
Flowering Season : Summer
Flower Color : Yellow
Propagation : Seeds
Human Hazards : None
Common Uses : Small flowering tree
Major Problems : None
Additional Notes : A spineless acacia with a somewhat straggly growth habit.

Family : Leguminosae   **Zone** : 10B-11

Typical Height : 15 Ft.
Drought Tolerance : High
Nutritional Requirements : Low
Light Requirements : High
Leaf Type : Pinnately compound
Texture : Medium
Flower Characteristics : Showy

Environmental Problems : None

Acacia farnesiana

Common Name(s) : Sweet Acacia
Origin : Subtropical & Tropical America
Growth Rate : Medium
Salt Tolerance : High
Soil Requirements : Wide
Plant Type : Evergreen tree or shrub
Foliage Color : Green
Flowering Season : Spring
Flower Color : Yellow
Propagation : Seed
Human Hazards : Spiny
Common Uses : Flowering shrub; small flowering tree
Major Problems : None
Additional Notes : Small, thorny, bushy tree. Perfume made from flowers.

Family : Leguminosae   **Zone** : 10A-11

Typical Height : 10 Ft.
Drought Tolerance : High
Nutritional Requirements : Low
Light Requirements : High
Leaf Type : Bipinnately compound
Texture : Fine
Flower Characteristics : Showy; fragrant

Environmental Problems : None

Acacia nilotica

Common Name(s) : Gum-arabic Tree; Stuntwood
Origin : Tropical Africa
Growth Rate : Fast
Salt Tolerance : Low
Soil Requirements : Wide
Plant Type : Evergreen tree
Foliage Color : Green
Flowering Season : n/a
Flower Color : Yellow
Propagation : Seed
Human Hazards : Spiny
Common Uses : Tree
Major Problems : None
Additional Notes : A source of gum arabic. Has long spines.

Family : Leguminosae   **Zone** : 10A-11

Typical Height : 60 Ft.
Drought Tolerance : High
Nutritional Requirements : Low
Light Requirements : High
Leaf Type : Bipinnately compound
Texture : Fine
Flower Characteristics : Insignificant

Environmental Problems : None

Acacia pinetorum

Common Name(s) : Pineland Acacia
Origin : South Florida
Growth Rate : Medium
Salt Tolerance : High
Soil Requirements : Wide
Plant Type : Evergreen shrub or tree
Foliage Color : Green
Flowering Season : Summer
Flower Color : Yellow
Propagation : Seeds
Human Hazards : Spiny
Common Uses : Flowering shrub; small flowering tree
Major Problems : None
Additional Notes : Excellent barrier plant.

Family : Leguminosae   **Zone** : 10B-11

Typical Height : 10 Ft.
Drought Tolerance : High
Nutritional Requirements : Low
Light Requirements : High
Leaf Type : Pinnately compound
Texture : Fine
Flower Characteristics : Showy

Environmental Problems : None

Acalypha hispida *(Photograph p. 172)*

Common Name(s) : Chenille Plant
Origin : East Indies
Growth Rate : Fast
Salt Tolerance : Medium
Soil Requirements : Wide
Plant Type : Evergreen shrub
Foliage Color : Green
Flowering Season : Summer; fall; winter; spring
Flower Color : Red; white
Propagation : Cuttings
Human Hazards : None
Common Uses : Foliage plant; flowering shrub
Major Problems : Mealybugs; mites
Additional Notes : Prune to retain shape.
Cultivars
'ALBA' has creamy white flowers.

Family : Euphorbiaceae   **Zone** : 10B-11

Typical Height : 5 Ft.
Drought Tolerance : Low
Nutritional Requirements : Medium
Light Requirements : High
Leaf Type : Simple
Texture : Coarse
Flower Characteristics : Showy

Environmental Problems : None

Acalypha wilkesiana *(Photograph p. 172)*

Common Name(s) : Copperleaf; Jacob's Coat
Origin : Pacific Islands
Growth Rate : Fast
Salt Tolerance : Medium
Soil Requirements : Wide
Plant Type : Evergreen shrub
Foliage Color : Red; green; pink
Flowering Season : Summer; fall
Flower Color : Red
Propagation : Cuttings
Human Hazards : None
Common Uses : Shrub; foliage plant
Major Problems : Mealybugs
Additional Notes : Requires frequent pruning; wilts easily.
Cultivars

Family : Euphorbiaceae   **Zone** : 10B-11

Typical Height : 8 Ft.
Drought Tolerance : Low
Nutritional Requirements : Medium
Light Requirements : High
Leaf Type : Simple
Texture : Coarse
Flower Characteristics : Insignificant

Environmental Problems : None

'GODSEFFIANA' has green leaves with white margins; 'MACAFEEANA' has red and bronze leaves; 'MARGINATA' has red leaf margins; 'MACROPHYLLA' has large heart-shaped bronze colored leaves; 'HOFFMANNII' has ruffled green leaves with white margins.

Acer barbatum

Common Name(s) : Florida Maple
Origin : Southeastern United States
Growth Rate : Fast
Salt Tolerance : Low
Soil Requirements : Wide
Plant Type : Deciduous tree
Foliage Color : Green
Flowering Season : Spring
Flower Color : Green
Propagation : Seeds
Human Hazards : None
Common Uses : Small tree
Major Problems : Aphids; cottony maple scale
Additional Notes : Holds on to dead leaves in winter.

Family : Aceraceae   **Zone** : 7-9

Typical Height : 25 Ft.
Drought Tolerance : Medium
Nutritional Requirements : Medium
Light Requirements : Medium
Leaf Type : Simple; palmate
Texture : Medium
Flower Characteristics : Insignificant

Environmental Problems : None

Acer negundo

Common Name(s) : Box Elder; Ash-leaved Maple
Origin : North America
Growth Rate : Fast
Salt Tolerance : Low
Soil Requirements : Wide
Plant Type : Deciduous tree
Foliage Color : Green
Flowering Season : Spring
Flower Color : Yellow
Propagation : Seeds
Human Hazards : None
Common Uses : Shade tree
Major Problems : Aphids; boxelder bugs; cottony maple scale; borers; gall mites
Additional Notes : Has brittle wood and an irregular growth habit.
Cultivars

Family : Aceraceae   **Zone** : 3-9

Typical Height : 40 Ft.
Drought Tolerance : Medium
Nutritional Requirements : Medium
Light Requirements : Medium; high
Leaf Type : Pinnately compound
Texture : Medium
Flower Characteristics : Insignificant

Environmental Problems : Weak

'AURATUM' has light green leaves with yellow fall color; 'AUREO-MARGINATUM' has whitish-green twigs and yellow-margined leaves; 'VARIEGATUM' has white-margined leaves.

Acer palmatum *(Photograph p. 172)*

Common Name(s) : Japanese Maple
Origin : Korea, China, and Japan
Growth Rate : Slow
Salt Tolerance : Low
Soil Requirements : Wide
Plant Type : Deciduous tree or shrub
Foliage Color : Green; red
Flowering Season : Spring
Flower Color : Red
Propagation : Seeds; cuttings; grafting
Human Hazards : None
Common Uses : Small tree; shrub
Major Problems : Aphids; root rot
Additional Notes : Some green-leaved cultivars have excellent red or yellow fall color.
Cultivars

Family : Aceraceae   Zone : 5-9

Typical Height : 12 Ft.
Drought Tolerance : Low
Nutritional Requirements : Medium
Light Requirements : Medium
Leaf Type : Simple; palmately lobed
Texture : Fine
Flower Characteristics : Inconspicuous

Environmental Problems : None

'AUREUM' has pale golden-yellow foliage; 'ATROPURPUREUM' has dark red leaves throughout the season; 'ACONITIFOLIUM' has deeply dissected foliage; 'BURGUNDY LACE' is a dwarf variety with deeply cut wine red leaves; 'DISSECTUM' has very fine lacy foliage.

Acer rubrum *(Photograph p. 153)*

Common Name(s) : Red Maple
Origin : Eastern North America
Growth Rate : Fast
Salt Tolerance : Low
Soil Requirements : Wide
Plant Type : Deciduous tree
Foliage Color : Green
Flowering Season : Winter; spring
Flower Color : Red
Propagation : Seeds; cuttings; grafting
Human Hazards : None
Common Uses : Shade tree
Major Problems : Aphids; cottony maple scale; gall mites
Additional Notes : Excellent red fall color. Good for wet sites; shallow-rooted
Cultivars

Family : Aceraceae   Zone : 3-10B

Typical Height : 40 Ft.
Drought Tolerance : Low
Nutritional Requirements : Low
Light Requirements : High
Leaf Type : Simple; palmately lobed
Texture : Medium
Flower Characteristics : Showy

Environmental Problems : None

Var. drummondii is a more southerly form of this widespread species; 'AUTUMN FLAME' and 'OCTOBER GLORY' are noted for their outstanding red fall color.

Acer saccharinum

Common Name(s) : Silver Maple
Origin : Eastern United States
Growth Rate : Fast
Salt Tolerance : Low
Soil Requirements : Wide
Plant Type : Deciduous tree
Foliage Color : Green & silver
Flowering Season : Spring
Flower Color : Pink
Propagation : Seeds; cuttings
Human Hazards : None
Common Uses : Shade tree
Major Problems : Anthracnose; cottony maple scale; aphids; borers; gall mites
Additional Notes : Weak-wooded. Yellow fall color.
Cultivars

Family : Aceraceae   Zone : 3-9

Typical Height : 50 Ft.
Drought Tolerance : Low
Nutritional Requirements : Medium
Light Requirements : High
Leaf Type : Simple; palmately lobed
Texture : Medium
Flower Characteristics : Inconspicuous

Environmental Problems : None

'CRISPUM' has dense foliage and deeply-lobed leaves; 'LACINIATUM BEEBE' has deeply cut leaves; 'PYRAMIDALE' has a pyramidal habit; 'SILVER QUEEN' is a male clone and is fruitless; 'WIERI' has pendulous branches and deeply cut leaves.

Achillea spp.

Common Name(s) : Yarrow
Origin : Northern Hemisphere
Growth Rate : Medium
Salt Tolerance : Medium
Soil Requirements : Wide
Plant Type : Herbaceous perennial
Foliage Color : Green; silver-green
Flowering Season : Spring; summer; fall
Flower Color : Red; white; yellow
Propagation : Division; seeds
Human Hazards : None
Common Uses : Specimen plant; cut flowers; rock gardens
Major Problems : None
Additional Notes : Lacy fern-like foliage. Flowers often dried.

Family : Compositae   Zone : 3-9

Typical Height : 3 Ft.
Drought Tolerance : High
Nutritional Requirements : Low
Light Requirements : High
Leaf Type : Bipinnately compound
Texture : Fine
Flower Characteristics : Showy

Environmental Problems : None

Achimenes spp. *(Photograph p. 189)*

Common Name(s) : Achimenes
Origin : Mexico and Central America
Growth Rate : Medium
Salt Tolerance : Low
Soil Requirements : Acid
Plant Type : Herbaceous perennial
Foliage Color : Green; red
Flowering Season : Spring; summer; fall
Flower Color : Red; blue; purple; pink; white
Propagation : Division; seeds
Human Hazards : None
Common Uses : Beds; specimen plant; flowering pot plant
Major Problems : Root rots
Additional Notes : Best in pots or baskets; dry off in winter.
Cultivars
Many cultivars exist.

Family : Gesneriaceae   **Zone** : 10A-11

Typical Height : .8 Ft.
Drought Tolerance : Low
Nutritional Requirements : High
Light Requirements : Medium
Leaf Type : Simple
Texture : Medium
Flower Characteristics : Showy

Environmental Problems : None

Acidanthera bicolor

Common Name(s) : Abyssinian Gladiolus; Peacock Orchid
Origin : Ethiopia
Growth Rate : Medium
Salt Tolerance : Low
Soil Requirements : Wide
Plant Type : Herbaceous perennial
Foliage Color : Green
Flowering Season : Summer
Flower Color : White & brown
Propagation : Division
Human Hazards : None
Common Uses : Beds; borders; cut flowers
Major Problems : Stem rots (on corm)
Additional Notes : Similar to gladiolus; does poorly in south Florida summers.

Family : Iridaceae   **Zone** : 9-11

Typical Height : 1.5 Ft.
Drought Tolerance : Low
Nutritional Requirements : High
Light Requirements : Medium
Leaf Type : Simple; linear
Texture : Medium
Flower Characteristics : Showy; fragrant

Environmental Problems : None

Acoelorrhaphe wrightii *(Photograph p. 202)*

Common Name(s) : Paurotis Palm; Everglades Palm
Origin : Caribbean Region
Growth Rate : Slow
Salt Tolerance : Medium
Soil Requirements : Wide
Plant Type : Palm
Foliage Color : Green
Flowering Season : Spring
Flower Color : White
Propagation : Seeds
Human Hazards : Spiny
Common Uses : Multi-trunked tree
Major Problems : Mn deficiency
Additional Notes : Tolerates wet conditions.

Family : Palmae   **Zone** : 10A-11

Typical Height : 20 Ft.
Drought Tolerance : Medium
Nutritional Requirements : Medium
Light Requirements : Medium; high
Leaf Type : Simple; palmately lobed
Texture : Very coarse
Flower Characteristics : Insignificant

Environmental Problems : None

Acorus calamus

Common Name(s) : Sweet Flag
Origin : Temperate Northern Hemisphere
Growth Rate : Medium
Salt Tolerance : n/a
Soil Requirements : Wide
Plant Type : Herbaceous perennial
Foliage Color : Green
Flowering Season : Summer
Flower Color : Yellow-green
Propagation : Seeds; division
Human Hazards : None
Common Uses : Aquatic
Major Problems : None
Additional Notes : This plant is grown primarily for its foliage in wet sites.
Cultivars
'VARIEGATUS' has yellow-striped foliage; var. <u>angustifolius</u> has very narrow leaves.

Family : Araceae   **Zone** : 2-10B

Typical Height : 6 Ft.
Drought Tolerance : Low
Nutritional Requirements : Low
Light Requirements : High
Leaf Type : Simple; linear
Texture : Medium
Flower Characteristics : Insignificant

Environmental Problems : None

Acorus gramineus

Common Name(s) : Grassy-leaved Sweet Flag
Origin : China, Southeast Asia, and Japan
Growth Rate : Medium
Salt Tolerance : n/a
Soil Requirements : Wide
Plant Type : Herbaceous perennial
Foliage Color : Green
Flowering Season : Summer
Flower Color : Yellow-green
Propagation : Seeds; division
Human Hazards : None
Common Uses : Aquatic
Major Problems : None

Family : Araceae   Zone : 9-10B

Typical Height : 1.5 Ft.
Drought Tolerance : Low
Nutritional Requirements : Low
Light Requirements : High
Leaf Type : Simple; linear
Texture : Medium
Flower Characteristics : Insignificant

Environmental Problems : None

Additional Notes : Smaller and much less hardy than A. calamus . Good for wet sites.
Cultivars
'PUSILLUS' is a dwarf form; 'VARIEGATUS' and 'ALBOVARIEGATUS' have white-striped leaves.

Acrocomia totai

Common Name(s) : Grugru Palm
Origin : Northern Argentina and Paraguay
Growth Rate : Slow
Salt Tolerance : Medium
Soil Requirements : Wide
Plant Type : Palm
Foliage Color : Green
Flowering Season : Summer
Flower Color : White
Propagation : Seeds
Human Hazards : Spiny
Common Uses : Tree
Major Problems : None

Family : Palmae   Zone : 10A-11

Typical Height : 30 Ft.
Drought Tolerance : High
Nutritional Requirements : Medium
Light Requirements : High
Leaf Type : Pinnately compound
Texture : Medium
Flower Characteristics : Insignificant

Environmental Problems : None

Additional Notes : Vicious thorns arm trunk and leafstalks.

Acrostichum daneifolium

Common Name(s) : Leather Fern
Origin : New World Tropics
Growth Rate : Medium
Salt Tolerance : High
Soil Requirements : Wide
Plant Type : Herbaceous perennial
Foliage Color : Green
Flowering Season : n/a
Flower Color : n/a
Propagation : Spores; division
Human Hazards : None
Common Uses : Aquatic; specimen plant; foliage plant
Major Problems : None

Family : Adiantaceae   Zone : 9-11

Typical Height : 8 Ft.
Drought Tolerance : Low
Nutritional Requirements : Low
Light Requirements : Medium
Leaf Type : Pinnately compound
Texture : Coarse
Flower Characteristics : n/a

Environmental Problems : None

Additional Notes : A large fern for wet sites.

Adansonia digitata

Common Name(s) : Baobab
Origin : Africa
Growth Rate : Medium
Salt Tolerance : Medium
Soil Requirements : Wide
Plant Type : Deciduous tree
Foliage Color : Green
Flowering Season : Summer
Flower Color : White
Propagation : Seeds
Human Hazards : None
Common Uses : Shade tree; flowering tree
Major Problems : None

Family : Bombacaceae   Zone : 10B-11

Typical Height : 50 Ft.
Drought Tolerance : High
Nutritional Requirements : Medium
Light Requirements : High
Leaf Type : Palmately compound
Texture : Medium
Flower Characteristics : Showy

Environmental Problems : None

Additional Notes : Large swollen trunk with unusual branching pattern.

Adenium obesum *(Photograph p. 172)*

Common Name(s) : Desert Rose
Origin : South Africa
Growth Rate : Slow
Salt Tolerance : Medium
Soil Requirements : Wide
Plant Type : Succulent shrub
Foliage Color : Green
Flowering Season : Year-round
Flower Color : Pink; red & white; red; pink & white
Propagation : Cuttings; seeds
Human Hazards : Poisonous
Common Uses : Rock gardens; flowering pot plant
Major Problems : Mites
Additional Notes : Will not tolerate wet conditions. Sap is poisonous.
Cultivars
'MULTIFLORUM' is a free-flowering variety with red and white flowers.

Family : Apocynaceae   **Zone** : 10B-11

Typical Height : 4 Ft.
Drought Tolerance : High
Nutritional Requirements : Medium
Light Requirements : High
Leaf Type : Simple
Texture : Medium
Flower Characteristics : Fragrant; showy

Environmental Problems : None

Adiantum spp. *(Photograph p. 189)*

Common Name(s) : Maidenhair Ferns
Origin : New World
Growth Rate : Medium
Salt Tolerance : Low
Soil Requirements : Acid
Plant Type : Herbaceous perennial
Foliage Color : Green
Flowering Season : n/a
Flower Color : n/a
Propagation : Division; spores
Human Hazards : None
Common Uses : Specimen plant; foliage plant; hanging basket
Major Problems : None
Additional Notes : Some native species occur. Grown for the delicate emerald foliage.

Family : Adiantaceae   **Zone** : 9-11

Typical Height : 2 Ft.
Drought Tolerance : Low
Nutritional Requirements : Medium
Light Requirements : Low; medium
Leaf Type : Pinnately compound
Texture : Fine
Flower Characteristics : n/a

Environmental Problems : None

Aechmea bracteata

Common Name(s) : Vase Bromeliad
Origin : Mexico to Colombia
Growth Rate : Slow
Salt Tolerance : Low
Soil Requirements : Wide
Plant Type : Perennial epiphyte
Foliage Color : Green
Flowering Season : Spring; summer
Flower Color : Red & yellow
Propagation : Seeds; division
Human Hazards : Spiny
Common Uses : Foliage plant; groundcover
Major Problems : Scales
Additional Notes : Usually grown as epiphytes. Sometimes grown terrestrially in beds.

Family : Bromeliaceae   **Zone** : 10B-11

Typical Height : 5 Ft.
Drought Tolerance : High
Nutritional Requirements : Low
Light Requirements : Medium
Leaf Type : Simple; linear
Texture : Coarse
Flower Characteristics : Showy

Environmental Problems : None

Aechmea chantinii

Common Name(s) : Amazonian Zebra Plant
Origin : Brazil
Growth Rate : Slow
Salt Tolerance : Low
Soil Requirements : Wide
Plant Type : Perennial epiphyte
Foliage Color : Green & silver
Flowering Season : Spring; summer
Flower Color : Orange
Propagation : Seeds; division
Human Hazards : Spiny
Common Uses : Foliage plant; groundcover
Major Problems : Scales
Additional Notes : Has attractive zebra-striped foliage.

Family : Bromeliaceae   **Zone** : 10B-11

Typical Height : 2 Ft.
Drought Tolerance : High
Nutritional Requirements : Low
Light Requirements : Medium
Leaf Type : Simple; linear
Texture : Coarse
Flower Characteristics : Showy

Environmental Problems : None

Aechmea fasciata *(Photograph p. 189)*

Common Name(s) : Silver Vase
Origin : Brazil
Growth Rate : Slow
Salt Tolerance : Low
Soil Requirements : Wide
Plant Type : Perennial epiphyte
Foliage Color : Silver
Flowering Season : Spring; summer
Flower Color : Pink
Propagation : Seeds; division; tissue culture
Human Hazards : Spiny
Common Uses : Foliage plant; groundcover
Major Problems : Scales
Additional Notes : Has attractive silver foliage and pink bracts.

Family : Bromeliaceae   Zone : 10B-11

Typical Height : 2 Ft.
Drought Tolerance : High
Nutritional Requirements : Low
Light Requirements : Medium
Leaf Type : Simple; linear
Texture : Coarse
Flower Characteristics : Showy

Environmental Problems : None

Aechmea fulgens

Common Name(s) : Coral Berry Vase
Origin : Brazil
Growth Rate : Slow
Salt Tolerance : Low
Soil Requirements : Wide
Plant Type : Perennial epiphyte
Foliage Color : Green & purple
Flowering Season : Spring; summer
Flower Color : Purple
Propagation : Seeds; division
Human Hazards : None
Common Uses : Foliage plant; groundcover
Major Problems : Scales
Additional Notes : Has attractive reddish berries and purple flowers.

Family : Bromeliaceae   Zone : 10B-11

Typical Height : 2 Ft.
Drought Tolerance : High
Nutritional Requirements : Low
Light Requirements : Medium
Leaf Type : Simple; linear
Texture : Coarse
Flower Characteristics : Showy

Environmental Problems : None

Aechmea mexicana

Common Name(s) : Mexican Vase
Origin : Mexico
Growth Rate : Slow
Salt Tolerance : Low
Soil Requirements : Wide
Plant Type : Perennial epiphyte
Foliage Color : Green & pink
Flowering Season : Spring; summer
Flower Color : Pink
Propagation : Seeds; division
Human Hazards : None
Common Uses : Foliage plant; groundcover
Major Problems : Scales
Additional Notes : Has attractive white berries and pinkish flowers.

Family : Bromeliaceae   Zone : 10B-11

Typical Height : 2.5 Ft.
Drought Tolerance : High
Nutritional Requirements : Low
Light Requirements : Medium
Leaf Type : Simple; linear
Texture : Coarse
Flower Characteristics : Showy

Environmental Problems : None

Aesculus pavia *(Photograph p. 172)*

Common Name(s) : Red Buckeye; Florida Buckeye
Origin : Southeastern United States
Growth Rate : Medium
Salt Tolerance : Low
Soil Requirements : Acid
Plant Type : Deciduous shrub or tree
Foliage Color : Green
Flowering Season : Spring
Flower Color : Red
Propagation : Seeds
Human Hazards : Poisonous
Common Uses : Flowering shrub; small flowering tree
Major Problems : None
Additional Notes : Can be trained as a small tree. Flowers at an early age. Fruits poisonous.

Family : Hippocastanaceae   Zone : 6-9

Typical Height : 10 Ft.
Drought Tolerance : Medium
Nutritional Requirements : Medium
Light Requirements : Medium; high
Leaf Type : Palmately compound
Texture : Coarse
Flower Characteristics : Showy

Environmental Problems : None

Agapanthus africanus *(Photograph p. 189)*

Common Name(s) : Lily-of-the-Nile; African Lily
Origin : Southern Africa
Growth Rate : Slow
Salt Tolerance : Low
Soil Requirements : Wide
Plant Type : Herbaceous perennial
Foliage Color : Green
Flowering Season : Spring; summer
Flower Color : Blue; white
Propagation : Division; seeds
Human Hazards : None
Common Uses : Flowering perennial
Major Problems : Botrytis; borers
Additional Notes : Produces fleshy underground rhizomes. Short-lived in south Florida.
Cultivars
'ALBUS' has white flowers; 'PETER PAN' is a dwarf blue flowered variety; 'QUEEN ANNE' is an intermediate-sized variety with blue flowers.

Family : Alliaceae   **Zone** : 9-11

Typical Height : 2.5 Ft.
Drought Tolerance : Medium
Nutritional Requirements : Medium
Light Requirements : Medium
Leaf Type : Simple; linear
Texture : Coarse
Flower Characteristics : Showy

Environmental Problems : None

Agave americana *(Photograph p. 172)*

Common Name(s) : Century Plant
Origin : Western Mexico
Growth Rate : Slow
Salt Tolerance : High
Soil Requirements : Wide
Plant Type : Succulent perennial
Foliage Color : Blue
Flowering Season : Summer; fall
Flower Color : Yellow
Propagation : Division
Human Hazards : Irritant; spiny
Common Uses : Rock gardens
Major Problems : None
Additional Notes : Leaves tipped with dangerous spines. Flowers once after several years.
Cultivars
'MARGINATA' has yellow leaf margins; 'MEDIO-PICTA' has a broad central yellow leaf stripe; 'VARIEGATA' has yellow and green twisted leaves; 'STRIATA' has leaves striped with white or yellow.

Family : Agavaceae   **Zone** : 9-11

Typical Height : 5 Ft.
Drought Tolerance : High
Nutritional Requirements : Low
Light Requirements : High
Leaf Type : Simple
Texture : Coarse
Flower Characteristics : Showy

Environmental Problems : None

Agave angustifolia

Common Name(s) : Caribbean Agave
Origin : Caribbean Basin
Growth Rate : Slow
Salt Tolerance : High
Soil Requirements : Wide
Plant Type : Succulent perennial
Foliage Color : Blue-green; variegated
Flowering Season : Summer; fall
Flower Color : Green
Propagation : Division
Human Hazards : Irritant; spiny
Common Uses : Rock gardens
Major Problems : None
Additional Notes : Leaves tipped with dangerous spines.
Cultivars
'MARGINATA' has white leaf margins.

Family : Agavaceae   **Zone** : 10A-11

Typical Height : 2 Ft.
Drought Tolerance : High
Nutritional Requirements : Low
Light Requirements : High
Leaf Type : Simple; linear
Texture : Coarse
Flower Characteristics : Showy

Environmental Problems : None

Agave atrovirens

Common Name(s) : Maguey Del Cumbre; Pulque Agave
Origin : Mexico
Growth Rate : Slow
Salt Tolerance : High
Soil Requirements : Wide
Plant Type : Succulent perennial
Foliage Color : Green
Flowering Season : Summer; fall
Flower Color : Red
Propagation : Division
Human Hazards : Irritant; spiny
Common Uses : Rock gardens
Major Problems : None
Additional Notes : Leaves tipped with dangerous spines.

Family : Agavaceae   **Zone** : 10A-11

Typical Height : 6 Ft.
Drought Tolerance : High
Nutritional Requirements : Low
Light Requirements : High
Leaf Type : Simple
Texture : Coarse
Flower Characteristics : Showy

Environmental Problems : None

Agave attenuata

Common Name(s) : Spineless Century Plant
Origin : Mexico
Growth Rate : Slow
Salt Tolerance : Medium
Soil Requirements : Wide
Plant Type : Succulent perennial
Foliage Color : Green
Flowering Season : Summer
Flower Color : Yellow
Propagation : Division; seeds
Human Hazards : Irritant
Common Uses : Rock gardens
Major Problems : None

Family : Agavaceae   **Zone** : 10B-11

Typical Height : 4 Ft.
Drought Tolerance : High
Nutritional Requirements : Low
Light Requirements : High
Leaf Type : Simple; linear
Texture : Coarse
Flower Characteristics : Showy

Environmental Problems : None

Additional Notes : Spineless, flowers once and then that stalk dies.

Agave desmettiana

Common Name(s) : Dwarf Century Plant
Origin : Eastern Mexico
Growth Rate : Slow
Salt Tolerance : High
Soil Requirements : Wide
Plant Type : Succulent perennial
Foliage Color : Green
Flowering Season : Summer; fall
Flower Color : Yellow
Propagation : Division
Human Hazards : Irritant
Common Uses : Rock gardens
Major Problems : None

Family : Agavaceae   **Zone** : 10A-11

Typical Height : 2 Ft.
Drought Tolerance : High
Nutritional Requirements : Low
Light Requirements : High
Leaf Type : Simple
Texture : Coarse
Flower Characteristics : Showy

Environmental Problems : None

Additional Notes : A smaller agave generally not so spiny as most.

Agave neglecta

Common Name(s) : Wild Century Plant
Origin : Florida
Growth Rate : Slow
Salt Tolerance : High
Soil Requirements : Wide
Plant Type : Succulent perennial
Foliage Color : Green
Flowering Season : Summer; fall
Flower Color : Yellow
Propagation : Division
Human Hazards : Irritant; spiny
Common Uses : Rock gardens; specimen plant
Major Problems : None

Family : Agavaceae   **Zone** : 9-11

Typical Height : 4 Ft.
Drought Tolerance : High
Nutritional Requirements : Low
Light Requirements : High
Leaf Type : Simple
Texture : Coarse
Flower Characteristics : Showy

Environmental Problems : None

Additional Notes : Flowers once when several years old and then that rosette dies.

Aglaonema commutatum *(Photograph p. 189)*

Common Name(s) : Aglaonema
Origin : Philippines, Celebes Islands
Growth Rate : Medium
Salt Tolerance : Low
Soil Requirements : Wide
Plant Type : Herbaceous perennial
Foliage Color : Green; variegated
Flowering Season : Spring
Flower Color : Green
Propagation : Cuttings; division
Human Hazards : None
Common Uses : Beds; foliage plant
Major Problems : Nematodes; pythium root rots

Family : Araceae   **Zone** : 11

Typical Height : 2 Ft.
Drought Tolerance : Low
Nutritional Requirements : Medium
Light Requirements : Low
Leaf Type : Simple
Texture : Coarse
Flower Characteristics : Insignificant

Environmental Problems : None

Additional Notes : Many cultivars with variable leaf patterns. Cold sensitive.
Cultivars
'MALAY BEAUTY' produces few suckers and has green and white leaves; 'PSEUDOBRACTEATUM' has gray-green and green leaves with green and white stems; 'SILVER KING' has attractive silver and dark green leaves;
'SILVER QUEEN' is similar to 'SILVER KING', but grows more rapidly.
'TRUEBII' is smaller and has narrower leaves than the species.

Aglaonema crispum

Common Name(s) : Painted Drop-tongue
Origin : Philippines
Growth Rate : Medium
Salt Tolerance : Low
Soil Requirements : Wide
Plant Type : Herbaceous perennial
Foliage Color : Green & grayish green
Flowering Season : Spring
Flower Color : Green
Propagation : Cuttings; division
Human Hazards : None
Common Uses : Beds; foliage plant
Major Problems : Nematodes; pythium root rots
Additional Notes : Has attractive grayish green leaves with darker green margins.

Family : Araceae   **Zone** : 11

Typical Height : 3 Ft.
Drought Tolerance : Low
Nutritional Requirements : Medium
Light Requirements : Low
Leaf Type : Simple
Texture : Coarse
Flower Characteristics : Insignificant

Environmental Problems : None

Aglaonema modestum

Common Name(s) : Chinese Evergreen
Origin : South China to N. Thailand
Growth Rate : Medium
Salt Tolerance : Low
Soil Requirements : Wide
Plant Type : Herbaceous perennial
Foliage Color : Green
Flowering Season : Spring
Flower Color : Green
Propagation : Cuttings; division
Human Hazards : None
Common Uses : Beds; foliage plant
Major Problems : Nematodes; pythium root rots
Additional Notes : Very cold sensitive.

Family : Araceae   **Zone** : 11

Typical Height : 1.5 Ft.
Drought Tolerance : Low
Nutritional Requirements : Medium
Light Requirements : Low
Leaf Type : Simple
Texture : Coarse
Flower Characteristics : Insignificant

Environmental Problems : None

Aglaonema simplex

Common Name(s) : Aglaonema
Origin : Philippines, Malaysia
Growth Rate : Medium
Salt Tolerance : Low
Soil Requirements : Wide
Plant Type : Herbaceous perennial
Foliage Color : Green
Flowering Season : Spring
Flower Color : Green
Propagation : Cuttings; division
Human Hazards : None
Common Uses : Beds; foliage plant
Major Problems : Nematodes; pythium root rots
Additional Notes : Similar to A. modestum .
Cultivars
'ANGUSTIFOLIUM' has narrower leaves than the species.

Family : Araceae   **Zone** : 11

Typical Height : 2 Ft.
Drought Tolerance : Low
Nutritional Requirements : Medium
Light Requirements : Low
Leaf Type : Simple
Texture : Coarse
Flower Characteristics : Insignificant

Environmental Problems : None

Ajuga reptans

Common Name(s) : Bugleweed; Carpet Bugleweed
Origin : Europe
Growth Rate : Medium
Salt Tolerance : Low
Soil Requirements : Wide
Plant Type : Herbaceous perennial
Foliage Color : Green;purple; variegated
Flowering Season : Summer; spring
Flower Color : White; pink; blue; purple
Propagation : Division
Human Hazards : None
Common Uses : Groundcover
Major Problems : Nematodes
Additional Notes : An excellent cold hardy groundcover. A. pyramidalis is similar.
Cultivars
'ALBA' has white flowers; 'ATROPURPUREA' has dark bronze foliage and purple flowers; 'RUBRA' has purple-red flowers; 'VARIEGATA'has variegated foliage; 'ROSEA' has rose-pink flowers; 'PURPUREA' has purple foliage and flowers; 'TOTTENHAMII' has green foliage that turns bronze-purple in the fall; 'JUNGLE BRONZE' is a tall bronze-leaved cultivar.

Family : Labiatae   **Zone** : 4-10A

Typical Height : .9 Ft.
Drought Tolerance : Medium
Nutritional Requirements : Low
Light Requirements : Low; medium; high
Leaf Type : Simple
Texture : Medium
Flower Characteristics : Showy

Environmental Problems : None

Albizia julibrissin *(Photograph p. 153)*

Common Name(s) : Mimosa
Origin : Asia
Growth Rate : Fast
Salt Tolerance : Medium
Soil Requirements : Wide
Plant Type : Deciduous tree
Foliage Color : Green
Flowering Season : Spring
Flower Color : Pink
Propagation : Seeds
Human Hazards : None
Common Uses : Flowering tree
Major Problems : Mimosa wilt
Additional Notes : Weedy, short-lived tree.
Cultivars

Family : Leguminosae   Zone : 7-9

Typical Height : 35 Ft.
Drought Tolerance : High
Nutritional Requirements : Medium
Light Requirements : High
Leaf Type : Bipinnately compound
Texture : Fine
Flower Characteristics : Showy

Environmental Problems : Weedy; weak

'RUBRA' has deep pink flowers; 'ALBA' has white flowers; 'CHARLOTTE', 'TRYON', and 'UNION' are supposedly resistant to mimosa wilt.

Albizia lebbeck

Common Name(s) : Mother In Law's Tongue; Lebbek Tree
Origin : Tropical Asia
Growth Rate : Fast
Salt Tolerance : Medium
Soil Requirements : Wide
Plant Type : Deciduous tree
Foliage Color : Green
Flowering Season : Spring
Flower Color : Green-yellow
Propagation : Seeds
Human Hazards : None
Common Uses : Flowering tree
Major Problems : None
Additional Notes : Susceptible to wind damage. A nuisance tree not recommended.

Family : Leguminosae   Zone : 10A-11

Typical Height : 50 Ft.
Drought Tolerance : High
Nutritional Requirements : Low
Light Requirements : High
Leaf Type : Bipinnately compound
Texture : Fine
Flower Characteristics : Showy

Environmental Problems : Weak

Aleurites fordii

Common Name(s) : Tung Oil Tree; China Wood-oil Tree
Origin : Central Asia
Growth Rate : Fast
Salt Tolerance : Medium
Soil Requirements : Wide
Plant Type : Evergreen tree
Foliage Color : Green
Flowering Season : Spring
Flower Color : White
Propagation : Seeds; cuttings
Human Hazards : Poisonous
Common Uses : Flowering tree
Major Problems : None
Additional Notes : Orange-red fall color; fruit is poisonous and a nuisance.

Family : Euphorbiaceae   Zone : 9-10A

Typical Height : 20 Ft.
Drought Tolerance : High
Nutritional Requirements : Medium
Light Requirements : High
Leaf Type : Simple
Texture : Coarse
Flower Characteristics : Showy

Environmental Problems : Messy

Aleurites moluccana

Common Name(s) : Candlenut
Origin : Southeast Asia
Growth Rate : Fast
Salt Tolerance : Medium
Soil Requirements : Wide
Plant Type : Evergreen tree
Foliage Color : Green & silver
Flowering Season : Spring
Flower Color : White
Propagation : Seeds; cuttings
Human Hazards : Poisonous
Common Uses : Flowering tree
Major Problems : None
Additional Notes : Large tree with a silvery cast to leaves. Seeds oily. Can be weedy.

Family : Euphorbiaceae   Zone : 10B-11

Typical Height : 55 Ft.
Drought Tolerance : High
Nutritional Requirements : Low
Light Requirements : High
Leaf Type : Simple
Texture : Coarse
Flower Characteristics : Showy

Environmental Problems : Weedy

Allagoptera arenaria

Family : Palmae   **Zone** : 9B-11

Common Name(s) : Seashore Palm
Origin : Brazil
Growth Rate : Slow
Salt Tolerance : High
Soil Requirements : Wide
Plant Type : Palm
Foliage Color : Silver-green
Flowering Season : Spring; summer; fall
Flower Color : Green-yellow
Propagation : Seeds
Human Hazards : None
Common Uses : Seasides; shrub
Major Problems : None
Additional Notes : An excellent shrubby palm for seashore environments.

Typical Height : 6 Ft.
Drought Tolerance : High
Nutritional Requirements : Low
Light Requirements : High
Leaf Type : Pinnately compound
Texture : Medium
Flower Characteristics : Insignificant

Environmental Problems : None

Allamanda cathartica

Family : Apocynaceae   **Zone** : 10A-11

Common Name(s) : Yellow Allamanda
Origin : Brazil
Growth Rate : Fast
Salt Tolerance : Low
Soil Requirements : Wide
Plant Type : Evergreen shrub or vine
Foliage Color : Green
Flowering Season : Spring; summer; fall
Flower Color : Yellow
Propagation : Cuttings
Human Hazards : Poisonous
Common Uses : Flowering shrub; flowering vine
Major Problems : Caterpillars; mites
Additional Notes : Requires pruning to maintain shrub form. Otherwise a rambling vine.
Cultivars

Typical Height : Not applicable
Drought Tolerance : Medium
Nutritional Requirements : Medium
Light Requirements : High
Leaf Type : Simple
Texture : Medium
Flower Characteristics : Showy; fragrant

Environmental Problems : None

'HENDERSONI' has a brown flower bud and yellow flowers; 'WILLIAMSII' has yellow flowers with a brown throat.

Allamanda neriifolia

Family : Apocynaceae   **Zone** : 10B-11

Common Name(s) : Bush Allamanda
Origin : South America
Growth Rate : Medium
Salt Tolerance : Medium
Soil Requirements : Wide
Plant Type : Evergreen shrub
Foliage Color : Green
Flowering Season : Summer; fall
Flower Color : Yellow
Propagation : Cuttings
Human Hazards : None
Common Uses : Shrub
Major Problems : None
Additional Notes : Other vining species may also be pruned into shrubs.

Typical Height : 5 Ft.
Drought Tolerance : Medium
Nutritional Requirements : Medium
Light Requirements : High
Leaf Type : Simple
Texture : Medium
Flower Characteristics : Showy

Environmental Problems : None

Allamanda violacea (*Photograph p. 210*)

Family : Apocynaceae   **Zone** : 10B-11

Common Name(s) : Purple Allamanda
Origin : Brazil
Growth Rate : Medium
Salt Tolerance : Low
Soil Requirements : Wide
Plant Type : Evergreen vine or shrub
Foliage Color : Green
Flowering Season : Summer; fall
Flower Color : Purple
Propagation : Cuttings
Human Hazards : Poisonous; irritant
Common Uses : Flowering vine; flowering groundcover; flowering shrub
Major Problems : Scales; mites
Additional Notes : Often pruned to maintain a shrub-like form.

Typical Height : Not applicable
Drought Tolerance : Medium
Nutritional Requirements : Medium
Light Requirements : High
Leaf Type : Simple
Texture : Medium
Flower Characteristics : Showy

Environmental Problems : None

Allium spp.

Family : Alliaceae   Zone : 4-9

Common Name(s) : Flowering Onions
Origin : Northern Hemisphere
Growth Rate : Medium
Salt Tolerance : Low
Soil Requirements : Wide
Plant Type : Herbaceous perennial
Foliage Color : Green
Flowering Season : Spring; summer; fall
Flower Color : Red; pink; white
Propagation : Seeds; division
Human Hazards : None
Common Uses : Beds; borders; rock gardens; cut flowers
Major Problems : None
Additional Notes : Not all available species adaptable to Florida; onion odor.

Typical Height : 1.5 Ft.
Drought Tolerance : Medium
Nutritional Requirements : Medium
Light Requirements : High
Leaf Type : Simple; linear
Texture : Fine
Flower Characteristics : Showy

Environmental Problems : None

Alocasia cucullata *(Photograph p. 190)*

Family : Araceae   Zone : 10B-11

Common Name(s) : Chinese Taro
Origin : India, Sri Lanka, and Burma
Growth Rate : Medium
Salt Tolerance : Low
Soil Requirements : Wide
Plant Type : Herbaceous perennial
Foliage Color : Green
Flowering Season : Summer
Flower Color : Green
Propagation : Division
Human Hazards : None
Common Uses : Specimen; edible; cut foliage
Major Problems : None
Additional Notes : Corms of this species are used as food in India.

Typical Height : 2 Ft.
Drought Tolerance : Low
Nutritional Requirements : Medium
Light Requirements : Low; medium
Leaf Type : Simple
Texture : Medium
Flower Characteristics : Insignificant

Environmental Problems : None

Alocasia cuprea

Family : Araceae   Zone : 10B-11

Common Name(s) : Giant Caladium
Origin : Borneo
Growth Rate : Medium
Salt Tolerance : Low
Soil Requirements : Wide
Plant Type : Herbaceous perennial
Foliage Color : Green; purple
Flowering Season : Summer
Flower Color : Green
Propagation : Division
Human Hazards : None
Common Uses : Beds; foliage plant
Major Problems : None
Additional Notes : Both green and bronze-leaved varieties exist.

Typical Height : 2 Ft.
Drought Tolerance : Low
Nutritional Requirements : Medium
Light Requirements : Low; medium
Leaf Type : Simple
Texture : Coarse
Flower Characteristics : Insignificant

Environmental Problems : None

Alocasia macrorrhiza

Family : Araceae   Zone : 10B-11

Common Name(s) : Giant Alocasia; Taro
Origin : India, Sri Lanka, and Southeast Asia
Growth Rate : Fast
Salt Tolerance : Low
Soil Requirements : Wide
Plant Type : Herbaceous perennial
Foliage Color : Green; variegated
Flowering Season : Summer
Flower Color : Green
Propagation : Division
Human Hazards : Irritant
Common Uses : Edible; specimen plant
Major Problems : None
Additional Notes : Corms of this species are used as food in many tropical areas.
Cultivars
'VARIEGATA' has variegated foliage; 'VIOLACEA' has purple foliage.

Typical Height : 12 Ft.
Drought Tolerance : Low
Nutritional Requirements : Medium
Light Requirements : Medium; high
Leaf Type : Simple
Texture : Very coarse
Flower Characteristics : Insignificant

Environmental Problems : None

Alocasia odora

Common Name(s) : Elephant Ear
Origin : India to China
Growth Rate : Fast
Salt Tolerance : Low
Soil Requirements : Wide
Plant Type : Herbaceous perennial
Foliage Color : Green
Flowering Season : Summer
Flower Color : Green
Propagation : Division
Human Hazards : None
Common Uses : Specimen plant
Major Problems : None
Additional Notes : Similar to <u>A. macrorrhiza</u> .

Family : Araceae   **Zone** : 10B-11

Typical Height : 8 Ft.
Drought Tolerance : Low
Nutritional Requirements : Medium
Light Requirements : Medium; high
Leaf Type : Simple
Texture : Very coarse
Flower Characteristics : Insignificant; fragrant

Environmental Problems : None

Alocasia plumbea

Common Name(s) : Elephant Ear
Origin : Java
Growth Rate : Fast
Salt Tolerance : Low
Soil Requirements : Wide
Plant Type : Herbaceous perennial
Foliage Color : Green & purple
Flowering Season : Summer
Flower Color : Purple
Propagation : Division
Human Hazards : None
Common Uses : Specimen plant
Major Problems : None
Additional Notes : Similar to <u>A. macrorrhiza</u> , but with purplish leaf undersides.

Family : Araceae   **Zone** : 10B-11

Typical Height : 8 Ft.
Drought Tolerance : Low
Nutritional Requirements : Medium
Light Requirements : Medium; high
Leaf Type : Simple
Texture : Very coarse
Flower Characteristics : Insignificant

Environmental Problems : None

Alocasia sanderana

Common Name(s) : Sander's Elephant Ear
Origin : Philippine Islands
Growth Rate : Medium
Salt Tolerance : Low
Soil Requirements : Wide
Plant Type : Herbaceous perennial
Foliage Color : Green & purple & silver
Flowering Season : Spring; summer
Flower Color : White
Propagation : Division
Human Hazards : None
Common Uses : Foliage plant; specimen plant
Major Problems : None
Additional Notes : Similar to <u>A. amazonica</u> .

Family : Araceae   **Zone** : 10B-11

Typical Height : 1.5 Ft.
Drought Tolerance : Low
Nutritional Requirements : Medium
Light Requirements : Low; medium
Leaf Type : Simple
Texture : Coarse
Flower Characteristics : Insignificant; fragrant

Environmental Problems : None

Alocasia X amazonica *(Photograph p. 190)*

Common Name(s) : Amazon Elephant's Ear
Origin : Hybrid
Growth Rate : Medium
Salt Tolerance : Low
Soil Requirements : Wide
Plant Type : Herbaceous perennial
Foliage Color : Green & purple & silver
Flowering Season : Summer
Flower Color : Green
Propagation : Division
Human Hazards : None
Common Uses : Beds; foliage plant
Major Problems : None
Additional Notes : Leaves have silvery veins and purple undersides. Dies back in winter.

Family : Araceae   **Zone** : 10B-11

Typical Height : 2 Ft.
Drought Tolerance : Low
Nutritional Requirements : Medium
Light Requirements : Low; medium
Leaf Type : Simple
Texture : Coarse
Flower Characteristics : Insignificant; fragrant

Environmental Problems : None

Aloe arborescens

Common Name(s) : Candelabra Aloe; Candelabra Plant
Origin : South Africa
Growth Rate : Slow
Salt Tolerance : High
Soil Requirements : Wide
Plant Type : Succulent perennial
Foliage Color : Green
Flowering Season : Spring
Flower Color : Red
Propagation : Division
Human Hazards : Spiny
Common Uses : Rock gardens
Major Problems : None
Additional Notes : A taller, shrubby aloe.

Family : Liliaceae   Zone : 10A-11

Typical Height : 10 Ft.
Drought Tolerance : High
Nutritional Requirements : Low
Light Requirements : High; medium
Leaf Type : Simple; linear
Texture : Medium
Flower Characteristics : Showy

Environmental Problems : None

Aloe barbadensis *(Photograph p. 189)*

Common Name(s) : Barbados Aloe; Mediterranean Aloe
Origin : Mediterranean Region
Growth Rate : Slow
Salt Tolerance : High
Soil Requirements : Wide
Plant Type : Succulent perennial
Foliage Color : Green
Flowering Season : Winter
Flower Color : Yellow
Propagation : Division
Human Hazards : None
Common Uses : Rock gardens; specimen plant
Major Problems : None
Additional Notes : The jelly-like pulp of A. barbadensis is used to soothe burns and cuts.

Family : Lilaceae   Zone : 10A-11

Typical Height : 1.5 Ft.
Drought Tolerance : High
Nutritional Requirements : Low
Light Requirements : High; medium
Leaf Type : Simple; linear
Texture : Medium
Flower Characteristics : Showy

Environmental Problems : None

Aloe saponaria

Common Name(s) : Soap Aloe
Origin : South Africa
Growth Rate : Slow
Salt Tolerance : High
Soil Requirements : Wide
Plant Type : Succulent perennial
Foliage Color : Green & white
Flowering Season : Spring
Flower Color : Red
Propagation : Division
Human Hazards : Spiny
Common Uses : Rock gardens
Major Problems : None
Additional Notes : A compact aloe with white-speckled leaves.

Family : Liliaceae   Zone : 10A-11

Typical Height : 1.5 Ft.
Drought Tolerance : High
Nutritional Requirements : Low
Light Requirements : High; medium
Leaf Type : Simple; linear
Texture : Medium
Flower Characteristics : Showy

Environmental Problems : None

Aloe thraskii

Common Name(s) : Thrask Aloe
Origin : South Africa
Growth Rate : Slow
Salt Tolerance : High
Soil Requirements : Wide
Plant Type : Succulent perennial
Foliage Color : Green & red
Flowering Season : Spring
Flower Color : Yellow; orange
Propagation : Division
Human Hazards : Spiny
Common Uses : Rock gardens
Major Problems : None
Additional Notes : Margins of leaves tinged with red.

Family : Liliaceae   Zone : 10A-11

Typical Height : 4 Ft.
Drought Tolerance : High
Nutritional Requirements : Low
Light Requirements : High; medium
Leaf Type : Simple; linear
Texture : Coarse
Flower Characteristics : Showy

Environmental Problems : None

Alpinia mutica

Family : Zingiberaceae   **Zone** : 10A-11

Common Name(s) : Small Shell Ginger; Orchid Ginger
Origin : Malay Peninsula
Growth Rate : Medium
Salt Tolerance : Medium
Soil Requirements : Wide
Plant Type : Herbaceous perennial
Foliage Color : Green
Flowering Season : Summer; fall; winter
Flower Color : White & yellow
Propagation : Division
Human Hazards : None
Common Uses : Specimen plant
Major Problems : None

Typical Height : 6 Ft.
Drought Tolerance : Medium
Nutritional Requirements : Medium
Light Requirements : Medium
Leaf Type : Simple
Texture : Coarse
Flower Characteristics : Showy

Environmental Problems : None

Additional Notes : Has terminal flowers similar in color to that of <u>A.</u> zerumbet .

Alpinia purpurata *(Photograph p. 190)*

Family : Zingiberaceae   **Zone** : 11

Common Name(s) : Red Ginger
Origin : Solomon Islands
Growth Rate : Fast
Salt Tolerance : Low
Soil Requirements : Wide
Plant Type : Herbaceous perennial
Foliage Color : Green
Flowering Season : Year-round
Flower Color : Red; pink
Propagation : Plantlets; division
Human Hazards : None
Common Uses : Cut flowers; flowering shrub; foliage plant
Major Problems : Scales; mealybugs; aphids

Typical Height : 8 Ft.
Drought Tolerance : Medium
Nutritional Requirements : High
Light Requirements : Medium; high
Leaf Type : Simple
Texture : Coarse
Flower Characteristics : Showy

Environmental Problems : None

Additional Notes : Large clumping tender plant. Excellent for cut flowers.

Alpinia sanderae

Family : Zingiberaceae   **Zone** : 10A-11

Common Name(s) : Variegated Ginger
Origin : New Guinea
Growth Rate : Medium
Salt Tolerance : Low
Soil Requirements : Wide
Plant Type : Herbaceous perennial
Foliage Color : Variegated
Flowering Season : Summer; fall; winter
Flower Color : Red
Propagation : Division
Human Hazards : None
Common Uses : Specimen plant; foliage plant
Major Problems : None

Typical Height : 2 Ft.
Drought Tolerance : Medium
Nutritional Requirements : Medium
Light Requirements : Medium
Leaf Type : Simple
Texture : Medium
Flower Characteristics : Insignificant

Environmental Problems : None

Additional Notes : Has attractive green and white variegated foliage, but rarely flowers.

Alpinia zerumbet *(Photograph p. 190)*

Family : Zingiberaceae   **Zone** : 10A-11

Common Name(s) : Shellflower; Shell Ginger
Origin : East Asia
Growth Rate : Fast
Salt Tolerance : Medium
Soil Requirements : Wide
Plant Type : Herbaceous perennial
Foliage Color : Green
Flowering Season : Summer; fall; winter
Flower Color : White & yellow
Propagation : Division
Human Hazards : None
Common Uses : Specimen plant; cut foliage; foliage plant
Major Problems : None

Typical Height : 8 Ft.
Drought Tolerance : Medium
Nutritional Requirements : Medium
Light Requirements : Medium; high
Leaf Type : Simple
Texture : Coarse
Flower Characteristics : Showy

Environmental Problems : None

Additional Notes : A large clumping plant with attractive pendulous flowers.
Cultivars
'VARIEGATA' has yellow and green foliage.

Alstroemeria pulchella

Common Name(s) : Inca Lily; Parrot Flower
Origin : Brazil
Growth Rate : Medium
Salt Tolerance : Low
Soil Requirements : Acid
Plant Type : Herbaceous perennial
Foliage Color : Green
Flowering Season : Summer; fall
Flower Color : Red; green
Propagation : Division; seeds
Human Hazards : None
Common Uses : Beds; groundcover; cut flowers
Major Problems : None
Additional Notes : Sterile shoots form excellent groundcover in partial shade

Family : Alstroemeriaceae   **Zone** : 8-10B

Typical Height : 3 Ft.
Drought Tolerance : Low
Nutritional Requirements : Medium
Light Requirements : Medium
Leaf Type : Simple
Texture : Medium
Flower Characteristics : Showy

Environmental Problems : Invasive

Amelanchier arborea

Common Name(s) : Serviceberry; Shadbush
Origin : Eastern United States
Growth Rate : Medium
Salt Tolerance : Low
Soil Requirements : Acid
Plant Type : Deciduous tree or shrub
Foliage Color : Green
Flowering Season : Spring
Flower Color : White
Propagation : Seeds
Human Hazards : None
Common Uses : Edible fruit; small flowering tree; flowering shrub
Major Problems : None
Additional Notes : Small purple fruits are an excellent wildlife attractant.

Family : Rosaceae   **Zone** : 4-10A

Typical Height : 10 Ft.
Drought Tolerance : Medium
Nutritional Requirements : Medium
Light Requirements : Medium; high
Leaf Type : Simple
Texture : Medium
Flower Characteristics : Showy; fragrant

Environmental Problems : None

Amomum compactum

Common Name(s) : Round Cardamon
Origin : Java
Growth Rate : Medium
Salt Tolerance : n/a
Soil Requirements : Wide
Plant Type : Herbaceous perennial
Foliage Color : Green
Flowering Season : n/a
Flower Color : White
Propagation : Division
Human Hazards : None
Common Uses : Specimen plant; edible fruit
Major Problems : None
Additional Notes : Seeds of this ginger are sometimes used as a substitute for cardamon.

Family : Zingiberaceae   **Zone** : 10A-11

Typical Height : 3 Ft.
Drought Tolerance : Low
Nutritional Requirements : High
Light Requirements : Medium
Leaf Type : Simple
Texture : Medium
Flower Characteristics : Showy

Environmental Problems : None

Amorphophallus spp.

Common Name(s) : Voodoo Lily; Snake Lily
Origin : Old World Tropics
Growth Rate : Medium
Salt Tolerance : Low
Soil Requirements : Wide
Plant Type : Herbaceous perennial
Foliage Color : Green
Flowering Season : Summer
Flower Color : Brown; red
Propagation : Division
Human Hazards : None
Common Uses : Specimen plant
Major Problems : None
Additional Notes : A novelty plant with attractive foliage; flowers have foul odor.

Family : Araceae   **Zone** : 9-11

Typical Height : 6 Ft.
Drought Tolerance : Low
Nutritional Requirements : High
Light Requirements : Medium
Leaf Type : Bipinnately lobed
Texture : Coarse
Flower Characteristics : Showy

Environmental Problems : None

Ampelopsis arborea

Common Name(s) : Pepper Vine
Origin : Southeastern United States & Mexico
Growth Rate : Fast
Salt Tolerance : Medium
Soil Requirements : Wide
Plant Type : Deciduous vine
Foliage Color : Green
Flowering Season : Summer
Flower Color : Green
Propagation : Cuttings; air layering
Human Hazards : None
Common Uses : Vine
Major Problems : None
Additional Notes : Best restricted to wild gardens or perimeter areas; wildlife attractant.

Family : Vitaceae   **Zone** : 7-10B

Typical Height : Not applicable
Drought Tolerance : Medium
Nutritional Requirements : Medium
Light Requirements : High; medium
Leaf Type : Bipinnately compound
Texture : Medium
Flower Characteristics : Insignificant

Environmental Problems : Weedy

Amphitecna latifolia

Common Name(s) : Black Calabash
Origin : West Indies
Growth Rate : Medium
Salt Tolerance : High
Soil Requirements : Wide
Plant Type : Evergreen tree
Foliage Color : Green
Flowering Season : Spring
Flower Color : Yellow
Propagation : Seeds
Human Hazards : None
Common Uses : Small tree
Major Problems : None
Additional Notes : Not particularly wind resistant; weak rooted.

Family : Bignoniaceae   **Zone** : 10B-11

Typical Height : 20 Ft.
Drought Tolerance : High
Nutritional Requirements : Low
Light Requirements : High
Leaf Type : Simple
Texture : Medium
Flower Characteristics : Insignificant

Environmental Problems : Weak

Amyris elemifera

Common Name(s) : Torchwood
Origin : Caribbean Region
Growth Rate : Medium
Salt Tolerance : High
Soil Requirements : Wide
Plant Type : Evergreen shrub or tree
Foliage Color : Green
Flowering Season : Fall
Flower Color : White
Propagation : Seeds
Human Hazards : None
Common Uses : Shrub; tree
Major Problems : None
Additional Notes : A native shrub. Green wood burns.

Family : Rutaceae   **Zone** : 10B-11

Typical Height : 15 Ft.
Drought Tolerance : High
Nutritional Requirements : Low
Light Requirements : Medium; high
Leaf Type : Pinnately compound
Texture : Medium
Flower Characteristics : Insignificant

Environmental Problems : None

Ananas comosus *(Photograph p. 190)*

Common Name(s) : Pineapple
Origin : Tropical America
Growth Rate : Medium
Salt Tolerance : Medium
Soil Requirements : Wide
Plant Type : Herbaceous perennial
Foliage Color : Green; variegated
Flowering Season : Year-round
Flower Color : Purple
Propagation : Division; cuttings
Human Hazards : Spiny
Common Uses : Edible fruit; rock gardens
Major Problems : Scales; mealybugs; nematodes; root rots
Additional Notes : Many varieties, some spineless. Fruiting can be forced with ethylene.
Cultivars
'SMOOTH CAYENNE' is spineless; 'VARIEGATUS' has marginal white stripes; 'PORTEANUS' has a central yellow stripe; tricolored cultivars also exist.

Family : Bromeliaceae   **Zone** : 10A-11

Typical Height : 4 Ft.
Drought Tolerance : High
Nutritional Requirements : Medium
Light Requirements : High
Leaf Type : Simple; linear
Texture : Coarse
Flower Characteristics : Insignificant

Environmental Problems : None

Andira inermis

Common Name(s) : Cabbage Angelin
Origin : Tropical America and West Africa
Growth Rate : Fast
Salt Tolerance : Medium
Soil Requirements : Wide
Plant Type : Evergreen tree
Foliage Color : Green
Flowering Season : Summer; winter
Flower Color : Pink
Propagation : Seeds; cuttings
Human Hazards : Poisonous
Common Uses : Flowering tree
Major Problems : None
Additional Notes : Barks and seeds poisonous.

Family : Leguminosae   Zone : 11

Typical Height : 50 Ft.
Drought Tolerance : Medium
Nutritional Requirements : Medium
Light Requirements : High
Leaf Type : Pinnately compound
Texture : Medium
Flower Characteristics : Showy; fragrant

Environmental Problems : None

Angadenia berterii

Common Name(s) : Pineland Allamanda
Origin : South Florida and West Indies
Growth Rate : Slow
Salt Tolerance : Medium
Soil Requirements : Alkaline
Plant Type : Evergreen shrub
Foliage Color : Green
Flowering Season : Year-round
Flower Color : Yellow
Propagation : Cuttings; seeds
Human Hazards : None
Common Uses : Specimen plant; flowering shrub
Major Problems : None
Additional Notes : A Florida native well adapted for alkaline soils.

Family : Apocynaceae   Zone : 10B-11

Typical Height : 3 Ft.
Drought Tolerance : High
Nutritional Requirements : Low
Light Requirements : High
Leaf Type : Simple
Texture : Fine
Flower Characteristics : Showy

Environmental Problems : None

Annona glabra

Common Name(s) : Pond Apple; Alligator Apple
Origin : Caribbean Region and Tropical America
Growth Rate : Medium
Salt Tolerance : Medium
Soil Requirements : Wide
Plant Type : Deciduous tree
Foliage Color : Green
Flowering Season : Spring
Flower Color : Yellow
Propagation : Seeds
Human Hazards : None
Common Uses : Tree; edible fruit
Major Problems : None
Additional Notes : Good for swampy sites. Fruit edible, but inferior.

Family : Annonaceae   Zone : 10A-11

Typical Height : 25 Ft.
Drought Tolerance : Low
Nutritional Requirements : Low
Light Requirements : High
Leaf Type : Simple
Texture : Coarse
Flower Characteristics : Insignificant

Environmental Problems : None

Annona muricata *(Photograph p. 153)*

Common Name(s) : Soursop; Guanabana
Origin : Tropical America
Growth Rate : Medium
Salt Tolerance : Medium
Soil Requirements : Wide
Plant Type : Evergreen tree
Foliage Color : Green
Flowering Season : Year-round
Flower Color : Yellow
Propagation : Seeds; grafting
Human Hazards : Poisonous
Common Uses : Edible fruit; small tree
Major Problems : Scales; mealybugs; lace-wing bugs
Additional Notes : Grows only in the warmest parts of Florida. Edible fruit; poisonous bark

Family : Annonaceae   Zone : 11

Typical Height : 20 Ft.
Drought Tolerance : Medium
Nutritional Requirements : Medium
Light Requirements : Medium; high
Leaf Type : Simple
Texture : Coarse
Flower Characteristics : Insignificant; fragrant

Environmental Problems : None

Annona reticulata

Common Name(s) : Custard Apple; Bullock's Heart
Origin : Tropical America
Growth Rate : Medium
Salt Tolerance : Low
Soil Requirements : Wide
Plant Type : Deciduous tree
Foliage Color : Green
Flowering Season : Spring
Flower Color : Greenish-yellow
Propagation : Seeds
Human Hazards : Irritant; poisonous
Common Uses : Edible fruit; small tree
Major Problems : Beetle and fly larvae
Additional Notes : Selected varieties exist. Bark contains poison and eye irritant.

Family : Annonaceae   **Zone** : 10B-11

Typical Height : 30 Ft.
Drought Tolerance : Medium
Nutritional Requirements : Medium
Light Requirements : High
Leaf Type : Simple
Texture : Coarse
Flower Characteristics : Insignificant

Environmental Problems : None

Annona squamosa

Common Name(s) : Sweetsop; Sugar Apple
Origin : Tropical America
Growth Rate : Medium
Salt Tolerance : Medium
Soil Requirements : Wide
Plant Type : Evergreen tree
Foliage Color : Green
Flowering Season : Spring
Flower Color : Green-yellow
Propagation : Seed; grafting
Human Hazards : None
Common Uses : Small tree; edible fruit
Major Problems : None
Additional Notes : Atemoya is a hybrid of this species and A. cherimola.
Cultivars
Several cultivars exist.

Family : Annonaceae   **Zone** : 10B-11

Typical Height : 20 Ft.
Drought Tolerance : Medium
Nutritional Requirements : Medium
Light Requirements : High
Leaf Type : Simple
Texture : Medium
Flower Characteristics : Insignificant

Environmental Problems : None

Anthurium 'Lady Jane' *(Photograph p. 191)*

Common Name(s) : Lady Jane Anthurium
Origin : Hybrid
Growth Rate : Medium
Salt Tolerance : Low
Soil Requirements : Well-drained
Plant Type : Epiphyte
Foliage Color : Green
Flowering Season : Year-round
Flower Color : Pink
Propagation : Division; tissue culture
Human Hazards : Irritant
Common Uses : Flowering pot plant; specimen plant; beds; cut flower
Major Problems : Bacterial blight
Additional Notes : Compact with small rose colored flowers; 'SOUTHERN BLUSH' is similar.

Family : Araceae   **Zone** : 10B-11

Typical Height : 1.5 Ft.
Drought Tolerance : Medium
Nutritional Requirements : Medium
Light Requirements : Low; medium
Leaf Type : Simple
Texture : Coarse
Flower Characteristics : Showy

Environmental Problems : None

Anthurium andraeanum *(Photograph p. 191)*

Common Name(s) : Flamingo Flower
Origin : Colombia
Growth Rate : Medium
Salt Tolerance : Low
Soil Requirements : Well-drained
Plant Type : Epiphyte
Foliage Color : Green
Flowering Season : Year-round
Flower Color : Orange; pink; red; white
Propagation : Division; cuttings; seed; tissue culture
Human Hazards : Irritant
Common Uses : Flowering pot plant; cut flowers
Major Problems : Bacterial blight; scales; mealybugs
Additional Notes : Widely used as a cut flower. Requires protection and perfect drainage.
Cultivars
Many cultivars exist.

Family : Araceae   **Zone** : 10B-11

Typical Height : 2 Ft.
Drought Tolerance : Medium
Nutritional Requirements : Medium
Light Requirements : Low; medium
Leaf Type : Simple
Texture : Coarse
Flower Characteristics : Showy

Environmental Problems : None

Anthurium clarinervium *(Photograph p. 191)*

Common Name(s) : Anthurium
Origin : Southern Mexico
Growth Rate : Slow
Salt Tolerance : Low
Soil Requirements : Well-drained
Plant Type : Herbaceous perennial
Foliage Color : Green & silver
Flowering Season : Year-round
Flower Color : Green
Propagation : Division; cuttings; seeds
Human Hazards : Irritant
Common Uses : Foliage plant; specimen plant
Major Problems : Bacterial blights; scales
Additional Notes : Attractive heart-shaped leaves have prominent silver veins.
Cultivars
A. crystallinum is similar in appearance.

Family : Araceae   **Zone** : 10B-11

Typical Height : 1 Ft.
Drought Tolerance : Medium
Nutritional Requirements : Medium
Light Requirements : Low; medium
Leaf Type : Simple
Texture : Coarse
Flower Characteristics : Insignificant

Environmental Problems : None

Anthurium guayanum

Common Name(s) : Birdsnest Anthurium
Origin : Surinam
Growth Rate : Medium
Salt Tolerance : Low
Soil Requirements : Well-drained
Plant Type : Epiphyte
Foliage Color : Green & red
Flowering Season : Year-round
Flower Color : Purple
Propagation : Seeds; cuttings
Human Hazards : None
Common Uses : Specimen plant; foliage plant; epiphyte
Major Problems : None
Additional Notes : A birdsnest anthurium with leathery foliage; new leaves wine red.

Family : Araceae   **Zone** : 10B-11

Typical Height : 5 Ft.
Drought Tolerance : Medium
Nutritional Requirements : Medium
Light Requirements : Low; medium
Leaf Type : Simple
Texture : Coarse
Flower Characteristics : Insignificant

Environmental Problems : None

Anthurium hookeri

Common Name(s) : Birdsnest Anthurium
Origin : Guianas
Growth Rate : Medium
Salt Tolerance : Low
Soil Requirements : Well-drained
Plant Type : Epiphyte
Foliage Color : Green
Flowering Season : Year-round
Flower Color : Green
Propagation : Seeds; cuttings
Human Hazards : Irritant
Common Uses : Specimen plant; foliage plant
Major Problems : None
Additional Notes : Bold tropical foliage and rosette form. Can be grown as an epiphyte.
Cultivars
'ALICIA' is a superior selection.

Family : Araceae   **Zone** : 10B-11

Typical Height : 3.5 Ft.
Drought Tolerance : Medium
Nutritional Requirements : Medium
Light Requirements : Low; medium
Leaf Type : Simple
Texture : Coarse
Flower Characteristics : Insignificant

Environmental Problems : None

Anthurium salviniae *(Photograph p. 191)*

Common Name(s) : Birdsnest Anthurium
Origin : Guatemala
Growth Rate : Medium
Salt Tolerance : Low
Soil Requirements : Wide
Plant Type : Epiphyte
Foliage Color : Green
Flowering Season : Spring; summer; fall
Flower Color : Pink
Propagation : Seeds
Human Hazards : Irritant
Common Uses : Specimen plant; foliage plant
Major Problems : None
Additional Notes : A very large spreading birdsnest anthurium.

Family : Araceae   **Zone** : 10B-11

Typical Height : 5 Ft.
Drought Tolerance : Medium
Nutritional Requirements : Medium
Light Requirements : Low
Leaf Type : Simple
Texture : Very coarse
Flower Characteristics : Insignificant

Environmental Problems : None

Anthurium watermaliense

Common Name(s) : Black Anthurium
Origin : Colombia
Growth Rate : Medium
Salt Tolerance : Medium
Soil Requirements : Well-drained
Plant Type : Epiphyte
Foliage Color : Green
Flowering Season : Year-round
Flower Color : Brown
Propagation : Cuttings; division; see
Human Hazards : Irritant
Common Uses : Foliage plant; specimen plant
Major Problems : None
Additional Notes : Has triangular reflexed leaves.

Family : Araceae   **Zone** : 10B-11

Typical Height : 2 Ft.
Drought Tolerance : Medium
Nutritional Requirements : Medium
Light Requirements : Medium; low
Leaf Type : Simple
Texture : Coarse
Flower Characteristics : Insignificant

Environmental Problems : None

Antigonon leptopus *(Photograph p. 210)*

Common Name(s) : Coral Vine
Origin : Mexico
Growth Rate : Fast
Salt Tolerance : Low
Soil Requirements : Wide
Plant Type : Evergreen vine
Foliage Color : Green
Flowering Season : Summer; fall
Flower Color : Pink
Propagation : Seeds; cuttings; tubers
Human Hazards : None
Common Uses : Flowering vine
Major Problems : Chewing insects
Additional Notes : A vigorous vine often grown on fences. Tubers are edible.
Cultivars
'ALBUM' has white flowers.

Family : Polygonaceae   **Zone** : 9-11

Typical Height : Not applicable
Drought Tolerance : High
Nutritional Requirements : Medium
Light Requirements : High
Leaf Type : Simple
Texture : Medium
Flower Characteristics : Showy

Environmental Problems : Weedy

Aphanostephus skirrhobasis

Common Name(s) : Lazy Daisy
Origin : Southeastern United States
Growth Rate : Medium
Salt Tolerance : Low
Soil Requirements : Wide
Plant Type : Herbaceous perennial
Foliage Color : Green
Flowering Season : Summer
Flower Color : White & red
Propagation : Seeds
Human Hazards : None
Common Uses : Specimen plant; beds; cut flower
Major Problems : None
Additional Notes : A well adapted native daisy relative.

Family : Compositae   **Zone** : 6-10A

Typical Height : 1.5 Ft.
Drought Tolerance : High
Nutritional Requirements : Low
Light Requirements : High
Leaf Type : Simple
Texture : Medium
Flower Characteristics : Showy

Environmental Problems : None

Aphelandra spp.

Common Name(s) : Zebra Plant
Origin : Brazil
Growth Rate : Medium
Salt Tolerance : Low
Soil Requirements : Acid
Plant Type : Herbaceous perennial
Foliage Color : Variegated
Flowering Season : Spring; summer; fall
Flower Color : Orange; red; yellow
Propagation : Cuttings
Human Hazards : None
Common Uses : Specimen plant; foliage plant
Major Problems : Aphids; mites; mealybugs
Additional Notes : Several species often with bold banded foliage.

Family : Acanthaceae   **Zone** : 10B-11

Typical Height : 1.5 Ft.
Drought Tolerance : Low
Nutritional Requirements : Medium
Light Requirements : Low; medium
Leaf Type : Simple
Texture : Coarse
Flower Characteristics : Showy

Environmental Problems : None

Aptenia cordifolia

Common Name(s) : Baby Sun Rose
Origin : South Africa
Growth Rate : Medium
Salt Tolerance : High
Soil Requirements : Dry
Plant Type : Evergreen succulent
Foliage Color : Green
Flowering Season : Spring; summer; fall
Flower Color : Purple
Propagation : Cuttings; seeds
Human Hazards : None
Common Uses : Groundcover; beds; rock gardens
Major Problems : None
Additional Notes : A prostrate succulent for dry sites.

Family : Aizoaceae   Zone : 10A-11

Typical Height : .5 Ft.
Drought Tolerance : High
Nutritional Requirements : Low
Light Requirements : High
Leaf Type : Simple
Texture : Medium
Flower Characteristics : Showy

Environmental Problems : None

Araucaria bidwillii

Common Name(s) : Bunya-bunya Tree
Origin : Australia
Growth Rate : Medium
Salt Tolerance : Medium
Soil Requirements : Wide
Plant Type : Evergreen tree
Foliage Color : Green
Flowering Season : Spring
Flower Color : Green
Propagation : Seeds
Human Hazards : Spiny
Common Uses : Tree
Major Problems : Scales; sooty mold; leafspots
Additional Notes : Spiny leaves. This is the hardiest of the araucarias.

Family : Araucariaceae   Zone : 9-10B

Typical Height : 65 Ft.
Drought Tolerance : Medium
Nutritional Requirements : Medium
Light Requirements : High
Leaf Type : Simple
Texture : Fine
Flower Characteristics : Insignificant

Environmental Problems : None

Araucaria heterophylla *(Photograph p. 153)*

Common Name(s) : Norfolk Island Pine
Origin : Norfolk Islands
Growth Rate : Fast
Salt Tolerance : Medium
Soil Requirements : Wide
Plant Type : Evergreen tree
Foliage Color : Green
Flowering Season : Spring
Flower Color : Brown
Propagation : Seeds; cuttings
Human Hazards : None
Common Uses : Tree; foliage plant
Major Problems : Scales; mealybugs; fungal blight
Additional Notes : Too tall for residential areas. May blow over in high winds.

Family : Araucariaceae   Zone : 10A-11

Typical Height : 80 Ft.
Drought Tolerance : High
Nutritional Requirements : Low
Light Requirements : High; medium
Leaf Type : Needle
Texture : Fine
Flower Characteristics : Insignificant

Environmental Problems : None

Archontophoenix alexandrae *(Photograph p. 202)*

Common Name(s) : Alexandra Palm; King Alexander Palm
Origin : Australia
Growth Rate : Medium
Salt Tolerance : Low
Soil Requirements : Wide
Plant Type : Palm
Foliage Color : Green
Flowering Season : Summer
Flower Color : White
Propagation : Seeds
Human Hazards : None
Common Uses : Tree
Major Problems : None
Additional Notes : This palm does not transplant well from field nurseries.

Family : Palmae   Zone : 10B-11

Typical Height : 40 Ft.
Drought Tolerance : High
Nutritional Requirements : Medium
Light Requirements : Medium; high
Leaf Type : Pinnately compound
Texture : Medium
Flower Characteristics : Insignificant

Environmental Problems : None

Archontophoenix cunninghamiana

Common Name(s) : Piccabeen Palm
Origin : Australia
Growth Rate : Medium
Salt Tolerance : Low
Soil Requirements : Wide
Plant Type : Palm
Foliage Color : Green
Flowering Season : Summer
Flower Color : White
Propagation : Seeds
Human Hazards : None
Common Uses : Tree
Major Problems : None
Additional Notes : Slightly more cold hardy than A. alexandrae .

Family : Palmae   **Zone** : 10A-11

Typical Height : 40 Ft.
Drought Tolerance : High
Nutritional Requirements : Medium
Light Requirements : Medium; high
Leaf Type : Pinnately compound
Texture : Medium
Flower Characteristics : Insignificant

Environmental Problems : None

Ardisia crenata *(Photograph p. 173)*

Common Name(s) : Coral Ardisia; Coralberry
Origin : India to Japan
Growth Rate : Slow
Salt Tolerance : Low
Soil Requirements : Acid
Plant Type : Evergreen shrub
Foliage Color : Green
Flowering Season : Spring
Flower Color : Pink; white
Propagation : Seeds; cuttings
Human Hazards : None
Common Uses : Groundcover; flowering shrub
Major Problems : None
Additional Notes : Very shade tolerant; attractive red or white fruit; may naturalize.
Cultivars
'ALBA' has white fruit.

Family : Myrsinaceae   **Zone** : 9-10A

Typical Height : 4 Ft.
Drought Tolerance : Low
Nutritional Requirements : Medium
Light Requirements : Low
Leaf Type : Simple
Texture : Medium
Flower Characteristics : Showy

Environmental Problems : None

Ardisia escallonioides

Common Name(s) : Marlberry; Marbleberry
Origin : South Florida and Caribbean Region
Growth Rate : Medium
Salt Tolerance : High
Soil Requirements : Wide
Plant Type : Evergreen tree or shrub
Foliage Color : Green
Flowering Season : Spring; summer; fall
Flower Color : White
Propagation : Seeds
Human Hazards : None
Common Uses : Small tree; shrub
Major Problems : None
Additional Notes : Fruit attracts wildlife.

Family : Myrsinaceae   **Zone** : 10A-11

Typical Height : 20 Ft.
Drought Tolerance : Medium
Nutritional Requirements : Low
Light Requirements : Medium; high
Leaf Type : Simple
Texture : Medium
Flower Characteristics : Insignificant; fragrant

Environmental Problems : None

Ardisia japonica

Common Name(s) : Japanese Ardisia
Origin : Japan and China
Growth Rate : Medium
Salt Tolerance : Low
Soil Requirements : Wide
Plant Type : Evergreen shrub
Foliage Color : Green
Flowering Season : Summer; fall
Flower Color : White
Propagation : Division; cuttings; seeds
Human Hazards : None
Common Uses : Groundcover
Major Problems : None
Additional Notes : An excellent groundcover for heavy shade.

Family : Myrsinaceae   **Zone** : 9-10B

Typical Height : 1.5 Ft.
Drought Tolerance : Medium
Nutritional Requirements : Low
Light Requirements : Low
Leaf Type : Simple
Texture : Medium
Flower Characteristics : Insignificant

Environmental Problems : None

Arenga pinnata

Common Name(s) : Sugar Palm
Origin : East Indies
Growth Rate : Medium
Salt Tolerance : n/a
Soil Requirements : Wide
Plant Type : Palm
Foliage Color : Green
Flowering Season : n/a
Flower Color : Brown
Propagation : Seeds
Human Hazards : Irritant
Common Uses : Tree
Major Problems : None

Family : Palmae   Zone : 10B-11

Typical Height : 25 Ft.
Drought Tolerance : Medium
Nutritional Requirements : Low
Light Requirements : High
Leaf Type : Pinnately compound
Texture : Coarse
Flower Characteristics : Insignificant

Environmental Problems : None

Additional Notes : Fruit is extremely irritating to skin; flowers once and dies.

Argyreia nervosa

Common Name(s) : Wooly Morning-glory
Origin : Tropical Asia
Growth Rate : Fast
Salt Tolerance : Low
Soil Requirements : Wide
Plant Type : Evergreen vine
Foliage Color : Green
Flowering Season : Spring; summer; fall
Flower Color : Pink; purple
Propagation : Cuttings; seeds
Human Hazards : None
Common Uses : Flowering vine
Major Problems : None

Family : Convolvulaceae   Zone : 10B-11

Typical Height : Not applicable
Drought Tolerance : Medium
Nutritional Requirements : Medium
Light Requirements : High
Leaf Type : Simple
Texture : Coarse
Flower Characteristics : Showy

Environmental Problems : None

Additional Notes : Decorative seed pods used for dried arrangements. Needs wind protection.

Arisaema dracontium

Common Name(s) : Green Dragons
Origin : Eastern North America
Growth Rate : Medium
Salt Tolerance : Low
Soil Requirements : Acid
Plant Type : Herbaceous perennial
Foliage Color : Green
Flowering Season : Spring
Flower Color : Green
Propagation : Seeds; division
Human Hazards : Irritant
Common Uses : Specimen plant
Major Problems : None

Family : Araceae   Zone : 6-10A

Typical Height : 1.5 Ft.
Drought Tolerance : Low
Nutritional Requirements : High
Light Requirements : Low
Leaf Type : Simple
Texture : Medium
Flower Characteristics : Showy

Environmental Problems : None

Additional Notes : Best in woodland setting.

Arisaema triphylla

Common Name(s) : Jack In The Pulpit
Origin : Northeastern United States
Growth Rate : Medium
Salt Tolerance : Low
Soil Requirements : Acid
Plant Type : Herbaceous perennial
Foliage Color : Green
Flowering Season : Spring
Flower Color : Brown; purple
Propagation : Seeds; division
Human Hazards : Irritant
Common Uses : Specimen plant
Major Problems : None

Family : Araceae   Zone : 5-9

Typical Height : 1.5 Ft.
Drought Tolerance : Low
Nutritional Requirements : High
Light Requirements : Low
Leaf Type : Simple
Texture : Medium
Flower Characteristics : Showy

Environmental Problems : None

Additional Notes : Attractive plant for woodland, shady setting.

Aristolochia elegans

Common Name(s) : Calico Flower
Origin : Brazil
Growth Rate : Fast
Salt Tolerance : Low
Soil Requirements : Wide
Plant Type : Evergreen vine
Foliage Color : Green
Flowering Season : Summer; fall
Flower Color : Red-purple & white
Propagation : Seeds; cuttings
Human Hazards : None
Common Uses : Flowering vine
Major Problems : Caterpillars
Additional Notes : Unusual flowers without the characteristic foul odor of aristolochias.

Family : Aristolochiaceae   **Zone** : 10B-11

Typical Height : Not applicable
Drought Tolerance : Medium
Nutritional Requirements : Medium
Light Requirements : Medium; high
Leaf Type : Simple
Texture : Medium
Flower Characteristics : Showy

Environmental Problems : None

Aristolochia grandiflora *(Photograph p. 210)*

Common Name(s) : Pelican Flower
Origin : Caribbean Region
Growth Rate : Fast
Salt Tolerance : Low
Soil Requirements : Wide
Plant Type : Evergreen vine
Foliage Color : Green
Flowering Season : Summer; fall
Flower Color : Purple-white
Propagation : Cuttings; seeds
Human Hazards : None
Common Uses : Flowering vine
Major Problems : Caterpillars
Additional Notes : Has pelican-shaped flowers with a foul odor.

Family : Aristolochiaceae   **Zone** : 10B-11

Typical Height : Not applicable
Drought Tolerance : Medium
Nutritional Requirements : Medium
Light Requirements : Medium; high
Leaf Type : Simple
Texture : Medium
Flower Characteristics : Showy

Environmental Problems : None

Asclepias tuberosa

Common Name(s) : Butterfly Weed
Origin : United States
Growth Rate : Medium
Salt Tolerance : Low
Soil Requirements : Wide
Plant Type : Herbaceous perennial
Foliage Color : Green
Flowering Season : Summer
Flower Color : Orange
Propagation : Seeds
Human Hazards : None
Common Uses : Specimen plant; flowering shrub
Major Problems : None
Additional Notes : Attracts butterflies to the garden.

Family : Asclepiadaceae   **Zone** : 3-10B

Typical Height : 3 Ft.
Drought Tolerance : High
Nutritional Requirements : Low
Light Requirements : High
Leaf Type : Simple
Texture : Medium
Flower Characteristics : Showy

Environmental Problems : None

Asparagus densiflorus *(Photograph p. 213)*

Common Name(s) : Asparagus Fern
Origin : South Africa
Growth Rate : Medium
Salt Tolerance : Medium
Soil Requirements : Wide
Plant Type : Herbaceous perennial
Foliage Color : Green
Flowering Season : Spring; summer
Flower Color : White
Propagation : Seeds; division
Human Hazards : Spiny
Common Uses : Beds; specimen plant; foliage plant; hanging baskets
Major Problems : None
Additional Notes : Arching stems with small spines. Fine textured foliage. Red berries.
Cultivars
'SPRENGERI' has cascading stems with 1 inch leaves; 'MYERS' has rather stiff upright stems with very dense fine leaves.

Family : Liliaceae   **Zone** : 10A-11

Typical Height : 2 Ft.
Drought Tolerance : High
Nutritional Requirements : Low
Light Requirements : Low; medium; high
Leaf Type : Needle-like
Texture : Very fine
Flower Characteristics : Insignificant

Environmental Problems : None

Asparagus falcatus

Common Name(s) : Sicklethorn Vine
Origin : Tropical Asia and Africa
Growth Rate : Medium
Salt Tolerance : Low
Soil Requirements : Wide
Plant Type : Evergreen shrub or vine
Foliage Color : Green
Flowering Season : Winter
Flower Color : White
Propagation : Seeds; division
Human Hazards : Spiny
Common Uses : Vine; shrub
Major Problems : None
Additional Notes : This durable vine has very spiny stems.

Family : Liliaceae   **Zone** : 9-11

Typical Height : 6 Ft.
Drought Tolerance : High
Nutritional Requirements : Medium
Light Requirements : Low; medium
Leaf Type : Simple; linear
Texture : Fine
Flower Characteristics : Showy; fragrant

Environmental Problems : None

Asparagus setaceus

Common Name(s) : Asparagus Fern
Origin : South Africa
Growth Rate : Medium
Salt Tolerance : Low
Soil Requirements : Wide
Plant Type : Evergreen shrub
Foliage Color : Green
Flowering Season : Spring; summer
Flower Color : White
Propagation : Seeds; division
Human Hazards : Spiny
Common Uses : Foliage plant; specimen plant; cut foliage; hanging basket
Major Problems : None
Additional Notes : Has very fine lacy foliage on wiry rambling stems.
Cultivars
'NANUS' is a dwarf variety; 'PYRAMIDALIS' has a stiff upright habit.

Family : Liliaceae   **Zone** : 10A-11

Typical Height : Not applicable
Drought Tolerance : High
Nutritional Requirements : Medium
Light Requirements : Medium
Leaf Type : Bipinnately compound
Texture : Very fine
Flower Characteristics : Insignificant

Environmental Problems : None

Aspidistra elatior

Common Name(s) : Cast Iron Plant
Origin : Japan
Growth Rate : Slow
Salt Tolerance : Medium
Soil Requirements : Wide
Plant Type : Herbaceous perennial
Foliage Color : Green; variegated
Flowering Season : Spring
Flower Color : Purple
Propagation : Division
Human Hazards : None
Common Uses : Foliage plant; groundcover
Major Problems : K deficiency
Additional Notes : A slow-growing plant. Excellent for low light interiorscapes.
Cultivars
'VARIEGATA' has green and white striped foliage.

Family : Liliaceae   **Zone** : 9-11

Typical Height : 2 Ft.
Drought Tolerance : Medium
Nutritional Requirements : Low
Light Requirements : Low; medium
Leaf Type : Simple
Texture : Coarse
Flower Characteristics : Insignificant

Environmental Problems : None

Asplenium nidus *(Photograph p. 191)*

Common Name(s) : Birdsnest Fern
Origin : Tropical Asia and Polynesia
Growth Rate : Medium
Salt Tolerance : Low
Soil Requirements : Acid
Plant Type : Epiphyte
Foliage Color : Green
Flowering Season : n/a
Flower Color : n/a
Propagation : Tissue culture; spores
Human Hazards : None
Common Uses : Foliage plant
Major Problems : Foliar nematodes
Additional Notes : An epiphyte with vase-shaped entire foliage.

Family : Aspleniaceae   **Zone** : 10B-11

Typical Height : 2.5 Ft.
Drought Tolerance : Low
Nutritional Requirements : Medium
Light Requirements : Low; medium
Leaf Type : Simple
Texture : Coarse
Flower Characteristics : n/a

Environmental Problems : None

Asplenium serratum

Common Name(s) : Wild Birdsnest Fern
Origin : South Florida and West Indies
Growth Rate : Medium
Salt Tolerance : Low
Soil Requirements : Acid
Plant Type : Herbaceous perennial
Foliage Color : Green
Flowering Season : n/a
Flower Color : n/a
Propagation : Spores
Human Hazards : None
Common Uses : Foliage plant; specimen plant
Major Problems : None
Additional Notes : Similar to A. nidus , but native and not an epiphyte.

Family : Aspleniaceae   **Zone** : 10B-11

Typical Height : 2 Ft.
Drought Tolerance : Medium
Nutritional Requirements : Medium
Light Requirements : Low; medium
Leaf Type : Simple
Texture : Coarse
Flower Characteristics : n/a

Environmental Problems : None

Asystasia gangetica

Common Name(s) : Ganges Primrose
Origin : India, Malay Peninsula, and Africa
Growth Rate : Medium
Salt Tolerance : Medium
Soil Requirements : Wide
Plant Type : Herbaceous perennial
Foliage Color : Green
Flowering Season : Year-round
Flower Color : Lavender; white; yellow
Propagation : Cuttings; layers
Human Hazards : None
Common Uses : Flowering groundcover
Major Problems : None
Additional Notes : Foliage can be cooked and eaten.

Family : Acanthaceae   **Zone** : 10B-11

Typical Height : 3 Ft.
Drought Tolerance : High
Nutritional Requirements : Low
Light Requirements : Medium; high
Leaf Type : Simple
Texture : Medium
Flower Characteristics : Showy

Environmental Problems : None

Aucuba japonica

Common Name(s) : Japanese Aucuba
Origin : Himalayas to Japan
Growth Rate : Medium
Salt Tolerance : Low
Soil Requirements : Acid
Plant Type : Evergreen shrub
Foliage Color : Green; yellow & green
Flowering Season : Summer
Flower Color : Purple
Propagation : Cuttings
Human Hazards : None
Common Uses : Shrub; foliage plant
Major Problems : Scales; nematodes; sooty mold
Additional Notes : Many leaf-color patterns are available. Highly smog-resistant
Cultivars
'CROTONIFOLIA' has white-spotted leaves; 'FRUCTO-ALBA' has silver variegation; 'GOLDIEANA' has leaves mostly yellow; 'LONGIFOLIA' has narrow, deep green leaves; 'MACROPHYLLA' has large broad leaves; 'PICTURATA' has a large yellow blotch in the leaf center; 'SERRATIFOLIA' has serrate leaf margins; 'VARIEGATA' has yellow-spotted leaves; 'VIRIDIS' has green foliage

Family : Cornaceae   **Zone** : 8-10A

Typical Height : 5 Ft.
Drought Tolerance : Medium
Nutritional Requirements : Medium
Light Requirements : Medium; low
Leaf Type : Simple
Texture : Coarse
Flower Characteristics : Insignificant

Environmental Problems : None

Averrhoa carambola

Common Name(s) : Carambola; Star Fruit
Origin : Malaysia
Growth Rate : Medium
Salt Tolerance : Low
Soil Requirements : Acid
Plant Type : Evergreen tree
Foliage Color : Green
Flowering Season : Summer; fall; spring
Flower Color : Pink
Propagation : Seeds; air layers; grafting
Human Hazards : None
Common Uses : Edible fruit; shade tree; flowering tree
Major Problems : None
Additional Notes : Edible orange star-shaped fruits are produced summer through winter.
Cultivars
Popular cultivars include: 'ARKIN', 'GOLDEN STAR', 'NEWCOMB', and 'THAYER'.

Family : Oxalidaceae   **Zone** : 10B-11

Typical Height : 30 Ft.
Drought Tolerance : Medium
Nutritional Requirements : Medium
Light Requirements : Medium; high
Leaf Type : Pinnately compound
Texture : Medium
Flower Characteristics : Showy

Environmental Problems : Messy

Avicennia germinans

Family : Avicenniaceae   **Zone** : 10B-11

Common Name(s) : Black Mangrove
Origin : South Florida and Tropical America
Growth Rate : Medium
Salt Tolerance : High
Soil Requirements : Wide
Plant Type : Evergreen tree
Foliage Color : Green
Flowering Season : Year-round
Flower Color : White
Propagation : Seeds
Human Hazards : None
Common Uses : Seasides; tree
Major Problems : None
Additional Notes : Grows well in brackish water sites.

Typical Height : 25 Ft.
Drought Tolerance : Low
Nutritional Requirements : Low
Light Requirements : High
Leaf Type : Simple
Texture : Medium
Flower Characteristics : Insignificant; fragrant

Environmental Problems : None

Azadirachta indica

Family : Meliaceae   **Zone** : 10A-11

Common Name(s) : Neem Tree
Origin : India to Malay Peninsula
Growth Rate : Medium
Salt Tolerance : Medium
Soil Requirements : Wide
Plant Type : Evergreen tree
Foliage Color : Green
Flowering Season : Spring
Flower Color : Green
Propagation : Cuttings; seed
Human Hazards : None
Common Uses : Shade tree
Major Problems : None
Additional Notes : This tree has lacy foliage, a slight weeping habit, & insecticidal leaves.

Typical Height : 45 Ft.
Drought Tolerance : High
Nutritional Requirements : Medium
Light Requirements : High
Leaf Type : Pinnately compound
Texture : Medium
Flower Characteristics : Insignificant

Environmental Problems : None

Babiana spp.

Family : Iridaceae   **Zone** : 8-10B

Common Name(s) : Baboon Flower
Origin : South Africa
Growth Rate : Medium
Salt Tolerance : Low
Soil Requirements : Wide
Plant Type : Herbaceous perennial
Foliage Color : Green
Flowering Season : Summer
Flower Color : Blue; red; pink; white
Propagation : Seeds; division
Human Hazards : None
Common Uses : Beds; rock gardens
Major Problems : None
Additional Notes : Easy from seed; may be short-lived in Florida.

Typical Height : .5 Ft.
Drought Tolerance : Low
Nutritional Requirements : Medium
Light Requirements : Medium
Leaf Type : Simple
Texture : Medium
Flower Characteristics : Showy

Environmental Problems : None

Baccharis halimifolia

Family : Compositae   **Zone** : 4-10B

Common Name(s) : Groundsel Bush; Salt Bush
Origin : Eastern United States
Growth Rate : Fast
Salt Tolerance : High
Soil Requirements : Wide
Plant Type : Evergreen shrub
Foliage Color : Gray-green
Flowering Season : Fall
Flower Color : White
Propagation : Seeds; cuttings
Human Hazards : Poisonous
Common Uses : Seasides; shrub
Major Problems : None
Additional Notes : Tolerates brackish water. Male and female flowers on separate plants.
Cultivars
 B. angustifolia is similar, but has long willow-like leaves.

Typical Height : 12 Ft.
Drought Tolerance : High
Nutritional Requirements : Low
Light Requirements : High
Leaf Type : Simple
Texture : Fine
Flower Characteristics : Showy

Environmental Problems : Weedy

Bambusa arundinacea

Common Name(s) : Giant Thorny Bamboo
Origin : India
Growth Rate : Fast
Salt Tolerance : Medium
Soil Requirements : Wide
Plant Type : Evergreen shrub
Foliage Color : Green
Flowering Season : n/a
Flower Color : n/a
Propagation : Division
Human Hazards : Spiny
Common Uses : Large shrub; specimen plant; edible
Major Problems : None
Additional Notes : A very large spiny bamboo. Can become invasive. Shoots edible.

Family : Gramineae   Zone : 9-10B

Typical Height : 80 Ft.
Drought Tolerance : Medium
Nutritional Requirements : Low
Light Requirements : High
Leaf Type : Simple; linear
Texture : Medium
Flower Characteristics : n/a

Environmental Problems : Invasive

Bambusa glaucescens

Common Name(s) : Hedge Bamboo
Origin : China
Growth Rate : Fast
Salt Tolerance : Medium
Soil Requirements : Wide
Plant Type : Evergreen shrub
Foliage Color : Green
Flowering Season : n/a
Flower Color : n/a
Propagation : Division; cuttings
Human Hazards : None
Common Uses : Shrub; hedge; foliage plant
Major Problems : None
Additional Notes : Many cultivars, some larger. Bamboos can become invasive in landscapes.
Cultivars
'ALPHONSE KARR' is larger and has yellow and green striped canes; 'FERNLEAF' grows to about 8 feet and has fine fern-like foliage; 'STRIPESTEM FERNLEAF' has yellow and green striped stems and fine green fern-like foliage; 'SILVER STRIPE' has white stripes in the foliage.

Family : Gramineae   Zone : 9-10B

Typical Height : 10 Ft.
Drought Tolerance : High
Nutritional Requirements : Low
Light Requirements : High
Leaf Type : Simple; linear
Texture : Medium
Flower Characteristics : n/a

Environmental Problems : Invasive

Bambusa oldhamii

Common Name(s) : Oldham Bamboo
Origin : China and Taiwan
Growth Rate : Fast
Salt Tolerance : n/a
Soil Requirements : Wide
Plant Type : Evergreen shrub
Foliage Color : Green
Flowering Season : n/a
Flower Color : n/a
Propagation : Division
Human Hazards : None
Common Uses : Large shrub; specimen plant; foliage plant
Major Problems : None
Additional Notes : Has pale green stems and pendent branches.

Family : Gramineae   Zone : 10A-11

Typical Height : 50 Ft.
Drought Tolerance : Medium
Nutritional Requirements : Low
Light Requirements : High
Leaf Type : Simple; linear
Texture : Medium
Flower Characteristics : n/a

Environmental Problems : Invasive

Bambusa ventricosa

Common Name(s) : Buddha Bamboo; Buddha's Belly Bamboo
Origin : Southern China
Growth Rate : Fast
Salt Tolerance : n/a
Soil Requirements : Wide
Plant Type : Evergreen shrub
Foliage Color : Green
Flowering Season : n/a
Flower Color : n/a
Propagation : Division
Human Hazards : None
Common Uses : Large shrub; specimen plant; foliage plant
Major Problems : None
Additional Notes : Dwarfed plants have swollen and shortened internodes.

Family : Gramineae   Zone : 10A-11

Typical Height : 50 Ft.
Drought Tolerance : Medium
Nutritional Requirements : Low
Light Requirements : High
Leaf Type : Simple; linear
Texture : Medium
Flower Characteristics : n/a

Environmental Problems : None

Bambusa vulgaris *(Photograph p. 173)*

Common Name(s) : Common Bamboo
Origin : East Indies
Growth Rate : Fast
Salt Tolerance : Medium
Soil Requirements : Wide
Plant Type : Evergreen shrub
Foliage Color : Green
Flowering Season : n/a
Flower Color : n/a
Propagation : Division
Human Hazards : None
Common Uses : Large shrub; specimen plant; foliage plant
Major Problems : None
Additional Notes : This large bamboo has attractive yellow and green striped stems.

Family : Gramineae   **Zone** : 10A-11

Typical Height : 60 Ft.
Drought Tolerance : Medium
Nutritional Requirements : Low
Light Requirements : High
Leaf Type : Simple; linear
Texture : Medium
Flower Characteristics : n/a

Environmental Problems : Invasive

Baptisia spp.

Common Name(s) : False Indigo
Origin : North America
Growth Rate : Medium
Salt Tolerance : Low
Soil Requirements : Wide
Plant Type : Herbaceous perennial
Foliage Color : Green
Flowering Season : Spring
Flower Color : Blue; yellow
Propagation : Seeds; division
Human Hazards : None
Common Uses : Beds; cut flowers; specimen plant
Major Problems : None
Additional Notes : Plants take two to three years to flower from seed.

Family : Leguminosae   **Zone** : 4-10B

Typical Height : 2.5 Ft.
Drought Tolerance : High
Nutritional Requirements : Low
Light Requirements : Medium; high
Leaf Type : Pinnately compound
Texture : Fine
Flower Characteristics : Showy

Environmental Problems : None

Barleria cristata

Common Name(s) : Bluebell Barleria; Philippine Violet
Origin : India and East Indies
Growth Rate : Fast
Salt Tolerance : Low
Soil Requirements : Wide
Plant Type : Evergreen shrub
Foliage Color : Green
Flowering Season : Fall
Flower Color : Lavender; pink; white
Propagation : Seeds; cuttings
Human Hazards : None
Common Uses : Hedge; shrub
Major Problems : None
Additional Notes : The white flowering variety is naturalized in south Florida.

Family : Acanthaceae   **Zone** : 10B-11

Typical Height : 4 Ft.
Drought Tolerance : Low
Nutritional Requirements : Medium
Light Requirements : Medium; low
Leaf Type : Simple
Texture : Medium
Flower Characteristics : Showy

Environmental Problems : Weedy

Bauhinia blakeana

Common Name(s) : Hong Kong Orchid Tree
Origin : Southeast Asia
Growth Rate : Fast
Salt Tolerance : Low
Soil Requirements : Wide
Plant Type : Evergreen tree
Foliage Color : Green
Flowering Season : Fall; winter
Flower Color : Purple
Propagation : Cuttings; air layers
Human Hazards : None
Common Uses : Flowering tree
Major Problems : K deficiency; borers
Additional Notes : Vegetatively propagated. Can be weak-wooded and messy.

Family : Leguminosae   **Zone** : 9-11

Typical Height : 35 Ft.
Drought Tolerance : High
Nutritional Requirements : Medium
Light Requirements : High
Leaf Type : Simple; two-lobed
Texture : Coarse
Flower Characteristics : Showy

Environmental Problems : Weak; messy

Bauhinia forficata

Common Name(s) : Brazilian Orchid Tree
Origin : South America
Growth Rate : Medium
Salt Tolerance : Low
Soil Requirements : Wide
Plant Type : Evergreen tree
Foliage Color : Green
Flowering Season : Summer
Flower Color : White
Propagation : Seeds
Human Hazards : Spiny
Common Uses : Small flowering tree
Major Problems : K deficiency
Additional Notes : Branches tend to weep in this species.

Family : Leguminosae   **Zone** : 10A-11

Typical Height : 20 Ft.
Drought Tolerance : Medium
Nutritional Requirements : Medium
Light Requirements : High
Leaf Type : Simple; two-lobed
Texture : Medium
Flower Characteristics : Showy

Environmental Problems : Messy

Bauhinia monandra

Common Name(s) : Butterfly Flower
Origin : Burma
Growth Rate : Fast
Salt Tolerance : Low
Soil Requirements : Wide
Plant Type : Deciduous shrub or tree
Foliage Color : Green
Flowering Season : Summer
Flower Color : Pink
Propagation : Seeds; air layering; cuttings
Human Hazards : None
Common Uses : Small tree;
Major Problems : K deficiency
Additional Notes : Butterfly shaped leaves. Weak-wooded and messy.

Family : Leguminosae   **Zone** : 10B-11

Typical Height : 20 Ft.
Drought Tolerance : High
Nutritional Requirements : Medium
Light Requirements : High
Leaf Type : Simple
Texture : Medium
Flower Characteristics : Showy

Environmental Problems : Weak; messy

Bauhinia punctata *(Photograph p. 173)*

Common Name(s) : Red Bauhinia
Origin : Tropical Africa
Growth Rate : Medium
Salt Tolerance : Medium
Soil Requirements : Wide
Plant Type : Evergreen shrub
Foliage Color : Green
Flowering Season : Spring; summer; fall
Flower Color : Orange-red
Propagation : Seeds
Human Hazards : None
Common Uses : Flowering shrub; groundcover
Major Problems : None
Additional Notes : A sprawling, vine-like shrub. Formerly B. galpinii

Family : Leguminosae   **Zone** : 10A-11

Typical Height : 7 Ft.
Drought Tolerance : High
Nutritional Requirements : Medium
Light Requirements : High
Leaf Type : Simple; two-lobed
Texture : Medium
Flower Characteristics : Showy

Environmental Problems : None

Bauhinia purpurea

Common Name(s) : Fall Orchid Tree
Origin : Asia
Growth Rate : Fast
Salt Tolerance : Low
Soil Requirements : Wide
Plant Type : Deciduous tree
Foliage Color : Green
Flowering Season : Fall
Flower Color : Purple; lavender
Propagation : Seeds; grafting
Human Hazards : None
Common Uses : Flowering tree
Major Problems : K deficiency; borers
Additional Notes : Often confused with B. variegata . Weak wooded and messy.

Family : Leguminosae   **Zone** : 9-11

Typical Height : 35 Ft.
Drought Tolerance : High
Nutritional Requirements : Medium
Light Requirements : High
Leaf Type : Simple; two-lobed
Texture : Medium
Flower Characteristics : Showy; fragrant

Environmental Problems : Weak; messy

Bauhinia tomentosa

Common Name(s) : Yellow Bauhinia; St. Thomas Tree
Origin : Asia and Africa
Growth Rate : Medium
Salt Tolerance : Low
Soil Requirements : Acid
Plant Type : Evergreen tree or shrub
Foliage Color : Green
Flowering Season : Spring; summer; fall
Flower Color : Yellow
Propagation : Seeds
Human Hazards : None
Common Uses : Flowering tree; flowering shrub
Major Problems : K deficiency; Fe deficiency
Additional Notes : Yellow flowers never fully open.

Family : Leguminosae   **Zone** : 10B-11

Typical Height : 15 Ft.
Drought Tolerance : Medium
Nutritional Requirements : Medium
Light Requirements : High
Leaf Type : Simple; two-lobed
Texture : Medium
Flower Characteristics : Showy

Environmental Problems : None

Bauhinia variegata *(Photograph p. 154)*

Common Name(s) : Orchid Tree; Buddhist Bauhinia
Origin : India
Growth Rate : Fast
Salt Tolerance : Low
Soil Requirements : Wide
Plant Type : Deciduous tree
Foliage Color : Green
Flowering Season : Spring
Flower Color : White; purple; lavender
Propagation : Seeds
Human Hazards : None
Common Uses : Flowering tree
Major Problems : K deficiency; borers
Additional Notes : Showy trees but weak-wooded and messy.
Cultivars
'CANDIDA' has white flowers.

Family : Leguminosae   **Zone** : 9-11

Typical Height : 30 Ft.
Drought Tolerance : High
Nutritional Requirements : Medium
Light Requirements : High
Leaf Type : Simple; two-lobed
Texture : Coarse
Flower Characteristics : Showy

Environmental Problems : Weak; messy

Beaucarnea gracilis

Common Name(s) : Bottle Ponytail
Origin : Mexico
Growth Rate : Slow
Salt Tolerance : Medium
Soil Requirements : Wide
Plant Type : Evergreen tree
Foliage Color : Green
Flowering Season : Spring
Flower Color : Red
Propagation : Seeds
Human Hazards : None
Common Uses : Small tree; foliage plant
Major Problems : None
Additional Notes : Large swollen base. Often erroneously called a palm.

Family : Agavaceae   **Zone** : 9-11

Typical Height : 15 Ft.
Drought Tolerance : High
Nutritional Requirements : Medium
Light Requirements : High
Leaf Type : Simple; linear
Texture : Medium
Flower Characteristics : Showy

Environmental Problems : None

Beaucarnea recurvata *(Photograph p. 153)*

Common Name(s) : Ponytail
Origin : Mexico
Growth Rate : Slow
Salt Tolerance : Medium
Soil Requirements : Wide
Plant Type : Evergreen tree
Foliage Color : Green
Flowering Season : Spring
Flower Color : White
Propagation : Seeds
Human Hazards : None
Common Uses : Small tree; foliage plant
Major Problems : Root rot
Additional Notes : Large swollen base. Often erroneously called a palm.

Family : Agavaceae   **Zone** : 9-11

Typical Height : 15 Ft.
Drought Tolerance : High
Nutritional Requirements : Medium
Light Requirements : High
Leaf Type : Simple; linear
Texture : Medium
Flower Characteristics : Showy

Environmental Problems : None

Beaumontia grandiflora

Common Name(s) : Herald's Trumpet
Origin : Northeastern India
Growth Rate : Fast
Salt Tolerance : Low
Soil Requirements : Wide
Plant Type : Evergreen vine
Foliage Color : Green
Flowering Season : Spring
Flower Color : White
Propagation : Root cuttings
Human Hazards : None
Common Uses : Flowering vine
Major Problems : None
Additional Notes : Large heavy vine requires strong support; large trumpet-shaped flowers.

Family : Apocynaceae   **Zone** : 10B-11

Typical Height : Not applicable
Drought Tolerance : Medium
Nutritional Requirements : Medium
Light Requirements : Medium; high
Leaf Type : Simple
Texture : Coarse
Flower Characteristics : Showy; fragrant

Environmental Problems : None

Befaria racemosa

Common Name(s) : Tarflower
Origin : Southeastern United States
Growth Rate : Slow
Salt Tolerance : Low
Soil Requirements : Acid
Plant Type : Evergreen shrub
Foliage Color : Green
Flowering Season : Spring; winter
Flower Color : White
Propagation : Seeds
Human Hazards : None
Common Uses : Flowering shrub; specimen plant
Major Problems : None
Additional Notes : Attractive in mass. Petals sticky, once used as flypaper.

Family : Ericaceae   **Zone** : 8-10B

Typical Height : 5 Ft.
Drought Tolerance : Medium
Nutritional Requirements : Medium
Light Requirements : Medium; high
Leaf Type : Simple
Texture : Medium
Flower Characteristics : Showy; fragrant

Environmental Problems : None

Begonia heracleifolia

Common Name(s) : Star Begonia
Origin : Mexico
Growth Rate : Medium
Salt Tolerance : Low
Soil Requirements : Wide
Plant Type : Herbaceous perennial
Foliage Color : Green; green & purple
Flowering Season : Spring
Flower Color : Pink
Propagation : Division; leaf cuttings
Human Hazards : None
Common Uses : Flowering groundcover; foliage plant
Major Problems : None
Additional Notes : Needs good drainage. Succulent star-shaped leaves.

Family : Begoniaceae   **Zone** : 10B-11

Typical Height : 2 Ft.
Drought Tolerance : Medium
Nutritional Requirements : Medium
Light Requirements : Medium
Leaf Type : Simple; palmately lobed
Texture : Coarse
Flower Characteristics : Showy

Environmental Problems : None

Begonia X rex-cultorum *(Photograph p. 191)*

Common Name(s) : Rex Begonia
Origin : Hybrid
Growth Rate : Medium
Salt Tolerance : Low
Soil Requirements : Wide
Plant Type : Herbaceous perennial
Foliage Color : Green; pink; purple; red
Flowering Season : Spring; winter
Flower Color : Pink; white
Propagation : Leaf cuttings; division
Human Hazards : None
Common Uses : Beds; foliage plant
Major Problems : Root rots
Additional Notes : Many cultivars with variable foliage. Does not like the heat in summer.

Family : Begoniaceae   **Zone** : 10B-11

Typical Height : 1 Ft.
Drought Tolerance : Low
Nutritional Requirements : Medium
Light Requirements : Low; medium
Leaf Type : Simple
Texture : Coarse
Flower Characteristics : Insignificant

Environmental Problems : None

Begonia X ricinifolia

Common Name(s) : Castor Bean Begonia
Origin : Hybrid
Growth Rate : Medium
Salt Tolerance : Low
Soil Requirements : Wide
Plant Type : Herbaceous perennial
Foliage Color : Green & red
Flowering Season : Winter; spring
Flower Color : Pink
Propagation : Division; leaf cuttings
Human Hazards : None
Common Uses : Specimen plant
Major Problems : None
Additional Notes : Has star-shaped leaves with green tops and reddish-purple undersides.

Family : Begoniaceae   Zone : 10B-11

Typical Height : 1.5 Ft.
Drought Tolerance : Medium
Nutritional Requirements : Medium
Light Requirements : Low; medium
Leaf Type : Simple; palmately lobed
Texture : Coarse
Flower Characteristics : Showy

Environmental Problems : None

Belamcanda chinensis

Common Name(s) : Blackberry Lily
Origin : China and Japan
Growth Rate : Fast
Salt Tolerance : Medium
Soil Requirements : Wide
Plant Type : Herbaceous perennial
Foliage Color : Green
Flowering Season : Summer; spring; fall
Flower Color : Orange; yellow
Propagation : Seeds; division
Human Hazards : None
Common Uses : Beds; borders; cut flowers
Major Problems : None
Additional Notes : Will naturalize where adapted; seed heads attractive.

Family : Iridaceae   Zone : 5-10A

Typical Height : 2 Ft.
Drought Tolerance : Medium
Nutritional Requirements : Low
Light Requirements : Medium; high
Leaf Type : Simple; linear
Texture : Fine
Flower Characteristics : Showy

Environmental Problems : None

Berberis julianae *(Photograph p. 173)*

Common Name(s) : Wintergreen Barberry
Origin : China
Growth Rate : Slow
Salt Tolerance : Medium
Soil Requirements : Wide
Plant Type : Evergreen shrub
Foliage Color : Green
Flowering Season : Spring
Flower Color : Yellow
Propagation : Cuttings
Human Hazards : Spiny
Common Uses : Shrub
Major Problems : None
Additional Notes : Very spiny; good barrier.

Family : Berberidaceae   Zone : 5-9

Typical Height : 5 Ft.
Drought Tolerance : Medium
Nutritional Requirements : Medium
Light Requirements : Medium; high
Leaf Type : Simple
Texture : Medium
Flower Characteristics : Insignificant

Environmental Problems : None

Berberis thunbergii *(Photograph p. 173)*

Common Name(s) : Japanese Barberry
Origin : Japan
Growth Rate : Medium
Salt Tolerance : Low
Soil Requirements : Wide
Plant Type : Deciduous shrub
Foliage Color : Green; red
Flowering Season : Spring
Flower Color : Yellow
Propagation : Cuttings; seeds
Human Hazards : Spiny
Common Uses : Hedge; shrub
Major Problems : None
Additional Notes : Persistant fruit in winter; excellent barrier plants.

Family : Berberidaceae   Zone : 4-9

Typical Height : 4 Ft.
Drought Tolerance : Medium
Nutritional Requirements : Medium
Light Requirements : Medium; high
Leaf Type : Simple
Texture : Fine
Flower Characteristics : Showy

Environmental Problems : None

Cultivars
'ATROPURPUREA' is a deep red-leaved culitvar; 'NANA', 'RED BIRD', and 'CRIMSON PYGMY' are dwarf red-leaved cultivars; 'AUREA' has yellowish foliage; 'STARKI' is thornless, spreading, and compact; 'ERECTA' is compact, but erect; 'VARIEGATA' is variegated

Berberis X mentorensis

Family : Berberidaceae   **Zone** : 5-9

Common Name(s) : Mentor Barberry
Origin : Hybrid
Growth Rate : Medium
Salt Tolerance : Low
Soil Requirements : Wide
Plant Type : Evergreen shrub
Foliage Color : Green; red
Flowering Season : Spring
Flower Color : Yellow
Propagation : Cuttings
Human Hazards : Spiny
Common Uses : Flowering shrub; hedge
Major Problems : None

Typical Height : 6 Ft.
Drought Tolerance : Medium
Nutritional Requirements : Medium
Light Requirements : Medium; high
Leaf Type : Simple
Texture : Fine
Flower Characteristics : Showy

Environmental Problems : None

Additional Notes : Thorny; hybrid of B. thunbergii and B. julianae . Good barrier plant.

Betula nigra

Family : Betulaceae   **Zone** : 4-9

Common Name(s) : River Birch
Origin : Eastern United States
Growth Rate : Fast
Salt Tolerance : Low
Soil Requirements : Wide
Plant Type : Deciduous tree
Foliage Color : Green
Flowering Season : Spring
Flower Color : Brown
Propagation : Seeds
Human Hazards : None
Common Uses : Shade tree
Major Problems : None

Typical Height : 40 Ft.
Drought Tolerance : Low
Nutritional Requirements : Medium
Light Requirements : High
Leaf Type : Simple
Texture : Medium
Flower Characteristics : Insignificant

Environmental Problems : None

Additional Notes : Suitable for wet sites in southeastern United States; attractive bark.

Bignonia capreolata

Family : Bignoniaceae   **Zone** : 7-10B

Common Name(s) : Cross Vine
Origin : Southeastern United States
Growth Rate : Fast
Salt Tolerance : Low
Soil Requirements : Wide
Plant Type : Deciduous vine
Foliage Color : Green
Flowering Season : Spring
Flower Color : Red; yellow
Propagation : Cuttings; seeds
Human Hazards : None
Common Uses : Flowering vine
Major Problems : None

Typical Height : 50 Ft.
Drought Tolerance : Low
Nutritional Requirements : Medium
Light Requirements : Medium
Leaf Type : Pinnately compound
Texture : Medium
Flower Characteristics : Showy

Environmental Problems : None

Additional Notes : A colorful native trumpet vine.

Billbergia spp.

Family : Bromeliaceae   **Zone** : 10B-11

Common Name(s) : Vase Plant
Origin : Tropical America
Growth Rate : Slow
Salt Tolerance : Low
Soil Requirements : Well-drained
Plant Type : Epiphyte
Foliage Color : Green; red; silver
Flowering Season : Spring
Flower Color : Red; pink; blue
Propagation : Seeds; division
Human Hazards : Spiny
Common Uses : Specimen plant; foliage plant; epiphyte
Major Problems : None

Typical Height : 1.5 Ft.
Drought Tolerance : Medium
Nutritional Requirements : Low
Light Requirements : Medium; high
Leaf Type : Simple; linear
Texture : Coarse
Flower Characteristics : Showy

Environmental Problems : None

Additional Notes : Sometimes used as border in deep woodchip mulch. Cup should be watered.
Cultivars
B. nutans and B. pyramidalis are most common.

Bischofia javanica

Common Name(s) : Bishopwood; Bischofia; Toog Tree
Origin : Asia
Growth Rate : Fast
Salt Tolerance : Medium
Soil Requirements : Wide
Plant Type : Evergreen tree
Foliage Color : Green
Flowering Season : Spring
Flower Color : Green-yellow
Propagation : Seeds
Human Hazards : None
Common Uses : Shade tree
Major Problems : Scales

Family : Euphorbiaceae   **Zone** : 10A-11

Typical Height : 60 Ft.
Drought Tolerance : Medium
Nutritional Requirements : Medium
Light Requirements : High
Leaf Type : Simple
Texture : Medium
Flower Characteristics : Insignificant

Environmental Problems : Weak; weedy

Additional Notes : A weak-wooded weedy tree prone to scale infestations. Not recommended.

Bismarckia nobilis *(Photograph p. 202)*

Common Name(s) : Bismarck Palm
Origin : Madagascar
Growth Rate : Slow
Salt Tolerance : Medium
Soil Requirements : Wide
Plant Type : Palm
Foliage Color : Blue-green
Flowering Season : Spring
Flower Color : White
Propagation : Seeds
Human Hazards : None
Common Uses : Tree
Major Problems : None

Family : Palmae   **Zone** : 10A-11

Typical Height : 30 Ft.
Drought Tolerance : High
Nutritional Requirements : Medium
Light Requirements : Medium; high
Leaf Type : Simple; palmately lobed
Texture : Very coarse
Flower Characteristics : Insignificant

Environmental Problems : None

Additional Notes : A beautiful fan palm. Can not be transplanted until it forms a trunk.

Bixa orellana *(Photograph p. 153)*

Common Name(s) : Annatto
Origin : Tropical America
Growth Rate : Medium
Salt Tolerance : Low
Soil Requirements : Acid
Plant Type : Evergreen tree
Foliage Color : Green
Flowering Season : Summer
Flower Color : Pink
Propagation : Seeds; cuttings
Human Hazards : None
Common Uses : Small tree; shrub
Major Problems : None

Family : Bixaceae   **Zone** : 10B-11

Typical Height : 15 Ft.
Drought Tolerance : Medium
Nutritional Requirements : Medium
Light Requirements : High
Leaf Type : Simple
Texture : Medium
Flower Characteristics : Showy

Environmental Problems : None

Additional Notes : Needs wind protection. Has showy fruit used as a dye.

Blechnum gibbum

Common Name(s) : Dwarf Tree Fern
Origin : New Caledonia and New Hebrides
Growth Rate : Medium
Salt Tolerance : Low
Soil Requirements : Acid
Plant Type : Herbaceous perennial
Foliage Color : Green
Flowering Season : n/a
Flower Color : n/a
Propagation : Spores
Human Hazards : None
Common Uses : Foliage plant; specimen plant
Major Problems : None

Family : Polypodiaceae   **Zone** : 9-11

Typical Height : 5 Ft.
Drought Tolerance : Low
Nutritional Requirements : Medium
Light Requirements : Low; medium
Leaf Type : Pinnately compound
Texture : Medium
Flower Characteristics : n/a

Environmental Problems : None

Additional Notes : Can produce a trunk up to 5 ft tall.

Blechnum serrulatum

Common Name(s) : Swamp Fern; Saw Fern
Origin : Florida to South America
Growth Rate : Medium
Salt Tolerance : Low
Soil Requirements : Acid
Plant Type : Herbaceous perennial
Foliage Color : Green
Flowering Season : n/a
Flower Color : n/a
Propagation : Spores
Human Hazards : None
Common Uses : Foliage plant; specimen plant
Major Problems : None
Additional Notes : Very tolerant of low light conditions.

Family : Polypodiaceae   **Zone** : 9-11

Typical Height : 2 Ft.
Drought Tolerance : Low
Nutritional Requirements : Medium
Light Requirements : Low; medium
Leaf Type : Pinnately compound
Texture : Medium
Flower Characteristics : n/a

Environmental Problems : None

Bletilla striata

Common Name(s) : Bletia
Origin : China and Japan
Growth Rate : Slow
Salt Tolerance : Low
Soil Requirements : Acid; well-drained
Plant Type : Herbaceous perennial
Foliage Color : Green
Flowering Season : Summer
Flower Color : Pink
Propagation : Division
Human Hazards : None
Common Uses : Rock gardens
Major Problems : None
Additional Notes : A hardy, terrestrial orchid of fairly easy culture; needs good drainage.
Cultivars
'ALBA' has white flowers.

Family : Orchidaceae   **Zone** : 8-10A

Typical Height : 1 Ft.
Drought Tolerance : Medium
Nutritional Requirements : High
Light Requirements : Medium
Leaf Type : Simple
Texture : Medium
Flower Characteristics : Showy

Environmental Problems : None

Blighia sapida *(Photograph p. 154)*

Common Name(s) : Akee; Vegetable Brain
Origin : West Africa
Growth Rate : Fast
Salt Tolerance : Medium
Soil Requirements : Wide
Plant Type : Evergreen tree
Foliage Color : Green
Flowering Season : Spring
Flower Color : White
Propagation : Seeds; air layering
Human Hazards : Poisonous
Common Uses : Shade tree; edible fruit
Major Problems : None
Additional Notes : Attractive red fruit can be messy; immature and overripe fruit poisonous.

Family : Sapindaceae   **Zone** : 10B-11

Typical Height : 35 Ft.
Drought Tolerance : High
Nutritional Requirements : Medium
Light Requirements : High
Leaf Type : Pinnately compound
Texture : Medium
Flower Characteristics : Insignificant

Environmental Problems : Messy

Bombacopsis fendleri

Common Name(s) : Fence Pochote
Origin : Nicaragua to Colombia
Growth Rate : Fast
Salt Tolerance : Low
Soil Requirements : Wide
Plant Type : Deciduous tree
Foliage Color : Green
Flowering Season : Spring
Flower Color : Brown & white
Propagation : Seeds
Human Hazards : Spiny
Common Uses : Large flowering tree
Major Problems : None
Additional Notes : A large tree with buttressed trunk covered with stout spines.

Family : Bombacaceae   **Zone** : 10B-11

Typical Height : 80 Ft.
Drought Tolerance : Medium
Nutritional Requirements : Medium
Light Requirements : High
Leaf Type : Palmately compound
Texture : Medium
Flower Characteristics : Showy

Environmental Problems : None

Bombax ceiba

Common Name(s) : Red Silk-cotton Tree
Origin : Southeast Asia, Australia, East Indies
Growth Rate : Medium
Salt Tolerance : Low
Soil Requirements : Wide
Plant Type : Deciduous tree
Foliage Color : Green
Flowering Season : Winter
Flower Color : Red
Propagation : Seeds; large cuttings; air layers
Human Hazards : None
Common Uses : Flowering tree
Major Problems : None
Additional Notes : Spectacular flowers after leaves drop.

Family : Bombacaceae   **Zone** : 10A-11

Typical Height : 60 Ft.
Drought Tolerance : Medium
Nutritional Requirements : Medium
Light Requirements : High
Leaf Type : Palmately compound
Texture : Medium
Flower Characteristics : Showy

Environmental Problems : None

Borrichia arborescens

Common Name(s) : Silver Sea Oxeye
Origin : South Florida
Growth Rate : Medium
Salt Tolerance : High
Soil Requirements : Well-drained
Plant Type : Evergreen shrub
Foliage Color : Silver-green; green;
Flowering Season : Spring; summer
Flower Color : Yellow
Propagation : Seeds; cuttings
Human Hazards : None
Common Uses : Flowering perennial; flowering groundcover
Major Problems : Root rots
Additional Notes : A green species (B. frutescens) also exists.

Family : Compositae   **Zone** : 10A-11

Typical Height : 3 Ft.
Drought Tolerance : High
Nutritional Requirements : Low
Light Requirements : High
Leaf Type : Simple
Texture : Medium
Flower Characteristics : Showy

Environmental Problems : None

Bougainvillea glabra *(Photograph p. 173)*

Common Name(s) : Lesser Bougainvillea; Paper Flower
Origin : Brazil
Growth Rate : Medium
Salt Tolerance : High
Soil Requirements : Wide
Plant Type : Evergreen shrub or vine
Foliage Color : Green
Flowering Season : Year-round
Flower Color : Purple
Propagation : Cuttings
Human Hazards : Spiny
Common Uses : Flowering shrub; flowering vine
Major Problems : Caterpillars
Additional Notes : Similar to B. spectabilis , but leaves have a narrow base.

Family : Nyctaginaceae   **Zone** : 10B-11

Typical Height : 8 Ft.
Drought Tolerance : High
Nutritional Requirements : Low
Light Requirements : High
Leaf Type : Simple
Texture : Medium
Flower Characteristics : Showy

Environmental Problems : None

Bougainvillea spectabilis

Common Name(s) : Bougainvillea
Origin : Brazil
Growth Rate : Medium
Salt Tolerance : High
Soil Requirements : Wide
Plant Type : Evergreen shrub or vine
Foliage Color : Green; variegated
Flowering Season : Year-round
Flower Color : Red; pink; white; orange; purple
Propagation : Cuttings
Human Hazards : Spiny
Common Uses : Flowering shrub; flowering vine
Major Problems : Caterpillars
Additional Notes : A rambling, drought resistant vine. Blooms on new growth.
Cultivars

Family : Nyctaginaceae   **Zone** : 10B-11

Typical Height : 20 Ft.
Drought Tolerance : High
Nutritional Requirements : Medium
Light Requirements : High
Leaf Type : Simple
Texture : Medium
Flower Characteristics : Showy

Environmental Problems : None

'BARBARA KARST' has red single flowers; 'CALIFORNIA GOLD' has golden single flowers; 'JAMAICA WHITE'
has white single flowers; 'SCARLETT O'HARA' has red single flowers; 'TEXAS DAWN' has rose-colored single
flowers; 'TAHITIAN DAWN' has golden single flowers darkening to mauve with age;
  'CHERRY BLOSSOM' and 'TAHITIAN MAID' are double pink varieties.

Bourreria succulenta var. revoluta

Common Name(s) : Strongbark
Origin : South Florida and West Indies
Growth Rate : Medium
Salt Tolerance : Medium
Soil Requirements : Wide
Plant Type : Evergreen tree or shrub
Foliage Color : Green
Flowering Season : Year-round
Flower Color : White
Propagation : Seeds
Human Hazards : None
Common Uses : Small tree; shrub
Major Problems : None
Additional Notes : Can be a large shrub. Native to the Keys.

Family : Boraginaceae   **Zone** : 10B-11

Typical Height : 20 Ft.
Drought Tolerance : High
Nutritional Requirements : Low
Light Requirements : High
Leaf Type : Simple
Texture : Medium
Flower Characteristics : Insignificant

Environmental Problems : None

Brachychiton acerifolius *(Photograph p. 154)*

Common Name(s) : Flame Bottle Tree
Origin : Eastern Australia
Growth Rate : Fast
Salt Tolerance : Medium
Soil Requirements : Wide
Plant Type : Deciduous tree
Foliage Color : Green
Flowering Season : Spring; summer
Flower Color : Red
Propagation : Seeds; cuttings
Human Hazards : None
Common Uses : Flowering tree; shade tree
Major Problems : None
Additional Notes : Leafless when in flower. Leaves deeply lobed. Other species exist.

Family : Sterculiaceae   **Zone** : 10A-11

Typical Height : 40 Ft.
Drought Tolerance : High
Nutritional Requirements : Medium
Light Requirements : High
Leaf Type : Simple; palmately lobed
Texture : Medium
Flower Characteristics : Showy

Environmental Problems : None

Brachychiton discolor

Common Name(s) : Scrub Bottle Tree
Origin : Australia
Growth Rate : Fast
Salt Tolerance : Medium
Soil Requirements : Wide
Plant Type : Evergreen tree
Foliage Color : Green
Flowering Season : Spring
Flower Color : Pink
Propagation : Seeds; cuttings
Human Hazards : None
Common Uses : Flowering tree
Major Problems : None
Additional Notes : May be deciduous in cooler areas

Family : Sterculiaceae   **Zone** : 10A-11

Typical Height : 80 Ft.
Drought Tolerance : High
Nutritional Requirements : Low
Light Requirements : High
Leaf Type : Palmately lobed
Texture : Medium
Flower Characteristics : Showy

Environmental Problems : None

Brassaia actinophylla *(Photograph p. 174)*

Common Name(s) : Schefflera; Umbrella Tree; Octopus Tree
Origin : Australia
Growth Rate : Medium
Salt Tolerance : Medium
Soil Requirements : Wide
Plant Type : Evergreen tree or shrub
Foliage Color : Green
Flowering Season : Summer
Flower Color : Red
Propagation : Seeds
Human Hazards : None
Common Uses : Small tree; large shrub; foliage plant
Major Problems : Scales; sooty mold
Additional Notes : Unusual red inflorescences. Now reclassified as <u>Schefflera</u> .
Cultivars

Family : Araliaceae   **Zone** : 10B-11

Typical Height : 25 Ft.
Drought Tolerance : High
Nutritional Requirements : Medium
Light Requirements : High; medium
Leaf Type : Palmately compound
Texture : Coarse
Flower Characteristics : Showy

Environmental Problems : Invasive; messy

'AMATE' has thicker leaves and is resistant to alternaria leafspot; 'DANIA' has more pointed leaflets and is resistant to alternaria.

Breynia disticha *(Photograph p. 174)*

Common Name(s) : Snowbush
Origin : Pacific Islands
Growth Rate : Medium
Salt Tolerance : Low
Soil Requirements : Wide
Plant Type : Evergreen shrub
Foliage Color : Variegated;purple; pink
Flowering Season : Summer
Flower Color : White
Propagation : Cuttings
Human Hazards : None
Common Uses : Specimen plant; shrub
Major Problems : Caterpillars; mites
Additional Notes : Fine textured variegated foliage. Requires pruning; can become a pest.
Cultivars
'ATROPURPUREA' has dark purple leaves; 'ROSEO-PICTA' has leaves mottled with pink and red.

Family : Euphorbiaceae   **Zone** : 10B-11

Typical Height : 6 Ft.
Drought Tolerance : Medium
Nutritional Requirements : Medium
Light Requirements : High; medium
Leaf Type : Simple
Texture : Fine
Flower Characteristics : Insignificant

Environmental Problems : Weedy

Broussonetia papyrifera

Common Name(s) : Paper Mulberry
Origin : East Asia to Polynesia
Growth Rate : Fast
Salt Tolerance : Medium
Soil Requirements : Wide
Plant Type : Deciduous tree
Foliage Color : Green
Flowering Season : Spring
Flower Color : Green
Propagation : Seeds; cuttings; suckers
Human Hazards : None
Common Uses : Shade tree
Major Problems : None
Additional Notes : Has variable-shaped leaves; a tough, fast tree for cities.

Family : Moraceae   **Zone** : 6-10A

Typical Height : 30 Ft.
Drought Tolerance : High
Nutritional Requirements : Low
Light Requirements : High
Leaf Type : Simple
Texture : Medium
Flower Characteristics : Insignificant

Environmental Problems : Weedy

Brugmansia versicolor

Common Name(s) : Angel's Trumpet
Origin : Ecuador
Growth Rate : Medium
Salt Tolerance : Low
Soil Requirements : Wide
Plant Type : Evergreen shrub or tree
Foliage Color : Green
Flowering Season : Summer
Flower Color : White; pink
Propagation : Cuttings
Human Hazards : Poisonous
Common Uses : Flowering shrub; small flowering tree
Major Problems : Mealybugs; nematodes
Additional Notes : Flowers are poisonous.

Family : Solanaceae   **Zone** : 10B-11

Typical Height : 12 Ft.
Drought Tolerance : Low
Nutritional Requirements : Medium
Light Requirements : Medium; high
Leaf Type : Simple
Texture : Coarse
Flower Characteristics : Showy; fragrant

Environmental Problems : None

Brugmansia X candida *(Photograph p. 174)*

Common Name(s) : Angel's Trumpet
Origin : Hybrid
Growth Rate : Fast
Salt Tolerance : Low
Soil Requirements : Wide
Plant Type : Evergreen shrub or tree
Foliage Color : Green
Flowering Season : Summer
Flower Color : White; pink; yellow
Propagation : Cuttings
Human Hazards : Poisonous
Common Uses : Flowering shrub; small flowering tree
Major Problems : Mealybugs; nematodes
Additional Notes : Flowers are poisonous.

Family : Solanaceae   **Zone** : 10B-11

Typical Height : 14 Ft.
Drought Tolerance : Low
Nutritional Requirements : Medium
Light Requirements : Medium; high
Leaf Type : Simple
Texture : Coarse
Flower Characteristics : Showy; fragrant

Environmental Problems : None

Brunfelsia americana

Common Name(s) : Lady-of-the-night
Origin : Tropical America and West Indies
Growth Rate : Medium
Salt Tolerance : Medium
Soil Requirements : Wide
Plant Type : Evergreen shrub
Foliage Color : Green
Flowering Season : Spring; summer; fall
Flower Color : White
Propagation : Seeds; cuttings
Human Hazards : None
Common Uses : Flowering shrub
Major Problems : None
Additional Notes : White tubular flowers turn yellow with age.

Family : Solanaceae   Zone : 10B-11

Typical Height : 10 Ft.
Drought Tolerance : Medium
Nutritional Requirements : Medium
Light Requirements : High
Leaf Type : Simple
Texture : Medium
Flower Characteristics : Showy; fragrant

Environmental Problems : None

Brunfelsia australis *(Photograph p. 174)*

Common Name(s) : Yesterday-today-and-tomorrow
Origin : Southern Brazil
Growth Rate : Medium
Salt Tolerance : Low
Soil Requirements : Wide
Plant Type : Evergreen shrub
Foliage Color : Green
Flowering Season : Summer; fall
Flower Color : Lavender; white
Propagation : Seeds; cuttings
Human Hazards : None
Common Uses : Specimen plant; flowering shrub
Major Problems : None
Additional Notes : Flowers fade from lavender to white.

Family : Solanaceae   Zone : 10B-11

Typical Height : 8 Ft.
Drought Tolerance : Medium
Nutritional Requirements : Medium
Light Requirements : High; medium
Leaf Type : Simple
Texture : Medium
Flower Characteristics : Showy; fragrant

Environmental Problems : None

Brunfelsia grandiflora

Common Name(s) : n/a
Origin : Venezuela to Bolivia
Growth Rate : Medium
Salt Tolerance : Medium
Soil Requirements : Wide
Plant Type : Evergreen shrub
Foliage Color : Green
Flowering Season : Spring; summer; fall
Flower Color : Purple & white
Propagation : Seeds; cuttings
Human Hazards : None
Common Uses : Flowering shrub
Major Problems : None
Additional Notes : Has purple flowers with white centers.

Family : Solanaceae   Zone : 10B-11

Typical Height : 10 Ft.
Drought Tolerance : Medium
Nutritional Requirements : Medium
Light Requirements : High
Leaf Type : Simple
Texture : Medium
Flower Characteristics : Showy

Environmental Problems : None

Brunfelsia pauciflora

Common Name(s) : Yesterday-today-and-tomorrow
Origin : Brazil
Growth Rate : Medium
Salt Tolerance : Medium
Soil Requirements : Wide
Plant Type : Evergreen shrub
Foliage Color : Green
Flowering Season : Spring; summer; fall
Flower Color : Purple & white
Propagation : Seeds; cuttings
Human Hazards : None
Common Uses : Flowering shrub
Major Problems : None
Additional Notes : Has purple flowers that fade to white as they age.
Cultivars
'FLORIBUNDA' is a more free-flowering form; 'MACRANTHA' has very large flowers.

Family : Solanaceae   Zone : 10B-11

Typical Height : 9 Ft.
Drought Tolerance : Medium
Nutritional Requirements : Medium
Light Requirements : High
Leaf Type : Simple
Texture : Medium
Flower Characteristics : Showy

Environmental Problems : None

Brya ebenus

Common Name(s) : Jamaican Rain Tree; West Indian Ebony

Family : Leguminosae   Zone : 10B-11

Origin : West Indies
Growth Rate : Medium
Salt Tolerance : Medium
Soil Requirements : Wide
Plant Type : Evergreen shrub or tree
Foliage Color : Green
Flowering Season : Year-round
Flower Color : Yellow-orange
Propagation : Seeds
Human Hazards : Spiny
Common Uses : Flowering shrub; small flowering tree
Major Problems : None
Additional Notes : Can be grown as a shrub; flowers at a young age; spiny.

Typical Height : 30 Ft.
Drought Tolerance : High
Nutritional Requirements : Low
Light Requirements : High
Leaf Type : Simple
Texture : Fine
Flower Characteristics : Showy

Environmental Problems : None

Bucida buceras

Common Name(s) : Black Olive

Family : Combretaceae   Zone : 10B-11

Origin : West Indies; Central America
Growth Rate : Medium
Salt Tolerance : High
Soil Requirements : Wide
Plant Type : Evergreen tree
Foliage Color : Green
Flowering Season : Spring
Flower Color : Green
Propagation : Seeds; air layers
Human Hazards : Spiny
Common Uses : Shade tree
Major Problems : Eriophyd mites
Additional Notes : Leaves variable in size; can be spiny; leaves stain masonry.
Cultivars
'SHADY LADY' has smaller leaves and more compact growth and some shade tolerance.

Typical Height : 45 Ft.
Drought Tolerance : High
Nutritional Requirements : Medium
Light Requirements : High
Leaf Type : Simple
Texture : Medium
Flower Characteristics : Insignificant

Environmental Problems : None

Bucida spinosa

Common Name(s) : Spiny Black Olive

Family : Combretaceae   Zone : 10B-11

Origin : Bahamas, Cuba
Growth Rate : Slow
Salt Tolerance : Medium
Soil Requirements : Wide
Plant Type : Evergreen shrub or tree
Foliage Color : Green
Flowering Season : Year-round
Flower Color : White
Propagation : Seeds
Human Hazards : Spiny
Common Uses : Small tree; shrub
Major Problems : None
Additional Notes : A small, spiny cousin of the black olive; excellent for bonsai.

Typical Height : 18 Ft.
Drought Tolerance : High
Nutritional Requirements : Medium
Light Requirements : High
Leaf Type : Simple
Texture : Fine
Flower Characteristics : Insignificant

Environmental Problems : None

Buddleia asiatica

Common Name(s) : Asian Butterfly Bush

Family : Loganiaceae   Zone : 9-10A

Origin : Southeast Asia and South Pacific
Growth Rate : Medium
Salt Tolerance : Low
Soil Requirements : Wide
Plant Type : Evergreen shrub or tree
Foliage Color : Green
Flowering Season : Winter; spring
Flower Color : White
Propagation : Seeds; cuttings
Human Hazards : Poisonous
Common Uses : Flowering shrub; small flowering tree
Major Problems : Nematodes; mites; caterpillars
Additional Notes : Several other species also cultivated. Best in north & central Florida.

Typical Height : 12 Ft.
Drought Tolerance : Medium
Nutritional Requirements : Medium
Light Requirements : High
Leaf Type : Simple
Texture : Coarse
Flower Characteristics : Showy; fragrant

Environmental Problems : None

Buddleia officinalis

Common Name(s) : Butterfly Bush
Origin : Western China
Growth Rate : Fast
Salt Tolerance : Medium
Soil Requirements : Wide
Plant Type : Evergreen shrub
Foliage Color : Green
Flowering Season : Winter
Flower Color : Lavender
Propagation : Seeds; cuttings
Human Hazards : None
Common Uses : Specimen plant; flowering shrub
Major Problems : Nematodes; caterpillars
Additional Notes : Small fragrant flowers. Dies to ground in north Florida.

Family : Loganiaceae   **Zone** : 8-10B

Typical Height : 13 Ft.
Drought Tolerance : Medium
Nutritional Requirements : Medium
Light Requirements : High
Leaf Type : Simple
Texture : Medium
Flower Characteristics : Showy; fragrant

Environmental Problems : None

Bulnesia arborea *(Photograph p. 154)*

Common Name(s) : Bulnesia
Origin : Colombia and Venezuela
Growth Rate : Medium
Salt Tolerance : Low
Soil Requirements : Wide
Plant Type : Evergreen tree
Foliage Color : Green
Flowering Season : Spring; summer; fall
Flower Color : Yellow-orange
Propagation : Seeds; cuttings; air layering
Human Hazards : None
Common Uses : Flowering tree; shade tree
Major Problems : None
Additional Notes : A beautiful flowering tree. Pot-bound plants produce weak-rooted trees.

Family : Zygophyllaceae   **Zone** : 10B-11

Typical Height : 30 Ft.
Drought Tolerance : High
Nutritional Requirements : Medium
Light Requirements : High
Leaf Type : Pinnately compound
Texture : Fine
Flower Characteristics : Showy

Environmental Problems : Weak

Bumelia reclinata

Common Name(s) : Slender Buckthorn
Origin : Florida
Growth Rate : Medium
Salt Tolerance : High
Soil Requirements : Wide
Plant Type : Evergreen shrub
Foliage Color : Green
Flowering Season : Fall
Flower Color : White
Propagation : Seeds
Human Hazards : Spiny
Common Uses : Shrub
Major Problems : None

Family : Sapotaceae   **Zone** : 9-10B

Typical Height : 6 Ft.
Drought Tolerance : High
Nutritional Requirements : Low
Light Requirements : High
Leaf Type : Simple
Texture : Medium
Flower Characteristics : Insignificant

Environmental Problems : None

Bumelia tenax

Common Name(s) : Tough Buckhorn
Origin : Coastal Southeastern United States
Growth Rate : Slow
Salt Tolerance : High
Soil Requirements : Wide
Plant Type : Evergreen shrub or tree
Foliage Color : Green
Flowering Season : Year-round
Flower Color : White
Propagation : Seeds
Human Hazards : Spiny
Common Uses : Small tree; shrub
Major Problems : None
Additional Notes : Stems are silky pubescent.

Family : Sapotaceae   **Zone** : 8-11

Typical Height : 20 Ft.
Drought Tolerance : High
Nutritional Requirements : Low
Light Requirements : High
Leaf Type : Simple
Texture : Medium
Flower Characteristics : Insignificant

Environmental Problems : None

Burbidgea schizocheila *(Photograph p. 192)*   Family : Zingiberaceae   Zone : 10B-11

Common Name(s) : Burbidgea
Origin : Malaysia   Typical Height : 1.5 Ft.
Growth Rate : Medium   Drought Tolerance : Medium
Salt Tolerance : Medium   Nutritional Requirements : Medium
Soil Requirements : Wide   Light Requirements : Low; medium
Plant Type : Herbaceous perennial   Leaf Type : Simple
Foliage Color : Green   Texture : Medium
Flowering Season : Year-round   Flower Characteristics : Showy
Flower Color : Orange
Propagation : Seeds; division
Human Hazards : None   Environmental Problems : None
Common Uses : Specimen plant; foliage plant; flowering pot plant
Major Problems : None
Additional Notes : Cut out stems after flowering to force new growth and more flowers.

Bursera simaruba *(Photograph p. 154)*   Family : Burseraceae   Zone : 10B-11

Common Name(s) : Gumbo Limbo; Tourist Tree
Origin : Caribbean Region   Typical Height : 50 Ft.
Growth Rate : Medium   Drought Tolerance : High
Salt Tolerance : High   Nutritional Requirements : Low
Soil Requirements : Wide   Light Requirements : High
Plant Type : Deciduous tree   Leaf Type : Pinnately compound
Foliage Color : Green   Texture : Medium
Flowering Season : Winter; spring   Flower Characteristics : Insignificant
Flower Color : Green
Propagation : Seeds; large cuttings
Human Hazards : None   Environmental Problems : Weak
Common Uses : Shade tree
Major Problems : None
Additional Notes : Large branches root directly in the ground; attractive bark; weak wood.

Butea monosperma *(Photograph p. 155)*   Family : Leguminosae   Zone : 10B-11

Common Name(s) : Flame of The Forest
Origin : India to Burma   Typical Height : 45 Ft.
Growth Rate : Medium   Drought Tolerance : High
Salt Tolerance : Medium   Nutritional Requirements : Medium
Soil Requirements : Wide   Light Requirements : High
Plant Type : Deciduous tree   Leaf Type : Pinnately compound
Foliage Color : Green   Texture : Coarse
Flowering Season : Winter   Flower Characteristics : Showy
Flower Color : Orange; red
Propagation : Seeds; suckers
Human Hazards : None   Environmental Problems : None
Common Uses : Flowering tree
Major Problems : None
Additional Notes : Trunk generally crooked. Leafless when in flower.

Butia capitata *(Photograph p. 202)*   Family : Palmae   Zone : 8-10B

Common Name(s) : Pindo Palm; Jelly Palm
Origin : Brazil, Argentina, Paraguay   Typical Height : 15 Ft.
Growth Rate : Slow   Drought Tolerance : High
Salt Tolerance : Medium   Nutritional Requirements : Medium
Soil Requirements : Wide   Light Requirements : Medium; high
Plant Type : Palm   Leaf Type : Pinnately compound
Foliage Color : Blue-green   Texture : Medium
Flowering Season : Spring   Flower Characteristics : Insignificant
Flower Color : White
Propagation : Seeds
Human Hazards : Spiny   Environmental Problems : None
Common Uses : Edible fruit; small tree
Major Problems : Scales
Additional Notes : Edible fruit used for jelly.

Buxus microphylla var. japonica

Common Name(s) : Japanese Boxwood; Littleleaf Box
Origin : Japan
Growth Rate : Medium
Salt Tolerance : Low
Soil Requirements : Acid
Plant Type : Evergreen shrub
Foliage Color : Green
Flowering Season : Summer
Flower Color : White
Propagation : Cuttings; suckers; seeds
Human Hazards : Poisonous
Common Uses : Shrub; hedge; groundcover
Major Problems : Nematodes
Additional Notes : Requires nematode-free soil. Grows best in central & north Florida.
Cultivars

Family : Buxaceae   **Zone** : 6-10A

Typical Height : 4 Ft.
Drought Tolerance : Medium
Nutritional Requirements : Medium
Light Requirements : Medium; high
Leaf Type : Simple
Texture : Fine
Flower Characteristics : Insignificant

Environmental Problems : None

'COMPACTA' is a very compact cultivar; 'GREEN PILLOW' is similar to 'COMPACTA' but has leaves twice as large; 'GREEN BEAUTY' is an upright form; 'WINTER GEM' has dark green foliage, even in winter.

Buxus microphylla var. koreana

Common Name(s) : Korean Boxwood
Origin : China
Growth Rate : Slow
Salt Tolerance : Low
Soil Requirements : Acid
Plant Type : Evergreen shrub
Foliage Color : Green
Flowering Season : Summer
Flower Color : White
Propagation : Cuttings
Human Hazards : Poisonous
Common Uses : Hedge; groundcover; shrub
Major Problems : Nematodes; stem and root rots

Family : Buxaceae   **Zone** : 8-10B

Typical Height : 2 Ft.
Drought Tolerance : Medium
Nutritional Requirements : Medium
Light Requirements : Medium; high
Leaf Type : Simple
Texture : Fine
Flower Characteristics : Insignificant

Environmental Problems : None

Byrsonima lucida

Common Name(s) : Locustberry
Origin : South Florida and West Indies
Growth Rate : Medium
Salt Tolerance : Medium
Soil Requirements : Wide
Plant Type : Evergreen shrub or tree
Foliage Color : Green
Flowering Season : Spring; summer
Flower Color : Pink; white; yellow
Propagation : Seeds
Human Hazards : None
Common Uses : Flowering shrub; small flowering tree
Major Problems : None
Additional Notes : Variable flower color. Somewhat sensitive to overwatering.

Family : Malpighiaceae   **Zone** : 10B-11

Typical Height : 20 Ft.
Drought Tolerance : High
Nutritional Requirements : Medium
Light Requirements : High
Leaf Type : Simple
Texture : Medium
Flower Characteristics : Showy

Environmental Problems : None

Caesalpinia gilliesii

Common Name(s) : Bird of Paradise Shrub
Origin : Argentina and Uruguay
Growth Rate : Medium
Salt Tolerance : Low
Soil Requirements : Wide
Plant Type : Evergreen shrub
Foliage Color : Green
Flowering Season : Summer
Flower Color : Yellow & red
Propagation : Seeds
Human Hazards : None
Common Uses : Flowering shrub
Major Problems : None
Additional Notes : A scraggly shrub with attractive filamentous flowers.

Family : Leguminosae   **Zone** : 8-10B

Typical Height : 10 Ft.
Drought Tolerance : Medium
Nutritional Requirements : Medium
Light Requirements : High
Leaf Type : Bipinnately compound
Texture : Fine
Flower Characteristics : Showy

Environmental Problems : None

Caesalpinia granadillo *(Photograph p. 154, 155)*

Common Name(s) : Bridalveil Tree
Origin : Northern South America
Growth Rate : Medium
Salt Tolerance : Low
Soil Requirements : Wide
Plant Type : Evergreen tree
Foliage Color : Green
Flowering Season : Summer; fall
Flower Color : Yellow
Propagation : Seeds
Human Hazards : None
Common Uses : Flowering tree; shade tree
Major Problems : None

Family : Leguminosae   Zone : 10B-11

Typical Height : 35 Ft.
Drought Tolerance : Medium
Nutritional Requirements : Medium
Light Requirements : High
Leaf Type : Pinnately compound
Texture : Fine
Flower Characteristics : Showy

Environmental Problems : None

Additional Notes : A new tree with beautiful exfoliating bark. Tends to cross branches.

Caesalpinia mexicana

Common Name(s) : Mexican Caesalpinea
Origin : Mexico
Growth Rate : Medium
Salt Tolerance : Low
Soil Requirements : Wide
Plant Type : Evergreen tree
Foliage Color : Green
Flowering Season : Summer
Flower Color : Yellow
Propagation : Seeds
Human Hazards : None
Common Uses : Flowering tree; shade tree
Major Problems : None

Family : Leguminosae   Zone : 10B-11

Typical Height : 25 Ft.
Drought Tolerance : Medium
Nutritional Requirements : Medium
Light Requirements : High
Leaf Type : Pinnately compound
Texture : Fine
Flower Characteristics : Showy

Environmental Problems : None

Additional Notes : Similar to C. granadillo , but not as large.

Caesalpinia pulcherrima *(Photograph p. 174)*

Common Name(s) : Dwarf Poinciana
Origin : West Indies
Growth Rate : Fast
Salt Tolerance : Medium
Soil Requirements : Wide
Plant Type : Evergreen shrub
Foliage Color : Green
Flowering Season : Spring; summer; fall
Flower Color : Orange; yellow
Propagation : Seeds
Human Hazards : Poisonous
Common Uses : Flowering shrub
Major Problems : Scales; mushroom root rot
Additional Notes : Deciduous in colder areas.

Family : Leguminosae   Zone : 9-11

Typical Height : 9 Ft.
Drought Tolerance : High
Nutritional Requirements : Medium
Light Requirements : High
Leaf Type : Bipinnately compound
Texture : Fine
Flower Characteristics : Showy

Environmental Problems : None

Caladium X hortulanum *(Photograph p. 192)*

Common Name(s) : Fancy-leaved Caladium; Caladium
Origin : Hybrid
Growth Rate : Medium
Salt Tolerance : Low
Soil Requirements : Wide
Plant Type : Herbaceous perennial
Foliage Color : Green; pink; purple; red
Flowering Season : Summer
Flower Color : Green
Propagation : Division
Human Hazards : None
Common Uses : Beds; foliage plant
Major Problems : Whiteflies; mealybugs; mites

Family : Araceae   Zone : 9-11

Typical Height : 1.5 Ft.
Drought Tolerance : Low
Nutritional Requirements : Medium
Light Requirements : Medium; high
Leaf Type : Simple
Texture : Coarse
Flower Characteristics : Insignificant

Environmental Problems : None

Additional Notes : Dormant in the winter. Many cultivars. Susceptible to nematodes.
Cultivars
'CANDIDUM' has white leaves with green borders; 'PINK CLOUD' and 'PINK BEAUTY' have pink foliage marked with green; 'CAROLYN WHORTON' has dark rosy-pink and white foliage.

Calathea bachemiana

Common Name(s) : Calathea
Origin : Brazil
Growth Rate : Medium
Salt Tolerance : Low
Soil Requirements : Wide
Plant Type : Herbaceous perennial
Foliage Color : Green & silver
Flowering Season : Summer
Flower Color : n/a
Propagation : Division; tissue culture
Human Hazards : None
Common Uses : Beds; specimen plant; foliage plant
Major Problems : K deficiency
Additional Notes : Has attractive green and silver striped leaves. Narrower than C. bella .

Family : Marantaceae   Zone : 10B-11

Typical Height : 1.5 Ft.
Drought Tolerance : Low
Nutritional Requirements : Medium
Light Requirements : Low; medium
Leaf Type : Simple
Texture : Coarse
Flower Characteristics : Insignificant

Environmental Problems : None

Calathea bella

Common Name(s) : Bella Calathea
Origin : Brazil
Growth Rate : Medium
Salt Tolerance : Low
Soil Requirements : Wide
Plant Type : Herbaceous perennial
Foliage Color : Green & silver
Flowering Season : Summer
Flower Color : n/a
Propagation : Division; tissue culture
Human Hazards : None
Common Uses : Beds; specimen plant; foliage plant
Major Problems : K deficiency
Additional Notes : Has attractive green and silver striped leaves.

Family : Marantaceae   Zone : 10B-11

Typical Height : 1.5 Ft.
Drought Tolerance : Low
Nutritional Requirements : Medium
Light Requirements : Low; medium
Leaf Type : Simple
Texture : Coarse
Flower Characteristics : Insignificant

Environmental Problems : None

Calathea lancifolia (Photograph p. 192)

Common Name(s) : Rattlesnake Plant
Origin : Brazil
Growth Rate : Slow
Salt Tolerance : Low
Soil Requirements : Wide
Plant Type : Herbaceous perennial
Foliage Color : Green & red
Flowering Season : n/a
Flower Color : n/a
Propagation : Division; tissue culture
Human Hazards : None
Common Uses : Cut foliage; foliage plant; specimen plant; groundcover; borders
Major Problems : K deficiency
Additional Notes : Has narrow leaves with green and dark green blotches above and red below.

Family : Marantaceae   Zone : 10A-11

Typical Height : 1.5 Ft.
Drought Tolerance : Low
Nutritional Requirements : Medium
Light Requirements : Low; medium
Leaf Type : Simple
Texture : Coarse
Flower Characteristics : Insignificant

Environmental Problems : None

Calathea louisae

Common Name(s) : Calathea
Origin : Brazil
Growth Rate : Medium
Salt Tolerance : Low
Soil Requirements : Wide
Plant Type : Herbaceous perennial
Foliage Color : Green & white & purple
Flowering Season : Summer
Flower Color : White
Propagation : Division; tissue culture
Human Hazards : None
Common Uses : Beds; specimen plant; foliage plant
Major Problems : K deficiency
Additional Notes : Has attractive green and white patterned leaves with purplish undersides.

Family : Marantaceae   Zone : 10B-11

Typical Height : 2.5 Ft.
Drought Tolerance : Low
Nutritional Requirements : Medium
Light Requirements : Low; medium
Leaf Type : Simple
Texture : Coarse
Flower Characteristics : Insignificant

Environmental Problems : None

Calathea makoyana *(Photograph p. 192)*

Common Name(s) : Peacock Plant
Origin : Brazil
Growth Rate : Slow
Salt Tolerance : Low
Soil Requirements : Wide
Plant Type : Herbaceous perennial
Foliage Color : Green and purple
Flowering Season : Summer
Flower Color : White
Propagation : Division; tissue culture
Human Hazards :

Family : Marantaceae   Zone : 10B-11

Typical Height : 1.5 Ft.
Drought Tolerance : Medium
Nutritional Requirements : Medium
Light Requirements : Low; medium
Leaf Type : Simple
Texture : Coarse
Flower Characteristics : Insignificant

Environmental Problems :

Common Uses : Foliage plant; specimen plant; groundcover; borders.
Major Problems : K deficiency
Additional Notes : Leaves have dark green spots on lighter background and purple undersides.

Calathea picturata

Common Name(s) : Calathea
Origin : Brazil and Venezuela
Growth Rate : Medium
Salt Tolerance : Low
Soil Requirements : Wide
Plant Type : Herbaceous perennial
Foliage Color : Green, silver & purple
Flowering Season : Summer
Flower Color : White
Propagation : Tissue culture; division; cuttings
Human Hazards : None

Family : Marantaceae   Zone : 10B-11

Typical Height : .8 Ft.
Drought Tolerance : Low
Nutritional Requirements : Medium
Light Requirements : Low; medium
Leaf Type : Simple
Texture : Coarse
Flower Characteristics : Insignificant

Environmental Problems : None

Common Uses : Beds; specimen plant; foliage plant
Major Problems : K deficiency
Additional Notes : Attractive foliage varies in color with the cultivar.
Cultivars
'VANDENHECKEI' has 3 silver bands along upper surface of leaves and purple undersides; 'ARGENTEA' has silver upper leaf surface with dark green margin and purple undersides.

Calathea roseopicta

Common Name(s) : Calathea
Origin : Brazil
Growth Rate : Medium
Salt Tolerance : Low
Soil Requirements : Wide
Plant Type : Herbaceous perennial
Foliage Color : Green & red & purple
Flowering Season : Summer
Flower Color : White
Propagation : Tissue culture; division; cuttings
Human Hazards : None

Family : Marantaceae   Zone : 10B-11

Typical Height : .8 Ft.
Drought Tolerance : Low
Nutritional Requirements : Medium
Light Requirements : Low; medium
Leaf Type : Simple
Texture : Coarse
Flower Characteristics : Insignificant

Environmental Problems : None

Common Uses : Beds; specimen plant; foliage plant
Major Problems : K deficiency
Additional Notes : Attractive leaves have red midrib and purple undersides.

Calathea warscewiczii

Common Name(s) : Calathea
Origin : Costa Rica
Growth Rate : Medium
Salt Tolerance : Low
Soil Requirements : Wide
Plant Type : Herbaceous perennial
Foliage Color : Green & purple
Flowering Season : Summer
Flower Color : White
Propagation : Tissue culture; division; cuttings
Human Hazards : None

Family : Marantaceae   Zone : 10B-11

Typical Height : .8 Ft.
Drought Tolerance : Low
Nutritional Requirements : Medium
Light Requirements : Low; medium
Leaf Type : Simple
Texture : Coarse
Flower Characteristics : Insignificant

Environmental Problems : None

Common Uses : Beds; specimen plant; foliage plant
Major Problems : K deficiency
Additional Notes : Upper leaf surface is dark & light green patterned; undersides are purple.

Calathea zebrina *(Photograph p. 192)*

Common Name(s) : Zebra Calathea
Origin : Southeast Brazil
Growth Rate : Medium
Salt Tolerance : Low
Soil Requirements : Wide
Plant Type : Herbaceous perennial
Foliage Color : Green & purple
Flowering Season : Summer
Flower Color : White
Propagation : Division; tissue culture
Human Hazards : None
Common Uses : Beds; specimen plant; foliage plant
Major Problems : K deficiency

Family : Marantaceae   **Zone** : 10B-11

Typical Height : 2 Ft.
Drought Tolerance : Low
Nutritional Requirements : Medium
Light Requirements : Low; medium
Leaf Type : Simple
Texture : Coarse
Flower Characteristics : Insignificant

Environmental Problems : None

Additional Notes : Attractive green and light-green striped leaves have purple undersides.

Calliandra haematocephala *(Photograph p. 175)*

Common Name(s) : Red Powderpuff
Origin : Tropical America
Growth Rate : Medium
Salt Tolerance : Low
Soil Requirements : Wide
Plant Type : Evergreen shrub
Foliage Color : Green
Flowering Season : Winter
Flower Color : Red; white
Propagation : Seeds; cuttings
Human Hazards : None
Common Uses : Flowering shrub
Major Problems : Thornbugs

Family : Leguminosae   **Zone** : 10A-11

Typical Height : 15 Ft.
Drought Tolerance : High
Nutritional Requirements : Medium
Light Requirements : High
Leaf Type : Pinnately compound
Texture : Fine
Flower Characteristics : Showy

Environmental Problems : None

Additional Notes : Susceptible to scale, mealybugs, and thornbugs.
Cultivars
'NANA' is a dwarf variety; a white flowering variety also exists.

Calliandra surinamensis

Common Name(s) : Pink Powderpuff
Origin : Northeastern South America
Growth Rate : Medium
Salt Tolerance : Low
Soil Requirements : Wide
Plant Type : Evergreen shrub
Foliage Color : Green
Flowering Season : Spring
Flower Color : Pink
Propagation : Seeds
Human Hazards : None
Common Uses : Flowering shrub
Major Problems : Thornbugs; scales; mealybugs

Family : Leguminosae   **Zone** : 10B-11

Typical Height : 10 Ft.
Drought Tolerance : High
Nutritional Requirements : Medium
Light Requirements : High
Leaf Type : Pinnately compound
Texture : Fine
Flower Characteristics : Showy; fragrant

Environmental Problems : None

Callicarpa americana

Common Name(s) : Beautyberry
Origin : Southeastern United States & W. Indies
Growth Rate : Fast
Salt Tolerance : Low
Soil Requirements : Wide
Plant Type : Evergreen shrub
Foliage Color : Green
Flowering Season : Spring
Flower Color : Lavender
Propagation : Cuttings; air layering; seeds
Human Hazards : None
Common Uses : Shrub
Major Problems : None

Family : Verbenaceae   **Zone** : 7-11

Typical Height : 6 Ft.
Drought Tolerance : High
Nutritional Requirements : Low
Light Requirements : High; medium
Leaf Type : Simple
Texture : Medium
Flower Characteristics : Insignificant

Environmental Problems : None

Additional Notes : Attractive purple fruits attract many birds. A white-berried form exists.

Callisia fragrans *(Photograph p. 213)*

Common Name(s) : Fragrant Callisia
Origin : Mexico and Guatemala
Growth Rate : Medium
Salt Tolerance : Medium
Soil Requirements : Wide
Plant Type : Herbaceous perennial
Foliage Color : Green; variegated
Flowering Season : Spring
Flower Color : White
Propagation : Cuttings; division
Human Hazards : None
Common Uses : Groundcover; foliage plant
Major Problems : None
Additional Notes : Although tolerant of full sun, this plant looks better in light shade.
Cultivars
'MELNICKOFF' has light green and white striped foliage.

Family : Commelinaceae   Zone : 10B-11

Typical Height : 1.5 Ft.
Drought Tolerance : High
Nutritional Requirements : Low
Light Requirements : Medium; high
Leaf Type : Simple; linear
Texture : Coarse
Flower Characteristics : Showy; fragrant

Environmental Problems : None

Callistemon citrinus

Common Name(s) : Lemon Bottlebrush
Origin : Australia
Growth Rate : Medium
Salt Tolerance : Medium
Soil Requirements : Wide
Plant Type : Evergreen tree
Foliage Color : Green
Flowering Season : Spring
Flower Color : Red
Propagation : Seeds
Human Hazards : None
Common Uses : Small flowering tree
Major Problems : Witch's broom; nematodes
Additional Notes : Has attractive bottlebrush-shaped red flowers.

Family : Myrtaceae   Zone : 9-11

Typical Height : 20 Ft.
Drought Tolerance : Medium
Nutritional Requirements : Medium
Light Requirements : High
Leaf Type : Simple
Texture : Fine
Flower Characteristics : Showy

Environmental Problems : None

Callistemon rigidus *(Photograph p. 155)*

Common Name(s) : Erect Bottlebrush
Origin : Australia
Growth Rate : Medium
Salt Tolerance : Medium
Soil Requirements : Wide
Plant Type : Evergreen tree
Foliage Color : Green
Flowering Season : Spring
Flower Color : Red
Propagation : Seeds
Human Hazards : None
Common Uses : Small flowering tree
Major Problems : Witch's broom; nematodes
Additional Notes : Similar to <u>C. citrinus.</u>

Family : Myrtaceae   Zone : 9-11

Typical Height : 15 Ft.
Drought Tolerance : Medium
Nutritional Requirements : Medium
Light Requirements : High
Leaf Type : Simple
Texture : Fine
Flower Characteristics : Showy

Environmental Problems : None

Callistemon viminalis *(Photograph p. 155)*

Common Name(s) : Weeping Bottlebrush
Origin : Australia
Growth Rate : Medium
Salt Tolerance : Medium
Soil Requirements : Wide
Plant Type : Evergreen tree
Foliage Color : Green
Flowering Season : Spring
Flower Color : Red
Propagation : Seeds
Human Hazards : None
Common Uses : Small flowering tree
Major Problems : Witch's broom; nematodes
Additional Notes : Has a weeping habit.

Family : Myrtaceae   Zone : 9-11

Typical Height : 15 Ft.
Drought Tolerance : Medium
Nutritional Requirements : Medium
Light Requirements : High
Leaf Type : Simple
Texture : Fine
Flower Characteristics : Showy

Environmental Problems : None

Calophyllum brasiliense

Common Name(s) : Santa Maria; Brazil Beautyleaf
Origin : West Indies and Mexico
Growth Rate : Fast
Salt Tolerance : High
Soil Requirements : Wide
Plant Type : Evergreen tree
Foliage Color : Green
Flowering Season : Summer
Flower Color : White
Propagation : Seeds
Human Hazards : None
Common Uses : Shade tree
Major Problems : None
Additional Notes : Dark glossy leaves with parallel veins.

Family : Guttiferae   **Zone** : 10B-11

Typical Height : 60 Ft.
Drought Tolerance : Medium
Nutritional Requirements : Medium
Light Requirements : High
Leaf Type : Simple
Texture : Medium
Flower Characteristics : Insignificant; fragrant

Environmental Problems : None

Calophyllum inophyllum *(Photograph p. 155)*

Common Name(s) : Mastwood; Laurelwood; Indian Laurel
Origin : Southeast Asia
Growth Rate : Fast
Salt Tolerance : High
Soil Requirements : Wide
Plant Type : Evergreen tree
Foliage Color : Green
Flowering Season : Summer
Flower Color : White
Propagation : Seeds
Human Hazards : Poisonous
Common Uses : Shade tree
Major Problems : None
Additional Notes : Dark glossy leaves with parallel veins. Fruit messy.

Family : Guttiferae   **Zone** : 10B-11

Typical Height : 40 Ft.
Drought Tolerance : Medium
Nutritional Requirements : Medium
Light Requirements : High
Leaf Type : Simple
Texture : Medium
Flower Characteristics : Insignificant

Environmental Problems : Messy

Calycanthus floridus

Common Name(s) : Sweet Shrub; Carolina Allspice; Pineapple Shrub
Origin : Southeastern United States
Growth Rate : Medium
Salt Tolerance : Low
Soil Requirements : Acid
Plant Type : Deciduous shrub
Foliage Color : Green; purple
Flowering Season : Spring
Flower Color : Red
Propagation : Seeds; air layering; suckers; division
Human Hazards : None
Common Uses : Flowering shrub
Major Problems : None
Additional Notes : Aromatic leaves; yellow foliage in the fall.
Cultivars
'PURPUREUS' has purple foliage.

Family : Calycanthaceae   **Zone** : 7-10A

Typical Height : 8 Ft.
Drought Tolerance : Medium
Nutritional Requirements : Medium
Light Requirements : Medium; low
Leaf Type : Simple
Texture : Medium
Flower Characteristics : Showy; fragrant

Environmental Problems : None

Calyptranthes pallens *(Photograph p. 174)*

Common Name(s) : Spicewood; Pale Lid Flower
Origin : South Florida
Growth Rate : Slow
Salt Tolerance : Medium
Soil Requirements : Wide
Plant Type : Evergreen shrub
Foliage Color : Green
Flowering Season : Spring; summer; fall
Flower Color : White
Propagation : Seeds
Human Hazards : None
Common Uses : Shrub; hedge
Major Problems : None
Additional Notes : Excellent native hedge material; can be sheared.

Family : Myrtaceae   **Zone** : 10B-11

Typical Height : 15 Ft.
Drought Tolerance : High
Nutritional Requirements : Medium
Light Requirements : Medium
Leaf Type : Simple
Texture : Medium
Flower Characteristics : Insignificant

Environmental Problems : None

Calyptranthes zuzygium

Common Name(s) : Myrtle of The River
Origin : South Florida and West Indies
Growth Rate : Medium
Salt Tolerance : Medium
Soil Requirements : Wide
Plant Type : Evergreen shrub
Foliage Color : Green
Flowering Season : Summer
Flower Color : White
Propagation : Seeds
Human Hazards : None
Common Uses : Shrub; small tree
Major Problems : None
Additional Notes : Good for wet sites.

Family : Myrtaceae   **Zone** : 10B-11

Typical Height : 25 Ft.
Drought Tolerance : Low
Nutritional Requirements : Low
Light Requirements : Medium; high
Leaf Type : Simple
Texture : Medium
Flower Characteristics : Insignificant

Environmental Problems : None

Camellia japonica *(Photograph p. 175)*

Common Name(s) : Common Camellia
Origin : Japan, Korea, and Taiwan
Growth Rate : Medium
Salt Tolerance : Low
Soil Requirements : Acid
Plant Type : Evergreen shrub
Foliage Color : Green
Flowering Season : Winter
Flower Color : White; pink; red
Propagation : Cuttings
Human Hazards : None
Common Uses : Flowering shrub
Major Problems : Scales; aphids
Additional Notes : Best in north Florida. Flowers often frost-killed.
Cultivars
Hundreds of culitvars with single or double flowers exist.

Family : Theaceae   **Zone** : 7-9

Typical Height : 12 Ft.
Drought Tolerance : Low
Nutritional Requirements : Medium
Light Requirements : Medium; high
Leaf Type : Simple
Texture : Medium
Flower Characteristics : Showy

Environmental Problems : None

Camellia sasanqua

Common Name(s) : Sasanqua Camellia
Origin : Japan and Ryukyu Islands
Growth Rate : Medium
Salt Tolerance : Low
Soil Requirements : Acid
Plant Type : Evergreen shrub
Foliage Color : Green
Flowering Season : Fall
Flower Color : White; pink; red
Propagation : Cuttings
Human Hazards : None
Common Uses : Flowering shrub; hedge
Major Problems : Scales; mites; aphids
Additional Notes : Best for central and northern Florida. Subject to tea scale.
Cultivars
Many cultivars having single to double flowers exist, some with red new foliage.

Family : Theaceae   **Zone** : 7B-9

Typical Height : 15 Ft.
Drought Tolerance : Low
Nutritional Requirements : Medium
Light Requirements : High
Leaf Type : Simple
Texture : Medium
Flower Characteristics : Showy; fragrant

Environmental Problems : None

Campanula spp.

Common Name(s) : Bellflowers
Origin : Southern Europe
Growth Rate : Medium
Salt Tolerance : Low
Soil Requirements : Wide
Plant Type : Herbaceous perennial
Foliage Color : Green
Flowering Season : Summer
Flower Color : Blue; purple; white
Propagation : Seeds; division
Human Hazards : None
Common Uses : Borders; rock gardens; hanging baskets
Major Problems : None
Additional Notes : Perennial and biennial species exist. Bell-shaped flowers.
Cultivars
Many species, cultivars, and hybrids of campanula exist.

Family : Campanulaceae   **Zone** : 4-10B

Typical Height : 2 Ft.
Drought Tolerance : Medium
Nutritional Requirements : Medium
Light Requirements : Medium; high
Leaf Type : Simple
Texture : Medium
Flower Characteristics : Showy

Environmental Problems : None

Campsis radicans

Common Name(s) : Trumpet Vine; Trumpet Creeper
Origin : Eastern United States
Growth Rate : Fast
Salt Tolerance : Low
Soil Requirements : Wide
Plant Type : Deciduous vine
Foliage Color : Green
Flowering Season : Summer
Flower Color : Orange
Propagation : Seeds; cuttings
Human Hazards : Irritant
Common Uses : Flowering vine
Major Problems : None
Additional Notes : A rampant vine that climbs by holdfast roots.
Cultivars
'FLAVA' has orange-yellow flowers.

Family : Bignoniaceae   **Zone** : 5-10A

Typical Height : Not applicable
Drought Tolerance : High
Nutritional Requirements : Low
Light Requirements : Medium; high
Leaf Type : Pinnately compound
Texture : Medium
Flower Characteristics : Showy

Environmental Problems : None

Cananga odorata *(Photograph p. 155)*

Common Name(s) : Ylang Ylang; Ilang Ilang
Origin : Southeast Asia, East Indies
Growth Rate : Fast
Salt Tolerance : Low
Soil Requirements : Wide
Plant Type : Evergreen tree
Foliage Color : Green
Flowering Season : Year-round
Flower Color : Yellow
Propagation : Seeds
Human Hazards : None
Common Uses : Flowering tree
Major Problems : None
Additional Notes : Very fragrant flowers are used in perfume. Open growth habit. Weak wood.

Family : Annonaceae   **Zone** : 10B-11

Typical Height : 35 Ft.
Drought Tolerance : Medium
Nutritional Requirements : Medium
Light Requirements : High
Leaf Type : Simple
Texture : Coarse
Flower Characteristics : Showy; fragrant

Environmental Problems : Weak

Canavallia maritima

Common Name(s) : Beach Bean
Origin : World Tropics
Growth Rate : Fast
Salt Tolerance : High
Soil Requirements : Wide
Plant Type : Herbaceous vine
Foliage Color : Green
Flowering Season : Year-round
Flower Color : Purple
Propagation : Seeds
Human Hazards : None
Common Uses : Seasides; groundcover
Major Problems : None
Additional Notes : An excellent sand-binding groundcover for coastal areas.

Family : Leguminosae   **Zone** : 10B-11

Typical Height : 1 Ft.
Drought Tolerance : High
Nutritional Requirements : Low
Light Requirements : High
Leaf Type : Trifoliate
Texture : Coarse
Flower Characteristics : Showy

Environmental Problems : None

Canella winterana

Common Name(s) : Wild Cinnamon
Origin : South Florida and Tropical America
Growth Rate : Slow
Salt Tolerance : Medium
Soil Requirements : Wide
Plant Type : Evergreen tree
Foliage Color : Green
Flowering Season : Summer; fall
Flower Color : Purple; white
Propagation : Seeds
Human Hazards : None
Common Uses : Flowering tree
Major Problems : None
Additional Notes : An attractive native flowering tree.

Family : Canellaceae   **Zone** : 10B-11

Typical Height : 25 Ft.
Drought Tolerance : High
Nutritional Requirements : Low
Light Requirements : High
Leaf Type : Simple
Texture : Medium
Flower Characteristics : Showy

Environmental Problems : None

Canna flaccida

Family : Cannaceae   **Zone** : 8-10B

Common Name(s) : Golden Canna; Bandana of The Everglades
Origin : Southeastern United States
Growth Rate : Fast
Salt Tolerance : Low
Soil Requirements : Wide
Plant Type : Herbaceous perennial
Foliage Color : Green
Flowering Season : Summer
Flower Color : Yellow
Propagation : Division; seeds
Human Hazards : None
Common Uses : Aquatic; specimen plant
Major Problems : None
Additional Notes : Good for wet sites.

Typical Height : 5 Ft.
Drought Tolerance : Low
Nutritional Requirements : Medium
Light Requirements : High
Leaf Type : Simple
Texture : Coarse
Flower Characteristics : Showy

Environmental Problems : None

Canna X generalis *(Photograph p. 192)*

Family : Cannaceae   **Zone** : 9-11

Common Name(s) : Garden Canna
Origin : Hybrid
Growth Rate : Fast
Salt Tolerance : Low
Soil Requirements : Wide
Plant Type : Herbaceous perennial
Foliage Color : Green; red; variegated
Flowering Season : Summer; fall
Flower Color : Orange; pink; red; yellow; yellow & red
Propagation : Division
Human Hazards : None
Common Uses : Beds; borders
Major Problems : Canna leafroller; rust
Additional Notes : Many cultivars exist.

Typical Height : 3.5 Ft.
Drought Tolerance : Medium
Nutritional Requirements : Medium
Light Requirements : High
Leaf Type : Simple
Texture : Coarse
Flower Characteristics : Showy

Environmental Problems : None

Capparis cynophallophora

Family : Capparaceae   **Zone** : 10B-11

Common Name(s) : Jamaican Caper
Origin : South Florida and The Caribbean
Growth Rate : Slow
Salt Tolerance : High
Soil Requirements : Wide
Plant Type : Evergreen shrub
Foliage Color : Green
Flowering Season : Spring
Flower Color : Pink-white
Propagation : Cuttings; seeds
Human Hazards : None
Common Uses : Flowering shrub
Major Problems : None
Additional Notes : Undersides of leaves rust-colored.

Typical Height : 9 Ft.
Drought Tolerance : High
Nutritional Requirements : Low
Light Requirements : High
Leaf Type : Simple
Texture : Medium
Flower Characteristics : Showy

Environmental Problems : None

Capparis flexuosa

Family : Capparaceae   **Zone** : 10B-11

Common Name(s) : Bay-leaved Caper Tree
Origin : South Florida to South America
Growth Rate : Medium
Salt Tolerance : High
Soil Requirements : Wide
Plant Type : Evergreen shrub
Foliage Color : Green
Flowering Season : Summer
Flower Color : White; pink
Propagation : Seeds
Human Hazards : None
Common Uses : Shrub
Major Problems : None
Additional Notes : Good beach plant.

Typical Height : 20 Ft.
Drought Tolerance : High
Nutritional Requirements : Low
Light Requirements : High
Leaf Type : Simple
Texture : Medium
Flower Characteristics : Insignificant

Environmental Problems : None

Carica papaya *(Photograph p. 156)*
Common Name(s) : Papaya
Origin : Tropical America
Growth Rate : Fast
Salt Tolerance : Low
Soil Requirements : Wide
Plant Type : Evergreen tree
Foliage Color : Green
Flowering Season : All year
Flower Color : Yellow
Propagation : Seeds
Human Hazards : Irritant
Common Uses : Edible fruit
Major Problems : Virus; nematodes
Additional Notes : Short-lived; can naturalize.
Cultivars
Many cultivars exist.

Family : Caricaceae   Zone : 10B-11

Typical Height : 15 Ft.
Drought Tolerance : Low
Nutritional Requirements : Medium
Light Requirements : High
Leaf Type : Simple; palmately lobed
Texture : Coarse
Flower Characteristics : Insignificant

Environmental Problems : Weedy

Carissa macrocarpa *(Photograph p. 175)*
Common Name(s) : Natal Plum
Origin : South Africa
Growth Rate : Medium
Salt Tolerance : High
Soil Requirements : Wide
Plant Type : Evergreen shrub
Foliage Color : Green
Flowering Season : Spring; summer; fall
Flower Color : White
Propagation : Seeds; cuttings
Human Hazards : Spiny
Common Uses : Hedge; edible fruit; flowering shrub
Major Problems : None
Additional Notes : Has edible red fruit, thorny stems, and glossy green leaves.
Cultivars
'EMERALD BLANKET', 'GREEN CARPET', and 'HORIZONTALIS' are dwarf cultivars; 'BOXWOOD BEAUTY'
is a thornless dwarf variety.

Family : Apocynaceae   Zone : 10B-11

Typical Height : 10 Ft.
Drought Tolerance : High
Nutritional Requirements : Medium
Light Requirements : Medium; high
Leaf Type : Simple
Texture : Medium
Flower Characteristics : Showy; fragrant

Environmental Problems : None

Carludovica palmata
Common Name(s) : Panama Hat Plant
Origin : Central America to Bolivia
Growth Rate : Medium
Salt Tolerance : Low
Soil Requirements : Wide
Plant Type : Herbaceous perennial
Foliage Color : Green
Flowering Season : Spring; summer
Flower Color : Yellow
Propagation : Division; seeds
Human Hazards : None
Common Uses : Specimen plant; foliage plant
Major Problems : None
Additional Notes : Leaves of this plant are used to make hats. Very cold sensitive.

Family : Cyclanthaceae   Zone : 11

Typical Height : 10 Ft.
Drought Tolerance : Low
Nutritional Requirements : Medium
Light Requirements : Low; medium
Leaf Type : Palmately lobed
Texture : Coarse
Flower Characteristics : Insignificant

Environmental Problems : None

Carpentaria acuminata *(Photograph p. 202)*
Common Name(s) : Carpentaria Palm
Origin : Australia
Growth Rate : Fast
Salt Tolerance : Low
Soil Requirements : Wide
Plant Type : Palm
Foliage Color : Green
Flowering Season : Spring; summer; fall
Flower Color : White
Propagation : Seeds
Human Hazards : Irritant
Common Uses : Tree
Major Problems : Thrips
Additional Notes : Fruit irritates skin.

Family : Palmae   Zone : 10B-11

Typical Height : 40 Ft.
Drought Tolerance : Low
Nutritional Requirements : Medium
Light Requirements : High
Leaf Type : Pinnately compound
Texture : Medium
Flower Characteristics : Insignificant

Environmental Problems : None

Carpinus caroliniana

Common Name(s) : American Hornbeam
Origin : Eastern United States
Growth Rate : Slow
Salt Tolerance : Low
Soil Requirements : Wide
Plant Type : Deciduous tree
Foliage Color : Green
Flowering Season : Spring
Flower Color : Green
Propagation : Seeds; grafting
Human Hazards : None
Common Uses : Small tree
Major Problems : None
Additional Notes : Grows well in wet sites in southeastern United States.

Family : Betulaceae   **Zone** : 2-9

Typical Height : 25 Ft.
Drought Tolerance : Medium
Nutritional Requirements : Low
Light Requirements : Medium; high
Leaf Type : Simple
Texture : Medium
Flower Characteristics : Insignificant

Environmental Problems : None

Carpobrotus spp.

Common Name(s) : Hottentot Fig
Origin : South Africa, Australia, & California
Growth Rate : Medium
Salt Tolerance : High
Soil Requirements : Wide
Plant Type : Herbaceous perennial
Foliage Color : Green
Flowering Season : Summer
Flower Color : Yellow; purple
Propagation : Cuttings; seeds
Human Hazards : None
Common Uses : Beds; rock gardens; seasides; groundcover
Major Problems : None
Additional Notes : Excellent succulent groundcover for seaside dunes. Common in California.

Family : Aizoaceae   **Zone** : 10A-10B

Typical Height : .5 Ft.
Drought Tolerance : High
Nutritional Requirements : Low
Light Requirements : High
Leaf Type : Simple
Texture : Medium
Flower Characteristics : Showy

Environmental Problems : None

Carya aquatica

Common Name(s) : Water Hickory
Origin : Eastern United States
Growth Rate : Slow
Salt Tolerance : Low
Soil Requirements : Wide
Plant Type : Deciduous tree
Foliage Color : Green
Flowering Season : Spring
Flower Color : Green
Propagation : Seeds
Human Hazards : None
Common Uses : Shade tree
Major Problems : None
Additional Notes : Best for moist sites in southeastern United States.

Family : Juglandaceae   **Zone** : 7-9

Typical Height : 60 Ft.
Drought Tolerance : Low
Nutritional Requirements : Low
Light Requirements : High
Leaf Type : Pinnately compound
Texture : Medium
Flower Characteristics : Insignificant

Environmental Problems : None

Carya floridana

Common Name(s) : Scrub Hickory
Origin : Florida
Growth Rate : Slow
Salt Tolerance : Medium
Soil Requirements : Wide
Plant Type : Deciduous tree
Foliage Color : Green
Flowering Season : Spring
Flower Color : Brown
Propagation : Seeds
Human Hazards : None
Common Uses : Shade tree
Major Problems : None
Additional Notes : This hickory is excellent for dry sandy sites.

Family : Juglandaceae   **Zone** : 8-10B

Typical Height : 40 Ft.
Drought Tolerance : High
Nutritional Requirements : Low
Light Requirements : High
Leaf Type : Pinnately compound
Texture : Medium
Flower Characteristics : Insignificant

Environmental Problems : None

Carya glabra

Common Name(s) : Pignut Hickory
Origin : Eastern United States
Growth Rate : Medium
Salt Tolerance : Low
Soil Requirements : Wide
Plant Type : Deciduous tree
Foliage Color : Green
Flowering Season : Spring
Flower Color : Green
Propagation : Seeds
Human Hazards : None
Common Uses : Shade tree
Major Problems : Borers
Additional Notes : Has excellent yellow fall color.

Family : Juglandaceae   **Zone** : 5-9

Typical Height : 100 Ft.
Drought Tolerance : High
Nutritional Requirements : Low
Light Requirements : High
Leaf Type : Pinnately compound
Texture : Medium
Flower Characteristics : Insignificant

Environmental Problems : None

Carya illinoinensis

Common Name(s) : Pecan
Origin : Eastern United States
Growth Rate : Medium
Salt Tolerance : Low
Soil Requirements : Acid
Plant Type : Deciduous tree
Foliage Color : Green
Flowering Season : Spring
Flower Color : Yellow
Propagation : Seeds; grafting
Human Hazards : None
Common Uses : Edible fruit; shade tree
Major Problems : Borers; scales
Additional Notes : Many regional cultivars exist; yellow fall color.

Family : Juglandaceae   **Zone** : 6-9

Typical Height : 70 Ft.
Drought Tolerance : High
Nutritional Requirements : Medium
Light Requirements : High
Leaf Type : Pinnately compound
Texture : Medium
Flower Characteristics : Insignificant

Environmental Problems : None

Caryota mitis

Common Name(s) : Clustering Fishtail Palm
Origin : Southeast Asia
Growth Rate : Medium
Salt Tolerance : Low
Soil Requirements : Wide
Plant Type : Palm
Foliage Color : Green
Flowering Season : Spring; summer
Flower Color : White
Propagation : Seeds
Human Hazards : Irritant
Common Uses : Tree; large shrub
Major Problems : None
Additional Notes : Stems die after flowering. Fruit is irritating.

Family : Palmae   **Zone** : 10B-11

Typical Height : 18 Ft.
Drought Tolerance : Medium
Nutritional Requirements : Medium
Light Requirements : Medium; high
Leaf Type : Bipinnately compound
Texture : Medium
Flower Characteristics : Insignificant

Environmental Problems : None

Caryota rumphiana

Common Name(s) : Giant Fishtail Palm
Origin : Southeast Asia to Australia
Growth Rate : Fast
Salt Tolerance : Low
Soil Requirements : Wide
Plant Type : Palm
Foliage Color : Green
Flowering Season : Spring; summer
Flower Color : White
Propagation : Seeds
Human Hazards : Irritant
Common Uses : Tree
Major Problems : None
Additional Notes : Tree dies after flowering. Fruit irritating to skin.

Family : Palmae   **Zone** : 10B-11

Typical Height : 60 Ft.
Drought Tolerance : Medium
Nutritional Requirements : Medium
Light Requirements : Medium; high
Leaf Type : Bipinnately compound
Texture : Medium
Flower Characteristics : Insignificant

Environmental Problems : None

Caryota urens *(Photograph p. 202)*

Family : Palmae   **Zone** : 10B-11

Common Name(s) : Toddy Fishtail Palm
Origin : India to Malay Peninsula
Growth Rate : Medium
Salt Tolerance : Low
Soil Requirements : Wide
Plant Type : Palm
Foliage Color : Green
Flowering Season : Spring
Flower Color : White
Propagation : Seeds
Human Hazards : Irritant
Common Uses : Tree
Major Problems : None

Typical Height : 40 Ft.
Drought Tolerance : Medium
Nutritional Requirements : Medium
Light Requirements : High
Leaf Type : Bipinnately compound
Texture : Medium
Flower Characteristics : Insignificant

Environmental Problems : None

Additional Notes : Susceptible to lethal yellowing, dies after flowering (20 years).

Casasia clusiifolia

Family : Rubiaceae   **Zone** : 10B-11

Common Name(s) : Seven-year Apple
Origin : South Florida and West Indies
Growth Rate : Slow
Salt Tolerance : High
Soil Requirements : Wide
Plant Type : Evergreen shrub
Foliage Color : Green
Flowering Season : Summer
Flower Color : White
Propagation : Seeds
Human Hazards : None
Common Uses : Flowering shrub
Major Problems : None

Typical Height : 8 Ft.
Drought Tolerance : High
Nutritional Requirements : Low
Light Requirements : High; medium
Leaf Type : Simple
Texture : Coarse
Flower Characteristics : Showy; fragrant

Environmental Problems : None

Additional Notes : Good for seaside plantings.

Cassia alata *(Photograph p. 175)*

Family : Leguminosae   **Zone** : 10A-11

Common Name(s) : Candle Bush
Origin : Tropics
Growth Rate : Fast
Salt Tolerance : Medium
Soil Requirements : Wide
Plant Type : Evergreen shrub
Foliage Color : Green
Flowering Season : Fall
Flower Color : Yellow
Propagation : Cuttings; seeds
Human Hazards : None
Common Uses : Flowering shrub;
Major Problems : None

Typical Height : 7 Ft.
Drought Tolerance : Medium
Nutritional Requirements : Medium
Light Requirements : High
Leaf Type : Pinnately compound
Texture : Medium
Flower Characteristics : Showy

Environmental Problems : None

Additional Notes : Cut back severely after blooming.

Cassia bahamensis

Family : Leguminosae   **Zone** : 10B-11

Common Name(s) : Bahama Cassia
Origin : South Florida and Caribbean Region
Growth Rate : Fast
Salt Tolerance : High
Soil Requirements : Wide
Plant Type : Evergreen shrub
Foliage Color : Green
Flowering Season : Fall; winter
Flower Color : Yellow
Propagation : Seeds
Human Hazards : None
Common Uses : Flowering shrub
Major Problems : None

Typical Height : 8 Ft.
Drought Tolerance : High
Nutritional Requirements : Low
Light Requirements : High
Leaf Type : Pinnately compound
Texture : Fine
Flower Characteristics : Showy

Environmental Problems : None

Additional Notes : A good late-blooming informal flowering shrub for south Florida.

Cassia bicapsularis

Common Name(s) : Cassia
Origin : Caribbean Region
Growth Rate : Fast
Salt Tolerance : Medium
Soil Requirements : Wide
Plant Type : Evergreen shrub
Foliage Color : Green
Flowering Season : Fall
Flower Color : Yellow
Propagation : Seeds
Human Hazards : Poisonous
Common Uses : Flowering shrub
Major Problems : Caterpillars; twig borers
Additional Notes : Requires pruning to maintain shape. Naturalized. Given support will vine.

Family : Leguminosae   Zone : 10A-11

Typical Height : 11 Ft.
Drought Tolerance : Medium
Nutritional Requirements : Medium
Light Requirements : High
Leaf Type : Pinnately compound
Texture : Fine
Flower Characteristics : Showy

Environmental Problems : None

Cassia fistula *(Photograph p. 156)*

Common Name(s) : Golden Shower
Origin : India
Growth Rate : Fast
Salt Tolerance : Medium
Soil Requirements : Wide
Plant Type : Deciduous tree
Foliage Color : Green
Flowering Season : Summer
Flower Color : Yellow
Propagation : Seeds
Human Hazards : Poisonous
Common Uses : Flowering tree
Major Problems : None
Additional Notes : Very attractive when in flower.

Family : Leguminosae   Zone : 10B-11

Typical Height : 35 Ft.
Drought Tolerance : Medium
Nutritional Requirements : Medium
Light Requirements : High
Leaf Type : Pinnately compound
Texture : Medium
Flower Characteristics : Showy

Environmental Problems : None

Cassia javanica *(Photograph p. 156)*

Common Name(s) : Pink and White Shower; Apple Blossom Shower
Origin : Indonesia
Growth Rate : Fast
Salt Tolerance : Medium
Soil Requirements : Wide
Plant Type : Deciduous tree
Foliage Color : Green
Flowering Season : Spring; summer
Flower Color : Red-pink
Propagation : Seeds; cuttings
Human Hazards : None
Common Uses : Flowering tree
Major Problems : None
Additional Notes : Very showy when in bloom. May be the same as C. nodosa .

Family : Leguminosae   Zone : 10B-11

Typical Height : 45 Ft.
Drought Tolerance : Medium
Nutritional Requirements : Medium
Light Requirements : High
Leaf Type : Pinnately compound
Texture : Fine
Flower Characteristics : Showy

Environmental Problems : None

Cassia multijuga

Common Name(s) : November Shower Tree
Origin : Brazil and Guyana
Growth Rate : Fast
Salt Tolerance : Low
Soil Requirements : Wide
Plant Type : Evergreen tree or shrub
Foliage Color : Green
Flowering Season : Fall
Flower Color : Yellow
Propagation : Seeds
Human Hazards : None
Common Uses : Small flowering tree; flowering shrub
Major Problems : None
Additional Notes : Can be shrub-like if not pruned.

Family : Leguminosae   Zone : 10B-11

Typical Height : 15 Ft.
Drought Tolerance : Medium
Nutritional Requirements : Medium
Light Requirements : High
Leaf Type : Pinnately compound
Texture : Fine
Flower Characteristics : Showy

Environmental Problems : None

Cassia siamea

Common Name(s) : Kassod Tree
Origin : Indonesia and Malay Peninsula
Growth Rate : Fast
Salt Tolerance : Low
Soil Requirements : Wide
Plant Type : Evergreen tree
Foliage Color : Green
Flowering Season : Spring; summer
Flower Color : Yellow
Propagation : Seeds
Human Hazards : None
Common Uses : Flowering tree
Major Problems : None
Additional Notes : Showy yellow flowers.

Family : Leguminosae   **Zone** : 10B-11

Typical Height : 35 Ft.
Drought Tolerance : Medium
Nutritional Requirements : Medium
Light Requirements : High
Leaf Type : Pinnately compound
Texture : Medium
Flower Characteristics : Showy

Environmental Problems : None

Cassia splendida

Common Name(s) : Golden Wonder
Origin : Brazil
Growth Rate : Fast
Salt Tolerance : Medium
Soil Requirements : Wide
Plant Type : Evergreen shrub
Foliage Color : Green
Flowering Season : Fall
Flower Color : Yellow
Propagation : Seeds
Human Hazards : None
Common Uses : Flowering shrub
Major Problems : None
Additional Notes : Requires pruning to maintain mound shape.

Family : Leguminosae   **Zone** : 10A-11

Typical Height : 8 Ft.
Drought Tolerance : Medium
Nutritional Requirements : Medium
Light Requirements : High
Leaf Type : Pinnately compound
Texture : Fine
Flower Characteristics : Showy

Environmental Problems : None

Cassia surattensis

Common Name(s) : Glaucous Cassia; Bush Cassia
Origin : Southeast Asia, Australia
Growth Rate : Fast
Salt Tolerance : Low
Soil Requirements : Wide
Plant Type : Evergreen tree or shrub
Foliage Color : Green
Flowering Season : Fall
Flower Color : Yellow
Propagation : Seeds; root cuttings
Human Hazards : None
Common Uses : Small flowering tree; flowering shrub
Major Problems : None
Additional Notes : May grow shrub-like if not pruned.

Family : Leguminosae   **Zone** : 10B-11

Typical Height : 15 Ft.
Drought Tolerance : Medium
Nutritional Requirements : Medium
Light Requirements : High
Leaf Type : Pinnately compound
Texture : Medium
Flower Characteristics : Showy

Environmental Problems : None

Catalpa bignonioides

Common Name(s) : Catalpa
Origin : Eastern United States
Growth Rate : Fast
Salt Tolerance : Low
Soil Requirements : Wide
Plant Type : Deciduous tree
Foliage Color : Green
Flowering Season : Spring
Flower Color : White
Propagation : Seeds; cuttings; grafting
Human Hazards : Irritant
Common Uses : Flowering tree; shade tree
Major Problems : Catalpa moth
Additional Notes : Weak-wooded; fruits unsightly; flowers contain irritant.

Family : Bignoniaceae   **Zone** : 5-9

Typical Height : 50 Ft.
Drought Tolerance : Low
Nutritional Requirements : Medium
Light Requirements : High
Leaf Type : Simple
Texture : Coarse
Flower Characteristics : Showy

Environmental Problems : Weak

Catharanthus roseus

Common Name(s) : Periwinkle
Origin : Old World Tropics
Growth Rate : Medium
Salt Tolerance : High
Soil Requirements : Wide
Plant Type : Herbaceous perennial
Foliage Color : Green
Flowering Season : Year-round
Flower Color : White; purple; pink
Propagation : Seeds
Human Hazards : Poisonous
Common Uses : Bedding plant;
Major Problems : Aster yellows

Family : Apocynaceae   **Zone** : 10B-11

Typical Height : 1 Ft.
Drought Tolerance : High
Nutritional Requirements : Low
Light Requirements : High; medium
Leaf Type : Simple
Texture : Medium
Flower Characteristics : Showy

Environmental Problems : None

Additional Notes : Great for color in dry areas. Plants reseed themselves.
Cultivars
'MAGIC CARPET SERIES' and 'HOT STREAK SERIES' are very low-growing prostrate varieties;
'LITTLE SERIES' are compact 10 inch tall varieties.

Cattleya spp. *(Photograph p. 193)*

Common Name(s) : Cattleya Orchid
Origin : Tropical America
Growth Rate : Slow
Salt Tolerance : Low
Soil Requirements : Well-drained
Plant Type : Epiphyte
Foliage Color : Green
Flowering Season : Year-round
Flower Color : White; yellow; red; pink; lavender; purple
Propagation : Division; tissue culture
Human Hazards : None
Common Uses : Cut flowers; epiphyte; flowering pot plant
Major Problems : Virus

Family : Orchidaceae   **Zone** : 10B-11

Typical Height : 1 Ft.
Drought Tolerance : High
Nutritional Requirements : Low
Light Requirements : Medium
Leaf Type : Simple; linear
Texture : Coarse
Flower Characteristics : Showy; fragrant

Environmental Problems : None

Additional Notes : Cattleyas need very well drained soils. Many cultivars exist.

Cecropia palmata *(Photograph p. 156)*

Common Name(s) : Snakewood; Cecropia
Origin : Caribbean Region
Growth Rate : Fast
Salt Tolerance : Medium
Soil Requirements : Wide
Plant Type : Evergreen tree
Foliage Color : Green
Flowering Season : Summer
Flower Color : Yellow
Propagation : Seeds
Human Hazards : None
Common Uses : Tree
Major Problems : None

Family : Moraceae   **Zone** : 10B-11

Typical Height : 45 Ft.
Drought Tolerance : Medium
Nutritional Requirements : Medium
Light Requirements : High
Leaf Type : Simple; palmately lobed
Texture : Very coarse
Flower Characteristics : Insignificant

Environmental Problems : Messy; weak

Additional Notes : Weak-wooded. Messy leaves often used in dried flower arrangements.

Cedrus atlantica *(Photograph p. 156)*

Common Name(s) : Atlas Cedar
Origin : North Africa
Growth Rate : Medium
Salt Tolerance : Low
Soil Requirements : Wide
Plant Type : Evergreen tree
Foliage Color : Blue-green
Flowering Season : n/a
Flower Color : n/a
Propagation : Seeds; cuttings; grafting
Human Hazards : None
Common Uses : Tree
Major Problems : Borers

Family : Pinaceae   **Zone** : 7-9

Typical Height : 30 Ft.
Drought Tolerance : Medium
Nutritional Requirements : Medium
Light Requirements : High
Leaf Type : Needle
Texture : Fine
Flower Characteristics : n/a

Environmental Problems : None

Additional Notes : This fine-textured evergreen has bluish-colored needles.
Cultivars
'GLAUCA' has bluish foliage and a pyramidal form; 'PENDULA' is a weeping blue variety; 'AUREA' has golden foliage; 'FASTIGIATA' is narrowly columnar ; 'ARGENTEA' has silvery foliage.

Cedrus deodara

Family : Pinaceae   **Zone** : 7-9

Common Name(s) : Deodar Cedar
Origin : Himalayas
Growth Rate : Medium
Salt Tolerance : Low
Soil Requirements : Wide
Plant Type : Evergreen tree
Foliage Color : Blue-green; green;
Flowering Season : n/a
Flower Color : n/a
Propagation : Seeds; cuttings
Human Hazards : None
Common Uses : Tree
Major Problems : Borers
Additional Notes : Graceful habit.

Typical Height : 60 Ft.
Drought Tolerance : Medium
Nutritional Requirements : Medium
Light Requirements : High
Leaf Type : Needle
Texture : Fine
Flower Characteristics : n/a

Environmental Problems : None

Cultivars
'AUREA' has golden foliage; 'COMPACTA' is a slow-growing rounded form; 'PROSTRATA' is a prostrate form; 'PENDULA' is a weeping form; 'VIRIDIS' has deep green foliage.

Ceiba aesculifolia

Family : Bombacaceae   **Zone** : 10B-11

Common Name(s) : n/a
Origin : Mexico and Guatemala
Growth Rate : Fast
Salt Tolerance : Medium
Soil Requirements : Wide
Plant Type : Deciduous tree
Foliage Color : Green
Flowering Season : Spring
Flower Color : White & purple
Propagation : Seeds
Human Hazards : Spiny
Common Uses : Flowering tree
Major Problems : None
Additional Notes : A smaller relative of the silk-cotton tree.

Typical Height : 40 Ft.
Drought Tolerance : High
Nutritional Requirements : Medium
Light Requirements : High
Leaf Type : Palmately compound
Texture : Coarse
Flower Characteristics : Showy

Environmental Problems : None

Ceiba pentandra *(Photograph p. 156)*

Family : Bombacaceae   **Zone** : 10B-11

Common Name(s) : Silk-cotton Tree; Kapok Tree
Origin : Old and New World Tropics
Growth Rate : Fast
Salt Tolerance : Medium
Soil Requirements : Wide
Plant Type : Deciduous tree
Foliage Color : Green
Flowering Season : Spring
Flower Color : White; pink
Propagation : Seeds
Human Hazards : Spiny
Common Uses : Flowering tree
Major Problems : None
Additional Notes : A very large tree with a buttress trunk. Seed pods yield kapok.

Typical Height : 100 Ft.
Drought Tolerance : High
Nutritional Requirements : Medium
Light Requirements : High
Leaf Type : Palmately compound
Texture : Coarse
Flower Characteristics : Showy

Environmental Problems : None

Celtis laevigata

Family : Ulmaceae   **Zone** : 5-9

Common Name(s) : Sugarberry
Origin : Southern United States
Growth Rate : Medium
Salt Tolerance : Low
Soil Requirements : Wide
Plant Type : Deciduous tree
Foliage Color : Green
Flowering Season : Spring
Flower Color : Green
Propagation : Seeds; cuttings
Human Hazards : None
Common Uses : Shade tree
Major Problems : None
Additional Notes : Resistant to witch's broom; yellow fall color

Typical Height : 50 Ft.
Drought Tolerance : High
Nutritional Requirements : Low
Light Requirements : High
Leaf Type : Simple
Texture : Medium
Flower Characteristics : Insignificant

Environmental Problems : None

Centranthus ruber

Common Name(s) : Jupiter's Beard; Red Valerian
Origin : Europe, North Africa, and Asia Minor
Growth Rate : Medium
Salt Tolerance : Low
Soil Requirements : Wide
Plant Type : Herbaceous perennial
Foliage Color : Green
Flowering Season : Summer
Flower Color : Red; white; pink
Propagation : Seeds; division
Human Hazards : None
Common Uses : Specimen plant
Major Problems : None

Family : Valerianaceae   Zone : 4-10B

Typical Height : 2.5 Ft.
Drought Tolerance : High
Nutritional Requirements : Low
Light Requirements : Medium; high
Leaf Type : Simple
Texture : Medium
Flower Characteristics : Showy

Environmental Problems : None

Additional Notes : Easy to grow, blooms second year from seed. Sometimes escapes cultivation

Cephalanthus occidentalis

Common Name(s) : Buttonbush
Origin : Eastern United States
Growth Rate : Medium
Salt Tolerance : Low
Soil Requirements : Wide
Plant Type : Deciduous shrub
Foliage Color : Green
Flowering Season : Summer
Flower Color : White
Propagation : Seeds; cuttings
Human Hazards : Poisonous
Common Uses : Shrub
Major Problems : None

Family : Rubiaceae   Zone : 4-10A

Typical Height : 15 Ft.
Drought Tolerance : Low
Nutritional Requirements : Medium
Light Requirements : Medium; high
Leaf Type : Simple
Texture : Medium
Flower Characteristics : Showy

Environmental Problems : None

Additional Notes : This native grows best in wet sites.

Cephalotaxus harringtonia

Common Name(s) : Japanese Plum Yew
Origin : Japan
Growth Rate : Slow
Salt Tolerance : Low
Soil Requirements : Wide
Plant Type : Evergreen shrub
Foliage Color : Green
Flowering Season : Spring; summer
Flower Color : n/a
Propagation : Seeds; cuttings
Human Hazards : None
Common Uses : Hedge; groundcover; shrub
Major Problems : Nematodes; mushroom root rot

Family : Cephalotaxaceae   Zone : 6-9

Typical Height : 10 Ft.
Drought Tolerance : Medium
Nutritional Requirements : Medium
Light Requirements : Medium; high
Leaf Type : Needle
Texture : Fine
Flower Characteristics : Insignificant

Environmental Problems : None

Additional Notes : Usually a low spreading shrub, but other forms exist.
Cultivars
'FASTIGIATA' is an upright, columnar cultivar.

Ceratiola ericoides

Common Name(s) : Rosemary
Origin : Southeastern United States
Growth Rate : Medium
Salt Tolerance : High
Soil Requirements : Acid
Plant Type : Evergreen shrub
Foliage Color : Green
Flowering Season : Year-round
Flower Color : Red; yellow
Propagation : Seeds
Human Hazards : None
Common Uses : Shrub
Major Problems : None

Family : Empetraceae   Zone : 8-10B

Typical Height : 5 Ft.
Drought Tolerance : High
Nutritional Requirements : Low
Light Requirements : High
Leaf Type : Simple
Texture : Fine
Flower Characteristics : Insignificant

Environmental Problems : None

Additional Notes : Well adapted to the sand pine areas of Florida. Difficult to propagate.

Ceratozamia mexicana

Family : Zamiaceae   Zone : 10A-11

Common Name(s) : Ceratozamia
Origin : Mexico
Growth Rate : Slow
Salt Tolerance : Low
Soil Requirements : Wide
Plant Type : Evergreen shrub (cycad)
Foliage Color : Green
Flowering Season : n/a
Flower Color : n/a
Propagation : Seeds
Human Hazards : Poisonous
Common Uses : Shrub; specimen plant
Major Problems : None
Additional Notes : A Zamia relative with narrow leaflets.

Typical Height : 6 Ft.
Drought Tolerance : Medium
Nutritional Requirements : Medium
Light Requirements : High; medium
Leaf Type : Pinnately compound
Texture : Medium
Flower Characteristics : n/a

Environmental Problems : None

Cercis canadensis *(Photograph p. 157)*

Family : Leguminosae   Zone : 4-9

Common Name(s) : Redbud
Origin : Eastern United States
Growth Rate : Medium
Salt Tolerance : Low
Soil Requirements : Wide
Plant Type : Deciduous tree
Foliage Color : Green
Flowering Season : Spring
Flower Color : Pink; white
Propagation : Seeds; grafting
Human Hazards : None
Common Uses : Small flowering tree
Major Problems : Leafspots; borers; canker
Additional Notes : Attractive pink flowers appear before foliage in spring. Yellow fall color.
Cultivars

Typical Height : 25 Ft.
Drought Tolerance : High
Nutritional Requirements : Medium
Light Requirements : Medium; high
Leaf Type : Simple
Texture : Coarse
Flower Characteristics : Showy

Environmental Problems : None

'ALBA' has white flowers; 'FOREST PANSY' has reddish-purple foliage; 'OKLAHOMA' has new foliage pink becoming green with maturity; 'FLAME' has rose-colored double flowers.

Cercis chinensis

Family : Leguminosae   Zone : 7-9

Common Name(s) : Chinese Redbud
Origin : Southern China
Growth Rate : Slow
Salt Tolerance : Low
Soil Requirements : Wide
Plant Type : Deciduous shrub
Foliage Color : Green
Flowering Season : Spring
Flower Color : Pink
Propagation : Seeds; grafting
Human Hazards : None
Common Uses : Flowering shrub
Major Problems : Root rots
Additional Notes : Similar to C. canadensis , but smaller and later blooming.

Typical Height : 12 Ft.
Drought Tolerance : High
Nutritional Requirements : Medium
Light Requirements : Medium; high
Leaf Type : Simple
Texture : Coarse
Flower Characteristics : Showy

Environmental Problems : None

Cereus peruvianus

Family : Cactaceae   Zone : 10A-11

Common Name(s) : Hedge Cactus; Peruvian Apple Cactus
Origin : South America
Growth Rate : Slow
Salt Tolerance : Medium
Soil Requirements : Wide
Plant Type : Succulent perennial
Foliage Color : Green
Flowering Season : Summer
Flower Color : White
Propagation : Cuttings
Human Hazards : Spiny
Common Uses : Shrub; edible fruit; rock gardens
Major Problems : None
Additional Notes : Spectacular blooms at night.
Cultivars

Typical Height : 10 Ft.
Drought Tolerance : High
Nutritional Requirements : Low
Light Requirements : High
Leaf Type : None
Texture : Coarse
Flower Characteristics : Showy; fragrant

Environmental Problems : None

'MONSTROSUS' is an unusual form with ribs divided into tubercles.

Cestrum nocturnum

Common Name(s) : Night-blooming Jessamine
Origin : West Indies
Growth Rate : Medium
Salt Tolerance : Medium
Soil Requirements : Wide
Plant Type : Evergreen shrub
Foliage Color : Green
Flowering Season : Spring; summer
Flower Color : Yellow
Propagation : Seeds; cuttings
Human Hazards : Poisonous
Common Uses : Flowering shrub
Major Problems : None
Additional Notes : White fruit is poisonous. Flowers at night.

Family : Solanaceae   Zone : 10A-11

Typical Height : 10 Ft.
Drought Tolerance : Medium
Nutritional Requirements : Medium
Light Requirements : High
Leaf Type : Simple
Texture : Medium
Flower Characteristics : Showy; fragrant

Environmental Problems : None

Chamaecyparis thyoides

Common Name(s) : Atlantic White Cedar
Origin : Eastern United States
Growth Rate : Slow
Salt Tolerance : Low
Soil Requirements : Acid
Plant Type : Evergreen tree
Foliage Color : Blue-green
Flowering Season : n/a
Flower Color : n/a
Propagation : Seeds; cuttings
Human Hazards : None
Common Uses : Tree
Major Problems : None
Additional Notes : Florida populations are sometimes considered a distinct species.
Cultivars
Several cultivars exist, but may not be well-adapted to Florida.

Family : Cupressaceae   Zone : 5-10A

Typical Height : 50 Ft.
Drought Tolerance : Low
Nutritional Requirements : Medium
Light Requirements : High
Leaf Type : Scale-like
Texture : Fine
Flower Characteristics : n/a

Environmental Problems : None

Chamaedaphne calyculata

Common Name(s) : Cassandra; Leatherleaf
Origin : Northern Europe, Asia and N. America
Growth Rate : Medium
Salt Tolerance : Low
Soil Requirements : Acid
Plant Type : Evergreen shrub
Foliage Color : Green
Flowering Season : Spring
Flower Color : White
Propagation : Cuttings
Human Hazards : None
Common Uses : Rock gardens; specimen plant; shrub
Major Problems : None
Additional Notes : Grows best in acid moist soils.

Family : Ericaceae   Zone : 2-9

Typical Height : 4 Ft.
Drought Tolerance : Low
Nutritional Requirements : Medium
Light Requirements : Medium
Leaf Type : Simple
Texture : Fine
Flower Characteristics : Showy

Environmental Problems : None

Chamaedorea cataractarum *(Photograph p. 203)*

Common Name(s) : Cat Palm
Origin : Southern Mexico
Growth Rate : Medium
Salt Tolerance : Low
Soil Requirements : Wide
Plant Type : Palm
Foliage Color : Green
Flowering Season : Summer
Flower Color : Yellow
Propagation : Seeds
Human Hazards : None
Common Uses : Shrub; foliage plant; palm
Major Problems : None
Additional Notes : A small suckering palm.

Family : Palmae   Zone : 10B-11

Typical Height : 5 Ft.
Drought Tolerance : Low
Nutritional Requirements : Medium
Light Requirements : Medium; low
Leaf Type : Pinnately compound
Texture : Fine
Flower Characteristics : Insignificant

Environmental Problems : None

Chamaedorea costaricana

Common Name(s) : Costa Rican Palm
Origin : Costa Rica
Growth Rate : Medium
Salt Tolerance : Low
Soil Requirements : Wide
Plant Type : Palm
Foliage Color : Green
Flowering Season : Summer
Flower Color : Yellow
Propagation : Seeds
Human Hazards : None
Common Uses : Specimen plant; shrub; palm
Major Problems : None
Additional Notes : A clumping chamaedorea with up to 40 leaflets per leaf.

Family : Palmae   Zone : 10B-11

Typical Height : 8 Ft.
Drought Tolerance : Medium
Nutritional Requirements : Medium
Light Requirements : Low; medium
Leaf Type : Pinnately compound
Texture : Medium
Flower Characteristics : Insignificant

Environmental Problems : None

Chamaedorea elegans

Common Name(s) : Parlor Palm; Neanthe Bella
Origin : Mexico and Central America
Growth Rate : Slow
Salt Tolerance : Low
Soil Requirements : Wide
Plant Type : Palm
Foliage Color : Green
Flowering Season : Summer
Flower Color : Yellow
Propagation : Seeds
Human Hazards : None
Common Uses : Foliage plant; specimen plant; palm
Major Problems : None
Additional Notes : A miniature single stemmed palm.

Family : Palmae   Zone : 10B-11

Typical Height : 3 Ft.
Drought Tolerance : Medium
Nutritional Requirements : Low
Light Requirements : Low; medium
Leaf Type : Pinnately compound
Texture : Fine
Flower Characteristics : Insignificant

Environmental Problems : None

Chamaedorea erumpens

Common Name(s) : Bamboo Palm
Origin : Mexico
Growth Rate : Medium
Salt Tolerance : Low
Soil Requirements : Wide
Plant Type : Palm
Foliage Color : Green
Flowering Season : Summer
Flower Color : Yellow
Propagation : Seeds
Human Hazards : Irritant
Common Uses : Foliage plant; shrub; palm
Major Problems : None
Additional Notes : A clumping palm similar to C. seifrizii , but with wider leaflets.
Cultivars
'FLORIDA HYBRID' is a hybrid between C. seifrizii and C. erumpens .

Family : Palmae   Zone : 10B-11

Typical Height : 9 Ft.
Drought Tolerance : Medium
Nutritional Requirements : Medium
Light Requirements : Low; medium
Leaf Type : Pinnately compound
Texture : Medium
Flower Characteristics : Insignificant

Environmental Problems : None

Chamaedorea metallica

Common Name(s) : Miniature Fishtail Palm
Origin : Mexico
Growth Rate : Slow
Salt Tolerance : Low
Soil Requirements : Wide
Plant Type : Palm
Foliage Color : Blue-green
Flowering Season : Summer
Flower Color : Yellow
Propagation : Seeds
Human Hazards : None
Common Uses : Specimen plant; palm
Major Problems : None
Additional Notes : This small single-stemmed palm has two-lobed leaves.

Family : Palmae   Zone : 10B-11

Typical Height : 4 Ft.
Drought Tolerance : Medium
Nutritional Requirements : Medium
Light Requirements : Low; medium
Leaf Type : Simple; two-lobed
Texture : Coarse
Flower Characteristics : Insignificant

Environmental Problems : None

a

Chamaedorea microspadix

Common Name(s) : Microspadix Palm
Origin : Mexico
Growth Rate : Medium
Salt Tolerance : Low
Soil Requirements : Wide
Plant Type : Palm
Foliage Color : Green
Flowering Season : Summer
Flower Color : Yellow
Propagation : Seeds
Human Hazards : None
Common Uses : Shrub; palm
Major Problems : None

Family : Palmae   **Zone** : 9-11

Typical Height : 8 Ft.
Drought Tolerance : Medium
Nutritional Requirements : Medium
Light Requirements : Low; medium
Leaf Type : Pinnately compound
Texture : Medium
Flower Characteristics : Insignificant

Environmental Problems : None

Additional Notes : This clustering palm is one of the most cold-hardy of the chamaedoreas..

Chamaedorea radicalis

Common Name(s) : Radicalis Palm
Origin : Mexico
Growth Rate : Slow
Salt Tolerance : Low
Soil Requirements : Wide
Plant Type : Palm
Foliage Color : Green
Flowering Season : Summer
Flower Color : Yellow
Propagation : Seeds
Human Hazards : None
Common Uses : Shrub; palm
Major Problems : None

Family : Palmae   **Zone** : 9-11

Typical Height : 3 Ft.
Drought Tolerance : Medium
Nutritional Requirements : Medium
Light Requirements : Low; medium
Leaf Type : Pinnately compound
Texture : Medium
Flower Characteristics : Insignificant

Environmental Problems : None

Additional Notes : This palm is virtually stemless.

Chamaedorea seifrizii

Common Name(s) : Reed Palm; Bamboo Palm
Origin : Mexico
Growth Rate : Medium
Salt Tolerance : Low
Soil Requirements : Wide
Plant Type : Palm
Foliage Color : Green
Flowering Season : Summer
Flower Color : Yellow
Propagation : Seeds
Human Hazards : Irritant
Common Uses : Foliage plant; shrub; palm
Major Problems : None

Family : Palmae   **Zone** : 10B-11

Typical Height : 7 Ft.
Drought Tolerance : Medium
Nutritional Requirements : Medium
Light Requirements : Low; medium
Leaf Type : Pinnately compound
Texture : Medium
Flower Characteristics : Insignificant

Environmental Problems : None

Additional Notes : A finer leaved clumping species than C. erumpens . Fruit irritating.
Cultivars
'FLORIDA HYBRID' is a hybrid between C. seifrizii and C. erumpens .

Chamaerops humilis *(Photograph p. 203)*

Common Name(s) : European Fan Palm
Origin : Mediterranean Region
Growth Rate : Slow
Salt Tolerance : Low
Soil Requirements : Wide
Plant Type : Palm
Foliage Color : Green
Flowering Season : Spring
Flower Color : Yellow
Propagation : Seeds
Human Hazards : Spiny
Common Uses : Shrub; palm
Major Problems : K deficiency

Family : Palmae   **Zone** : 8-11

Typical Height : 10 Ft.
Drought Tolerance : High
Nutritional Requirements : Medium
Light Requirements : High; medium
Leaf Type : Simple; palmately lobed
Texture : Coarse
Flower Characteristics : Insignificant

Environmental Problems : None

Additional Notes : A beautiful accent palm. Hardy throughout Florida. A clumping species.

Chimonobambusa falcata

Common Name(s) : Sickle Bamboo
Origin : Himalayas
Growth Rate : Fast
Salt Tolerance : n/a
Soil Requirements : Wide
Plant Type : Evergreen shrub
Foliage Color : Green
Flowering Season : n/a
Flower Color : n/a
Propagation : Division
Human Hazards : None
Common Uses : Shrub
Major Problems : None

Family : Gramineae   **Zone** : 8-10B

Typical Height : 20 Ft.
Drought Tolerance : Medium
Nutritional Requirements : Low
Light Requirements : High
Leaf Type : Simple; linear
Texture : Medium
Flower Characteristics : n/a

Environmental Problems : Invasive

Additional Notes : Slender canes are covered with a glaucous coating when young.

Chiococca alba

Common Name(s) : Snowberry
Origin : South Florida and West Indies
Growth Rate : Medium
Salt Tolerance : High
Soil Requirements : Wide
Plant Type : Evergreen shrub or vine
Foliage Color : Green
Flowering Season : Year-round
Flower Color : Yellow
Propagation : Seeds
Human Hazards : None
Common Uses : Shrub; vine
Major Problems : None

Family : Rubiaceae   **Zone** : 10A-11

Typical Height : 10 Ft.
Drought Tolerance : High
Nutritional Requirements : Low
Light Requirements : High
Leaf Type : Simple
Texture : Medium
Flower Characteristics : Insignificant

Environmental Problems : None

Additional Notes : A Florida native with white fruit. Can become a vine.

Chiococca pinetorum

Common Name(s) : Pineland Snowberry
Origin : South Florida
Growth Rate : Slow
Salt Tolerance : Low
Soil Requirements : Wide
Plant Type : Evergreen shrub
Foliage Color : Green
Flowering Season : Year-round
Flower Color : White; purple-white
Propagation : Seeds
Human Hazards : None
Common Uses : Groundcover
Major Problems : None

Family : Rubiaceae   **Zone** : 10B-11

Typical Height : 2.5 Ft.
Drought Tolerance : High
Nutritional Requirements : Low
Light Requirements : High
Leaf Type : Simple
Texture : Medium
Flower Characteristics : Insignificant

Environmental Problems : None

Additional Notes : A native vining shrub.

Chionanthus retusus

Common Name(s) : Chinese Fringe Tree
Origin : China
Growth Rate : Medium
Salt Tolerance : Low
Soil Requirements : Acid
Plant Type : Deciduous shrub
Foliage Color : Green
Flowering Season : Summer
Flower Color : White
Propagation : Seeds; cuttings; air layering; grafting
Human Hazards : None
Common Uses : Flowering shrub
Major Problems : None

Family : Oleaceae   **Zone** : 6-10A

Typical Height : 15 Ft.
Drought Tolerance : Low
Nutritional Requirements : Medium
Light Requirements : Medium
Leaf Type : Simple
Texture : Medium
Flower Characteristics : Showy

Environmental Problems : None

Additional Notes : Later-flowering and smaller than our native species but of easier culture.

Chionanthus virginicus *(Photograph p. 157)*

Common Name(s) : Fringe Tree
Origin : Eastern United States
Growth Rate : Slow
Salt Tolerance : Low
Soil Requirements : Acid
Plant Type : Deciduous tree
Foliage Color : Green
Flowering Season : Spring
Flower Color : White
Propagation : Seeds; grafting
Human Hazards : Poisonous
Common Uses : Small flowering tree; flowering shrub
Major Problems : Scales; mites
Additional Notes : Often shrubby; airy flowers late in spring.

Family : Oleaceae **Zone** : 5-9

Typical Height : 20 Ft.
Drought Tolerance : Medium
Nutritional Requirements : Medium
Light Requirements : Medium
Leaf Type : Simple
Texture : Coarse
Flower Characteristics : Fragrant; showy

Environmental Problems : None

Chlorophytum comosum

Common Name(s) : Spider Plant
Origin : South Africa
Growth Rate : Medium
Salt Tolerance : Low
Soil Requirements : Wide
Plant Type : Herbaceous perennial
Foliage Color : Green
Flowering Season : Year-round
Flower Color : White
Propagation : Plantlets; division
Human Hazards : None
Common Uses : Foliage plant; groundcover; hanging baskets
Major Problems : Mealybugs
Additional Notes : Plantlets produced at tips of leaves.
Cultivars
'MANDAIANUM' is a dwarf variety with a central yellow leaf stripe; 'PICTURATUM' has a central yellow leaf stripe; 'VITTATUM' has a central white leaf stripe; 'VARIEGATUM' has white leaf margins.

Family : Liliaceae **Zone** : 10B-11

Typical Height : .9 Ft.
Drought Tolerance : Medium
Nutritional Requirements : Medium
Light Requirements : Medium; low
Leaf Type : Simple; linear
Texture : Medium
Flower Characteristics : Insignificant

Environmental Problems : None

Chorisia insignis

Common Name(s) : White Floss-silk Tree;
Origin : Peru
Growth Rate : Medium
Salt Tolerance : Medium
Soil Requirements : Wide
Plant Type : Deciduous tree
Foliage Color : Green
Flowering Season : Fall
Flower Color : White
Propagation : Seeds; grafting
Human Hazards : Spiny
Common Uses : Flowering tree
Major Problems : None
Additional Notes : Spiny green trunk. Spectacular flowers.

Family : Bombacaceae **Zone** : 10B-11

Typical Height : 40 Ft.
Drought Tolerance : High
Nutritional Requirements : Medium
Light Requirements : High
Leaf Type : Palmately compound
Texture : Medium
Flower Characteristics : Showy

Environmental Problems : None

Chorisia speciosa *(Photograph p. 157)*

Common Name(s) : Floss-silk Tree; Silk-floss Tree
Origin : Brazil and Argentina
Growth Rate : Fast
Salt Tolerance : Medium
Soil Requirements : Wide
Plant Type : Deciduous tree
Foliage Color : Green
Flowering Season : Fall
Flower Color : Pink
Propagation : Seeds; grafting
Human Hazards : Spiny
Common Uses : Flowering tree
Major Problems : None
Additional Notes : Spiny green trunk. Spectacular pink flowers.

Family : Bombacaceae **Zone** : 10B-11

Typical Height : 45 Ft.
Drought Tolerance : High
Nutritional Requirements : Medium
Light Requirements : High
Leaf Type : Palmately compound
Texture : Medium
Flower Characteristics : Showy

Environmental Problems : None

Chrysalidocarpus cabadae

Common Name(s) : Cabada Palm
Origin : Madagascar
Growth Rate : Medium
Salt Tolerance : Medium
Soil Requirements : Wide
Plant Type : Palm
Foliage Color : Green
Flowering Season : Spring
Flower Color : White
Propagation : Seeds
Human Hazards : None
Common Uses : Shrub; multi-trunked tree; palm
Major Problems : K deficiency
Additional Notes : A multiple-stemmed palm. Larger than C. lutescens .

Family : Palmae   **Zone** : 10B-11

Typical Height : 30 Ft.
Drought Tolerance : High
Nutritional Requirements : Medium
Light Requirements : Medium; high
Leaf Type : Pinnately compound
Texture : Medium
Flower Characteristics : Insignificant

Environmental Problems : None

Chrysalidocarpus lutescens *(Photograph p. 203)*

Common Name(s) : Areca Palm; Butterfly Palm
Origin : Madagascar
Growth Rate : Medium
Salt Tolerance : Medium
Soil Requirements : Wide
Plant Type : Palm
Foliage Color : Green
Flowering Season : Spring
Flower Color : White
Propagation : Seeds
Human Hazards : None
Common Uses : Shrub; multi-trunked tree; palm
Major Problems : K deficiency; caterpillars
Additional Notes : A multiple-stemmed palm. Highly susceptible to potassium deficiency.

Family : Palmae   **Zone** : 10B-11

Typical Height : 20 Ft.
Drought Tolerance : High
Nutritional Requirements : High
Light Requirements : Medium; high
Leaf Type : Pinnately compound
Texture : Medium
Flower Characteristics : Insignificant

Environmental Problems : None

Chrysanthemum leucanthemum

Common Name(s) : Oxeye Daisy
Origin : Europe and Asia
Growth Rate : Fast
Salt Tolerance : Medium
Soil Requirements : Wide
Plant Type : Herbaceous perennial
Foliage Color : Green
Flowering Season : Summer
Flower Color : White
Propagation : Cuttings; seeds
Human Hazards : None
Common Uses : Beds; specimen plant
Major Problems : None
Additional Notes : This plant is widely naturalized throughout the United States.

Family : Compositae   **Zone** : 3-9

Typical Height : 3 Ft.
Drought Tolerance : High
Nutritional Requirements : Low
Light Requirements : High
Leaf Type : Pinnately lobed
Texture : Medium
Flower Characteristics : Showy

Environmental Problems : Weedy

Chrysobalanus icaco *(Photograph p. 175)*

Common Name(s) : Cocoplum
Origin : Caribbean Region
Growth Rate : Medium
Salt Tolerance : High
Soil Requirements : Wide
Plant Type : Evergreen shrub
Foliage Color : Green; green & red
Flowering Season : Year-round
Flower Color : White
Propagation : Cuttings; seeds; air layers
Human Hazards : None
Common Uses : Hedge; shrub; edible fruit
Major Problems : None
Additional Notes : An excellent native shrub for south Florida.
Cultivars
'RED TIP' has dark red new foliage.

Family : Chrysobalanaceae   **Zone** : 10B-11

Typical Height : 20 Ft.
Drought Tolerance : Medium
Nutritional Requirements : Low
Light Requirements : High
Leaf Type : Simple
Texture : Medium
Flower Characteristics : Insignificant

Environmental Problems : None

Chrysophyllum cainito

Common Name(s) : Star Apple; Caimito
Origin : Tropical America
Growth Rate : Medium
Salt Tolerance : Medium
Soil Requirements : Wide
Plant Type : Evergreen tree
Foliage Color : Green & brown
Flowering Season : Summer; fall
Flower Color : Purple-white
Propagation : Seeds; cuttings; grafting
Human Hazards : None
Common Uses : Edible fruit; shade tree
Major Problems : None
Additional Notes : Grown primarily for fruits with star-shaped centers.

Family : Sapotaceae   Zone : 10B-11

Typical Height : 40 Ft.
Drought Tolerance : Medium
Nutritional Requirements : Medium
Light Requirements : High
Leaf Type : Simple
Texture : Coarse
Flower Characteristics : Insignificant

Environmental Problems : None

Chrysophyllum oliviforme *(Photograph p. 157)*

Common Name(s) : Satin Leaf
Origin : South Florida and West Indies
Growth Rate : Slow
Salt Tolerance : Medium
Soil Requirements : Wide
Plant Type : Evergreen tree
Foliage Color : Green & brown
Flowering Season : Fall
Flower Color : Yellow
Propagation : Seeds
Human Hazards : None
Common Uses : Shade tree; edible fruit
Major Problems : Galls
Additional Notes : Leaves glossy on top and bronzy satin below. Fruit edible.

Family : Sapotaceae   Zone : 10B-11

Typical Height : 30 Ft.
Drought Tolerance : High
Nutritional Requirements : Low
Light Requirements : High
Leaf Type : Simple
Texture : Medium
Flower Characteristics : Insignificant

Environmental Problems : None

Cinnamomum camphora *(Photograph p. 157)*

Common Name(s) : Camphor Tree
Origin : China and Japan
Growth Rate : Medium
Salt Tolerance : Low
Soil Requirements : Acid
Plant Type : Evergreen tree
Foliage Color : Green
Flowering Season : Spring
Flower Color : Yellow
Propagation : Seeds
Human Hazards : Irritant
Common Uses : Shade tree
Major Problems : Scales
Additional Notes : Camphor aroma in bruised leaves. Can be weedy and messy.

Family : Lauraceae   Zone : 9-10B

Typical Height : 45 Ft.
Drought Tolerance : Medium
Nutritional Requirements : Medium
Light Requirements : High
Leaf Type : Simple
Texture : Medium
Flower Characteristics : Insignificant

Environmental Problems : Weedy; messy

Cissus incisa

Common Name(s) : Marine Ivy
Origin : Southern United States
Growth Rate : Fast
Salt Tolerance : High
Soil Requirements : Wide
Plant Type : Deciduous vine
Foliage Color : Green
Flowering Season : Summer
Flower Color : Green
Propagation : Cuttings; seeds
Human Hazards : None
Common Uses : Vine
Major Problems : None
Additional Notes : Excellent for seaside plantings.

Family : Vitaceae   Zone : 7-11

Typical Height : Not applicable
Drought Tolerance : High
Nutritional Requirements : Low
Light Requirements : Medium; high
Leaf Type : Simple; palmately lobed
Texture : Medium
Flower Characteristics : Insignificant

Environmental Problems : None

Cissus rhombifolia

Common Name(s) : Grape Ivy
Origin : Mexico to Colombia
Growth Rate : Fast
Salt Tolerance : n/a
Soil Requirements : Wide
Plant Type : Evergreen vine
Foliage Color : Green
Flowering Season : n/a
Flower Color : Green
Propagation : Cuttings
Human Hazards : None
Common Uses : Foliage plant; hanging basket; vine
Major Problems : Aphids; scales; mites; nematodes
Additional Notes : Often grown as a foliage plant in hanging baskets or on totem poles.
Cultivars
'ELLEN DANICA' has deeply lobed leaflets; 'MANDAIANA' is more upright and lacks tendrils.

Family : Vitaceae   **Zone** : 10B-11

Typical Height : Not applicable
Drought Tolerance : Medium
Nutritional Requirements : Medium
Light Requirements : Low; medium
Leaf Type : Trifoliate
Texture : Medium
Flower Characteristics : Insignificant

Environmental Problems : None

Citharexylum fruticosum

Common Name(s) : Fiddlewood
Origin : West Indies
Growth Rate : Slow
Salt Tolerance : Medium
Soil Requirements : Wide
Plant Type : Evergreen tree
Foliage Color : Green
Flowering Season : Year-round
Flower Color : White
Propagation : Seeds
Human Hazards : None
Common Uses : Small tree
Major Problems : None
Additional Notes : A Florida native.

Family : Verbenaceae   **Zone** : 10B-11

Typical Height : 25 Ft.
Drought Tolerance : High
Nutritional Requirements : Low
Light Requirements : High
Leaf Type : Simple
Texture : Medium
Flower Characteristics : Insignificant; fragrant

Environmental Problems : None

X Citrofortunella mitis

Common Name(s) : Calamondin Orange
Origin : Philippines
Growth Rate : Medium
Salt Tolerance : Low
Soil Requirements : Wide
Plant Type : Evergreen shrub
Foliage Color : Green
Flowering Season : Spring; summer; fall
Flower Color : White
Propagation : Cuttings
Human Hazards : None
Common Uses : Flowering shrub; foliage plant
Major Problems : Whiteflies; scales; sooty mold
Additional Notes : Attractive small, sour orange fruit most of the year.

Family : Rutaceae   **Zone** : 10B-11

Typical Height : 9 Ft.
Drought Tolerance : Medium
Nutritional Requirements : Medium
Light Requirements : High
Leaf Type : Simple
Texture : Medium
Flower Characteristics : Showy; fragrant

Environmental Problems : None

Citrus aurantiifolia

Common Name(s) : Key Lime
Origin : Southern Asia
Growth Rate : Medium
Salt Tolerance : Low
Soil Requirements : Wide
Plant Type : Evergreen tree
Foliage Color : Green
Flowering Season : Winter
Flower Color : White
Propagation : Grafting
Human Hazards : Spiny
Common Uses : Edible fruit
Major Problems : Scales; root rots; sooty mold
Additional Notes : The least cold hardy of citrus species; small round yellow fruits.

Family : Rutaceae   **Zone** : 10B-11

Typical Height : 15 Ft.
Drought Tolerance : Medium
Nutritional Requirements : High
Light Requirements : High
Leaf Type : Simple
Texture : Medium
Flower Characteristics : Insignificant; fragrant

Environmental Problems : Messy

Citrus aurantium

Common Name(s) : Sour Orange
Origin : Southern Asia
Growth Rate : Medium
Salt Tolerance : Low
Soil Requirements : Wide
Plant Type : Evergreen tree
Foliage Color : Green
Flowering Season : Winter
Flower Color : White
Propagation : Seeds
Human Hazards : Spiny
Common Uses : Edible fruit; rootstock
Major Problems : Scales; sooty mold
Additional Notes : Often used as a rootstock for other citrus species.

Family : Rutaceae   Zone : 9-11

Typical Height : 25 Ft.
Drought Tolerance : Medium
Nutritional Requirements : High
Light Requirements : High
Leaf Type : Simple
Texture : Medium
Flower Characteristics : Insignificant; fragrant

Environmental Problems : Messy

Citrus latifolia

Common Name(s) : Persian Lime; Lime
Origin : Southern Asia
Growth Rate : Medium
Salt Tolerance : Low
Soil Requirements : Wide
Plant Type : Evergreen tree
Foliage Color : Green
Flowering Season : Winter
Flower Color : White
Propagation : Grafting
Human Hazards : Spiny
Common Uses : Edible fruit
Major Problems : Scales; sooty mold; root rots
Additional Notes : This is the common green-fruited lime of commerce.
Cultivars
Widely grown cultivars include 'TAHITI' and 'BEARS'.

Family : Rutaceae   Zone : 10B-11

Typical Height : 15 Ft.
Drought Tolerance : Medium
Nutritional Requirements : High
Light Requirements : High
Leaf Type : Simple
Texture : Medium
Flower Characteristics : Insignificant; fragrant

Environmental Problems : Messy

Citrus limon

Common Name(s) : Lemon
Origin : Southern Asia
Growth Rate : Medium
Salt Tolerance : Low
Soil Requirements : Wide
Plant Type : Evergreen tree
Foliage Color : Green
Flowering Season : Winter
Flower Color : White
Propagation : Grafting
Human Hazards : Spiny
Common Uses : Edible fruit
Major Problems : Scales; nematodes; sooty mold
Additional Notes : The common commercial lemon.
Cultivars
'PONDEROSA' has a very large warty fruit; 'MEYER' has a nearly round fruit.

Family : Rutaceae   Zone : 9-11

Typical Height : 20 Ft.
Drought Tolerance : Medium
Nutritional Requirements : High
Light Requirements : High
Leaf Type : Simple
Texture : Medium
Flower Characteristics : Insignificant; fragrant

Environmental Problems : Messy

Citrus reticulata

Common Name(s) : Tangerine; Mandarin Orange; Satsuma Orange
Origin : China
Growth Rate : Medium
Salt Tolerance : Low
Soil Requirements : Wide
Plant Type : Evergreen tree
Foliage Color : Green
Flowering Season : Winter
Flower Color : White
Propagation : Grafting
Human Hazards : Spiny
Common Uses : Edible fruit
Major Problems : Scales; nematodes; sooty mold
Additional Notes : Many cultivars of this easily peeled fruit exist.
Cultivars
Cultivars include: 'DANCY', 'MURCOTT', 'OWARI', 'OBAWASE 891', 'ARMSTRONG'S EARLY', 'NORDMAN', 'CLEMENTINE', 'CLEOPATRA', 'SUNBURST', and 'ONECO'.

Family : Rutaceae   Zone : 9B-11

Typical Height : 15 Ft.
Drought Tolerance : Medium
Nutritional Requirements : High
Light Requirements : High
Leaf Type : Simple
Texture : Medium
Flower Characteristics : Insignificant; fragrant

Environmental Problems : Messy

Citrus sinensis

Common Name(s) : Sweet Orange
Origin : China
Growth Rate : Medium
Salt Tolerance : Low
Soil Requirements : Wide
Plant Type : Evergreen tree
Foliage Color : Green
Flowering Season : Winter
Flower Color : White
Propagation : Grafting
Human Hazards : Spiny
Common Uses : Edible fruit
Major Problems : Scales; nematodes; sooty mold
Additional Notes : Many cultivars of sweet orange exist. Some are seedless.
Cultivars
Cultivars include: 'HAMLIN', 'PARSON BROWN', 'PINEAPPLE', 'VALENCIA', 'WASHINGTON', 'DWARF NAVEL' 'MURCOT', and 'PAGE'.

Family : Rutaceae   Zone : 9B-11

Typical Height : 30 Ft.
Drought Tolerance : Medium
Nutritional Requirements : High
Light Requirements : High
Leaf Type : Simple
Texture : Medium
Flower Characteristics : Insignificant; fragrant

Environmental Problems : Messy

Citrus X nobilis

Common Name(s) : Tangor
Origin : Hybrid
Growth Rate : Medium
Salt Tolerance : Low
Soil Requirements : Wide
Plant Type : Evergreen tree
Foliage Color : Green
Flowering Season : Winter
Flower Color : White
Propagation : Grafting
Human Hazards : Spiny
Common Uses : Edible fruit
Major Problems : Scales; nematodes; sooty mold
Additional Notes : A hybrid between C. reticulata and C. sinensis .
Cultivars
Cultivars include: 'KING', 'TEMPLE', and 'TEMPLE DWARF'.

Family : Rutaceae   Zone : 9-11

Typical Height : 10 Ft.
Drought Tolerance : Medium
Nutritional Requirements : High
Light Requirements : High
Leaf Type : Simple
Texture : Medium
Flower Characteristics : Insignificant; fragrant

Environmental Problems : Messy

Citrus X paradisi

Common Name(s) : Grapefruit
Origin : Hybrid
Growth Rate : Medium
Salt Tolerance : Low
Soil Requirements : Wide
Plant Type : Evergreen tree
Foliage Color : Green
Flowering Season : Winter
Flower Color : White
Propagation : Grafting
Human Hazards : Spiny
Common Uses : Edible fruit
Major Problems : Scales; nematodes; sooty mold
Additional Notes : Large round yellow-peeled fruits. Many cultivars exist.
Cultivars
Cultivars include: 'MARSH', 'RUBY', 'STAR RUBY', 'THOMPSON', 'RED BLUSH', 'FLAME', 'DUNCAN', and 'MCCARTY'.

Family : Rutaceae   Zone : 9-11

Typical Height : 30 Ft.
Drought Tolerance : Medium
Nutritional Requirements : High
Light Requirements : High
Leaf Type : Simple
Texture : Medium
Flower Characteristics : Insignificant; fragrant

Environmental Problems : Messy

Citrus X tangelo

Common Name(s) : Tangelo
Origin : Hybrid
Growth Rate : Medium
Salt Tolerance : Low
Soil Requirements : Wide
Plant Type : Evergreen tree
Foliage Color : Green
Flowering Season : Winter
Flower Color : White
Propagation : Grafting
Human Hazards : Spiny
Common Uses : Edible fruit
Major Problems : Scales; nematodes; sooty mold
Additional Notes : A cross between C. X paradisi and C. reticulata .
Cultivars
Cultivars include: 'MINNEOLA', 'ORLANDO', 'SEMINOLE', and 'SAMPSON'.

Family : Rutaceae   Zone : 9-11

Typical Height : 15 Ft.
Drought Tolerance : Medium
Nutritional Requirements : High
Light Requirements : High
Leaf Type : Simple
Texture : Medium
Flower Characteristics : Insignificant; fragrant

Environmental Problems : Messy

Cladium jamaicensis

Common Name(s) : Sawgrass
Origin : Southeastern United States, W. Indies
Growth Rate : Fast
Salt Tolerance : Medium
Soil Requirements : Wide
Plant Type : Herbaceous perennial
Foliage Color : Green
Flowering Season : Fall
Flower Color : Brown
Propagation : Division; seeds
Human Hazards : Spiny
Common Uses : Aquatic
Major Problems : None
Additional Notes : Leaf edges are sharply serrated. Common in the Everglades.

Family : Cyperaceae   Zone : 8-11

Typical Height : 8 Ft.
Drought Tolerance : Medium
Nutritional Requirements : Low
Light Requirements : High
Leaf Type : Simple; linear
Texture : Medium
Flower Characteristics : Insignificant

Environmental Problems : None

Clematis dioscoreifolia

Common Name(s) : Japanese Clematis; Autumn Clematis
Origin : Korea
Growth Rate : Medium
Salt Tolerance : Low
Soil Requirements : Wide
Plant Type : Deciduous vine
Foliage Color : Green
Flowering Season : Summer; fall
Flower Color : White
Propagation : Division; cuttings
Human Hazards : None
Common Uses : Flowering vine
Major Problems : None
Additional Notes : This species is widely adaptable to all parts of Florida.

Family : Ranunculaceae   Zone : 5-10B

Typical Height : Not applicable
Drought Tolerance : Medium
Nutritional Requirements : Medium
Light Requirements : High
Leaf Type : Pinnately compound
Texture : Medium
Flower Characteristics : Showy; fragrant

Environmental Problems : None

Clerodendrum minahassae

Common Name(s) : Clerodendrum
Origin : Malay Archipeligo
Growth Rate : Medium
Salt Tolerance : Low
Soil Requirements : Wide
Plant Type : Evergreen shrub or tree
Foliage Color : Green
Flowering Season : Summer
Flower Color : White
Propagation : Seeds; cuttings
Human Hazards : None
Common Uses : Flowering shrub; small flowering tree
Major Problems : None
Additional Notes : Has attractive white flowers with red calyces.

Family : Verbenaceae   Zone : 10B-11

Typical Height : 10 Ft.
Drought Tolerance : Low
Nutritional Requirements : Medium
Light Requirements : Medium
Leaf Type : Simple
Texture : Medium
Flower Characteristics : Showy

Environmental Problems : None

Clerodendrum paniculatum *(Photograph p. 176)*

Common Name(s) : Pagoda Flower
Origin : Southeast Asia
Growth Rate : Fast
Salt Tolerance : Low
Soil Requirements : Wide
Plant Type : Evergreen shrub
Foliage Color : Green
Flowering Season : Summer; fall
Flower Color : Red
Propagation : Cuttings; seeds; suckers
Human Hazards : None
Common Uses : Flowering shrub
Major Problems : None
Additional Notes : Prune severely to maintain size; root suckers. Often weedy.

Family : Verbenaceae   Zone : 10B-11

Typical Height : 6 Ft.
Drought Tolerance : Medium
Nutritional Requirements : Medium
Light Requirements : Medium; high
Leaf Type : Simple
Texture : Coarse
Flower Characteristics : Showy

Environmental Problems : Invasive

Clerodendrum speciosissimum

Common Name(s) : Java Glorybower
Origin : Java
Growth Rate : Fast
Salt Tolerance : Low
Soil Requirements : Wide
Plant Type : Evergreen shrub
Foliage Color : Green
Flowering Season : Spring; fall
Flower Color : Red
Propagation : Cuttings; suckers; seeds
Human Hazards : None
Common Uses : Flowering shrub
Major Problems : None
Additional Notes : Root suckers vigorously, can be weedy; prune severely.

Family : Verbenaceae   Zone : 10B-11

Typical Height : 10 Ft.
Drought Tolerance : Medium
Nutritional Requirements : Low
Light Requirements : Medium; high
Leaf Type : Simple
Texture : Coarse
Flower Characteristics : Showy

Environmental Problems : Invasive

Clerodendrum thomsoniae

Common Name(s) : Bleeding Heart
Origin : West Africa
Growth Rate : Medium
Salt Tolerance : Low
Soil Requirements : Wide
Plant Type : Evergreen vine or shrub
Foliage Color : Green
Flowering Season : Summer
Flower Color : White & red
Propagation : Cuttings
Human Hazards : None
Common Uses : Flowering vine; flowering shrub
Major Problems : Nematodes; mites
Additional Notes : A twining shrub.

Family : Verbenaceae   Zone : 10A-11

Typical Height : Not applicable
Drought Tolerance : Low
Nutritional Requirements : Medium
Light Requirements : Medium
Leaf Type : Simple
Texture : Medium
Flower Characteristics : Showy

Environmental Problems : None

Clerodendrum ugandense

Common Name(s) : Ugandan Clerodendrum
Origin : Tropical Africa
Growth Rate : Medium
Salt Tolerance : Low
Soil Requirements : Wide
Plant Type : Evergreen shrub
Foliage Color : Green
Flowering Season : Summer
Flower Color : Blue
Propagation : Seeds; cuttings
Human Hazards : None
Common Uses : Flowering shrub
Major Problems : None
Additional Notes : A climbing shrub with attractive blue and lavender flowers.

Family : Verbenaceae   Zone : 10B-11

Typical Height : 10 Ft.
Drought Tolerance : Low
Nutritional Requirements : Medium
Light Requirements : Medium
Leaf Type : Simple
Texture : Medium
Flower Characteristics : Showy

Environmental Problems : None

Clerodendrum wallichii

Common Name(s) : Wallich Clerodendrum
Origin : India
Growth Rate : Medium
Salt Tolerance : Low
Soil Requirements : Wide
Plant Type : Evergreen shrub
Foliage Color : Green
Flowering Season : Summer
Flower Color : White
Propagation : Seeds; cuttings
Human Hazards : None
Common Uses : Flowering shrub
Major Problems : None
Additional Notes : Has attractive white flowers in a pendent inflorescence.

Family : Verbenaceae   Zone : 10B-11

Typical Height : 8 Ft.
Drought Tolerance : Low
Nutritional Requirements : Medium
Light Requirements : Medium
Leaf Type : Simple
Texture : Medium
Flower Characteristics : Showy

Environmental Problems : None

Cleyera japonica

Common Name(s) : Cleyera
Origin : Eastern Asia
Growth Rate : Medium
Salt Tolerance : Low
Soil Requirements : Acid
Plant Type : Evergreen shrub
Foliage Color : Green
Flowering Season : Spring
Flower Color : White
Propagation : Cuttings
Human Hazards : None
Common Uses : Shrub
Major Problems : Scales
Additional Notes : Showy red berries.

Family : Theaceae   **Zone** : 8-9

Typical Height : 20 Ft.
Drought Tolerance : Low
Nutritional Requirements : Medium
Light Requirements : Medium; high
Leaf Type : Simple
Texture : Coarse
Flower Characteristics : Insignificant; fragrant

Environmental Problems : None

Clivia miniata *(Photograph p. 193)*

Common Name(s) : Kaffir Lily
Origin : South Africa
Growth Rate : Slow
Salt Tolerance : Low
Soil Requirements : Acid
Plant Type : Herbaceous perennial
Foliage Color : Green
Flowering Season : Spring
Flower Color : Orange; yellow
Propagation : Division; seeds
Human Hazards : Poisonous
Common Uses : Beds; borders; specimen plant
Major Problems : Scales; root rots
Additional Notes : Evergreen; keep cool and dry in winter; fleshy roots rot easily.

Family : Amaryllidaceae   **Zone** : 10B-11

Typical Height : 2.5 Ft.
Drought Tolerance : Medium
Nutritional Requirements : High
Light Requirements : Low
Leaf Type : Simple; linear
Texture : Coarse
Flower Characteristics : Showy; fragrant

Environmental Problems : None

Clusia rosea *(Photograph p. 157)*

Common Name(s) : Pitch Apple; Autograph Tree
Origin : Caribbean Region
Growth Rate : Slow
Salt Tolerance : High
Soil Requirements : Wide
Plant Type : Evergreen tree
Foliage Color : Green
Flowering Season : Summer
Flower Color : Pink & white
Propagation : Seeds; cuttings
Human Hazards : Poisonous
Common Uses : Shade tree; flowering tree
Major Problems : Scales
Additional Notes : Has stilt roots. Leaves very leathery and tough.

Family : Guttiferae   **Zone** : 10B-11

Typical Height : 30 Ft.
Drought Tolerance : High
Nutritional Requirements : Low
Light Requirements : High
Leaf Type : Simple
Texture : Coarse
Flower Characteristics : Showy

Environmental Problems : None

Clytostoma callistegioides

Common Name(s) : Argentine Trumpet Vine
Origin : Brazil and Argentina
Growth Rate : Fast
Salt Tolerance : Low
Soil Requirements : Wide
Plant Type : Evergreen vine
Foliage Color : Green
Flowering Season : Spring; summer
Flower Color : Lavender
Propagation : Cuttings
Human Hazards : None
Common Uses : Flowering vine
Major Problems : None
Additional Notes : Flowers hang below foliage when grown on overhead support.

Family : Bignoniaceae   **Zone** : 9-11

Typical Height : Not applicable
Drought Tolerance : Medium
Nutritional Requirements : Medium
Light Requirements : High
Leaf Type : Bifoliate
Texture : Medium
Flower Characteristics : Showy

Environmental Problems : None

Coccoloba diversifolia *(Photograph p. 158)*

Common Name(s) : Pigeon Plum
Origin : Caribbean Region
Growth Rate : Medium
Salt Tolerance : High
Soil Requirements : Wide
Plant Type : Evergreen tree
Foliage Color : Green
Flowering Season : Spring
Flower Color : White
Propagation : Seeds
Human Hazards : None
Common Uses : Tree
Major Problems : None

Family : Polygonaceae   Zone : 10B-11

Typical Height : 35 Ft.
Drought Tolerance : High
Nutritional Requirements : Low
Light Requirements : High
Leaf Type : Simple
Texture : Medium
Flower Characteristics : Insignificant

Environmental Problems : None

Additional Notes : Attractive bark. Variable leaf shape and size. Good small native tree.

Coccoloba uvifera *(Photograph p. 158)*

Common Name(s) : Sea Grape
Origin : Caribbean Region
Growth Rate : Medium
Salt Tolerance : High
Soil Requirements : Wide
Plant Type : Evergreen tree or shrub
Foliage Color : Green
Flowering Season : Summer
Flower Color : White
Propagation : Seeds; cuttings; air layers
Human Hazards : None
Common Uses : Edible fruit; small tree; shrub
Major Problems : None

Family : Polygonaceae   Zone : 10B-11

Typical Height : 25 Ft.
Drought Tolerance : High
Nutritional Requirements : Low
Light Requirements : High
Leaf Type : Simple
Texture : Coarse
Flower Characteristics : Insignificant

Environmental Problems : None

Additional Notes : Edible fruit used for jelly. Good seaside plant. Broad spreading.

Coccothrinax alta

Common Name(s) : n/a
Origin : Puerto Rico
Growth Rate : Slow
Salt Tolerance : High
Soil Requirements : Wide
Plant Type : Palm
Foliage Color : Green
Flowering Season : Summer
Flower Color : White
Propagation : Seeds
Human Hazards : None
Common Uses : Small tree; palm
Major Problems : None

Family : Palmae   Zone : 10B-11

Typical Height : 25 Ft.
Drought Tolerance : High
Nutritional Requirements : Low
Light Requirements : Medium; high
Leaf Type : Simple; palmately lobed
Texture : Very coarse
Flower Characteristics : Insignificant

Environmental Problems : None

Additional Notes : Undersides of leaves are silver.

Coccothrinax argentata

Common Name(s) : Silver Palm
Origin : Caribbean Region
Growth Rate : Slow
Salt Tolerance : High
Soil Requirements : Wide
Plant Type : Palm
Foliage Color : Green & silver
Flowering Season : Summer
Flower Color : White
Propagation : Seeds
Human Hazards : None
Common Uses : Small tree; palm
Major Problems : None

Family : Palmae   Zone : 10B-11

Typical Height : 15 Ft.
Drought Tolerance : High
Nutritional Requirements : Low
Light Requirements : Medium; high
Leaf Type : Simple; palmately lobed
Texture : Very coarse
Flower Characteristics : Insignificant

Environmental Problems : None

Additional Notes : Excellent slow growing small native palm.

Coccothrinax crinita *(Photograph p. 203)*

Common Name(s) : Old Man Palm
Origin : Cuba
Growth Rate : Slow
Salt Tolerance : High
Soil Requirements : Wide
Plant Type : Palm
Foliage Color : Green
Flowering Season : Summer
Flower Color : White
Propagation : Seeds
Human Hazards : None
Common Uses : Small tree; palm
Major Problems : None
Additional Notes : Trunk is covered with curious long whitish hairs.

Family : Palmae   **Zone** : 10B-11

Typical Height : 15 Ft.
Drought Tolerance : High
Nutritional Requirements : Low
Light Requirements : Medium; high
Leaf Type : Simple; palmately lobed
Texture : Very coarse
Flower Characteristics : Insignificant

Environmental Problems : None

Coccothrinax miraguama

Common Name(s) : Miraguama Palm
Origin : Cuba
Growth Rate : Medium
Salt Tolerance : High
Soil Requirements : Wide
Plant Type : Palm
Foliage Color : Green & silver
Flowering Season : Summer
Flower Color : White
Propagation : Seeds
Human Hazards : None
Common Uses : Small tree; palm
Major Problems : K deficiency
Additional Notes : A variable species. Trunk is covered with mat of woven fibers.

Family : Palmae   **Zone** : 10B-11

Typical Height : 20 Ft.
Drought Tolerance : High
Nutritional Requirements : Low
Light Requirements : Medium; high
Leaf Type : Simple; palmately lobed
Texture : Very coarse
Flower Characteristics : Insignificant

Environmental Problems : None

Cocculus laurifolius

Common Name(s) : Snail Seed
Origin : Southern Asia
Growth Rate : Medium
Salt Tolerance : Low
Soil Requirements : Wide
Plant Type : Evergreen shrub
Foliage Color : Green
Flowering Season : Summer
Flower Color : Yellow
Propagation : Seeds; cuttings
Human Hazards : Poisonous
Common Uses : Hedge; shrub; cut foliage
Major Problems : Root rots
Additional Notes : Long lasting foliage used for wreaths; poisonous leaves.

Family : Menispermaceae   **Zone** : 9-10B

Typical Height : 13 Ft.
Drought Tolerance : Medium
Nutritional Requirements : Medium
Light Requirements : Medium; high
Leaf Type : Simple
Texture : Medium
Flower Characteristics : Insignificant

Environmental Problems : None

Cochlospermum vitifolium

Common Name(s) : Buttercup Tree
Origin : Mexico to Northern South America
Growth Rate : Fast
Salt Tolerance : Medium
Soil Requirements : Wide
Plant Type : Deciduous tree
Foliage Color : Green
Flowering Season : Winter; spring
Flower Color : Yellow
Propagation : Seeds; cuttings
Human Hazards : None
Common Uses : Flowering tree
Major Problems : None
Additional Notes : Soft-wooded branches break off in high wind. Double flower cultivar exists.

Family : Cochlospermaceae   **Zone** : 10B-11

Typical Height : 35 Ft.
Drought Tolerance : High
Nutritional Requirements : Medium
Light Requirements : High
Leaf Type : Simple; palmately lobed
Texture : Coarse
Flower Characteristics : Showy

Environmental Problems : Weak

Cocos nucifera *(Photograph p. 203)*

Common Name(s) : Coconut Palm
Origin : Pacific Islands
Growth Rate : Medium
Salt Tolerance : High
Soil Requirements : Wide
Plant Type : Palm
Foliage Color : Green
Flowering Season : Year-round
Flower Color : White
Propagation : Seeds
Human Hazards : None
Common Uses : Shade tree; edible fruit; palm
Major Problems : Lethal yellowing; K deficiency; mites;
Additional Notes : Varieties listed below show some resistance to lethal yellowing.

Family : Palmae   **Zone** : 10B-11

Typical Height : 80 Ft.
Drought Tolerance : High
Nutritional Requirements : Medium
Light Requirements : High
Leaf Type : Pinnately compound
Texture : Coarse
Flower Characteristics : Insignificant

Environmental Problems : None

Cultivars

'MALAYAN DWARF' has a slender straight trunk and either green, yellow, or golden fruits; 'MAYPAN' is a hybrid between 'MALAYAN DWARF' & 'PANAMA TALL' coconuts. 'PANAMA TALL' is a robust, moderately disease-resistant variety.

Codiaeum variegatum var. pictum *(Photo. p. 175)*

Common Name(s) : Croton
Origin : Malaysia
Growth Rate : Slow
Salt Tolerance : Medium
Soil Requirements : Wide
Plant Type : Evergreen shrub
Foliage Color : Red; yellow; green; pink
Flowering Season : Summer
Flower Color : White
Propagation : Cuttings
Human Hazards : Irritant
Common Uses : Shrub; foliage plant; hedge
Major Problems : Scales
Additional Notes : Many cultivars with varying leaf color patterns. Sap stains clothes.

Family : Euphorbiaceae   **Zone** : 10B-11

Typical Height : 8 Ft.
Drought Tolerance : High
Nutritional Requirements : Low
Light Requirements : Medium; high
Leaf Type : Simple
Texture : Coarse
Flower Characteristics : Insignificant

Environmental Problems : None

Coleus X hybridus

Common Name(s) : Coleus
Origin : Hybrid
Growth Rate : Fast
Salt Tolerance : Low
Soil Requirements : Wide
Plant Type : Herbaceous perennial
Foliage Color : Variegated; red; purple
Flowering Season : Summer
Flower Color : Blue
Propagation : Cuttings
Human Hazards : None
Common Uses : Beds; borders; foliage plant; specimen plant
Major Problems : Aphids; mealybugs
Additional Notes : Many cultivars having different leaf shapes and colors exist.

Family : Labiatae   **Zone** : 10B-11

Typical Height : 2 Ft.
Drought Tolerance : Low
Nutritional Requirements : Medium
Light Requirements : Medium; high
Leaf Type : Simple
Texture : Medium
Flower Characteristics : Insignificant

Environmental Problems : None

Colocasia esculenta

Common Name(s) : Taro
Origin : India
Growth Rate : Fast
Salt Tolerance : Low
Soil Requirements : Wide
Plant Type : Herbaceous perennial
Foliage Color : Green
Flowering Season : Summer; fall
Flower Color : Green
Propagation : Division
Human Hazards : None
Common Uses : Edible tubers
Major Problems : None
Additional Notes : Bold heart-shaped tropical foliage, edible tubers.

Family : Araceae   **Zone** : 10A-11

Typical Height : 4 Ft.
Drought Tolerance : Low
Nutritional Requirements : Medium
Light Requirements : Medium; high
Leaf Type : Simple
Texture : Very coarse
Flower Characteristics : Insignificant

Environmental Problems : None

Colubrina arborescens

Common Name(s) : Coffee Colubrina
Origin : Caribbean Region
Growth Rate : Slow
Salt Tolerance : High
Soil Requirements : Wide
Plant Type : Evergreen shrub or tree
Foliage Color : Green
Flowering Season : Year-round
Flower Color : White
Propagation : Seeds
Human Hazards : None
Common Uses : Shrub; small tree
Major Problems : None
Additional Notes : A Florida native that can become a small tree.

Family : Rhamnaceae   **Zone** : 10B-11

Typical Height : 20 Ft.
Drought Tolerance : High
Nutritional Requirements : Low
Light Requirements : Medium; high
Leaf Type : Simple
Texture : Medium
Flower Characteristics : Insignificant

Environmental Problems : None

Colvillea racemosa

Common Name(s) : Colville's Glory
Origin : Madagascar
Growth Rate : Medium
Salt Tolerance : Low
Soil Requirements : Wide
Plant Type : Deciduous tree
Foliage Color : Green
Flowering Season : Fall
Flower Color : Orange
Propagation : Seeds
Human Hazards : None
Common Uses : Flowering tree
Major Problems : None
Additional Notes : Beautiful flowers in late fall; sparsely branched.

Family : Leguminosae   **Zone** : 10B-11

Typical Height : 45 Ft.
Drought Tolerance : Medium
Nutritional Requirements : Medium
Light Requirements : High
Leaf Type : Bipinnately compound
Texture : Medium
Flower Characteristics : Showy

Environmental Problems : None

Combretum grandiflorum

Common Name(s) : Showy Combretum
Origin : West Africa
Growth Rate : Fast
Salt Tolerance : Low
Soil Requirements : Wide
Plant Type : Evergreen vine
Foliage Color : Green
Flowering Season : Summer
Flower Color : Red
Propagation : Seeds; cuttings
Human Hazards : None
Common Uses : Flowering vine
Major Problems : None
Additional Notes : New leaves emerge red. Other similar species exist.

Family : Combretaceae   **Zone** : 10B-11

Typical Height : Not applicable
Drought Tolerance : Medium
Nutritional Requirements : Medium
Light Requirements : High
Leaf Type : Simple
Texture : Medium
Flower Characteristics : Showy

Environmental Problems : None

Congea tomentosa *(Photograph p. 210)*

Common Name(s) : Wooly Congea
Origin : Burma and Thailand
Growth Rate : Medium
Salt Tolerance : Medium
Soil Requirements : Wide
Plant Type : Evergreen vine
Foliage Color : Green
Flowering Season : Winter; spring
Flower Color : Lavender; white
Propagation : Seeds; cuttings
Human Hazards : None
Common Uses : Flowering vine
Major Problems : None
Additional Notes : Bracts are the showy part of the inflorescence. Prune after flowering.

Family : Verbenaceae   **Zone** : 10B-11

Typical Height : Not applicable
Drought Tolerance : Medium
Nutritional Requirements : Medium
Light Requirements : High
Leaf Type : Simple
Texture : Medium
Flower Characteristics : Showy

Environmental Problems : None

Conocarpus erectus *(Photograph p. 158)*

Common Name(s) : Buttonwood
Origin : South Florida and West Indies
Growth Rate : Medium
Salt Tolerance : High
Soil Requirements : Wide
Plant Type : Evergreen tree
Foliage Color : Green; silver
Flowering Season : Year-round
Flower Color : Purple-white
Propagation : Seeds; cuttings; air layers
Human Hazards : None
Common Uses : Small tree; shrub
Major Problems : None
Additional Notes : A good native seaside plant.
Cultivars

Family : Combretaceae   Zone : 10B-11

Typical Height : 35 Ft.
Drought Tolerance : High
Nutritional Requirements : Low
Light Requirements : High
Leaf Type : Simple
Texture : Medium
Flower Characteristics : Insignificant

Environmental Problems : None

Var. sericeus has silver foliage; 'MOMBO' has particularly good growth characteristics and green foliage.

Conradina grandiflora

Common Name(s) : Conradina
Origin : South Florida
Growth Rate : Fast
Salt Tolerance : High
Soil Requirements : Wide
Plant Type : Evergreen shrub
Foliage Color : Green
Flowering Season : Year-round
Flower Color : Blue
Propagation : Cuttings
Human Hazards : None
Common Uses : Groundcover
Major Problems : None
Additional Notes : Sensitive to overwatering.

Family : Labiatae   Zone : 10A-10B

Typical Height : 2 Ft.
Drought Tolerance : High
Nutritional Requirements : Low
Light Requirements : High
Leaf Type : Simple
Texture : Fine
Flower Characteristics : Showy

Environmental Problems : None

Copernicia baileyana

Common Name(s) : Bailey Copernicia Palm
Origin : Cuba
Growth Rate : Slow
Salt Tolerance : Medium
Soil Requirements : Wide
Plant Type : Palm
Foliage Color : Green
Flowering Season : Spring
Flower Color : White
Propagation : Seeds
Human Hazards : Spiny
Common Uses : Palm
Major Problems : None
Additional Notes : This slow growing palm has a large diameter trunk.

Family : Palmae   Zone : 10B-11

Typical Height : 40 Ft.
Drought Tolerance : High
Nutritional Requirements : Low
Light Requirements : High
Leaf Type : Simple; palmately lobed
Texture : Very coarse
Flower Characteristics : Insignificant

Environmental Problems : None

Copernicia hospita *(Photograph p. 203)*

Common Name(s) : Hospita Copernicia
Origin : Cuba
Growth Rate : Slow
Salt Tolerance : Medium
Soil Requirements : Wide
Plant Type : Palm
Foliage Color : Green
Flowering Season : Spring
Flower Color : White
Propagation : Seeds
Human Hazards : Spiny
Common Uses : Palm
Major Problems : None
Additional Notes : This slow growing palm is well adapted to south Florida conditions.

Family : Palmae   Zone : 10B-11

Typical Height : 25 Ft.
Drought Tolerance : High
Nutritional Requirements : Low
Light Requirements : High
Leaf Type : Simple; palmately lobed
Texture : Very coarse
Flower Characteristics : Insignificant

Environmental Problems : None

Copernicia macroglossa

Common Name(s) : Cuban Petticoat Palm
Origin : Cuba
Growth Rate : Slow
Salt Tolerance : Medium
Soil Requirements : Wide
Plant Type : Palm
Foliage Color : Green
Flowering Season : Spring
Flower Color : White
Propagation : Seeds
Human Hazards : Spiny
Common Uses : Palm
Major Problems : None
Additional Notes : The leaves of this palm have virtually no petiole and are persistent.

Family : Palmae   **Zone** : 10B-11

Typical Height : 15 Ft.
Drought Tolerance : High
Nutritional Requirements : Low
Light Requirements : High
Leaf Type : Simple; palmately lobed
Texture : Very coarse
Flower Characteristics : Insignificant

Environmental Problems : None

Cordia boissieri *(Photograph p. 158)*

Common Name(s) : Texas Wild Olive
Origin : Texas and Mexico
Growth Rate : Medium
Salt Tolerance : Medium
Soil Requirements : Wide
Plant Type : Evergreen tree
Foliage Color : Green & silver
Flowering Season : Year-round
Flower Color : White
Propagation : Seeds; air layers
Human Hazards : None
Common Uses : Small flowering tree
Major Problems : None
Additional Notes : A cold hardy relative of C. sebestena .

Family : Boraginaceae   **Zone** : 9-10B

Typical Height : 20 Ft.
Drought Tolerance : High
Nutritional Requirements : Medium
Light Requirements : High
Leaf Type : Simple
Texture : Medium
Flower Characteristics : Showy

Environmental Problems : None

Cordia sebestena *(Photograph p. 158)*

Common Name(s) : Geiger Tree
Origin : South Florida and West Indies
Growth Rate : Medium
Salt Tolerance : High
Soil Requirements : Wide
Plant Type : Evergreen tree
Foliage Color : Green
Flowering Season : Year-round
Flower Color : Orange
Propagation : Seeds; air layers
Human Hazards : None
Common Uses : Small flowering tree
Major Problems : Geiger beetle
Additional Notes : Attractive small flowering tree.

Family : Boraginaceae   **Zone** : 10B-11

Typical Height : 25 Ft.
Drought Tolerance : High
Nutritional Requirements : Low
Light Requirements : High
Leaf Type : Simple
Texture : Medium
Flower Characteristics : Showy

Environmental Problems : None

Cordyline australis

Common Name(s) : Giant Dracaena; Cabbage Tree
Origin : New Zealand
Growth Rate : Medium
Salt Tolerance : Medium
Soil Requirements : Wide
Plant Type : Evergreen shrub or tree
Foliage Color : Green
Flowering Season : n/a
Flower Color : White
Propagation : Cuttings
Human Hazards : None
Common Uses : Shrub; foliage plant; small tree
Major Problems : None
Additional Notes : This species has narrower leaves than C. terminalis and is taller.
Cultivars
'ATROPURPUREA' has purple-bronze leaves.

Family : Agavaceae   **Zone** : 9-11

Typical Height : 30 Ft.
Drought Tolerance : High
Nutritional Requirements : Medium
Light Requirements : Medium
Leaf Type : Simple; linear
Texture : Medium
Flower Characteristics : Showy; fragrant

Environmental Problems : None

Cordyline terminalis (Photograph p. 176)

Common Name(s) : Ti Plant
Origin : Eastern Asia
Growth Rate : Slow
Salt Tolerance : Low
Soil Requirements : Wide
Plant Type : Evergreen shrub
Foliage Color : Red; green; pink; yellow
Flowering Season : Fall
Flower Color : White; pink
Propagation : Cuttings
Human Hazards : None
Common Uses : Shrub; foliage plant
Major Problems : Scales; mealybugs
Additional Notes : Showy multicolored leaves. Many cultivars exist.
Cultivars

Family : Agavaceae   Zone : 10B-11

Typical Height : 5 Ft.
Drought Tolerance : Medium
Nutritional Requirements : Medium
Light Requirements : Medium; high
Leaf Type : Simple; linear
Texture : Coarse
Flower Characteristics : Insignificant

Environmental Problems : None

'BABY DOLL' is a dwarf variety with pink and purple foliage; 'KIWI' has yellow and green striped leaves with pink margins; 'BLACK MAGIC' has nearly black foliage; 'MADAME EUGENE ANDRE' has mostly red leaves; 'TRICOLOR' has green, cream, and red foliage; 'RED SISTER' is similar to 'BABY DOLL', but
  has larger leaves.

Cornus drummondii

Common Name(s) : Rough-leaved Dogwood
Origin : Southeastern United States
Growth Rate : Fast
Salt Tolerance : Low
Soil Requirements : Wide
Plant Type : Deciduous shrub or tree
Foliage Color : Green
Flowering Season : Spring
Flower Color : White
Propagation : Seeds; cuttings
Human Hazards : None
Common Uses : Shrub; small tree
Major Problems : None
Additional Notes : A relatively short-lived species; tolerant of heavy soils.

Family : Cornaceae   Zone : 4-9

Typical Height : 20 Ft.
Drought Tolerance : Medium
Nutritional Requirements : Medium
Light Requirements : High
Leaf Type : Simple
Texture : Medium
Flower Characteristics : Insignificant

Environmental Problems : None

Cornus florida (Photograph p. 158)

Common Name(s) : Flowering Dogwood
Origin : Eastern North America
Growth Rate : Slow
Salt Tolerance : Low
Soil Requirements : Acid
Plant Type : Deciduous tree
Foliage Color : Green
Flowering Season : Spring
Flower Color : White; pink; red
Propagation : Seeds; cuttings; grafting
Human Hazards : None
Common Uses : Small flowering tree
Major Problems : Borers; anthracnose
Additional Notes : Red and pink flowered cultivars do poorly in Florida.
Cultivars

Family : Cornaceae   Zone : 4-9

Typical Height : 20 Ft.
Drought Tolerance : Low
Nutritional Requirements : Medium
Light Requirements : High
Leaf Type : Simple
Texture : Medium
Flower Characteristics : Showy

Environmental Problems : None

'RUBRA', 'SPRING SONG', 'GULF COAST' have rosy-pink bracts; 'CHEROKEE CHIEF' has reddish new growth and red bracts; 'BONNIE', 'CLOUD NINE' and 'WHITE CLOUD' have white bracts; 'VARIEGATA' has
  variegated foliage.

Cornus kousa

Common Name(s) : Kousa Dogwood; Japanese Dogwood
Origin : Japan and Korea
Growth Rate : Medium
Salt Tolerance : Low
Soil Requirements : Wide
Plant Type : Deciduous tree
Foliage Color : Green
Flowering Season : Summer
Flower Color : White; pink
Propagation : Seeds; cuttings; grafting
Human Hazards : None
Common Uses : Small flowering tree
Major Problems : None
Additional Notes : Similar to C. florida , but bracts are pointed rather than rounded.
Cultivars

Family : Cornaceae   Zone : 5-9

Typical Height : 20 Ft.
Drought Tolerance : Medium
Nutritional Requirements : Medium
Light Requirements : High
Leaf Type : Simple
Texture : Medium
Flower Characteristics : Showy

Environmental Problems : None

'RUBRA' has pink bracts; 'VARIEGATA' has variegated foliage.

Cornus sericea

Common Name(s) : Red Osier Dogwood
Origin : North America
Growth Rate : Fast
Salt Tolerance : Low
Soil Requirements : Wide
Plant Type : Deciduous shrub
Foliage Color : Green; red
Flowering Season : Spring
Flower Color : White
Propagation : Cuttings
Human Hazards : None
Common Uses : Shrub; windbreak
Major Problems : None
Additional Notes : Attractive red stems; tolerant of wet soils. Has red fall color

Family : Cornaceae   **Zone** : 2-9

Typical Height : 8 Ft.
Drought Tolerance : Low
Nutritional Requirements : Medium
Light Requirements : Medium
Leaf Type : Simple
Texture : Medium
Flower Characteristics : Insignificant

Environmental Problems : None

Cornus stricta

Common Name(s) : Stiff Dogwood; Swamp Dogwood
Origin : Southeastern United States
Growth Rate : Fast
Salt Tolerance : Low
Soil Requirements : Wide
Plant Type : Deciduous shrub
Foliage Color : Green
Flowering Season : Spring
Flower Color : White
Propagation : Seeds; cuttings
Human Hazards : None
Common Uses : Shrub
Major Problems : None
Additional Notes : This species has reddish young branches.

Family : Cornaceae   **Zone** : 7-9

Typical Height : 15 Ft.
Drought Tolerance : Low
Nutritional Requirements : Medium
Light Requirements : High
Leaf Type : Simple
Texture : Medium
Flower Characteristics : Insignificant

Environmental Problems : None

Cortaderia selloana *(Photograph p. 193)*

Common Name(s) : Pampas Grass
Origin : Brazil, Argentina, and Chile
Growth Rate : Fast
Salt Tolerance : High
Soil Requirements : Wide
Plant Type : Herbaceous perennial
Foliage Color : Green
Flowering Season : Summer; fall
Flower Color : White; pink
Propagation : Division; seeds
Human Hazards : Serrated leaves
Common Uses : Specimen plant
Major Problems : None
Additional Notes : An attractive ornamental grass with feathery plume-like flowers.
Cultivars
'VARIEGATA' has variegated foliage; 'RUBRA' has pink flowers.

Family : Gramineae   **Zone** : 9-11

Typical Height : 8 Ft.
Drought Tolerance : High
Nutritional Requirements : Low
Light Requirements : High
Leaf Type : Simple; linear
Texture : Medium
Flower Characteristics : Showy

Environmental Problems : None

Corylus colurna

Common Name(s) : Turkish Filbert
Origin : Asia Minor
Growth Rate : Medium
Salt Tolerance : n/a
Soil Requirements : Wide
Plant Type : Deciduous tree
Foliage Color : Green
Flowering Season : Spring
Flower Color : Green
Propagation : Seeds; cuttings
Human Hazards : None
Common Uses : Shade tree
Major Problems : None
Additional Notes : A broadly pyramidal tree with yellow to purple fall color.

Family : Betulaceae   **Zone** : 4-9

Typical Height : 70 Ft.
Drought Tolerance : High
Nutritional Requirements : Medium
Light Requirements : High
Leaf Type : Simple
Texture : Medium
Flower Characteristics : Insignificant

Environmental Problems : None

Corypha elata *(Photograph p. 204)*

Common Name(s) : Gebang Palm
Origin : Southeast Asia and East Indies
Growth Rate : Medium
Salt Tolerance : n/a
Soil Requirements : Wide
Plant Type : Palm
Foliage Color : Green
Flowering Season : n/a
Flower Color : White
Propagation : Seeds
Human Hazards : None
Common Uses : Palm
Major Problems : None
Additional Notes : This huge palm dies after a spectacular flowering.

Family : Palmae   **Zone** : 10B-11

Typical Height : 60 Ft.
Drought Tolerance : High
Nutritional Requirements : Medium
Light Requirements : High
Leaf Type : Simple; palmately lobed
Texture : Very coarse
Flower Characteristics : Showy

Environmental Problems : None

Costus igneus

Common Name(s) : Fiery Costus
Origin : Brazil
Growth Rate : Medium
Salt Tolerance : Medium
Soil Requirements : Wide
Plant Type : Herbaceous perennial
Foliage Color : Green & red
Flowering Season : Summer; fall
Flower Color : Orange
Propagation : Division; cuttings
Human Hazards : None
Common Uses : Flowering shrub
Major Problems : None
Additional Notes : Stems twist in a spiral fashion. Stems and leaf undersides red.

Family : Costaceae   **Zone** : 10A-11

Typical Height : 3 Ft.
Drought Tolerance : Medium
Nutritional Requirements : Medium
Light Requirements : Medium
Leaf Type : Simple
Texture : Coarse
Flower Characteristics : Showy

Environmental Problems : None

Costus pulverulentus

Common Name(s) : Velvet Spiral Flag
Origin : Mexico to Western South America
Growth Rate : Fast
Salt Tolerance : Medium
Soil Requirements : Wide
Plant Type : Herbaceous perennial
Foliage Color : Bronze & red
Flowering Season : Summer; fall
Flower Color : Red
Propagation : Division; cuttings
Human Hazards : None
Common Uses : Flowering shrub
Major Problems : None
Additional Notes : Stems twist in a spiral fashion. Stems and leaf undersides red.

Family : Costaceae   **Zone** : 10A-11

Typical Height : 8 Ft.
Drought Tolerance : Medium
Nutritional Requirements : Medium
Light Requirements : Medium
Leaf Type : Simple
Texture : Coarse
Flower Characteristics : Showy

Environmental Problems : None

Costus speciosus *(Photograph p. 193)*

Common Name(s) : Crepe Ginger
Origin : East Indies
Growth Rate : Fast
Salt Tolerance : Medium
Soil Requirements : Wide
Plant Type : Herbaceous perennial
Foliage Color : Green; variegated
Flowering Season : Summer; fall
Flower Color : White
Propagation : Division; cuttings
Human Hazards : None
Common Uses : Flowering shrub
Major Problems : None
Additional Notes : Stems twist in a spiral fashion.
Cultivars
'VARIEGATUS' has variegated foliage.

Family : Costaceae   **Zone** : 9-11

Typical Height : 8 Ft.
Drought Tolerance : Medium
Nutritional Requirements : Medium
Light Requirements : Medium; high
Leaf Type : Simple
Texture : Coarse
Flower Characteristics : Showy

Environmental Problems : None

Costus spiralis

Common Name(s) : Scarlet Spiral Flag
Origin : Northern South America
Growth Rate : Fast
Salt Tolerance : Medium
Soil Requirements : Wide
Plant Type : Herbaceous perennial
Foliage Color : Green
Flowering Season : Summer; fall
Flower Color : Red
Propagation : Division; cuttings
Human Hazards : None
Common Uses : Flowering shrub
Major Problems : None

Family : Costaceae   Zone : 10A-11

Typical Height : 8 Ft.
Drought Tolerance : Medium
Nutritional Requirements : Medium
Light Requirements : Medium
Leaf Type : Simple
Texture : Coarse
Flower Characteristics : Showy

Environmental Problems : None

Additional Notes : This species has red bracts and florets. Stems twist in a spiral fashion.

Crassula argentea *(Photograph p. 176)*

Common Name(s) : Jade Plant
Origin : South Africa
Growth Rate : Slow
Salt Tolerance : Medium
Soil Requirements : Well-drained
Plant Type : Succulent perennial
Foliage Color : Green
Flowering Season : Fall
Flower Color ; White
Propagation : Cuttings
Human Hazards : None
Common Uses : Rock gardens; foliage plant
Major Problems : Root rots

Family : Crassulaceae   Zone : 10A-11

Typical Height : 3 Ft.
Drought Tolerance : High
Nutritional Requirements : Low
Light Requirements : High
Leaf Type : Simple
Texture : Fine
Flower Characteristics : Showy

Environmental Problems : None

Additional Notes : Requires dry conditions and well-drained soil; C. obliqua is similar.
Cultivars
'VARIEGATA' has variegated foliage.

Crataegus spp.

Common Name(s) : Hawthorns
Origin : Northern Hemisphere
Growth Rate : Slow
Salt Tolerance : Low
Soil Requirements : Wide
Plant Type : Deciduous shrub or tree
Foliage Color : Green
Flowering Season : Spring
Flower Color : White
Propagation : Seeds; grafting
Human Hazards : Spiny
Common Uses : Small flowering tree; flowering shrub
Major Problems : Fireblight

Family : Rosaceae   Zone : 4-10A

Typical Height : 20 Ft.
Drought Tolerance : High
Nutritional Requirements : Medium
Light Requirements : High
Leaf Type : Simple
Texture : Fine
Flower Characteristics : Showy

Environmental Problems : None

Additional Notes : Many species and cultivars; best for north Florida.

Crescentia alata

Common Name(s) : Mexican Calabash
Origin : Western Mexico to Guatemala
Growth Rate : Fast
Salt Tolerance : Medium
Soil Requirements : Wide
Plant Type : Evergreen tree
Foliage Color : Green
Flowering Season : Summer
Flower Color : Green & bronze
Propagation : Seeds; cuttings
Human Hazards : None
Common Uses : Shade tree
Major Problems : None

Family : Bignoniaceae   Zone : 10B-11

Typical Height : 35 Ft.
Drought Tolerance : High
Nutritional Requirements : Low
Light Requirements : High
Leaf Type : Pinnately compound
Texture : Medium
Flower Characteristics : Insignificant

Environmental Problems : None

Additional Notes : This plant has curious whip-like branches and gourd-like fruits.

Crescentia cujete

Common Name(s) : Calabash
Origin : Tropical America
Growth Rate : Medium
Salt Tolerance : Medium
Soil Requirements : Wide
Plant Type : Evergreen tree
Foliage Color : Green
Flowering Season : Year-round
Flower Color : Yellow
Propagation : Seeds; air layers
Human Hazards : Poisonous
Common Uses : Flowering tree
Major Problems : None
Additional Notes : Grown for its curious gourd-like fruits.

Family : Bignoniaceae   **Zone** : 10B-11

Typical Height : 30 Ft.
Drought Tolerance : Medium
Nutritional Requirements : Medium
Light Requirements : High
Leaf Type : Simple
Texture : Medium
Flower Characteristics : Showy; fragrant

Environmental Problems : None

Crinum americanum

Common Name(s) : String Lily; Swamp Lily
Origin : Southeastern United States
Growth Rate : Medium
Salt Tolerance : High
Soil Requirements : Wide; moist
Plant Type : Herbaceous perennial
Foliage Color : Green
Flowering Season : Summer; fall
Flower Color : White
Propagation : Seeds; division
Human Hazards : Poisonous
Common Uses : Flowering perennial
Major Problems : None
Additional Notes : Will form solid cover in wet places; easy to grow from large seed.

Family : Amaryllidaceae   **Zone** : 7-11

Typical Height : 1.5 Ft.
Drought Tolerance : Medium
Nutritional Requirements : Medium
Light Requirements : Medium
Leaf Type : Simple; linear
Texture : Coarse
Flower Characteristics : Fragrant; showy

Environmental Problems : None

Crinum asiaticum *(Photograph p. 193)*

Common Name(s) : Tree Crinum; Poison Bulb
Origin : Tropical Asia
Growth Rate : Medium
Salt Tolerance : Medium
Soil Requirements : Wide
Plant Type : Herbaceous perennial
Foliage Color : Green; red; variegated
Flowering Season : Year-round
Flower Color : White; pink
Propagation : Seeds; division
Human Hazards : Poisonous
Common Uses : Flowering perennial; flowering shrub
Major Problems : Leafspots; grasshoppers
Additional Notes : Several cultivars exist, some with bronze, purple or variegated foliage.

Family : Amaryllidaceae   **Zone** : 8-11

Typical Height : 5 Ft.
Drought Tolerance : Medium
Nutritional Requirements : High
Light Requirements : Medium
Leaf Type : Simple; linear
Texture : Coarse
Flower Characteristics : Showy; fragrant

Environmental Problems : None

Crinum bulbispermum

Common Name(s) : Crinum
Origin : South Africa
Growth Rate : Medium
Salt Tolerance : Low
Soil Requirements : Wide
Plant Type : Herbaceous perennial
Foliage Color : Green
Flowering Season : Spring; summer
Flower Color : White; pink; red
Propagation : Seeds; division
Human Hazards : Poisonous
Common Uses : Specimen plant; beds
Major Problems : Leaf spot
Additional Notes : Flowers of this species are white with a red exterior. Much hybridized.
Cultivars
'ALBUM' has white flowers; 'ROSEUM' has pink flowers; 'ORANGE RIVER' has reddish flowers.

Family : Amaryllidaceae   **Zone** : 8-11

Typical Height : 3 Ft.
Drought Tolerance : Medium
Nutritional Requirements : Medium
Light Requirements : Medium
Leaf Type : Simple; linear
Texture : Coarse
Flower Characteristics : Showy

Environmental Problems : None

Crinum jagus *(Photograph p. 194)*

Common Name(s) : St. Christopher Lily
Origin : Africa
Growth Rate : Medium
Salt Tolerance : Low
Soil Requirements : Wide
Plant Type : Herbaceous perennial
Foliage Color : Green
Flowering Season : Fall; spring
Flower Color : White
Propagation : Division; seeds
Human Hazards : Poisonous
Common Uses : Specimen plant
Major Problems : None
Additional Notes : Has attractive foliage free of leafspot; well adapted for shady sites.

Family : Amaryllidaceae   **Zone** : 10A-11

Typical Height : 4 Ft.
Drought Tolerance : Low
Nutritional Requirements : Medium
Light Requirements : Medium; low
Leaf Type : Simple
Texture : Coarse
Flower Characteristics : Showy; fragrant

Environmental Problems : None

Crinum X amabile *(Photograph p. 193)*

Common Name(s) : Giant Spider Lily
Origin : Hybrid, Sumatra
Growth Rate : Medium
Salt Tolerance : Medium
Soil Requirements : Wide
Plant Type : Herbaceous perennial
Foliage Color : Green
Flowering Season : Year-round
Flower Color : Red & pink
Propagation : Division
Human Hazards : Poisonous
Common Uses : Flowering perennial; flowering shrub
Major Problems : Leafspot
Additional Notes : Sterile hybrid of C. asiaticum and perhaps C. zeylanicum .

Family : Amaryllidaceae   **Zone** : 10A-11

Typical Height : 4 Ft.
Drought Tolerance : Medium
Nutritional Requirements : High
Light Requirements : Medium
Leaf Type : Simple; linear
Texture : Coarse
Flower Characteristics : Showy; fragrant

Environmental Problems : None

Crinum X augustum

Common Name(s) : Milk and Wine Crinum
Origin : Sumatra
Growth Rate : Medium
Salt Tolerance : Medium
Soil Requirements : Wide
Plant Type : Herbaceous perennial
Foliage Color : Green
Flowering Season : Spring; summer
Flower Color : Purple & white
Propagation : Division
Human Hazards : Poisonous
Common Uses : Specimen plant; shrub
Major Problems : Leaf spot
Additional Notes : A sterile C. asiaticum hybrid generally smaller than C. X amabile .

Family : Amaryllidaceae   **Zone** : 10A-11

Typical Height : 5 Ft.
Drought Tolerance : Medium
Nutritional Requirements : Medium
Light Requirements : High; medium
Leaf Type : Simple; linear
Texture : Coarse
Flower Characteristics : Showy; fragrant

Environmental Problems : None

Crinum zeylanicum *(Photograph p. 194)*

Common Name(s) : Milk and Wine Lily
Origin : Tropical Asia and Africa
Growth Rate : Medium
Salt Tolerance : Low
Soil Requirements : Wide
Plant Type : Herbaceous perennial
Foliage Color : Green
Flowering Season : Spring; summer
Flower Color : White & purple
Propagation : Seeds; division
Human Hazards : Poisonous
Common Uses : Beds; specimen plant
Major Problems : None
Additional Notes : Can naturalize; foliage usually untidy.

Family : Amaryllidaceae   **Zone** : 8-11

Typical Height : 2.5 Ft.
Drought Tolerance : Medium
Nutritional Requirements : High
Light Requirements : High
Leaf Type : Simple; linear
Texture : Coarse
Flower Characteristics : Showy

Environmental Problems : None

Crocosmia X crocosmiiflora

Family : Iridaceae   **Zone** : 6-10B

Common Name(s) : Montebretia
Origin : Hybrid
Growth Rate : Medium
Salt Tolerance : Low
Soil Requirements : Wide
Plant Type : Herbaceous perennial
Foliage Color : Green
Flowering Season : Summer
Flower Color : Orange; red
Propagation : Division
Human Hazards : None
Common Uses : Beds; borders; cut flowers
Major Problems : None
Additional Notes : Culture similar to gladiolus; may be invasive.

Typical Height : 3.5 Ft.
Drought Tolerance : Medium
Nutritional Requirements : Medium
Light Requirements : Medium
Leaf Type : Simple; linear
Texture : Medium
Flower Characteristics : Showy

Environmental Problems : None

Crossandra infundibuliformis *(Photograph p. 194)*

Family : Acanthaceae   **Zone** : 10A-11

Common Name(s) : Crossandra
Origin : Southern India and Sri Lanka
Growth Rate : Medium
Salt Tolerance : Low
Soil Requirements : Acid
Plant Type : Herbaceous perennial
Foliage Color : Green
Flowering Season : Spring; summer
Flower Color : Orange
Propagation : Cuttings
Human Hazards : None
Common Uses : Flowering perennial; flowering pot plant
Major Problems : Mealybugs; nematodes
Additional Notes : Other species and other colors exist.

Typical Height : 3 Ft.
Drought Tolerance : Low
Nutritional Requirements : Medium
Light Requirements : Medium
Leaf Type : Simple
Texture : Medium
Flower Characteristics : Showy

Environmental Problems : None

Crossopetalum ilicifolium

Family : Celastraceae   **Zone** : 10B-11

Common Name(s) : Quail Berry
Origin : South Florida and West Indies
Growth Rate : Medium
Salt Tolerance : Low
Soil Requirements : Wide
Plant Type : Evergreen shrub
Foliage Color : Green
Flowering Season : Year-round
Flower Color : Red
Propagation : Seeds
Human Hazards : Spiny
Common Uses : Groundcover
Major Problems : None
Additional Notes : Has attractive red fruit and spiny leaf margins.

Typical Height : 2 Ft.
Drought Tolerance : High
Nutritional Requirements : Medium
Light Requirements : High
Leaf Type : Simple
Texture : Fine
Flower Characteristics : Insignificant

Environmental Problems : None

Cryptanthus spp. *(Photograph p. 194)*

Family : Bromeliaceae   **Zone** : 10B-11

Common Name(s) : Earth Star
Origin : Brazil
Growth Rate : Slow
Salt Tolerance : Medium
Soil Requirements : Wide
Plant Type : Herbaceous perennial
Foliage Color : Pink; red; variegated
Flowering Season : n/a
Flower Color : White
Propagation : Division
Human Hazards : None
Common Uses : Rock gardens; foliage plant
Major Problems : None
Additional Notes : Many species with varying foliage colors and patterns. Compact rosettes.

Typical Height : .3 Ft.
Drought Tolerance : High
Nutritional Requirements : Low
Light Requirements : High
Leaf Type : Simple; linear
Texture : Medium
Flower Characteristics : Insignificant

Environmental Problems : None

Cryptocereus anthonyanus

Common Name(s) : Anthony's Rick-rack; Zigzag Cactus
Origin : Southern Mexico
Growth Rate : Slow
Salt Tolerance : n/a
Soil Requirements : Wide
Plant Type : Succulent epiphyte
Foliage Color : Green
Flowering Season : Winter; spring
Flower Color : Yellow-white
Propagation : Cuttings
Human Hazards : None
Common Uses : Foliage plant; epiphyte; hanging basket
Major Problems : None
Additional Notes : This curious cactus has zig-zag stems and flowers only at night.

Family : Cactaceae   **Zone** : 10B-11

Typical Height : 2 Ft.
Drought Tolerance : High
Nutritional Requirements : Low
Light Requirements : Medium; high
Leaf Type : None
Texture : Coarse
Flower Characteristics : Showy; fragrant

Environmental Problems : None

Cryptomeria japonica

Common Name(s) : Japanese Cedar
Origin : Japan
Growth Rate : Fast
Salt Tolerance : Low
Soil Requirements : Wide
Plant Type : Evergreen tree
Foliage Color : Green
Flowering Season : Spring
Flower Color : Brown
Propagation : Cuttings; seeds
Human Hazards : None
Common Uses : Tree
Major Problems : None
Additional Notes : Many cultivars that vary in shape and size.

Family : Taxodiaceae   **Zone** : 5-9

Typical Height : 60 Ft.
Drought Tolerance : Medium
Nutritional Requirements : Medium
Light Requirements : High
Leaf Type : Needle
Texture : Fine
Flower Characteristics : Insignificant

Environmental Problems : None

Cryptostegia grandiflora

Common Name(s) : Palay Rubber Vine; Purple Allamanda
Origin : Africa
Growth Rate : Medium
Salt Tolerance : High
Soil Requirements : Wide
Plant Type : Evergreen shrub or vine
Foliage Color : Green
Flowering Season : Spring; summer; fall
Flower Color : Purple
Propagation : Cuttings
Human Hazards : Poisonous; irritant
Common Uses : Flowering shrub; flowering vine
Major Problems : Scales
Additional Notes : Can grow as a vine if not pruned.

Family : Asclepiadaceae   **Zone** : 10B-11

Typical Height : 7 Ft.
Drought Tolerance : High
Nutritional Requirements : Low
Light Requirements : High
Leaf Type : Simple
Texture : Medium
Flower Characteristics : Showy

Environmental Problems : None

Cryptostegia madagascariensis *(Photo. p. 210)*

Common Name(s) : Madagascar Rubber Vine
Origin : Madagascar
Growth Rate : Medium
Salt Tolerance : Medium
Soil Requirements : Wide
Plant Type : Evergreen vine
Foliage Color : Green
Flowering Season : Summer; fall
Flower Color : Purple
Propagation : Cuttings
Human Hazards : None
Common Uses : Flowering vine
Major Problems : Scales
Additional Notes : Erroneously called purple allamanda. Latex was used to make rubber.

Family : Asclepiadaceae   **Zone** : 10B-11

Typical Height : Not applicable
Drought Tolerance : High
Nutritional Requirements : Medium
Light Requirements : High
Leaf Type : Simple
Texture : Medium
Flower Characteristics : Showy

Environmental Problems : None

Cupaniopsis anacardiopsis

Common Name(s) : Carrotwood

Family : Sapindaceae   **Zone** : 10B-11

Origin : Australia

Growth Rate : Medium

Salt Tolerance : Medium

Soil Requirements : Wide

Plant Type : Evergreen tree

Foliage Color : Green

Flowering Season : Summer

Flower Color : White

Propagation : Seeds

Human Hazards : None

Common Uses : Shade tree

Major Problems : None

Typical Height : 35 Ft.

Drought Tolerance : Medium

Nutritional Requirements : Medium

Light Requirements : High

Leaf Type : Pinnately compound

Texture : Medium

Flower Characteristics : Insignificant

Environmental Problems : Invasive (?)

Additional Notes : A tough, pest-free landscape tree. May be beginning to naturalize.

Cuphea hyssopifolia *(Photograph p. 213)*

Common Name(s) : False Heather; Mexican Heather

Family : Lythraceae   **Zone** : 10B-11

Origin : Mexico and Guatemala

Growth Rate : Medium

Salt Tolerance : Low

Soil Requirements : Wide

Plant Type : Evergreen shrub

Foliage Color : Green

Flowering Season : Year-round

Flower Color : Lavender; pink; white

Propagation : Cuttings

Human Hazards : None

Typical Height : 1 Ft.

Drought Tolerance : Low

Nutritional Requirements : Medium

Light Requirements : Medium; high

Leaf Type : Simple

Texture : Fine

Flower Characteristics : Showy

Environmental Problems : None

Common Uses : Flowering groundcover; small flowering shrub

Major Problems : Nematodes; flea beetles

Cultivars

'ALBA' has white flowers; 'ALLYSON' has slightly larger leaves and more flowers.

Cuphea ignea *(Photograph p. 176)*

Common Name(s) : Cigar Plant

Family : Lythraceae   **Zone** : 10B-11

Origin : Mexico and Jamaica

Growth Rate : Medium

Salt Tolerance : Low

Soil Requirements : Wide

Plant Type : Evergreen shrub

Foliage Color : Green

Flowering Season : Year round

Flower Color : Red

Propagation : Seed; cuttings

Human Hazards : None

Common Uses : Flowering shrub; flowering pot plant

Major Problems : None

Typical Height : 2 Ft.

Drought Tolerance : Low

Nutritional Requirements : Medium

Light Requirements : Medium; high

Leaf Type : Simple

Texture : Fine

Flower Characteristics : Showy

Environmental Problems : None

Additional Notes : Small tubular red flowers in profusion.

Cupressus sempervirens

Common Name(s) : Italian Cypress

Family : Cupressaceae   **Zone** : 7-10B

Origin : Southern Europe

Growth Rate : Medium

Salt Tolerance : Medium

Soil Requirements : Wide

Plant Type : Evergreen tree

Foliage Color : Green; blue-green

Flowering Season : Summer

Flower Color : Brown

Propagation : Cuttings; air layers

Human Hazards : None

Common Uses : Tree

Major Problems : Fungal blight; mites

Typical Height : 70 Ft.

Drought Tolerance : Medium

Nutritional Requirements : Medium

Light Requirements : High

Leaf Type : Scale-like

Texture : Fine

Flower Characteristics : Cone

Environmental Problems : None

Additional Notes : A very formal slender evergreen tree.

Cultivars

'STRICTA' is a very narrow columnar variety; 'GLAUCA' is a narrow form with blue-green foliage; 'HORIZONTALIS' has horizontally spreading branches .

Curculigo capitulata

Common Name(s) : Palm Grass
Origin : Tropical Asia and Australia
Growth Rate : Medium
Salt Tolerance : Low
Soil Requirements : Wide
Plant Type : Herbaceous perennial
Foliage Color : Green
Flowering Season : Spring; summer
Flower Color : Yellow
Propagation : Division
Human Hazards : None
Common Uses : Groundcover; foliage plant
Major Problems : None
Additional Notes : Resembles a young palm; spreads by rhizomes.

Family : Hypoxidaceae   **Zone** : 10A-11

Typical Height : 3 Ft.
Drought Tolerance : Low
Nutritional Requirements : Medium
Light Requirements : Medium; low
Leaf Type : Simple; linear
Texture : Coarse
Flower Characteristics : Insignificant

Environmental Problems : None

Curcuma roscoeana

Common Name(s) : Pride of Burma
Origin : Burma
Growth Rate : Medium
Salt Tolerance : n/a
Soil Requirements : Wide
Plant Type : Herbaceous perennial
Foliage Color : Green
Flowering Season : n/a
Flower Color : Orange
Propagation : Division
Human Hazards : None
Common Uses : Specimen plant
Major Problems : None
Additional Notes : This ginger is grown primarily for its attractive orange floral bracts.

Family : Zingiberaceae   **Zone** : 10A-11

Typical Height : 3 Ft.
Drought Tolerance : Medium
Nutritional Requirements : Medium
Light Requirements : Medium
Leaf Type : Simple
Texture : Coarse
Flower Characteristics : Showy

Environmental Problems : None

Curcuma spp.

Common Name(s) : Hidden Lily
Origin : Burma
Growth Rate : Fast
Salt Tolerance : n/a
Soil Requirements : Wide
Plant Type : Deciduous herb
Foliage Color : Green & purple
Flowering Season : Spring
Flower Color : Pink & yellow
Propagation : Division
Human Hazards : None
Common Uses : Specimen plant
Major Problems : None
Additional Notes : Attractive pink inflorescences are borne on separate stalks.

Family : Zingiberaceae   **Zone** : 9-11

Typical Height : 5 Ft.
Drought Tolerance : Medium
Nutritional Requirements : Medium
Light Requirements : Medium
Leaf Type : Simple
Texture : Coarse
Flower Characteristics : Showy

Environmental Problems : None

Cycas circinalis *(Photograph p. 176)*

Common Name(s) : Queen Sago
Origin : East Indies and Africa
Growth Rate : Slow
Salt Tolerance : Medium
Soil Requirements : Wide
Plant Type : Evergreen shrub; cycad
Foliage Color : Green
Flowering Season : Summer
Flower Color : n/a
Propagation : Seeds; offshoots
Human Hazards : Poisonous; spiny
Common Uses : Shrub
Major Problems : Scales
Additional Notes : Dark green palm-like leaves are much larger than those of C. revoluta .

Family : Cycadaceae   **Zone** : 10B-11

Typical Height : 10 Ft.
Drought Tolerance : High
Nutritional Requirements : Medium
Light Requirements : Medium; high
Leaf Type : Pinnately compound
Texture : Medium
Flower Characteristics : Cone

Environmental Problems : None

Cycas revoluta *(Photograph p. 176)*

Common Name(s) : King Sago
Origin : Japan and Ryukyu Islands
Growth Rate : Slow
Salt Tolerance : Medium
Soil Requirements : Wide
Plant Type : Evergreen shrub; cycad
Foliage Color : Green
Flowering Season : Summer
Flower Color : Brown
Propagation : Seeds
Human Hazards : Poisonous; spiny
Common Uses : Shrub
Major Problems : K deficiency; scales
Additional Notes : Smaller and hardier than C. circinalis .

Family : Cycadaceae   **Zone** : 8-11

Typical Height : 8 Ft.
Drought Tolerance : High
Nutritional Requirements : Medium
Light Requirements : High; medium
Leaf Type : Pinnately compound
Texture : Coarse
Flower Characteristics : Cone

Environmental Problems : None

Cycas taiwaniana

Common Name(s) : Prince Sago
Origin : Taiwan
Growth Rate : Slow
Salt Tolerance : Medium
Soil Requirements : Wide
Plant Type : Evergreen shrub (cycad)
Foliage Color : Green
Flowering Season : Spring
Flower Color : Brown
Propagation : Seeds
Human Hazards : Spiny
Common Uses : Shrub; sprcimen plant
Major Problems : Scales; mealybugs
Additional Notes : Similar to C. revoluta , but has slightly larger leaves.

Family : Cycadaceae   **Zone** : 8-11

Typical Height : 6 Ft.
Drought Tolerance : High
Nutritional Requirements : Medium
Light Requirements : High
Leaf Type : Pinnately compound
Texture : Coarse
Flower Characteristics : Insignificant

Environmental Problems : None

Cydista aequinoctialis *(Photograph p. 210)*

Common Name(s) : Garlic Vine
Origin : Caribbean Region
Growth Rate : Fast
Salt Tolerance : Low
Soil Requirements : Wide
Plant Type : Evergreen vine
Foliage Color : Green
Flowering Season : Spring; fall
Flower Color : Lavender; pink; white
Propagation : Cuttings
Human Hazards : None
Common Uses : Flowering vine
Major Problems : None
Additional Notes : All parts of vine garlic scented when bruised. Flowers fade to white.

Family : Bignoniaceae   **Zone** : 10B-11

Typical Height : Not applicable
Drought Tolerance : High
Nutritional Requirements : Low
Light Requirements : High
Leaf Type : Pinnately compound
Texture : Medium
Flower Characteristics : Showy; fragrant

Environmental Problems : None

Cymbopogon citratus

Common Name(s) : Lemongrass
Origin : India and Sri Lanka
Growth Rate : Fast
Salt Tolerance : n/a
Soil Requirements : Wide
Plant Type : Herbaceous perennial
Foliage Color : Green
Flowering Season : n/a
Flower Color : n/a
Propagation : Division
Human Hazards : None
Common Uses : Specimen plant
Major Problems : None
Additional Notes : A lemon-scented essential oil is distilled from foliage of this plant.

Family : Gramineae   **Zone** : 10B-11

Typical Height : 6 Ft.
Drought Tolerance : Medium
Nutritional Requirements : Medium
Light Requirements : High
Leaf Type : Simple; linear
Texture : Medium
Flower Characteristics : Insignificant

Environmental Problems : None

Cyperus alternifolius *(Photograph p. 194)*

Common Name(s) : Umbrella Sedge
Origin : Madagascar and Mascarene Islands
Growth Rate : Medium
Salt Tolerance : Medium
Soil Requirements : Wide
Plant Type : Herbaceous perennial
Foliage Color : Green
Flowering Season : Summer
Flower Color : Brown
Propagation : Division; cuttings; seeds
Human Hazards : None
Common Uses : Aquatic; specimen plant
Major Problems : None
Additional Notes : Well adapted for planting in shallow water.

Family : Cyperaceae   Zone : 9-11

Typical Height : 5 Ft.
Drought Tolerance : Low
Nutritional Requirements : Medium
Light Requirements : Medium; high
Leaf Type : Simple; linear
Texture : Fine
Flower Characteristics : Insignificant

Environmental Problems : None

Cyperus haspan

Common Name(s) : American Papyrus
Origin : Southeastern USA to South America
Growth Rate : Medium
Salt Tolerance : Medium
Soil Requirements : Wide
Plant Type : Herbaceous perennial
Foliage Color : Green
Flowering Season : Summer
Flower Color : Brown
Propagation : Division; seeds
Human Hazards : None
Common Uses : Aquatic; specimen plant
Major Problems : None
Additional Notes : Inflorescences have lacy fluffy appearance.

Family : Cyperaceae   Zone : 7-11

Typical Height : 2 Ft.
Drought Tolerance : Low
Nutritional Requirements : Medium
Light Requirements : Medium; high
Leaf Type : Simple; linear
Texture : Fine
Flower Characteristics : Insignificant

Environmental Problems : None

Cyperus isocladus

Common Name(s) : Dwarf Papyrus
Origin : Southern Africa
Growth Rate : Medium
Salt Tolerance : Medium
Soil Requirements : Wide
Plant Type : Herbaceous perennial
Foliage Color : Green
Flowering Season : Summer
Flower Color : Brown
Propagation : Division; cuttings; seeds
Human Hazards : None
Common Uses : Aquatic; specimen plant
Major Problems : None
Additional Notes : Fluffy, globose inflorescence on strong vertical leafless stems.

Family : Cyperaceae   Zone : 9-11

Typical Height : 1 Ft.
Drought Tolerance : Low
Nutritional Requirements : Medium
Light Requirements : Medium; high
Leaf Type : Simple; linear
Texture : Fine
Flower Characteristics : Insignificant

Environmental Problems : None

Cyperus papyrus *(Photograph p. 195)*

Common Name(s) : Papyrus
Origin : North and Tropical Africa
Growth Rate : Medium
Salt Tolerance : Medium
Soil Requirements : Wide
Plant Type : Herbaceous perennial
Foliage Color : Green
Flowering Season : Summer
Flower Color : Brown
Propagation : Division; cuttings; seeds
Human Hazards : None
Common Uses : Aquatic; specimen plant
Major Problems : None
Additional Notes : Fluffy, globose inflorescence on strong vertical stems. Used to make paper.

Family : Cyperaceae   Zone : 9-11

Typical Height : 6 Ft.
Drought Tolerance : Low
Nutritional Requirements : Medium
Light Requirements : Medium; high
Leaf Type : Simple; linear
Texture : Fine
Flower Characteristics : Insignificant

Environmental Problems : None

Cyrtanthus mackenii

Family : Amaryllidaceae   **Zone** : 10A-11

Common Name(s) : Ifafa Lily
Origin : South Africa
Growth Rate : Medium
Salt Tolerance : Low
Soil Requirements : Wide
Plant Type : Herbaceous perennial
Foliage Color : Green
Flowering Season : Summer; fall
Flower Color : Yellow; white
Propagation : Seed; division
Human Hazards : None
Common Uses : Beds; borders; cut flowers
Major Problems : None

Typical Height : 1 Ft.
Drought Tolerance : Medium
Nutritional Requirements : Medium
Light Requirements : Medium
Leaf Type : Simple; linear
Texture : Fine
Flower Characteristics : Showy

Environmental Problems : None

Additional Notes : Will remain evergreen and flower in successive flushes in south Florida.

Cyrtanthus purpuratus

Family : Amaryllidaceae   **Zone** : 10B-11

Common Name(s) : Scarborough Lily
Origin : South Africa
Growth Rate : Medium
Salt Tolerance : Low
Soil Requirements : Wide
Plant Type : Herbaceous perennial
Foliage Color : Green
Flowering Season : Spring; summer
Flower Color : Red
Propagation : Division
Human Hazards : None
Common Uses : Beds; borders
Major Problems : Dislikes heat.

Typical Height : 1.5 Ft.
Drought Tolerance : Medium
Nutritional Requirements : High
Light Requirements : Medium
Leaf Type : Simple; linear
Texture : Medium
Flower Characteristics : Showy

Environmental Problems : None

Additional Notes : Rich soil; must dry off to flower. Formerly known as <u>Vallote</u> .

Cyrtomium falcatum

Family : Polypodiaceae   **Zone** : 9-11

Common Name(s) : Holly Fern
Origin : Asia, South Africa, and Polynesia
Growth Rate : Slow
Salt Tolerance : Medium
Soil Requirements : Acid
Plant Type : Herbaceous perennial
Foliage Color : Green
Flowering Season : n/a
Flower Color : n/a
Propagation : Spores; division
Human Hazards : None
Common Uses : Foliage plant; groundcover
Major Problems : Caterpillars

Typical Height : 1.5 Ft.
Drought Tolerance : Medium
Nutritional Requirements : Medium
Light Requirements : Medium; low
Leaf Type : Simple
Texture : Medium
Flower Characteristics : n/a

Environmental Problems : None

Additional Notes : Prefers moist shady area. Glossy green foliage.
Cultivars
'COMPACTUM' is a compact, dwarf form; 'ROCHFORDIANUM' has coarsely fringed leaf margins; 'BUTTERFIELDII' has deeply serrated leaf margins.

Cyrtostachys renda *(Photograph p. 204)*

Family : Palmae   **Zone** : 11

Common Name(s) : Sealing Wax Palm
Origin : Malay Peninsula and Borneo
Growth Rate : Slow
Salt Tolerance : n/a
Soil Requirements : Wide
Plant Type : Palm
Foliage Color : Green & red
Flowering Season : Spring
Flower Color : White
Propagation : Seeds; division
Human Hazards : None
Common Uses : Foliage plant; specimen plant; palm
Major Problems : None

Typical Height : 15 Ft.
Drought Tolerance : Medium
Nutritional Requirements : Medium
Light Requirements : Medium; high
Leaf Type : Pinnately compound
Texture : Medium
Flower Characteristics : Insignificant

Environmental Problems : None

Additional Notes : The crownshafts of this clumping palm are brilliant red.

Dalbergia ecastophyllum

Common Name(s) : Coin Vine
Origin : New and Old World Tropics
Growth Rate : Medium
Salt Tolerance : High
Soil Requirements : Wide
Plant Type : Evergreen shrub
Foliage Color : Green
Flowering Season : Spring
Flower Color : White; pink
Propagation : Seeds
Human Hazards : None
Common Uses : Specimen plant; shrub
Major Problems : None
Additional Notes : A Florida native that grows well in coastal landscapes.

Family : Leguminosae   Zone : 10A-11

Typical Height : 8 Ft.
Drought Tolerance : High
Nutritional Requirements : Low
Light Requirements : High
Leaf Type : Pinnately compound
Texture : Medium
Flower Characteristics : Insignificant

Environmental Problems : None

Dalbergia sissoo

Common Name(s) : Indian Rosewood; Sissoo
Origin : India
Growth Rate : Fast
Salt Tolerance : Medium
Soil Requirements : Wide
Plant Type : Deciduous tree
Foliage Color : Green
Flowering Season : Spring; summer
Flower Color : Yellowish-white
Propagation : Seeds
Human Hazards : None
Common Uses : Shade tree
Major Problems : None
Additional Notes : This fast growing tree has a very open branching habit.

Family : Leguminosae   Zone : 10A-11

Typical Height : 50 Ft.
Drought Tolerance : Medium
Nutritional Requirements : Medium
Light Requirements : High
Leaf Type : Simple
Texture : Medium
Flower Characteristics : Insignificant; fragrant

Environmental Problems : None

Davallia fejeensis

Common Name(s) : Rabbit's Foot Fern
Origin : Fiji Islands
Growth Rate : Medium
Salt Tolerance : Low
Soil Requirements : Acid
Plant Type : Epiphyte
Foliage Color : Green
Flowering Season : n/a
Flower Color : n/a
Propagation : Spores; division
Human Hazards : None
Common Uses : Specimen plant; foliage plant
Major Problems : None
Additional Notes : Often grown as an epiphyte on trees. Loses foliage during cool winters.

Family : Davalliaceae   Zone : 10B-11

Typical Height : 1.5 Ft.
Drought Tolerance : Medium
Nutritional Requirements : Medium
Light Requirements : Low; medium
Leaf Type : Bipinnately compound
Texture : Fine
Flower Characteristics : n/a

Environmental Problems : None

Decumaria barbara

Common Name(s) : Climbing Hydrangea
Origin : Southeastern United States
Growth Rate : Medium
Salt Tolerance : Low
Soil Requirements : Acid
Plant Type : Deciduous vine
Foliage Color : Green
Flowering Season : Spring
Flower Color : White
Propagation : Cuttings
Human Hazards : None
Common Uses : Flowering vine
Major Problems : None
Additional Notes : Attractive in flower; shade tolerant; yellow fall color.

Family : Saxifragaceae   Zone : 6-10A

Typical Height : Not applicable
Drought Tolerance : Medium
Nutritional Requirements : Medium
Light Requirements : Medium
Leaf Type : Simple
Texture : Coarse
Flower Characteristics : Showy

Environmental Problems : None

Delonix regia *(Photograph p. 159)*

Common Name(s) : Royal Poinciana; Flame Tree; Flamboyant Tree

Family : Leguminosae	**Zone** : 10B-11

Origin : Madagascar	**Typical Height** : 40 Ft.
Growth Rate : Fast	**Drought Tolerance** : High
Salt Tolerance : Medium	**Nutritional Requirements** : Low
Soil Requirements : Wide	**Light Requirements** : High
Plant Type : Deciduous tree	**Leaf Type** : Bipinnately compound
Foliage Color : Green	**Texture** : Fine
Flowering Season : Summer	**Flower Characteristics** : Showy
Flower Color : Red; yellow	
Propagation : Seeds	
Human Hazards : None	**Environmental Problems** : Weak; messy
Common Uses : Flowering tree	
Major Problems : None	

Additional Notes : Large spreading tree with brilliant, but messy flowers. Brittle wood.

Dendranthema X grandiflorum

Common Name(s) : Florist's Chrysanthemum

Family : Compositae	**Zone** : 8-10A

Origin : Hybrid	**Typical Height** : 3 Ft.
Growth Rate : Medium	**Drought Tolerance** : Low
Salt Tolerance : Medium	**Nutritional Requirements** : Medium
Soil Requirements : Wide	**Light Requirements** : Medium; high
Plant Type : Herbaceous perennial	**Leaf Type** : Simple
Foliage Color : Green	**Texture** : Medium
Flowering Season : Fall	**Flower Characteristics** : Showy
Flower Color : White; yellow; red; pink; purple; bronze	
Propagation : Cuttings	
Human Hazards : None	**Environmental Problems** : None
Common Uses : Flowering pot plant; cut flower; beds; specimen plant	
Major Problems : Leaf blights	

Additional Notes : Many cultivars for different purposes exist.

Dendrobium spp.

Common Name(s) : Dendrobium Orchid

Family : Orchidaceae	**Zone** : 10B-11

Origin : Old World Tropics	**Typical Height** : 2 Ft.
Growth Rate : Slow	**Drought Tolerance** : High
Salt Tolerance : Low	**Nutritional Requirements** : Low
Soil Requirements : Well-drained	**Light Requirements** : Medium
Plant Type : Epiphyte	**Leaf Type** : Simple; linear
Foliage Color : Green	**Texture** : Medium
Flowering Season : Year-round	**Flower Characteristics** : Showy
Flower Color : Yellow; brown; pink; white; orange; red; lavender	
Propagation : Division; tissue culture	
Human Hazards : None	**Environmental Problems** : None
Common Uses : Cut flower; flowering pot plant; epiphyte	
Major Problems : Virus	

Additional Notes : Many species and hybrids of <u>Dendrobium</u> exist.

Dendrocalamus strictus

Common Name(s) : Male Bamboo

Family : Gramineae	**Zone** : 10A-11

Origin : India and Java	**Typical Height** : 50 Ft.
Growth Rate : Fast	**Drought Tolerance** : High
Salt Tolerance : n/a	**Nutritional Requirements** : Medium
Soil Requirements : Wide	**Light Requirements** : High
Plant Type : Evergreen shrub	**Leaf Type** : Simple; linear
Foliage Color : Green	**Texture** : Medium
Flowering Season : n/a	**Flower Characteristics** : n/a
Flower Color : n/a	
Propagation : Division	
Human Hazards : None	**Environmental Problems** : None
Common Uses : Large shrub; specimen plant	
Major Problems : None	

Additional Notes : This giant bamboo is very drought resistant.

Dianella ensifolia

Family : Liliaceae **Zone** : 10A-11

Common Name(s) : Flax Lily; Umbrella Dracaena
Origin : Africa, Asia, Australia, & Hawaii
Growth Rate : Medium
Salt Tolerance : Medium
Soil Requirements : Wide
Plant Type : Herbaceous perennial
Foliage Color : Green
Flowering Season : Year-round
Flower Color : White
Propagation : Seeds; division
Human Hazards : None
Common Uses : Borders; screens
Major Problems : None
Additional Notes : Naturalizes and flowers constantly.

Typical Height : 4.5 Ft.
Drought Tolerance : Medium
Nutritional Requirements : Medium
Light Requirements : Medium
Leaf Type : Simple; linear
Texture : Medium
Flower Characteristics : Insignificant

Environmental Problems : Weedy

Dichorisandra thyrsiflora *(Photograph p. 194)*

Family : Commelinaceae **Zone** : 10B-1OC

Common Name(s) : Blue Ginger
Origin : Brazil
Growth Rate : Medium
Salt Tolerance : Low
Soil Requirements : Wide
Plant Type : Herbaceous perennial
Foliage Color : Green
Flowering Season : Spring; summer; fall
Flower Color : Purple
Propagation : Cuttings; division; seeds
Human Hazards : None
Common Uses : Beds; specimen plant
Major Problems : None
Additional Notes : This plant has spirally arranged leaves and terminal purple flowers.

Typical Height : 3 Ft.
Drought Tolerance : Medium
Nutritional Requirements : Low
Light Requirements : Medium
Leaf Type : Simple
Texture : Medium
Flower Characteristics : Showy

Environmental Problems : None

Dictyosperma album *(Photograph p. 204)*

Family : Palmae **Zone** : 10B-11

Common Name(s) : Hurricane Palm; Princess Palm
Origin : Mascarene Islands
Growth Rate : Slow
Salt Tolerance : High
Soil Requirements : Wide
Plant Type : Palm
Foliage Color : Green
Flowering Season : Spring
Flower Color : White
Propagation : Seeds
Human Hazards : None
Common Uses : Tree; palm
Major Problems : Lethal yellowing (moderately susceptible)
Additional Notes : This small palm is highly wind resistant.
Cultivars
Var. rubrum has red veins on leaves of young plants; var. aureum has golden petioles and veins on young plants; var. furfuraceum has petioles covered with white hairs when young.

Typical Height : 30 Ft.
Drought Tolerance : Medium
Nutritional Requirements : Medium
Light Requirements : High
Leaf Type : Pinnately compound
Texture : Medium
Flower Characteristics : Insignificant

Environmental Problems : None

Dieffenbachia amoena

Family : Araceae **Zone** : 10B-11

Common Name(s) : Dumbcane
Origin : Tropical America
Growth Rate : Medium
Salt Tolerance : Low
Soil Requirements : Acid
Plant Type : Herbaceous perennial
Foliage Color : Variegated
Flowering Season : Summer
Flower Color : Green
Propagation : Cuttings
Human Hazards : Irritant
Common Uses : Specimen plant; foliage plant
Major Problems : Mealybugs; bacterial rot
Additional Notes : Has dark green leaves with some white variegation between veins.
Cultivars
'TROPIC SNOW' has more white variegation on leaf centers than species.

Typical Height : 5 Ft.
Drought Tolerance : Low
Nutritional Requirements : Medium
Light Requirements : Low; medium
Leaf Type : Simple
Texture : Coarse
Flower Characteristics : Insignificant

Environmental Problems : None

Dieffenbachia hybrids

Family : Araceae   Zone : 10B-11

Common Name(s) : Dumbcane
Origin : Hybrid
Growth Rate : Medium
Salt Tolerance : Low
Soil Requirements : Acid
Plant Type : Herbaceous perennial
Foliage Color : Green; variegated
Flowering Season : Summer
Flower Color : Green
Propagation : Cuttings
Human Hazards : Irritant
Common Uses : Specimen plant; foliage plant
Major Problems : Mealybugs; bacterial rot
Additional Notes : Many species and cultivars. Sap irritating externally & internally.
Cultivars

Typical Height : 3 Ft.
Drought Tolerance : Low
Nutritional Requirements : Medium
Light Requirements : Low; medium
Leaf Type : Simple
Texture : Coarse
Flower Characteristics : Insignificant

Environmental Problems : None

'WILSON'S DELIGHT' has dark green leaves with white midveins; 'VICTORY' is a freely-branching cultivar with white, yellow, and green variegation; 'TROPIC STAR' is a green-spotted yellow foliage non-suckering cultivar; 'TRIUMPH' is a freely-branching variety with green-bordered yellow leaves.

Dieffenbachia maculata *(Photograph p. 195)*

Family : Araceae   Zone : 10B-11

Common Name(s) : Spotted Dumbcane
Origin : Tropical America
Growth Rate : Medium
Salt Tolerance : Low
Soil Requirements : Acid
Plant Type : Herbaceous perennial
Foliage Color : Green & yellow
Flowering Season : Summer
Flower Color : Green; variegated
Propagation : Cuttings
Human Hazards : Irritant
Common Uses : Specimen plant; foliage plant
Major Problems : Mealybugs; bacterial rot
Additional Notes : Many cultivars exist.
Cultivars

Typical Height : 3 Ft.
Drought Tolerance : Low
Nutritional Requirements : Medium
Light Requirements : Low; medium
Leaf Type : Simple
Texture : Coarse
Flower Characteristics : Insignificant

Environmental Problems : None

'CAMILLE' is a freely-branching variety with green-margined yellow leaves; 'RUDOLPH ROEHRS' is a non-branching variety with light green-yellow young leaves; 'EXOTICA' has boldly splashed white and green foliage; 'PERFECTION' is a freely-branching variety with boldly splashed green and white foliage.

Dieffenbachia X memoria-corsii

Family : Araceae   Zone : 10B-11

Common Name(s) : Memoria Corsii Dumbcane
Origin : Hybrid
Growth Rate : Medium
Salt Tolerance : Low
Soil Requirements : Acid
Plant Type : Herbaceous perennial
Foliage Color : Green & gray-green
Flowering Season : Summer
Flower Color : Green
Propagation : Cuttings
Human Hazards : Irritant
Common Uses : Specimen plant; foliage plant
Major Problems : Mealybugs; bacterial rot
Additional Notes : Has gray-green leaves with dark green veins. Produces few suckers.

Typical Height : 3 Ft.
Drought Tolerance : Low
Nutritional Requirements : Medium
Light Requirements : Low; medium
Leaf Type : Simple
Texture : Coarse
Flower Characteristics : Insignificant

Environmental Problems : None

Dietes bicolor

Family : Iridaceae   Zone : 9-10B

Common Name(s) : Yellow Moraea
Origin : South Africa
Growth Rate : Medium
Salt Tolerance : Low
Soil Requirements : Wide
Plant Type : Herbaceous perennial
Foliage Color : Green
Flowering Season : Year-round
Flower Color : Yellow & black
Propagation : Division; seeds
Human Hazards : None
Common Uses : Beds; specimen plant
Major Problems : None
Additional Notes : Has attractive yellow flowers with black spots in center.

Typical Height : 2 Ft.
Drought Tolerance : Low
Nutritional Requirements : Low
Light Requirements : High
Leaf Type : Simple; linear
Texture : Medium
Flower Characteristics : Showy

Environmental Problems : None

Dietes vegeta *(Photograph p. 213)*

Family : Iridaceae   Zone : 9-10B

Common Name(s) : African Iris; Fortnight Lily; Butterfly Iris

Origin : South Africa	Typical Height : 2 Ft.
Growth Rate : Medium	Drought Tolerance : Medium
Salt Tolerance : Low	Nutritional Requirements : Low
Soil Requirements : Wide	Light Requirements : High
Plant Type : Herbaceous perennial	Leaf Type : Simple; linear
Foliage Color : Green	Texture : Medium
Flowering Season : Year-round	Flower Characteristics : Showy
Flower Color : White, brown & blue	
Propagation : Division; seeds	
Human Hazards : None	Environmental Problems : None
Common Uses : Beds; specimen plant	
Major Problems : None	

Additional Notes : Has attractive white flowers with blue & brown highlights.

Dillenia indica

Family : Dilleniaceae   Zone : 10B-11

Common Name(s) : Hondapara; Elephant Apple

Origin : India to Indonesia	Typical Height : 40 Ft.
Growth Rate : Medium	Drought Tolerance : Medium
Salt Tolerance : Low	Nutritional Requirements : Medium
Soil Requirements : Wide	Light Requirements : High
Plant Type : Evergreen tree	Leaf Type : Simple
Foliage Color : Green	Texture : Coarse
Flowering Season : Spring	Flower Characteristics : Insignificant; fragrant
Flower Color : White	
Propagation : Seeds	
Human Hazards : None	Environmental Problems : Messy
Common Uses : Tree; edible fruit	
Major Problems : None	

Additional Notes : Long leaves conspicuously veined. Large fruit messy; strong odor.

Dioon edule

Family : Zamiaceae   Zone : 10B-11

Common Name(s) : Chamal

Origin : Mexico	Typical Height : 5 Ft.
Growth Rate : Slow	Drought Tolerance : High
Salt Tolerance : Medium	Nutritional Requirements : Medium
Soil Requirements : Wide	Light Requirements : Medium; high
Plant Type : Evergreen shrub; cycad	Leaf Type : Pinnately compound
Foliage Color : Green	Texture : Medium
Flowering Season : Summer	Flower Characteristics : Cone
Flower Color : n/a	
Propagation : Seeds	
Human Hazards : Spiny	Environmental Problems : None
Common Uses : Shrub	
Major Problems : Scales	

Additional Notes : Spiny leaves in a stiff rosette.

Dioon spinulosum *(Photograph p. 177)*

Family : Zamiaceae   Zone : 10B-11

Common Name(s) : Spiny Dioon

Origin : Mexico	Typical Height : 6 Ft.
Growth Rate : Slow	Drought Tolerance : High
Salt Tolerance : Medium	Nutritional Requirements : Medium
Soil Requirements : Wide	Light Requirements : Medium; high
Plant Type : Evergreen shrub; cycad	Leaf Type : Pinnately compound
Foliage Color : Green	Texture : Medium
Flowering Season : Summer	Flower Characteristics : Cone
Flower Color : n/a	
Propagation : Seeds	
Human Hazards : Spiny	Environmental Problems : None
Common Uses : Shrub	
Major Problems : Scales	

Additional Notes : Spiny leaves in a stiff rosette. Old plants have trunks up to 20ft or more.

Diospyros dignya

Common Name(s) : Black Sapote
Origin : Mexico and Central America
Growth Rate : Fast
Salt Tolerance : Low
Soil Requirements : Wide
Plant Type : Evergreen tree
Foliage Color : Green
Flowering Season : Spring
Flower Color : Green-yellow
Propagation : Seeds
Human Hazards : None
Common Uses : Edible fruit; tree
Major Problems : None

Family : Ebenaceae   **Zone** : 10B-11

Typical Height : 35 Ft.
Drought Tolerance : Medium
Nutritional Requirements : Medium
Light Requirements : High
Leaf Type : Simple
Texture : Coarse
Flower Characteristics : Insignificant

Environmental Problems : Messy

Additional Notes : Messy edible brown fruits. Sometimes called the chocolate pudding tree.
Cultivars
'MERIDA' is a new improved cultivar.

Diospyros kaki

Common Name(s) : Japanese Persimmon; Kaki
Origin : China and Korea
Growth Rate : Medium
Salt Tolerance : Low
Soil Requirements : Wide
Plant Type : Deciduous tree
Foliage Color : Green
Flowering Season : Spring
Flower Color : White
Propagation : Seeds; cuttings; grafting; root cuttings
Human Hazards : None
Common Uses : Edible fruit; shade tree
Major Problems : None

Family : Ebenaceae   **Zone** : 6-10B

Typical Height : 40 Ft.
Drought Tolerance : Medium
Nutritional Requirements : Medium
Light Requirements : High
Leaf Type : Simple
Texture : Medium
Flower Characteristics : Insignificant

Environmental Problems : None

Additional Notes : Improved cultivars exist. Fruit set difficult without cross-pollination.
Cultivars
Popular astringent cultivars include: 'GIOMBO', 'TANNENASHI', 'EUREKA', and 'SHENG'; popular non-astringent cultivars include: 'JIRO', 'FUYU', and 'ICHIKIKEIJIRO'.

Diospyros virginiana

Common Name(s) : Persimmon
Origin : Eastern United States
Growth Rate : Medium
Salt Tolerance : Low
Soil Requirements : Wide
Plant Type : Deciduous tree
Foliage Color : Green
Flowering Season : Spring
Flower Color : White
Propagation : Seeds; cuttings; grafting; root cuttings
Human Hazards : None
Common Uses : Edible fruit; shade tree
Major Problems : None

Family : Ebenaceae   **Zone** : 4-10A

Typical Height : 40 Ft.
Drought Tolerance : Medium
Nutritional Requirements : Medium
Light Requirements : High
Leaf Type : Simple
Texture : Medium
Flower Characteristics : Insignificant

Environmental Problems : None

Additional Notes : Improved cultivars exist; has yellow to red fall color.

Dipholis salicifolia

Common Name(s) : Willow-leaved Bustic
Origin : Caribbean Region
Growth Rate : Medium
Salt Tolerance : Medium
Soil Requirements : Wide
Plant Type : Evergreen tree
Foliage Color : Green
Flowering Season : Summer; spring
Flower Color : White
Propagation : Seeds
Human Hazards : None
Common Uses : Shade tree
Major Problems : None

Family : Sapotaceae   **Zone** : 10B-11

Typical Height : 40 Ft.
Drought Tolerance : High
Nutritional Requirements : Low
Light Requirements : High
Leaf Type : Simple
Texture : Medium
Flower Characteristics : Insignificant

Environmental Problems : None

Dizygotheca elegantissima

Common Name(s) : False Aralia
Origin : South Pacific Islands
Growth Rate : Medium
Salt Tolerance : Medium
Soil Requirements : Wide
Plant Type : Evergreen shrub
Foliage Color : Green
Flowering Season : Summer
Flower Color : White
Propagation : Seeds
Human Hazards : None
Common Uses : Foliage plant; shrub
Major Problems : Scales; mealybugs
Additional Notes : Fine textured juvenile foliage; older foliage is bolder.

Family : Araliaceae   Zone : 10B-11

Typical Height : 10 Ft.
Drought Tolerance : Medium
Nutritional Requirements : Medium
Light Requirements : Medium; high
Leaf Type : Palmately compound
Texture : Fine
Flower Characteristics : Insignificant

Environmental Problems : None

Dodanaea viscosa

Common Name(s) : Varnish Leaf
Origin : Pantropical
Growth Rate : Slow
Salt Tolerance : High
Soil Requirements : Wide
Plant Type : Evergreen shrub
Foliage Color : Green
Flowering Season : Summer
Flower Color : White
Propagation : Seeds
Human Hazards : None
Common Uses : Shrub
Major Problems : None
Additional Notes : Leaves variable in shape and very shiny; winged fruit showy.

Family : Sapindaceae   Zone : 9-11

Typical Height : 6 Ft.
Drought Tolerance : High
Nutritional Requirements : Low
Light Requirements : High
Leaf Type : Simple
Texture : Medium
Flower Characteristics : Insignificant

Environmental Problems : None

Dolichos lablab

Common Name(s) : Hyacinth Bean
Origin : Old World Tropics
Growth Rate : Medium
Salt Tolerance : Low
Soil Requirements : Wide
Plant Type : Evergreen vine
Foliage Color : Green
Flowering Season : Summer; fall
Flower Color : Purple; white
Propagation : Seeds; cuttings
Human Hazards : None
Common Uses : Flowering vine
Major Problems : None
Additional Notes : Rampant growth quickly fills a trellis. Best as an annual.

Family : Leguminosae   Zone : 10A-11

Typical Height : Not applicable
Drought Tolerance : Medium
Nutritional Requirements : Low
Light Requirements : High
Leaf Type : Trifoliate
Texture : Medium
Flower Characteristics : Showy

Environmental Problems : Invasive

Dombeya spp. *(Photograph p. 177)*

Common Name(s) : Tropical Snowball
Origin : Mascarene Islands and Africa
Growth Rate : Fast
Salt Tolerance : Low
Soil Requirements : Wide
Plant Type : Evergreen shrub
Foliage Color : Green
Flowering Season : Summer
Flower Color : White; pink; red
Propagation : Cuttings
Human Hazards : None
Common Uses : Flowering shrub
Major Problems : Aphids; scales; nematodes; sooty mold
Additional Notes : Prune regularly to keep shaped. D. wallichii most common.

Family : Byttneriaceae   Zone : 9-11

Typical Height : 9 Ft.
Drought Tolerance : Low
Nutritional Requirements : Medium
Light Requirements : High
Leaf Type : Simple; palmately lobed
Texture : Coarse
Flower Characteristics : Showy

Environmental Problems : None

Dovyalis hebecarpa

Common Name(s) : Ceylon Gooseberry
Origin : Sri Lanka
Growth Rate : Medium
Salt Tolerance : Low
Soil Requirements : Wide
Plant Type : Evergreen tree or shrub
Foliage Color : Green; variegated
Flowering Season : Fall
Flower Color : White
Propagation : Seeds; air layering
Human Hazards : None
Common Uses : Shrub; small tree; edible fruit
Major Problems : None
Additional Notes : Intolerant of shearing. A variegated, patented hybrid exists.

Family : Flacourtiaceae   **Zone** : 10B-11

Typical Height : 20 Ft.
Drought Tolerance : Medium
Nutritional Requirements : Medium
Light Requirements : High
Leaf Type : Simple
Texture : Medium
Flower Characteristics : Insignificant

Environmental Problems : None

Dracaena deremensis *(Photograph p. 177)*

Common Name(s) : Dracaena
Origin : Tropical Africa
Growth Rate : Medium
Salt Tolerance : Low
Soil Requirements : Wide
Plant Type : Evergreen shrub
Foliage Color : Green; variegated
Flowering Season : Summer
Flower Color : White
Propagation : Cuttings
Human Hazards : None
Common Uses : Foliage plant; shrub
Major Problems : Leaf tipburn
Additional Notes : Has gracefully arching leaves; good indoor plants.
Cultivars
'JANET CRAIG' has dark green foliage; 'WARNECKII' has white and light green-striped foliage;
 'JANET CRAIG COMPACTA' has short dark green leaves and is very compact;
'WARNECKII COMPACTA' is a compact version of 'WARNECKII'.

Family : Agavaceae   **Zone** : 10B-11

Typical Height : 9 Ft.
Drought Tolerance : Medium
Nutritional Requirements : Medium
Light Requirements : Medium; low
Leaf Type : Simple; linear
Texture : Coarse
Flower Characteristics : Insignificant

Environmental Problems : None

Dracaena draco *(Photograph p. 159)*

Common Name(s) : Dragon Tree
Origin : Canary Islands
Growth Rate : Slow
Salt Tolerance : High
Soil Requirements : Wide
Plant Type : Evergreen tree
Foliage Color : Green
Flowering Season : Summer
Flower Color : Yellow-green
Propagation : Cuttings; seeds
Human Hazards : None
Common Uses : Tree; foliage plant
Major Problems : None
Additional Notes : Succulent tree with lance-shaped foliage. Sap is red.

Family : Agavaceae   **Zone** : 9-11

Typical Height : 15 Ft.
Drought Tolerance : High
Nutritional Requirements : Medium
Light Requirements : Medium; high
Leaf Type : Simple; linear
Texture : Coarse
Flower Characteristics : Showy

Environmental Problems : None

Dracaena fragrans *(Photograph p. 177)*

Common Name(s) : Fragrant Dracaena
Origin : New Guinea
Growth Rate : Medium
Salt Tolerance : Low
Soil Requirements : Wide
Plant Type : Evergreen shrub
Foliage Color : Green; green & yellow
Flowering Season : Summer; fall; winter
Flower Color : Yellow
Propagation : Cuttings
Human Hazards : None
Common Uses : Foliage plant; shrub
Major Problems : Leaf tipburn
Additional Notes : Has gracefully arching leaves; good indoor plants.
Cultivars
'LINDENII' and 'VICTORIAE' have green leaves with broad light yellow marginal stripes; 'MASSANGEANA' has
dark green leaves with a broad yellow central leaf stripe.

Family : Agavaceae   **Zone** : 10B-11

Typical Height : 9 Ft.
Drought Tolerance : Medium
Nutritional Requirements : Medium
Light Requirements : Medium; low
Leaf Type : Simple; linear
Texture : Coarse
Flower Characteristics : Insignificant; fragrant

Environmental Problems : None

Dracaena marginata

Common Name(s) : Red-edged Dracaena
Origin : Madagascar
Growth Rate : Medium
Salt Tolerance : Low
Soil Requirements : Wide
Plant Type : Evergreen shrub
Foliage Color : Green & red; variegated
Flowering Season : Summer
Flower Color : White
Propagation : Cuttings
Human Hazards : None
Common Uses : Foliage plant; shrub
Major Problems : None
Additional Notes : Multiple stemmed plant with stiff lance-shaped leaves.
Cultivars
'TRICOLOR' and 'COLORAMA' have light yellow, green and red striped leaves; 'MAGENTA' has wine-red foliage.

Family : Agavaceae   **Zone** : 10B-11

Typical Height : 10 Ft.
Drought Tolerance : High
Nutritional Requirements : Medium
Light Requirements : Medium; high
Leaf Type : Simple; linear
Texture : Coarse
Flower Characteristics : Insignificant

Environmental Problems : None

Dracaena reflexa *(Photograph p. 177)*

Common Name(s) : Reflexed Dracaena
Origin : Madagascar, Mauritius
Growth Rate : Slow
Salt Tolerance : Low
Soil Requirements : Wide
Plant Type : Evergreen shrub
Foliage Color : Green; variegated
Flowering Season : Summer
Flower Color : White
Propagation : Cuttings
Human Hazards : None
Common Uses : Foliage plant; shrub
Major Problems : None
Additional Notes : Has short twisted or arching leaves; good indoor plants.
Cultivars
'HONORIAE' has green reflexed foliage with white margins; 'SONG OF INDIA' has straight leaves with broad yellow margins; 'SONG OF JAMAICA' has yellow-green striped foliage.

Family : Agavaceae   **Zone** : 10B-11

Typical Height : 14 Ft.
Drought Tolerance : High
Nutritional Requirements : Medium
Light Requirements : Medium; high
Leaf Type : Simple; linear
Texture : Medium
Flower Characteristics : Insignificant

Environmental Problems : None

Dracaena sanderana *(Photograph p. 177)*

Common Name(s) : Ribbon Plant
Origin : Cameroons
Growth Rate : Slow
Salt Tolerance : Low
Soil Requirements : Wide
Plant Type : Herbaceous perenial
Foliage Color : Variegated; green
Flowering Season : Summer
Flower Color : White
Propagation : Cuttings
Human Hazards : None
Common Uses : Foliage plant
Major Problems : None
Additional Notes : Slender stems with white-striped leaves; a good indoor plant.
Cultivars
'BORINQUEN' has green foliage.

Family : Agavaceae   **Zone** : 10B-11

Typical Height : 4 Ft.
Drought Tolerance : High
Nutritional Requirements : Medium
Light Requirements : Medium; low
Leaf Type : Simple; linear
Texture : Medium
Flower Characteristics : Insignificant

Environmental Problems : None

Dracaena surculosa

Common Name(s) : Gold Dust Dracaena
Origin : Tropical West Africa
Growth Rate : Slow
Salt Tolerance : Low
Soil Requirements : Wide
Plant Type : Evergreen shrub
Foliage Color : Green & yellow
Flowering Season : Summer
Flower Color : White
Propagation : Cuttings
Human Hazards : None
Common Uses : Foliage plant
Major Problems : None
Additional Notes : Has attractive gold-spotted foliage and slender stems.
Cultivars
'FLORIDA BEAUTY' has more golden leaves than species; 'JUANITAS' has center of leaves golden.

Family : Agavaceae   **Zone** : 10B-11

Typical Height : 4 Ft.
Drought Tolerance : Medium
Nutritional Requirements : Medium
Light Requirements : Medium; low
Leaf Type : Simple
Texture : Medium
Flower Characteristics : Insignificant

Environmental Problems : None

Dracaena thalioides

Common Name(s) : Lance Dracaena
Origin : Tropical Africa
Growth Rate : Slow
Salt Tolerance : Low
Soil Requirements : Wide
Plant Type : Evergreen shrub
Foliage Color : Green
Flowering Season : Summer
Flower Color : White
Propagation : Cuttings
Human Hazards : None
Common Uses : Foliage plant; shrub
Major Problems : None
Additional Notes : Has lance-shaped leaves on long narrow petioles.

Family : Agavaceae   Zone : 10B-11

Typical Height : 2 Ft.
Drought Tolerance : High
Nutritional Requirements : Medium
Light Requirements : Medium; high
Leaf Type : Simple
Texture : Coarse
Flower Characteristics : Insignificant

Environmental Problems : None

Dryopteris erythrosora

Common Name(s) : Japanese Shield Fern; Japanese Wood Fern
Origin : Japan and China
Growth Rate : Medium
Salt Tolerance : Low
Soil Requirements : Wide
Plant Type : Herbaceous perennial
Foliage Color : Green
Flowering Season : n/a
Flower Color : n/a
Propagation : Spores
Human Hazards : None
Common Uses : Foliage plant; specimen plant
Major Problems : None
Additional Notes : Sori of this fern are red when young.

Family : Aspleniaceae   Zone : 10B-11

Typical Height : 3 Ft.
Drought Tolerance : Low
Nutritional Requirements : Low
Light Requirements : Low; medium
Leaf Type : Bipinnately compound
Texture : Fine
Flower Characteristics : n/a

Environmental Problems : None

Drypetes lateriflora

Common Name(s) : Guiana Plum
Origin : Caribbean Region
Growth Rate : Medium
Salt Tolerance : Medium
Soil Requirements : Wide
Plant Type : Evergreen tree or shrub
Foliage Color : Green
Flowering Season : Fall
Flower Color : Green
Propagation : Seeds
Human Hazards : None
Common Uses : Tree; shrub
Major Problems : None
Additional Notes : Flowers of this tree have no petals; fruits are reddish.

Family : Euphorbiaceae   Zone : 10B-11

Typical Height : 25 Ft.
Drought Tolerance : High
Nutritional Requirements : Low
Light Requirements : High
Leaf Type : Simple
Texture : Medium
Flower Characteristics : Insignificant

Environmental Problems : None

Duranta repens *(Photograph p. 178)*

Common Name(s) : Golden Dewdrop
Origin : Caribbean Region
Growth Rate : Medium
Salt Tolerance : Medium
Soil Requirements : Wide
Plant Type : Evergreen shrub
Foliage Color : Green
Flowering Season : Spring; summer; fall
Flower Color : Blue; white
Propagation : Seeds; cuttings
Human Hazards : Poisonous
Common Uses : Flowering shrub; hedge
Major Problems : Scales; nematodes
Additional Notes : Yellow fruit is poisonous to humans.

Family : Verbenaceae   Zone : 9B-11

Typical Height : 14 Ft.
Drought Tolerance : High
Nutritional Requirements : Low
Light Requirements : Medium; high
Leaf Type : Simple
Texture : Medium
Flower Characteristics : Showy

Environmental Problems : None

Dyckia brevifolia

Common Name(s) : Dyckia
Origin : Brazil
Growth Rate : Slow
Salt Tolerance : Medium
Soil Requirements : Well-drained
Plant Type : Herbaceous perennial
Foliage Color : Green
Flowering Season : Spring
Flower Color : Yellow-orange
Propagation : Seeds; division
Human Hazards : Spiny
Common Uses : Rock gardens
Major Problems : None

Family : Bromeliaceae   **Zone** : 10A-11

Typical Height : 1.5 Ft.
Drought Tolerance : High
Nutritional Requirements : Low
Light Requirements : Medium; high
Leaf Type : Simple; linear
Texture : Medium
Flower Characteristics : Showy

Environmental Problems : None

Additional Notes : Unlike most bromeliads, dyckias are terrestrial.

Dyschoriste oblongifolia

Common Name(s) : Twinflower
Origin : Southeastern United States
Growth Rate : Fast
Salt Tolerance : Low
Soil Requirements : Wide
Plant Type : Herbaceous perennial
Foliage Color : Green
Flowering Season : Year-round
Flower Color : Blue-purple; white
Propagation : Cuttings; division
Human Hazards : None
Common Uses : Groundcover
Major Problems : None

Family : Acanthaceae   **Zone** : 8-11

Typical Height : 1 Ft.
Drought Tolerance : Medium
Nutritional Requirements : Low
Light Requirements : High; medium
Leaf Type : Simple
Texture : Fine
Flower Characteristics : Showy

Environmental Problems : None

Additional Notes : Plant close together for good coverage.

Echeveria rosea

Common Name(s) : Desert Rose
Origin : Eastern Mexico
Growth Rate : Slow
Salt Tolerance : High
Soil Requirements : Well-drained
Plant Type : Succulent perennial
Foliage Color : Green & red
Flowering Season : Fall; winter; spring
Flower Color : Red
Propagation : Division; cuttings
Human Hazards : None
Common Uses : Rock gardens
Major Problems : Root rots

Family : Crassulaceae   **Zone** : 10A-11

Typical Height : .3 Ft.
Drought Tolerance : High
Nutritional Requirements : Low
Light Requirements : High
Leaf Type : Simple
Texture : Medium
Flower Characteristics : Showy

Environmental Problems : None

Additional Notes : A low-growing succulent rosette type plant.

Echinacea purpurea

Common Name(s) : Purple Coneflower
Origin : Southeastern United States
Growth Rate : Medium
Salt Tolerance : Low
Soil Requirements : Wide
Plant Type : Herbaceous perennial
Foliage Color : Green
Flowering Season : Summer
Flower Color : Purple; white
Propagation : Seeds; division
Human Hazards : None
Common Uses : Cut flowers; specimen plant
Major Problems : None

Family : Compositae   **Zone** : 3-10B

Typical Height : 3 Ft.
Drought Tolerance : High
Nutritional Requirements : Medium
Light Requirements : High
Leaf Type : Simple
Texture : Medium
Flower Characteristics : Showy

Environmental Problems : None

Additional Notes : Coarse growing habit seen best from a distance. Native to eastern U.S.
Cultivars
'WHITE KING' has white flowers with bronze centers; 'ROBERT BLOOM' has purple flowers with orange centers; 'BRIGHT STAR' has red flowers with maroon centers.

Echites umbellata

Common Name(s) : Devil's Potato; Rubber Vine
Origin : South Florida to South America
Growth Rate : Fast
Salt Tolerance : Low
Soil Requirements : Wide
Plant Type : Evergreen vine
Foliage Color : Green
Flowering Season : Year-round
Flower Color : White
Propagation : Seeds; cuttings
Human Hazards : None
Common Uses : Flowering vine
Major Problems : None
Additional Notes : An adaptable, everblooming native vine.

Family : Apocynaceae   **Zone** : 10B-11

Typical Height : Not applicable
Drought Tolerance : Medium
Nutritional Requirements : Medium
Light Requirements : Medium; high
Leaf Type : Simple
Texture : Medium
Flower Characteristics : Showy

Environmental Problems : None

Elaeagnus angustifolia

Common Name(s) : Russian Olive
Origin : Europe and Western Asia
Growth Rate : Fast
Salt Tolerance : High
Soil Requirements : Wide
Plant Type : Deciduous tree or shrub
Foliage Color : Silver
Flowering Season : Spring
Flower Color : Silver
Propagation : Seeds; cuttings
Human Hazards : Spiny
Common Uses : Shrub; small tree; windbreak
Major Problems : None
Additional Notes : A tough plant with attractive silvery foliage. Old trees may be thorny.

Family : Elaeagnaceae   **Zone** : 2-9

Typical Height : 20 Ft.
Drought Tolerance : High
Nutritional Requirements : Low
Light Requirements : High
Leaf Type : Simple
Texture : Medium
Flower Characteristics : Insignificant; fragrant

Environmental Problems : None

Elaeagnus latifolia

Common Name(s) : Oleaster; Wild Olive
Origin : India to China
Growth Rate : Medium
Salt Tolerance : High
Soil Requirements : Wide
Plant Type : Evergreen shrub or tree
Foliage Color : Silver & green
Flowering Season : Winter
Flower Color : Brown
Propagation : Cuttings; seeds
Human Hazards : None
Common Uses : Shrub; small tree
Major Problems : None
Additional Notes : A variable plant that can be shrub-like, tree-like, or climbing.

Family : Elaeagnaceae   **Zone** : 7-10A

Typical Height : 15 Ft.
Drought Tolerance : High
Nutritional Requirements : Low
Light Requirements : High
Leaf Type : Simple
Texture : Medium
Flower Characteristics : Insignificant; fragrant

Environmental Problems : None

Elaeagnus philippensis

Common Name(s) : Lingaro
Origin : Philippines
Growth Rate : Medium
Salt Tolerance : High
Soil Requirements : Wide
Plant Type : Evergreen shrub
Foliage Color : Silver-green
Flowering Season : Winter
Flower Color : Yellow-white
Propagation : Seeds; cuttings
Human Hazards : None
Common Uses : Shrub; hedge; edible fruit
Major Problems : None
Additional Notes : Sprawling, weeping habit requires shearing; new growth is bronzy.

Family : Elaeagnaceae   **Zone** : 10B-11

Typical Height : 9 Ft.
Drought Tolerance : High
Nutritional Requirements : Low
Light Requirements : High
Leaf Type : Simple
Texture : Medium
Flower Characteristics : Insignificant; fragrant

Environmental Problems : None

Elaeagnus pungens

Common Name(s) : Silverthorn
Origin : China and Japan
Growth Rate : Medium
Salt Tolerance : High
Soil Requirements : Acid
Plant Type : Evergreen shrub or tree
Foliage Color : Silver-green; variegated
Flowering Season : Winter
Flower Color : Brown
Propagation : Cuttings; seeds
Human Hazards : Spiny
Common Uses : Shrub; small tree
Major Problems : None
Additional Notes : Develops micronutrient deficiencies on calcareous soils. Many cultivars.
Cultivars
'COMPACTA' is a more compact cultivar; 'FRUITLANDII' has rounded leaves with wavy margins; 'MACULATA' has dark green leaves with a yellow central blotch; 'AUREA' has yellow-margined green leaves; 'SIMONII' has leaves silver beneath and variegated above; 'SUNSET' has bright yellow foliage; 'NANA' is a dwarf variety; 'ROTUNDIFOLIA' has round leaves.

Family : Elaeagnaceae   Zone : 7-10A

Typical Height : 18 Ft.
Drought Tolerance : High
Nutritional Requirements : Low
Light Requirements : High
Leaf Type : Simple
Texture : Medium
Flower Characteristics : Insignificant; fragrant

Environmental Problems : None

Elaeis guineensis *(Photograph p. 204)*

Common Name(s) : African Oil Palm
Origin : Africa
Growth Rate : Medium
Salt Tolerance : Medium
Soil Requirements : Wide
Plant Type : Palm
Foliage Color : Green
Flowering Season : Spring
Flower Color : Cream
Propagation : Seed; tissue culture
Human Hazards : Spiny
Common Uses : Tree
Major Problems : None
Additional Notes : Tolerates wet soils; grown commercially for oily fruits and seeds.

Family : Palmae   Zone : 10B-11

Typical Height : 35 Ft.
Drought Tolerance : Medium
Nutritional Requirements : Medium
Light Requirements : High
Leaf Type : Pinnately compound
Texture : Coarse
Flower Characteristics : Insignificant

Environmental Problems : None

Eleocharis cellulosa

Common Name(s) : Spikerush
Origin : South Florida to South America
Growth Rate : Medium
Salt Tolerance : High
Soil Requirements : Wet
Plant Type : Herbaceous perennial
Foliage Color : Green & red
Flowering Season : Spring; summer
Flower Color : Brown
Propagation : Seeds; division
Human Hazards : None
Common Uses : Aquatic
Major Problems : None
Additional Notes : Good for marshy areas.

Family : Cyperaceae   Zone : 10A-11

Typical Height : 2 Ft.
Drought Tolerance : Low
Nutritional Requirements : Low
Light Requirements : High
Leaf Type : Simple; linear
Texture : Fine
Flower Characteristics : Insignificant

Environmental Problems : None

Elettaria cardamomum

Common Name(s) : Cardamon; Cardamon Ginger
Origin : India
Growth Rate : Medium
Salt Tolerance : n/a
Soil Requirements : Wide
Plant Type : Herbaceous perennial
Foliage Color : Green
Flowering Season : n/a
Flower Color : White & pink
Propagation : Division; seeds
Human Hazards : None
Common Uses : Edible fruit; foliage plant; specimen plant
Major Problems : None
Additional Notes : This is the commercial source of the spice cardamon.

Family : Zingiberaceae   Zone : 10A-11

Typical Height : 8 Ft.
Drought Tolerance : Medium
Nutritional Requirements : Medium
Light Requirements : Medium
Leaf Type : Simple
Texture : Coarse
Flower Characteristics : Showy

Environmental Problems : None

Encyclia spp.

Common Name(s) : Encyclia Orchids
Origin : Tropical America
Growth Rate : Slow
Salt Tolerance : Low
Soil Requirements : Acid; well-drained
Plant Type : Herbaceous perennial
Foliage Color : Green
Flowering Season : n/a
Flower Color : Yellow; green; white
Propagation : Division
Human Hazards : None
Common Uses : Epiphyte; specimen plant; flowering pot plant
Major Problems : None
Additional Notes : Grow as epiphyte on live oak and other coarse-barked trees. Some native.
Cultivars
Many species and cultivars exist.

Family : Orchidaceae   **Zone** : 10B-11

Typical Height : 1 Ft.
Drought Tolerance : Medium
Nutritional Requirements : High
Light Requirements : Medium
Leaf Type : Simple; linear
Texture : Medium
Flower Characteristics : Showy

Environmental Problems : None

Enterolobium cyclocarpum

Common Name(s) : Ear Tree
Origin : Tropical America
Growth Rate : Fast
Salt Tolerance : Low
Soil Requirements : Wide
Plant Type : Deciduous tree
Foliage Color : Green
Flowering Season : Spring
Flower Color : White
Propagation : Seeds
Human Hazards : None
Common Uses : Tree
Major Problems : None
Additional Notes : Large wind resistant tree with aggressive roots.

Family : Leguminosae   **Zone** : 10B-11

Typical Height : 90 Ft.
Drought Tolerance : Medium
Nutritional Requirements : Low
Light Requirements : High
Leaf Type : Pinnately compound
Texture : Medium
Flower Characteristics : Insignificant

Environmental Problems : Invasive

Epidendrum ibaguense *(Photograph p. 195)*

Common Name(s) : Reed-stem Epidendrum
Origin : Central and South America
Growth Rate : Medium
Salt Tolerance : Medium
Soil Requirements : Acid; well-drained
Plant Type : Epiphyte
Foliage Color : Green
Flowering Season : Spring; summer; fall
Flower Color : Orange; yellow
Propagation : Division; cuttings
Human Hazards : None
Common Uses : Beds; flowering perennial; epiphyte
Major Problems : None
Additional Notes : A tough, adaptable, even slightly weedy orchid useful in beds and borders.

Family : Orchidaceae   **Zone** : 10B-11

Typical Height : 3 Ft.
Drought Tolerance : High
Nutritional Requirements : Low
Light Requirements : High
Leaf Type : Simple
Texture : Medium
Flower Characteristics : Showy

Environmental Problems : None

Epiphyllum spp.

Common Name(s) : Orchid Cactus
Origin : Tropical America
Growth Rate : Medium
Salt Tolerance : Low
Soil Requirements : Wide
Plant Type : Succulent epiphyte
Foliage Color : Green
Flowering Season : Spring; summer; fall
Flower Color : Lavender; orange; pink; purple; red; white; yellow
Propagation : Cuttings
Human Hazards : None
Common Uses : Flowering perennial; epiphyte; flowering pot plant
Major Problems : Root rot
Additional Notes : Many species and hybrids of day or night blooming epiphytic cacti.

Family : Cactaceae   **Zone** : 10B-11

Typical Height : 3 Ft.
Drought Tolerance : Medium
Nutritional Requirements : Medium
Light Requirements : Medium
Leaf Type : None
Texture : Coarse
Flower Characteristics : Showy

Environmental Problems : None

Epipremnum aureum *(Photograph p. 211)*

Common Name(s) : Pothos
Origin : Solomon Islands
Growth Rate : Fast
Salt Tolerance : Medium
Soil Requirements : Wide
Plant Type : Evergreen vine
Foliage Color : Green; variegated
Flowering Season : n/a
Flower Color : Green
Propagation : Cuttings
Human Hazards : None
Common Uses : Vine; groundcover; foliage plant; hanging baskets
Major Problems : None
Additional Notes : Yellow & green foliage; mature foliage is large and often split.
Cultivars
'MARBLE QUEEN' has white and green variegated foliage; 'TROPIC GREEN' and 'JADE' have solid green foliage.

Family : Araceae   **Zone** : 10B-11

Typical Height : Not applicable
Drought Tolerance : High
Nutritional Requirements : Low
Light Requirements : Low; medium
Leaf Type : Simple
Texture : Coarse
Flower Characteristics : Insignificant

Environmental Problems : None

Eranthemum pulchellum

Common Name(s) : Blue Sage
Origin : India
Growth Rate : Fast
Salt Tolerance : Medium
Soil Requirements : Wide
Plant Type : Evergreen shrub
Foliage Color : Green
Flowering Season : Winter
Flower Color : Blue
Propagation : Cuttings
Human Hazards : None
Common Uses : Specimen plant; flowering shrub
Major Problems : None
Additional Notes : Should be pruned heavily to remain compact.

Family : Acanthaceae   **Zone** : 10B-11

Typical Height : 4 Ft.
Drought Tolerance : Low
Nutritional Requirements : Medium
Light Requirements : Medium; low
Leaf Type : Simple
Texture : Medium
Flower Characteristics : Showy

Environmental Problems : None

Eriobotrya deflexa

Common Name(s) : Bronze Loquat
Origin : Taiwan
Growth Rate : Medium
Salt Tolerance : Low
Soil Requirements : Wide
Plant Type : Evergreen tree
Foliage Color : Green; red
Flowering Season : Spring
Flower Color : White
Propagation : Seeds
Human Hazards : None
Common Uses : Small flowering tree
Major Problems : Fireblight; root rots
Additional Notes : Attractive small tree with bronzy new foliage.

Family : Rosaceae   **Zone** : 8-10B

Typical Height : 15 Ft.
Drought Tolerance : Medium
Nutritional Requirements : Medium
Light Requirements : High
Leaf Type : Simple
Texture : Coarse
Flower Characteristics : Showy

Environmental Problems : None

Eriobotrya japonica *(Photograph p. 159)*

Common Name(s) : Loquat
Origin : China and Japan
Growth Rate : Medium
Salt Tolerance : Medium
Soil Requirements : Wide
Plant Type : Evergreen tree
Foliage Color : Green
Flowering Season : Fall; winter
Flower Color : White
Propagation : Seeds; grafting
Human Hazards : None
Common Uses : Edible fruit; small flowering tree
Major Problems : Caribbean fruit fly; fireblight
Additional Notes : Many cultivars exist.

Family : Rosaceae   **Zone** : 7-11

Typical Height : 20 Ft.
Drought Tolerance : High
Nutritional Requirements : Low
Light Requirements : High
Leaf Type : Simple
Texture : Coarse
Flower Characteristics : Showy; fragrant

Environmental Problems : None

Ernodea littoralis

Common Name(s) : Golden Creeper
Origin : South Florida
Growth Rate : Medium
Salt Tolerance : High
Soil Requirements : Wide
Plant Type : Evergreen shrub
Foliage Color : Yellow-green
Flowering Season : Year-round
Flower Color : Pink & white
Propagation : Seed; cuttings
Human Hazards : None
Common Uses : Groundcover; seasides
Major Problems : None
Additional Notes : A drought resistant native. Pineland form more tolerant of overwatering.

Family : Rubiaceae   **Zone** : 10B-11

Typical Height : 2 Ft.
Drought Tolerance : High
Nutritional Requirements : Low
Light Requirements : High
Leaf Type : Simple
Texture : Medium
Flower Characteristics : Insignificant

Environmental Problems : None

Eryngium amethystinum

Common Name(s) : Amethyst Sea Holly
Origin : Europe
Growth Rate : Medium
Salt Tolerance : High
Soil Requirements : Wide
Plant Type : Herbaceous perennial
Foliage Color : Green
Flowering Season : Summer
Flower Color : Blue
Propagation : Seeds; division
Human Hazards : Spiny
Common Uses : Cut flowers; specimen plant
Major Problems : None
Additional Notes : Bold-textured plant suitable for seasides. Flowers dry well.

Family : Umbelliferae   **Zone** : 4-9

Typical Height : 2 Ft.
Drought Tolerance : High
Nutritional Requirements : Low
Light Requirements : High
Leaf Type : Simple; pinnately lobed
Texture : Medium
Flower Characteristics : Showy

Environmental Problems : None

Erythrina crista-gallii

Common Name(s) : Cockspur Coral Tree
Origin : Brazil to Northern Argentina
Growth Rate : Medium
Salt Tolerance : Medium
Soil Requirements : Wide
Plant Type : Deciduous tree
Foliage Color : Green
Flowering Season : Spring; summer
Flower Color : Red
Propagation : Seeds; cuttings
Human Hazards : Spiny
Common Uses : Flowering tree
Major Problems : Borers; nematodes
Additional Notes : Many other species of erythrina can be grown in Florida.

Family : Leguminosae   **Zone** : 9-11

Typical Height : 30 Ft.
Drought Tolerance : High
Nutritional Requirements : Medium
Light Requirements : High
Leaf Type : Trifoliate
Texture : Medium
Flower Characteristics : Showy

Environmental Problems : None

Erythrina herbacea

Common Name(s) : Coral Bean; Cardinal-spear
Origin : Southeastern United States
Growth Rate : Medium
Salt Tolerance : High
Soil Requirements : Wide
Plant Type : Deciduous shrub
Foliage Color : Green
Flowering Season : Spring
Flower Color : Red
Propagation : Seeds; cuttings
Human Hazards : Poisonous
Common Uses : Flowering shrub
Major Problems : None
Additional Notes : Attracts hummingbirds; seeds poisonous.

Family : Leguminosae   **Zone** : 8-11

Typical Height : 5 Ft.
Drought Tolerance : High
Nutritional Requirements : Medium
Light Requirements : Medium; high
Leaf Type : Trifoliate
Texture : Medium
Flower Characteristics : Showy

Environmental Problems : None

Erythrina variegata var. orientalis *(Photo. p. 159)*   Family : Leguminosae   Zone : 10A-11

Common Name(s) : Coral Tree; Lenten Tree
Origin : India to Indonesia and Philippines
Growth Rate : Fast
Salt Tolerance : Medium
Soil Requirements : Wide
Plant Type : Deciduous tree
Foliage Color : Variegated
Flowering Season : Spring
Flower Color : Red
Propagation : Seeds; cuttings; air layers
Human Hazards : Spiny; poisonous
Common Uses : Flowering tree
Major Problems : Borers
Additional Notes : Flowers appear before variegated foliage in spring; seeds poisonous.

Typical Height : 60 Ft.
Drought Tolerance : High
Nutritional Requirements : Medium
Light Requirements : High
Leaf Type : Trifoliate
Texture : Coarse
Flower Characteristics : Showy

Environmental Problems : None

Etlingera elatior *(Photograph p. 195)*   Family : Zingiberaceae   Zone : 10B-11

Common Name(s) : Torch Ginger
Origin : Celebes and Java
Growth Rate : Fast
Salt Tolerance : Medium
Soil Requirements : Wide
Plant Type : Herbaceous perennial
Foliage Color : Green; red
Flowering Season : Spring; summer
Flower Color : Red; pink
Propagation : Division
Human Hazards : None
Common Uses : Cut flowers; specimen plant
Major Problems : K deficiency
Additional Notes : A large ginger with red or pink flowers on separate stalks.

Typical Height : 15 Ft.
Drought Tolerance : Medium
Nutritional Requirements : Medium
Light Requirements : Medium; high
Leaf Type : Simple
Texture : Coarse
Flower Characteristics : Showy

Environmental Problems : None

Eucalyptus cinerea   Family : Myrtaceae   Zone : 9-11

Common Name(s) : Silver Dollar Tree
Origin : Australia
Growth Rate : Medium
Salt Tolerance : Medium
Soil Requirements : Wide
Plant Type : Evergreen tree
Foliage Color : Silver
Flowering Season : Spring
Flower Color : White
Propagation : Seeds
Human Hazards : Irritant
Common Uses : Tree; cut foliage
Major Problems : None
Additional Notes : Round silver juvenile foliage is often used by florists as cut foliage.

Typical Height : 20 Ft.
Drought Tolerance : High
Nutritional Requirements : Low
Light Requirements : High
Leaf Type : Simple
Texture : Medium
Flower Characteristics : Insignificant

Environmental Problems : None

Eucalyptus robusta   Family : Myrtaceae   Zone : 10A-11

Common Name(s) : Swamp Mahogany
Origin : Australia
Growth Rate : Fast
Salt Tolerance : Low
Soil Requirements : Wide
Plant Type : Evergreen tree
Foliage Color : Green
Flowering Season : Fall
Flower Color : White
Propagation : Seeds
Human Hazards : Irritant
Common Uses : Shade tree
Major Problems : None
Additional Notes : Very tolerant of wet or flooded soils.

Typical Height : 50 Ft.
Drought Tolerance : Medium
Nutritional Requirements : Low
Light Requirements : High
Leaf Type : Simple
Texture : Medium
Flower Characteristics : Insignificant

Environmental Problems : None

Eucalyptus torelliana

Common Name(s) : Cadaga
Origin : Australia
Growth Rate : Fast
Salt Tolerance : Medium
Soil Requirements : Wide
Plant Type : Evergreen tree
Foliage Color : Green
Flowering Season : Spring
Flower Color : White
Propagation : Seeds
Human Hazards : Irritant
Common Uses : Tree
Major Problems : None
Additional Notes : Has smooth green bark.

Family : Myrtaceae   **Zone** : 10A-11

Typical Height : 80 Ft.
Drought Tolerance : High
Nutritional Requirements : Medium
Light Requirements : High
Leaf Type : Simple
Texture : Medium
Flower Characteristics : Insignificant

Environmental Problems : None

Eucharis amazonica *(Photograph p. 195)*

Common Name(s) : Amazon Lily
Origin : Peru
Growth Rate : Medium
Salt Tolerance : Low
Soil Requirements : Acid
Plant Type : Herbaceous perennial
Foliage Color : Green
Flowering Season : Fall; winter; spring
Flower Color : White
Propagation : Division
Human Hazards : Poisonous
Common Uses : Beds; flowering perennial; foliage plant
Major Problems : Mealybugs; virus; bacterial and fungal bulb rots
Additional Notes : Attactive hosta-like foliage burns in sun; repeat blooms during year.

Family : Amaryllidaceae   **Zone** : 10A-10B

Typical Height : 2 Ft.
Drought Tolerance : Low
Nutritional Requirements : High
Light Requirements : Low
Leaf Type : Simple
Texture : Coarse
Flower Characteristics : Fragrant; showy

Environmental Problems : None

Eucomis spp.

Common Name(s) : Pineapple Lilies
Origin : South Africa
Growth Rate : Medium
Salt Tolerance : Low
Soil Requirements : Well-drained
Plant Type : Herbaceous perennial
Foliage Color : Green
Flowering Season : Summer
Flower Color : White; yellow
Propagation : Seeds; division
Human Hazards : None
Common Uses : Beds; borders; cut flowers
Major Problems : None
Additional Notes : Dormant in winter; flowers resemble pineapples.

Family : Liliaceae   **Zone** : 7-10B

Typical Height : 3 Ft.
Drought Tolerance : Medium
Nutritional Requirements : Medium
Light Requirements : Medium
Leaf Type : Simple; linear
Texture : Coarse
Flower Characteristics : Showy

Environmental Problems : None

Eugenia aggregata

Common Name(s) : Cherry of The Rio Grande
Origin : Brazil
Growth Rate : Medium
Salt Tolerance : Low
Soil Requirements : Wide
Plant Type : Evergreen tree or shrub
Foliage Color : Green
Flowering Season : Spring
Flower Color : White
Propagation : Seeds; cuttings
Human Hazards : None
Common Uses : Small tree; shrub; edible fruit
Major Problems : None
Additional Notes : Reddish-purple fruits are edible.

Family : Myrtaceae   **Zone** : 10B-11

Typical Height : 15 Ft.
Drought Tolerance : Medium
Nutritional Requirements : Medium
Light Requirements : High
Leaf Type : Simple
Texture : Medium
Flower Characteristics : Insignificant

Environmental Problems : None

Eugenia axillaris

Common Name(s) : White Stopper
Origin : Caribbean Region
Growth Rate : Medium
Salt Tolerance : High
Soil Requirements : Wide
Plant Type : Evergreen tree
Foliage Color : Green
Flowering Season : Spring; summer
Flower Color : White
Propagation : Seeds
Human Hazards : None
Common Uses : Small tree
Major Problems : None
Additional Notes : New foliage is reddish; edible fruits.

Family : Myrtaceae   **Zone** : 10B-11

Typical Height : 25 Ft.
Drought Tolerance : High
Nutritional Requirements : Low
Light Requirements : Medium; high
Leaf Type : Simple
Texture : Medium
Flower Characteristics : Insignificant

Environmental Problems : None

Eugenia brasiliensis *(Photograph p. 159)*

Common Name(s) : Grumichama
Origin : Southern Brazil
Growth Rate : Medium
Salt Tolerance : Medium
Soil Requirements : Wide
Plant Type : Evergreen tree or shrub
Foliage Color : Green
Flowering Season : Spring
Flower Color : White
Propagation : Seeds; cuttings
Human Hazards : None
Common Uses : Edible fruit; shrub; hedge; tree
Major Problems : None
Additional Notes : Has tasty, cherry-like fruit.

Family : Myrtaceae   **Zone** : 10B-11

Typical Height : 20 Ft.
Drought Tolerance : Low
Nutritional Requirements : Medium
Light Requirements : High
Leaf Type : Simple
Texture : Medium
Flower Characteristics : Showy

Environmental Problems : None

Eugenia confusa

Common Name(s) : Ironwood; Red Stopper
Origin : Florida and West Indies
Growth Rate : Medium
Salt Tolerance : High
Soil Requirements : Wide
Plant Type : Evergreen tree
Foliage Color : Green
Flowering Season : Spring
Flower Color : White
Propagation : Seeds; cuttings
Human Hazards : None
Common Uses : Small tree
Major Problems : None
Additional Notes : This plant has small red fruits.

Family : Myrtaceae   **Zone** : 10B-11

Typical Height : 35 Ft.
Drought Tolerance : High
Nutritional Requirements : Medium
Light Requirements : High; medium
Leaf Type : Simple
Texture : Medium
Flower Characteristics : Insignificant

Environmental Problems : None

Eugenia coronata

Common Name(s) : n/a
Origin : Tropical West Africa
Growth Rate : Medium
Salt Tolerance : n/a
Soil Requirements : Wide
Plant Type : Evergreen shrub or tree
Foliage Color : Green
Flowering Season : Spring
Flower Color : White
Propagation : Seeds; cuttings
Human Hazards : None
Common Uses : Small tree; shrub; hedge
Major Problems : None
Additional Notes : This plant has blue-black fruits. Often used in hedges.

Family : Myrtaceae   **Zone** : 10B-11

Typical Height : 15 Ft.
Drought Tolerance : High
Nutritional Requirements : Medium
Light Requirements : High
Leaf Type : Simple
Texture : Medium
Flower Characteristics : Insignificant; fragrant

Environmental Problems : None

Eugenia foetida

Common Name(s) : Spanish Stopper; Box-leaf Eugenia
Origin : Florida and West Indies
Growth Rate : Medium
Salt Tolerance : High
Soil Requirements : Wide
Plant Type : Evergreen shrub or tree
Foliage Color : Green
Flowering Season : Summer
Flower Color : White
Propagation : Seeds; cuttings
Human Hazards : None
Common Uses : Small tree; shrub
Major Problems : None
Additional Notes : Often used in tall hedges.

Family : Myrtaceae   **Zone** : 10A-11

Typical Height : 15 Ft.
Drought Tolerance : High
Nutritional Requirements : Medium
Light Requirements : High
Leaf Type : Simple
Texture : Medium
Flower Characteristics : Insignificant

Environmental Problems : None

Eugenia rhombea

Common Name(s) : Spiceberry; Red Stopper
Origin : Florida and West Indies
Growth Rate : Medium
Salt Tolerance : High
Soil Requirements : Wide
Plant Type : Evergreen tree or shrub
Foliage Color : Green
Flowering Season : Year-round
Flower Color : White
Propagation : Seeds; cuttings
Human Hazards : None
Common Uses : Small tree; shrub
Major Problems : None
Additional Notes : Has small black fruits.

Family : Myrtaceae   **Zone** : 10B-11

Typical Height : 20 Ft.
Drought Tolerance : High
Nutritional Requirements : Medium
Light Requirements : High
Leaf Type : Simple
Texture : Medium
Flower Characteristics : Insignificant

Environmental Problems : None

Eugenia uniflora *(Photograph p. 178)*

Common Name(s) : Surinam Cherry
Origin : Brazil
Growth Rate : Medium
Salt Tolerance : Medium
Soil Requirements : Wide
Plant Type : Evergreen shrub
Foliage Color : Green
Flowering Season : Spring
Flower Color : White
Propagation : Seeds
Human Hazards : None
Common Uses : Hedge; shrub; edible fruit
Major Problems : Scales
Additional Notes : Edible attractive fruits. Can be pruned to any size. Can naturalize.

Family : Myrtaceae   **Zone** : 10A-11

Typical Height : 10 Ft.
Drought Tolerance : Medium
Nutritional Requirements : Low
Light Requirements : Medium; high
Leaf Type : Simple
Texture : Medium
Flower Characteristics : Insignificant; fragrant

Environmental Problems : Weedy

Euonymus americana

Common Name(s) : Bursting Heart; Strawberry Bush
Origin : Eastern United States
Growth Rate : Fast
Salt Tolerance : Low
Soil Requirements : Wide
Plant Type : Deciduous shrub
Foliage Color : Green
Flowering Season : Spring
Flower Color : White
Propagation : Seeds; division
Human Hazards : None
Common Uses : Shrub
Major Problems : None
Additional Notes : Attractive fruit is eaten by wildlife; best in woodland setting.

Family : Celastraceae   **Zone** : 6-9

Typical Height : 7 Ft.
Drought Tolerance : Low
Nutritional Requirements : Medium
Light Requirements : Medium
Leaf Type : Simple
Texture : Medium
Flower Characteristics : Insignificant

Environmental Problems : None

Euonymus fortunei

Common Name(s) : Spreading Euonymus
Origin : China
Growth Rate : Medium
Salt Tolerance : Medium
Soil Requirements : Wide
Plant Type : Evergreen shrub
Foliage Color : Green; purple
Flowering Season : Spring
Flower Color : White
Propagation : Cuttings
Human Hazards : None
Common Uses : Groundcover; shrub
Major Problems : None
Additional Notes : Shear occasionally to control height; many cultivars exist.
Cultivars
'COLORATA' is semiprostrate and has purplish foliage in the fall and winter; 'GRACILIS' is a climbing form with variegated foliage; 'CARRIEREI' is an upright form; 'UNCINATA' has gray-green foliage.

Family : Celastraceae   Zone : 5-9

Typical Height : 2 Ft.
Drought Tolerance : Low
Nutritional Requirements : Medium
Light Requirements : Medium
Leaf Type : Simple
Texture : Medium
Flower Characteristics : Insignificant

Environmental Problems : None

Euonymus japonica

Common Name(s) : Spindle Tree; Japanese Euonymus
Origin : Japan
Growth Rate : Fast
Salt Tolerance : Low
Soil Requirements : Wide
Plant Type : Evergreen shrub or tree
Foliage Color : Green; silver; yellow
Flowering Season : Spring
Flower Color : Green
Propagation : Seeds; cuttings
Human Hazards : None
Common Uses : Shrub; hedge; small tree
Major Problems : Scales
Additional Notes : Many cultivars exist; can be sheared.
Cultivars
'ALBOMARGINATA' has narrow white border on leaves; 'AUREO-MARGINATA' has yellow leaf margins; 'AUREO-VARIEGATA' has leaves blotched with yellow; 'MICROPHYLLA' has small leaves; 'AUREA' has leaves marked with yellow; 'VARIEGATA' has small, silver-variegated leaves; 'PICTA' is dwarf with dark green leaves. 'MEDIOPICTA' has a large yellow leaf blotch.

Family : Celastraceae   Zone : 8-10A

Typical Height : 10 Ft.
Drought Tolerance : Medium
Nutritional Requirements : Low
Light Requirements : Low; medium; high
Leaf Type : Simple
Texture : Medium
Flower Characteristics : Insignificant

Environmental Problems : None

Eupatorium coelestinum

Common Name(s) : Mistflower
Origin : Eastern United States
Growth Rate : Medium
Salt Tolerance : Low
Soil Requirements : Wide
Plant Type : Herbaceous perennial
Foliage Color : Green
Flowering Season : Fall
Flower Color : Blue
Propagation : Division; seeds
Human Hazards : None
Common Uses : Cut flowers; specimen plant
Major Problems : None
Additional Notes : Mulch plants for best growth. Can become weedy.

Family : Compositae   Zone : 3-10B

Typical Height : 2 Ft.
Drought Tolerance : Low
Nutritional Requirements : Low
Light Requirements : Medium; high
Leaf Type : Simple
Texture : Medium
Flower Characteristics : Showy

Environmental Problems : Invasive

Euphorbia acrurensis

Common Name(s) : n/a
Origin : Ethiopia
Growth Rate : Slow
Salt Tolerance : High
Soil Requirements : Wide
Plant Type : Succulent shrub
Foliage Color : Green
Flowering Season : Summer
Flower Color : Yellow
Propagation : Cuttings
Human Hazards : Irritant; spiny
Common Uses : Shrub; rock gardens
Major Problems : None
Additional Notes : Can become tree-like with 7-angled stems. Milky sap may irritate skin.

Family : Euphorbiaceae   Zone : 10B-11

Typical Height : 12 Ft.
Drought Tolerance : High
Nutritional Requirements : Low
Light Requirements : High
Leaf Type : None
Texture : Coarse
Flower Characteristics : Insignificant

Environmental Problems : None

Euphorbia bergeri

Common Name(s) : Dwarf Euphorbia
Origin : South Africa
Growth Rate : Slow
Salt Tolerance : High
Soil Requirements : Wide
Plant Type : Evergreen succulent
Foliage Color : Green
Flowering Season : Summer
Flower Color : Green
Propagation : Cuttings
Human Hazards : Irritant
Common Uses : Rock gardens
Major Problems : None
Additional Notes : A very dwarf spineless succulent with many short branches.

Family : Euphorbiaceae   **Zone** : 10B-11

Typical Height : .8 Ft.
Drought Tolerance : High
Nutritional Requirements : Low
Light Requirements : High
Leaf Type : None
Texture : Coarse
Flower Characteristics : Insignificant

Environmental Problems : None

Euphorbia biglandulosa

Common Name(s) : Spurge
Origin : Asia Minor
Growth Rate : Medium
Salt Tolerance : Medium
Soil Requirements : Wide
Plant Type : Herbaceous perennial
Foliage Color : Green
Flowering Season : Summer
Flower Color : Yellow
Propagation : Seeds; division
Human Hazards : Irritant
Common Uses : Rock gardens; borders; specimen plant
Major Problems : None
Additional Notes : Unusual perennial for areas with good drainage.

Family : Euphorbiaceae   **Zone** : 7-9

Typical Height : 2 Ft.
Drought Tolerance : High
Nutritional Requirements : Medium
Light Requirements : High
Leaf Type : Simple
Texture : Medium
Flower Characteristics : Showy

Environmental Problems : None

Euphorbia cotinifolia *(Photograph p. 178)*

Common Name(s) : Red Spurge
Origin : Mexico to N. South America
Growth Rate : Fast
Salt Tolerance : Low
Soil Requirements : Wide
Plant Type : Evergreen shrub
Foliage Color : Red
Flowering Season : Summer
Flower Color : White
Propagation : Cuttings; air layering; seeds
Human Hazards : Irritant
Common Uses : Shrub
Major Problems : None
Additional Notes : Milky sap may irritate eyes and skin.

Family : Euphorbiaceae   **Zone** : 10B-11

Typical Height : 10 Ft.
Drought Tolerance : Medium
Nutritional Requirements : Medium
Light Requirements : High
Leaf Type : Simple
Texture : Medium
Flower Characteristics : Insignificant

Environmental Problems : None

Euphorbia epithymoides

Common Name(s) : Spurge
Origin : Eastern Europe
Growth Rate : Medium
Salt Tolerance : Medium
Soil Requirements : Wide
Plant Type : Herbaceous perennial
Foliage Color : Green
Flowering Season : Summer
Flower Color : Yellow-green
Propagation : Division
Human Hazards : Irritant
Common Uses : Beds; borders; groundcover
Major Problems : None
Additional Notes : Forms a low rounded clump. Sap may irritate skin.

Family : Euphorbiaceae   **Zone** : 3-10A

Typical Height : 1 Ft.
Drought Tolerance : Medium
Nutritional Requirements : Medium
Light Requirements : High
Leaf Type : Simple
Texture : Fine
Flower Characteristics : Showy

Environmental Problems : None

Euphorbia fulgens

Common Name(s) : Scarlet-plume
Origin : Mexico
Growth Rate : Medium
Salt Tolerance : High
Soil Requirements : Wide
Plant Type : Evergreen succulent shrub
Foliage Color : Green
Flowering Season : Year-round
Flower Color : Orange-red
Propagation : Cuttings
Human Hazards : Irritant
Common Uses : Rock gardens
Major Problems : None
Additional Notes : A spineless leafy euphorbia with showy scarlet flowers.

Family : Euphorbiaceae   **Zone** : 10B-11

Typical Height : 4 Ft.
Drought Tolerance : High
Nutritional Requirements : Low
Light Requirements : High
Leaf Type : Simple
Texture : Medium
Flower Characteristics : Showy

Environmental Problems : None

Euphorbia lactea

Common Name(s) : Milkstriped Euphorbia
Origin : East Indies
Growth Rate : Medium
Salt Tolerance : High
Soil Requirements : Wide
Plant Type : Succulent evergreen shrub
Foliage Color : Variegated; green
Flowering Season : Summer
Flower Color : Green; yellow
Propagation : Cuttings
Human Hazards : Irritant; spiny
Common Uses : Rock gardens; foliage plant; specimen plant
Major Problems : None
Additional Notes : Milky sap may cause skin irritation.
Cultivars
'CRISTATA' is a dwarf form with an unusual habit.

Family : Euphorbiaceae   **Zone** : 10B-11

Typical Height : 12 Ft.
Drought Tolerance : High
Nutritional Requirements : Low
Light Requirements : High
Leaf Type : Simple
Texture : Coarse
Flower Characteristics : Insignificant

Environmental Problems : None

Euphorbia leucocephala

Common Name(s) : Pascuita
Origin : Southern Mexico to El Salvador
Growth Rate : Fast
Salt Tolerance : Low
Soil Requirements : Wide
Plant Type : Evergreen shrub
Foliage Color : Green
Flowering Season : Winter
Flower Color : White
Propagation : Cuttings
Human Hazards : Irritant
Common Uses : Flowering shrub
Major Problems : None
Additional Notes : Milky sap may irritate skin or eyes.

Family : Euphorbiaceae   **Zone** : 10B-11

Typical Height : 8 Ft.
Drought Tolerance : Medium
Nutritional Requirements : Medium
Light Requirements : High
Leaf Type : Simple
Texture : Medium
Flower Characteristics : Showy

Environmental Problems : None

Euphorbia milii

Common Name(s) : Crown of Thorns
Origin : Madagascar
Growth Rate : Slow
Salt Tolerance : High
Soil Requirements : Wide
Plant Type : Evergreen succulent shrub
Foliage Color : Green
Flowering Season : Year-round
Flower Color : Yellow; red; pink
Propagation : Cuttings
Human Hazards : Irritant; spiny
Common Uses : Foliage plant; flowering groundcover; flowering shrub
Major Problems : None
Additional Notes : Many spiny, prostrate and upright forms available.

Family : Euphorbiaceae   **Zone** : 10B-11

Typical Height : 2 Ft.
Drought Tolerance : High
Nutritional Requirements : Low
Light Requirements : High
Leaf Type : Simple
Texture : Fine
Flower Characteristics : Showy

Environmental Problems : None

Euphorbia polycantha

Common Name(s) : Fishbone Cactus
Origin : Ethiopia
Growth Rate : Slow
Salt Tolerance : High
Soil Requirements : Wide
Plant Type : Succulent shrub
Foliage Color : Green
Flowering Season : n/a
Flower Color : n/a
Propagation : Cuttings
Human Hazards : Irritant; spiny
Common Uses : Rock gardens; shrub
Major Problems : None
Additional Notes : Has 4-5-angled stems with long spines.

Family : Euphorbiaceae   **Zone** : 10B-11

Typical Height : 4 Ft.
Drought Tolerance : High
Nutritional Requirements : Low
Light Requirements : High
Leaf Type : None
Texture : Coarse
Flower Characteristics : Insignificant

Environmental Problems : None

Euphorbia pulcherrima *(Photograph p. 178)*

Common Name(s) : Poinsettia
Origin : Mexico and Central America
Growth Rate : Fast
Salt Tolerance : Low
Soil Requirements : Wide
Plant Type : Evergreen shrub
Foliage Color : Green
Flowering Season : Winter
Flower Color : Red; white; pink
Propagation : Cuttings
Human Hazards : Irritant
Common Uses : Flowering shrub; hedge; flowering pot plant
Major Problems : Whiteflies; mealybugs
Additional Notes : Prune hard after flowering; many cultivars exist.

Family : Euphorbiaceae   **Zone** : 10B-11

Typical Height : 7 Ft.
Drought Tolerance : Low
Nutritional Requirements : Medium
Light Requirements : High
Leaf Type : Simple
Texture : Coarse
Flower Characteristics : Showy

Environmental Problems : None

Euphorbia punicea

Common Name(s) : n/a
Origin : West Indies
Growth Rate : Medium
Salt Tolerance : High
Soil Requirements : Wide
Plant Type : Evergreen succulent shrub
Foliage Color : Green
Flowering Season : Spring; summer; fall
Flower Color : Red
Propagation : Cuttings
Human Hazards : Irritant
Common Uses : Rock gardens; shrub
Major Problems : None
Additional Notes : A tree-like or shrubby succulent with showy red flowers.

Family : Euphorbiaceae   **Zone** : 10B-11

Typical Height : 15 Ft.
Drought Tolerance : High
Nutritional Requirements : Low
Light Requirements : High
Leaf Type : Simple
Texture : Medium
Flower Characteristics : Showy

Environmental Problems : None

Euphorbia tirucalli

Common Name(s) : Pencil Tree
Origin : Africa
Growth Rate : Medium
Salt Tolerance : High
Soil Requirements : Wide
Plant Type : Succulent shrub
Foliage Color : Green
Flowering Season : Summer
Flower Color : White
Propagation : Cuttings
Human Hazards : Irritant
Common Uses : Shrub; hedge
Major Problems : None
Additional Notes : Often grown near the beach. Milky sap irritating.

Family : Euphorbiaceae   **Zone** : 10B-11

Typical Height : 20 Ft.
Drought Tolerance : High
Nutritional Requirements : Low
Light Requirements : High
Leaf Type : Simple
Texture : Fine
Flower Characteristics : Insignificant

Environmental Problems : None

Euphorbia trigona *(Photograph p. 178)*

Common Name(s) : Cathedral Cactus; African Milk Tree
Origin : Tropical Southwest Africa
Growth Rate : Medium
Salt Tolerance : High
Soil Requirements : Wide
Plant Type : Succulent shrub
Foliage Color : Green
Flowering Season : n/a
Flower Color : n/a
Propagation : Cuttings
Human Hazards : Irritant; spiny
Common Uses : Rock gardens; shrub; foliage plant
Major Problems : None
Additional Notes : Has 3-angled stems with lighter green stripes between spiny ridges.

Family : Euphorbiaceae   **Zone** : 10B-11

Typical Height : 8 Ft.
Drought Tolerance : High
Nutritional Requirements : Low
Light Requirements : High
Leaf Type : Simple
Texture : Coarse
Flower Characteristics : Insignificant

Environmental Problems : None

Euphoria longan *(Photograph p. 160)*

Common Name(s) : Longan
Origin : India
Growth Rate : Medium
Salt Tolerance : Low
Soil Requirements : Wide
Plant Type : Evergreen tree
Foliage Color : Green
Flowering Season : Spring
Flower Color : White
Propagation : Seeds; air layers; grafting
Human Hazards : None
Common Uses : Edible fruit; shade tree
Major Problems : None
Additional Notes : Edible fruits. Desirable varieties are grafted or air-layered.
Cultivars
'KOHALA' is a popular cultivar.

Family : Sapindaceae   **Zone** : 10B-11

Typical Height : 35 Ft.
Drought Tolerance : Medium
Nutritional Requirements : Medium
Light Requirements : High
Leaf Type : Pinnately compound
Texture : Medium
Flower Characteristics : Insignificant

Environmental Problems : None

Euryops pectinatus

Common Name(s) : Silver Leaf Daisy; Golden Shrub Daisy
Origin : South Africa
Growth Rate : Medium
Salt Tolerance : Medium
Soil Requirements : Wide
Plant Type : Evergreen shrub
Foliage Color : Silver-green
Flowering Season : Summer
Flower Color : Yellow
Propagation : Seeds; cuttings
Human Hazards : None
Common Uses : Beds; flowering shrub
Major Problems : None
Additional Notes : Best adapted to Mediterranean type of climate.

Family : Compositae   **Zone** : 10A-11

Typical Height : 3 Ft.
Drought Tolerance : High
Nutritional Requirements : Low
Light Requirements : High
Leaf Type : Simple; pinnately lobed
Texture : Fine
Flower Characteristics : Showy

Environmental Problems : None

Euterpe edulis

Common Name(s) : Assai Palm
Origin : Brazil
Growth Rate : Fast
Salt Tolerance : Low
Soil Requirements : Acid
Plant Type : Palm
Foliage Color : Green
Flowering Season : Spring
Flower Color : White
Propagation : Seeds
Human Hazards : None
Common Uses : Multi-trunked tree; edible; palm
Major Problems : None
Additional Notes : A tall slender graceful multi-trunked palm. Palm heart is often eaten.

Family : Palmae   **Zone** : 11

Typical Height : 60 Ft.
Drought Tolerance : Medium
Nutritional Requirements : Medium
Light Requirements : High; medium
Leaf Type : Pinnately compound
Texture : Medium
Flower Characteristics : Insignificant

Environmental Problems : None

Evodia suaveolens var. ridleyi

Common Name(s) : Lacy Lady Aralia
Origin : Asia
Growth Rate : Fast
Salt Tolerance : Low
Soil Requirements : Wide
Plant Type : Evergreen shrub
Foliage Color : Green
Flowering Season : Summer
Flower Color : Yellow
Propagation : Cuttings
Human Hazards : None
Common Uses : Hedge; shrub
Major Problems : None
Additional Notes : Lacy light-green foliage; shear to maintain shape.

Family : Rutaceae   Zone : 10B-11

Typical Height : 6 Ft.
Drought Tolerance : Low
Nutritional Requirements : Medium
Light Requirements : High
Leaf Type : Simple
Texture : Fine
Flower Characteristics : Insignificant

Environmental Problems : None

Evolvulus glomeratus *(Photograph p. 213)*

Common Name(s) : Blue Daze
Origin : Tropical America
Growth Rate : Medium
Salt Tolerance : High
Soil Requirements : Wide
Plant Type : Herbaceous perennial
Foliage Color : Silver-green
Flowering Season : Year-round
Flower Color : Blue
Propagation : Cuttings
Human Hazards : None
Common Uses : Flowering groundcover
Major Problems : Fungal blight
Additional Notes : Develops disease problems if kept too wet.

Family : Convolvulaceae   Zone : 10B-11

Typical Height : .9 Ft.
Drought Tolerance : Medium
Nutritional Requirements : Medium
Light Requirements : Medium; high
Leaf Type : Simple
Texture : Fine
Flower Characteristics : Showy

Environmental Problems : None

Exostema caribaeum

Common Name(s) : Princewood
Origin : South Florida and West Indies
Growth Rate : Medium
Salt Tolerance : Medium
Soil Requirements : Wide
Plant Type : Evergreen tree or shrub
Foliage Color : Green
Flowering Season : Spring; summer
Flower Color : White
Propagation : Seeds
Human Hazards : None
Common Uses : Flowering shrub; small flowering tree
Major Problems : None
Additional Notes : Hard wood used for cabinetwork.

Family : Rubiaceae   Zone : 10B-11

Typical Height : 20 Ft.
Drought Tolerance : High
Nutritional Requirements : Medium
Light Requirements : High
Leaf Type : Simple
Texture : Medium
Flower Characteristics : Showy; fragrant

Environmental Problems : None

Fatsia japonica *(Photograph p. 179)*

Common Name(s) : Fatsia
Origin : Japan
Growth Rate : Medium
Salt Tolerance : Medium
Soil Requirements : Wide
Plant Type : Evergreen shrub
Foliage Color : Green; variegated
Flowering Season : Summer
Flower Color : White
Propagation : Cuttings; seeds
Human Hazards : None
Common Uses : Shrub; foliage plant
Major Problems : Scales
Additional Notes : Stiff upright growth habit.
Cultivars
'VARIEGATA' has white leaf margins.

Family : Araliaceae   Zone : 8-11

Typical Height : 6 Ft.
Drought Tolerance : Medium
Nutritional Requirements : Medium
Light Requirements : Medium
Leaf Type : Simple; palmately lobed
Texture : Coarse
Flower Characteristics : Insignificant

Environmental Problems : None

Feijoa sellowiana *(Photograph p. 178)*

Common Name(s) : Feijoa; Pineapple Guava
Origin : South America
Growth Rate : Medium
Salt Tolerance : Medium
Soil Requirements : Wide
Plant Type : Evergreen shrub
Foliage Color : Green
Flowering Season : Spring
Flower Color : White; red
Propagation : Seeds; air layers
Human Hazards : None
Common Uses : Hedge; flowering shrub; edible fruit
Major Problems : None
Additional Notes : Dependable, hardy broadleaved evergreen. Edible fruit and flowers.
Cultivars
Include: 'ANDRE', 'COOLIDGE', 'CHOICE', 'BESSON', and 'SUPERBA'.

Family : Myrtaceae   Zone : 9-11

Typical Height : 14 Ft.
Drought Tolerance : High
Nutritional Requirements : Low
Light Requirements : Medium; high
Leaf Type : Simple
Texture : Medium
Flower Characteristics : Showy

Environmental Problems : None

Festuca ovina var. glauca

Common Name(s) : Blue Fescue
Origin : Europe
Growth Rate : Medium
Salt Tolerance : High
Soil Requirements : Wide
Plant Type : Herbaceous perennial
Foliage Color : Blue-green
Flowering Season : Summer
Flower Color : Brown
Propagation : Division
Human Hazards : None
Common Uses : Groundcover; rock gardens
Major Problems : None
Additional Notes : Plant close together for a solid groundcover.

Family : Gramineae   Zone : 5-10B

Typical Height : 1 Ft.
Drought Tolerance : High
Nutritional Requirements : Low
Light Requirements : High
Leaf Type : Simple; linear
Texture : Fine
Flower Characteristics : Insignificant

Environmental Problems : None

Ficus altissima

Common Name(s) : Lofty Fig; Council Tree
Origin : Southeast Asia and Philippines
Growth Rate : Fast
Salt Tolerance : Medium
Soil Requirements : Wide
Plant Type : Evergreen tree
Foliage Color : Green
Flowering Season : Year-round
Flower Color : n/a
Propagation : Cuttings; air layering
Human Hazards : None
Common Uses : Shade tree
Major Problems : None
Additional Notes : A huge spreading tree with multiple trunks from aerial roots.

Family : Moraceae   Zone : 10B-11

Typical Height : 65 Ft.
Drought Tolerance : High
Nutritional Requirements : Medium
Light Requirements : High
Leaf Type : Simple
Texture : Coarse
Flower Characteristics : Insignificant

Environmental Problems : Invasive

Ficus aspera *(Photograph p. 160)*

Common Name(s) : Clown Fig
Origin : South Pacific Islands
Growth Rate : Medium
Salt Tolerance : Low
Soil Requirements : Wide
Plant Type : Evergreen tree
Foliage Color : Variegated
Flowering Season : n/a
Flower Color : n/a
Propagation : Cuttings; air layers
Human Hazards : None
Common Uses : Small tree
Major Problems : None
Additional Notes : Has bold, white-splashed foliage.

Family : Moraceae   Zone : 10B-11

Typical Height : 15 Ft.
Drought Tolerance : Medium
Nutritional Requirements : Medium
Light Requirements : Medium; high
Leaf Type : Simple
Texture : Coarse
Flower Characteristics : n/a

Environmental Problems : None

Ficus aurea

Common Name(s) : Strangler Fig
Origin : South Florida and West Indies
Growth Rate : Fast
Salt Tolerance : Medium
Soil Requirements : Wide
Plant Type : Evergreen tree
Foliage Color : Green
Flowering Season : n/a
Flower Color : n/a
Propagation : Seeds; air layers
Human Hazards : None
Common Uses : Shade tree
Major Problems : None
Additional Notes : This native ficus often begins its life as an epiphyte.

Family : Moraceae   **Zone** : 10B-11

Typical Height : 60 Ft.
Drought Tolerance : High
Nutritional Requirements : Low
Light Requirements : High
Leaf Type : Simple
Texture : Coarse
Flower Characteristics : Insignificant

Environmental Problems : Invasive

Ficus benghalensis *(Photograph p. 160)*

Common Name(s) : Banyan Tree
Origin : India to Malaya
Growth Rate : Fast
Salt Tolerance : Medium
Soil Requirements : Wide
Plant Type : Evergreen tree
Foliage Color : Green
Flowering Season : n/a
Flower Color : n/a
Propagation : Cuttings; air layers
Human Hazards : None
Common Uses : Shade tree
Major Problems : None
Additional Notes : This tree with invasive roots is too large for most home landscapes.

Family : Moraceae   **Zone** : 10B-11

Typical Height : 70 Ft.
Drought Tolerance : High
Nutritional Requirements : Low
Light Requirements : Medium; high
Leaf Type : Simple
Texture : Medium
Flower Characteristics : Insignificant

Environmental Problems : Invasive; messy

Ficus benjamina

Common Name(s) : Weeping Fig; Benjamin Fig
Origin : India, Southeast Asia
Growth Rate : Fast
Salt Tolerance : Medium
Soil Requirements : Wide
Plant Type : Evergreen tree
Foliage Color : Green
Flowering Season : n/a
Flower Color : n/a
Propagation : Cuttings; air layers
Human Hazards : None
Common Uses : Shade tree; hedge; foliage plant
Major Problems : None
Additional Notes : Aggressive root system; requires a large area or frequent pruning.
Cultivars
'VARIEGATA', 'JACQUELINE', 'WHITE PRINCESS', & 'SPEARMINT' have variegated foliage; 'NUDA' has longer, narrower leaves than the species; 'MINI' is a dwarf small-leaved variety; 'WINTERGREEN' is a low light, green-leaved variety.

Family : Moraceae   **Zone** : 10B-11

Typical Height : 45 Ft.
Drought Tolerance : High
Nutritional Requirements : Low
Light Requirements : Medium; high
Leaf Type : Simple
Texture : Medium
Flower Characteristics : Insignificant

Environmental Problems : Invasive

Ficus carica *(Photograph p. 160)*

Common Name(s) : Edible Fig
Origin : Asia Minor
Growth Rate : Medium
Salt Tolerance : Medium
Soil Requirements : Wide
Plant Type : Deciduous tree
Foliage Color : Green
Flowering Season : Spring; summer
Flower Color : n/a
Propagation : Cuttings; air layers
Human Hazards : Irritant
Common Uses : Edible fruit
Major Problems : Nematodes
Additional Notes : Should be grafted on nematode-resistant rootstock.
Cultivars
'CELESTE', 'BROWN TURKEY', and 'MAGNOLIA' are best adapted for Florida.

Family : Moraceae   **Zone** : 6-10B

Typical Height : 15 Ft.
Drought Tolerance : Medium
Nutritional Requirements : Medium
Light Requirements : High
Leaf Type : Simple; palmately lobed
Texture : Coarse
Flower Characteristics : Insignificant

Environmental Problems : None

Ficus citrifolia

Family : Moraceae   Zone : 10B-11

Common Name(s) : Shortleaf Fig
Origin : South Florida and West Indies
Growth Rate : Fast
Salt Tolerance : Medium
Soil Requirements : Wide
Plant Type : Evergreen tree
Foliage Color : Green
Flowering Season : n/a
Flower Color : n/a
Propagation : Seeds; air layers
Human Hazards : None
Common Uses : Shade tree
Major Problems : None
Additional Notes : A south Florida native fig without aerial roots.

Typical Height : 45 Ft.
Drought Tolerance : High
Nutritional Requirements : Low
Light Requirements : High
Leaf Type : Simple
Texture : Medium
Flower Characteristics : Insignificant

Environmental Problems : None

Ficus elastica

Family : Moraceae   Zone : 10B-11

Common Name(s) : Indian Rubber Tree
Origin : Tropical Asia
Growth Rate : Medium
Salt Tolerance : Medium
Soil Requirements : Wide
Plant Type : Evergreen tree
Foliage Color : Green; variegated;purple
Flowering Season : n/a
Flower Color : n/a
Propagation : Air layers
Human Hazards : None
Common Uses : Shade tree; foliage plant
Major Problems : None
Additional Notes : Large leaves can be messy in lawns.
Cultivars

Typical Height : 50 Ft.
Drought Tolerance : High
Nutritional Requirements : Medium
Light Requirements : Medium; high
Leaf Type : Simple
Texture : Coarse
Flower Characteristics : Insignificant

Environmental Problems : Invasive; messy

'DECORA' has large greenish-red leaves; 'ROBUSTA' has slightly smaller and redder leaves than 'DECORA';
'BURGUNDY' has deep purplish leaves; 'DOESCHERI' has narrower variegated foliage; 'HONDURAS' has dark
blotches on light green leaves; 'ASAHI' has variegated foliage with pink shading.

Ficus lyrata *(Photograph p. 161)*

Family : Moraceae   Zone : 10B-11

Common Name(s) : Fiddleleaf Fig
Origin : Tropical Africa
Growth Rate : Medium
Salt Tolerance : Medium
Soil Requirements : Wide
Plant Type : Evergreen tree
Foliage Color : Green
Flowering Season : n/a
Flower Color : n/a
Propagation : Cuttings; air layers
Human Hazards : None
Common Uses : Shade tree; foliage plant
Major Problems : None
Additional Notes : One of the best figs for landscaping in warm areas. Large, messy leaves.
Cultivars

Typical Height : 40 Ft.
Drought Tolerance : High
Nutritional Requirements : Medium
Light Requirements : High; medium
Leaf Type : Simple
Texture : Coarse
Flower Characteristics : Insignificant

Environmental Problems : Messy

'COMPACTA' has slightly smaller leaves and is more compact.

Ficus montana

Family : Moraceae   Zone : 10B-11

Common Name(s) : Oakleaf Fig
Origin : Asia
Growth Rate : Medium
Salt Tolerance : Low
Soil Requirements : Wide
Plant Type : Evergreen shrub
Foliage Color : Green
Flowering Season : n/a
Flower Color : n/a
Propagation : Cuttings
Human Hazards : None
Common Uses : Groundcover
Major Problems : None
Additional Notes : An attractive nonaggressive oak-leaved fig.

Typical Height : 1 Ft.
Drought Tolerance : Medium
Nutritional Requirements : Medium
Light Requirements : Medium; low
Leaf Type : Simple; pinnately lobed
Texture : Medium
Flower Characteristics : n/a

Environmental Problems : None

Ficus nota

Common Name(s) : Nota Fig
Origin : Philippines and Borneo
Growth Rate : Medium
Salt Tolerance : Medium
Soil Requirements : Wide
Plant Type : Evergreen tree
Foliage Color : Green
Flowering Season : n/a
Flower Color : n/a
Propagation : Cuttings; air layers
Human Hazards : None
Common Uses : Tree
Major Problems : None

Family : Moraceae   **Zone** : 10B-11

Typical Height : 25 Ft.
Drought Tolerance : Medium
Nutritional Requirements : Low
Light Requirements : Medium; high
Leaf Type : Simple
Texture : Coarse
Flower Characteristics : Insignificant

Environmental Problems : None

Additional Notes : Has large leaves with assymetrical bases. Figs borne on large branches.

Ficus perforata

Common Name(s) : West Indian Laurel
Origin : Caribbean Region
Growth Rate : Medium
Salt Tolerance : Medium
Soil Requirements : Wide
Plant Type : Evergreen tree
Foliage Color : Green
Flowering Season : n/a
Flower Color : n/a
Propagation : Cuttings; air layers
Human Hazards : None
Common Uses : Small tree
Major Problems : None

Family : Moraceae   **Zone** : 10B-11

Typical Height : 35 Ft.
Drought Tolerance : High
Nutritional Requirements : Low
Light Requirements : High
Leaf Type : Simple
Texture : Fine
Flower Characteristics : Insignificant

Environmental Problems : None

Additional Notes : A small, less aggressive fig.

Ficus pumila *(Photograph p. 211)*

Common Name(s) : Creeping Fig
Origin : Japan, China, and Australia
Growth Rate : Fast
Salt Tolerance : Medium
Soil Requirements : Wide
Plant Type : Evergreen vine
Foliage Color : Green; variegated
Flowering Season : n/a
Flower Color : n/a
Propagation : Cuttings
Human Hazards : Irritant
Common Uses : Hanging baskets; vine; foliage plant
Major Problems : None

Family : Moraceae   **Zone** : 10A-11

Typical Height : Not applicable
Drought Tolerance : High
Nutritional Requirements : Low
Light Requirements : Medium; high
Leaf Type : Simple
Texture : Fine
Flower Characteristics : Insignificant

Environmental Problems : Invasive

Additional Notes : Aggressively attaches to masonry, invasive. Adult foliage larger.
Cultivars
'VARIEGATA' has variegated foliage; 'QUERCIFOLIA' has oak-shaped leaves.

Ficus religiosa

Common Name(s) : Sacred Fig; Bo Tree
Origin : India to Southeast Asia
Growth Rate : Fast
Salt Tolerance : Medium
Soil Requirements : Wide
Plant Type : Evergreen tree
Foliage Color : Green
Flowering Season : n/a
Flower Color : n/a
Propagation : Cuttings; air layering
Human Hazards : None
Common Uses : Shade tree
Major Problems : None

Family : Moraceae   **Zone** : 10B-11

Typical Height : 60 Ft.
Drought Tolerance : High
Nutritional Requirements : Low
Light Requirements : High
Leaf Type : Simple
Texture : Medium
Flower Characteristics : Insignificant

Environmental Problems : Invasive

Additional Notes : This large fig has few if any aerial roots.

Ficus retusa *(Photograph p. 161)*

Common Name(s) : Indian Laurel
Origin : India
Growth Rate : Fast
Salt Tolerance : Medium
Soil Requirements : Wide
Plant Type : Evergreen tree
Foliage Color : Green; variegated
Flowering Season : n/a
Flower Color : n/a
Propagation : Cuttings; air layers
Human Hazards : None
Common Uses : Shade tree; foliage plant; hedge
Major Problems : Thrips
Additional Notes : Can be grown as a tree or hedge.
Cultivars
'NITIDA' is similar to species and is popular as a hedge; 'GREEN GEM' has larger leaves than species and is reportedly more resistant to thrips; 'VARIEGATA' has variegated foliage;

Family : Moraceae   **Zone** : 10A-11

Typical Height : 50 Ft.
Drought Tolerance : High
Nutritional Requirements : Medium
Light Requirements : Medium; high
Leaf Type : Simple
Texture : Medium
Flower Characteristics : Insignificant

Environmental Problems : Invasive

Ficus rubiginosa *(Photograph p. 160)*

Common Name(s) : Rusty Fig
Origin : Australia
Growth Rate : Slow
Salt Tolerance : Medium
Soil Requirements : Wide
Plant Type : Evergreen tree
Foliage Color : Green
Flowering Season : n/a
Flower Color : n/a
Propagation : Air layers
Human Hazards : None
Common Uses : Shade tree
Major Problems : None
Additional Notes : Lower surface of leaf is rusty pubescent.
Cultivars
'VARIEGATA' has variegated foliage.

Family : Moraceae   **Zone** : 10B-11

Typical Height : 35 Ft.
Drought Tolerance : Medium
Nutritional Requirements : Medium
Light Requirements : High
Leaf Type : Simple
Texture : Medium
Flower Characteristics : Insignificant

Environmental Problems : None

Ficus triangularis

Common Name(s) : Triangle Fig
Origin : Tropical Africa
Growth Rate : Medium
Salt Tolerance : Medium
Soil Requirements : Wide
Plant Type : Evergreen tree
Foliage Color : Green; variegated
Flowering Season : n/a
Flower Color : n/a
Propagation : Cuttings; air layers
Human Hazards : None
Common Uses : Small tree; foliage plant
Major Problems : None
Additional Notes : A small fig with triangular-shaped leaves. Figs light green.
Cultivars
'VARIEGATA' has variegated foliage.

Family : Moraceae   **Zone** : 10B-11

Typical Height : 10 Ft.
Drought Tolerance : Medium
Nutritional Requirements : Low
Light Requirements : Medium; high
Leaf Type : Simple
Texture : Medium
Flower Characteristics : Insignificant

Environmental Problems : None

Ficus 'Green Island'

Common Name(s) : Green Island Fig
Origin : n/a
Growth Rate : Slow
Salt Tolerance : Medium
Soil Requirements : Wide
Plant Type : Evergreen shrub
Foliage Color : Green
Flowering Season : n/a
Flower Color : n/a
Propagation : Cuttings; air layering
Human Hazards : None
Common Uses : Hedge; shrub;
Major Problems : None
Additional Notes : A slow growing, compact cultivar of ficus with round to oval leaves.

Family : Moraceae   **Zone** : 10B-11

Typical Height : 4 Ft.
Drought Tolerance : Medium
Nutritional Requirements : Medium
Light Requirements : Medium; high
Leaf Type : Simple
Texture : Medium
Flower Characteristics : Insignificant

Environmental Problems : None

Firmiana simplex

Common Name(s) : Chinese Parasol Tree
Origin : Eastern Asia
Growth Rate : Fast
Salt Tolerance : Low
Soil Requirements : Wide
Plant Type : Deciduous tree
Foliage Color : Green
Flowering Season : Summer
Flower Color : Green
Propagation : Seeds
Human Hazards : None
Common Uses : Shade tree
Major Problems : None

Family : Sterculiaceae   **Zone** : 8-10B

Typical Height : 40 Ft.
Drought Tolerance : Medium
Nutritional Requirements : Medium
Light Requirements : Medium
Leaf Type : Simple; palmately lobed
Texture : Coarse
Flower Characteristics : Insignificant

Environmental Problems : Weedy; messy

Additional Notes : Messy fruit and leaf litter; brittle; leafless for long period.

Fittonia verschaffeltii *(Photograph p. 213)*

Common Name(s) : Nerve Plant
Origin : Colombia and Peru
Growth Rate : Medium
Salt Tolerance : Low
Soil Requirements : Acid
Plant Type : Herbaceous perennial
Foliage Color : Variegated; pink & green
Flowering Season : Year-round
Flower Color : Yellow-green
Propagation : Cuttings
Human Hazards : None
Common Uses : Beds; specimen plant; groundcover; foliage plant; hanging baskets
Major Problems : Fungal blight

Family : Acanthaceae   **Zone** : 11

Typical Height : .5 Ft.
Drought Tolerance : Low
Nutritional Requirements : Medium
Light Requirements : Low
Leaf Type : Simple
Texture : Medium
Flower Characteristics : Insignificant

Environmental Problems : None

Additional Notes : Grown for attractive red or white veined foliage.
Cultivars
Var. argyroneura has white veins; var. verschafeltii has pink veins; dwarf forms of both varieties exist.

Flacourtia indica

Common Name(s) : Governor's Plum
Origin : Madagascar and Southern Asia
Growth Rate : Medium
Salt Tolerance : Low
Soil Requirements : Wide
Plant Type : Evergreen shrub or tree
Foliage Color : Green
Flowering Season : Spring; summer; fall
Flower Color : Yellow
Propagation : Seeds; cuttings; grafting
Human Hazards : Spiny
Common Uses : Shrub; hedge; small tree; edible fruit
Major Problems : None

Family : Flacourtiaceae   **Zone** : 10B-11

Typical Height : 20 Ft.
Drought Tolerance : Medium
Nutritional Requirements : Medium
Light Requirements : High
Leaf Type : Simple
Texture : Medium
Flower Characteristics : Insignificant

Environmental Problems : None

Additional Notes : Edible fruit eaten fresh or preserved.

Flaveria linearis

Common Name(s) : Yellowtop
Origin : South Florida, West Indies & Mexico
Growth Rate : Medium
Salt Tolerance : High
Soil Requirements : Wide
Plant Type : Herbaceous perennial
Foliage Color : Green
Flowering Season : Year-round
Flower Color : Yellow
Propagation : Seeds
Human Hazards : None
Common Uses : Specimen plant
Major Problems : None

Family : Compositae   **Zone** : 10B-11

Typical Height : 1.5 Ft.
Drought Tolerance : Medium
Nutritional Requirements : Low
Light Requirements : High
Leaf Type : Simple
Texture : Fine
Flower Characteristics : Showy

Environmental Problems : None

Additional Notes : Grows in the salt marshes in southern Florida.

Forestiera segregata

Common Name(s) : Florida Privet; Wild Olive
Origin : Southeastern United States
Growth Rate : Medium
Salt Tolerance : High
Soil Requirements : Wide
Plant Type : Evergreen shrub
Foliage Color : Green
Flowering Season : Spring
Flower Color : Green
Propagation : Seeds; cuttings
Human Hazards : None
Common Uses : Hedge; shrub
Major Problems : None

Family : Oleaceae   **Zone** : 8-10B

Typical Height : 10 Ft.
Drought Tolerance : High
Nutritional Requirements : Low
Light Requirements : High
Leaf Type : Simple
Texture : Medium
Flower Characteristics : Insignificant

Environmental Problems : None

Additional Notes : Native hedge plant with good salt, drought and alkali tolerance.

Forestiera segregata var. pinetorum

Common Name(s) : Pineland Privet
Origin : South Florida
Growth Rate : Medium
Salt Tolerance : Medium
Soil Requirements : Wide
Plant Type : Evergreen shrub
Foliage Color : Gray-green
Flowering Season : Spring
Flower Color : Green
Propagation : Seeds; cuttings
Human Hazards : None
Common Uses : Hedge; shrub
Major Problems : None

Family : Oleaceae   **Zone** : 9-10B

Typical Height : 5 Ft.
Drought Tolerance : High
Nutritional Requirements : Low
Light Requirements : High
Leaf Type : Simple
Texture : Medium
Flower Characteristics : Insignificant

Environmental Problems : None

Additional Notes : Similar to F. segregata , but has smaller grayer leaves. Compact shape.

Fortunella japonica

Common Name(s) : Kumquat
Origin : China
Growth Rate : Medium
Salt Tolerance : Medium
Soil Requirements : Wide
Plant Type : Evergreen shrub
Foliage Color : Green
Flowering Season : Winter; spring
Flower Color : White
Propagation : Grafting; air layering
Human Hazards : Spiny
Common Uses : Shrub; edible fruit
Major Problems : Scales; sooty mold

Family : Rutaceae   **Zone** : 9-11

Typical Height : 10 Ft.
Drought Tolerance : Medium
Nutritional Requirements : High
Light Requirements : High
Leaf Type : Simple
Texture : Medium
Flower Characteristics : Showy; fragrant

Environmental Problems : None

Additional Notes : Attractive edible orange fruit used in preserves.

Fortunella margarita

Common Name(s) : Oval Kumquat; Nagami Kumquat
Origin : China
Growth Rate : Medium
Salt Tolerance : Medium
Soil Requirements : Wide
Plant Type : Evergreen shrub
Foliage Color : Green
Flowering Season : Winter; spring
Flower Color : White
Propagation : Grafting; air layering
Human Hazards : None
Common Uses : Shrub; edible fruit
Major Problems : Scales; sooty mold

Family : Rutaceae   **Zone** : 9-11

Typical Height : 14 Ft.
Drought Tolerance : High
Nutritional Requirements : High
Light Requirements : High
Leaf Type : Simple
Texture : Medium
Flower Characteristics : Showy; fragrant

Environmental Problems : None

Additional Notes : Similar to F. japonica . Fruit used in preserves.

Fraxinus caroliniana

Common Name(s) : Water Ash; Pop Ash
Origin : Southeastern United States
Growth Rate : Fast
Salt Tolerance : Low
Soil Requirements : Wide
Plant Type : Deciduous tree
Foliage Color : Green
Flowering Season : Spring
Flower Color : Green
Propagation : Seeds
Human Hazards : None
Common Uses : Shade tree
Major Problems : None
Additional Notes : Best for wet sites in southeastern United States.

Family : Oleaceae   **Zone** : 7-10A

Typical Height : 50 Ft.
Drought Tolerance : Low
Nutritional Requirements : Low
Light Requirements : High
Leaf Type : Pinnately compound
Texture : Medium
Flower Characteristics : Insignificant

Environmental Problems : None

Fraxinus pennsylvanica

Common Name(s) : Green Ash
Origin : Eastern North America
Growth Rate : Fast
Salt Tolerance : Low
Soil Requirements : Wide
Plant Type : Deciduous tree
Foliage Color : Green
Flowering Season : Spring
Flower Color : Green
Propagation : Seeds; grafting; budding
Human Hazards : None
Common Uses : Shade tree
Major Problems : None
Additional Notes : A widely adaptable species with some seedless cultivars available.
Cultivars
'MARSHALL'S SEEDLESS' and 'SUMMIT' are improved male seedless cultivars.

Family : Oleaceae   **Zone** : 2-9

Typical Height : 50 Ft.
Drought Tolerance : Medium
Nutritional Requirements : Medium
Light Requirements : High
Leaf Type : Pinnately compound
Texture : Medium
Flower Characteristics : Insignificant

Environmental Problems : None

Gaillardia pulchella *(Photograph p. 214)*

Common Name(s) : Blanket Flower; Gaillardia
Origin : Southern United States
Growth Rate : Medium
Salt Tolerance : High
Soil Requirements : Wide
Plant Type : Herbaceous perennial
Foliage Color : Green
Flowering Season : Year-round
Flower Color : Yellow & red; red; yellow
Propagation : Seeds; cuttings
Human Hazards : None
Common Uses : Beds; flowering perennial
Major Problems : None
Additional Notes : Excellent for hot, dry windy sites. Does well in urns or other containers.
Cultivars
G. X grandiflora is a hybrid of this species and G. aristata from which many cultivars have been selected.

Family : Compositae   **Zone** : 3-11

Typical Height : 1.5 Ft.
Drought Tolerance : High
Nutritional Requirements : Low
Light Requirements : High
Leaf Type : Simple
Texture : Medium
Flower Characteristics : Showy

Environmental Problems : None

Galphimia glauca *(Photograph p. 179)*

Common Name(s) : Shower-of-gold
Origin : Mexico and Central America
Growth Rate : Medium
Salt Tolerance : Medium
Soil Requirements : Wide
Plant Type : Evergreen shrub
Foliage Color : Green
Flowering Season : Year-round
Flower Color : Yellow
Propagation : Seeds; cuttings
Human Hazards : None
Common Uses : Flowering shrub; hedge
Major Problems : None
Additional Notes : A compact, flowering shrub.

Family : Malpighiaceae   **Zone** : 10A-11

Typical Height : 8 Ft.
Drought Tolerance : Medium
Nutritional Requirements : Medium
Light Requirements : High
Leaf Type : Simple
Texture : Medium
Flower Characteristics : Showy

Environmental Problems : None

Galphimia gracilis

Common Name(s) : Thryallis
Origin : Mexico to Peru
Growth Rate : Medium
Salt Tolerance : Medium
Soil Requirements : Wide
Plant Type : Evergreen shrub
Foliage Color : Green
Flowering Season : Summer; fall
Flower Color : Yellow
Propagation : Seeds; cuttings
Human Hazards : None
Common Uses : Shrub
Major Problems : None
Additional Notes : Branches are brittle.

Family : Malpighiaceae   **Zone** : 10B-11

Typical Height : 5 Ft.
Drought Tolerance : Medium
Nutritional Requirements : Medium
Light Requirements : Medium; high
Leaf Type : Simple
Texture : Medium
Flower Characteristics : Showy

Environmental Problems : Weak

Gamolepis chrysanthemoides

Common Name(s) : African Daisy
Origin : Africa
Growth Rate : Medium
Salt Tolerance : Low
Soil Requirements : Wide
Plant Type : Evergreen shrub
Foliage Color : Green
Flowering Season : Year-round
Flower Color : Yellow
Propagation : Seeds
Human Hazards : None
Common Uses : Flowering shrub
Major Problems : None
Additional Notes : Becomes straggly when old.

Family : Compositae   **Zone** : 10B-11

Typical Height : 3 Ft.
Drought Tolerance : Medium
Nutritional Requirements : Medium
Light Requirements : High
Leaf Type : Simple; pinnately lobed
Texture : Fine
Flower Characteristics : Showy

Environmental Problems : None

Garberia fruticosa

Common Name(s) : Garberia
Origin : Florida
Growth Rate : Medium
Salt Tolerance : Medium
Soil Requirements : Acid
Plant Type : Evergreen shrub
Foliage Color : Green
Flowering Season : Summer; fall
Flower Color : Pink
Propagation : Seeds; cuttings
Human Hazards : None
Common Uses : Flowering shrub
Major Problems : None
Additional Notes : Attractive, fall-flowering native shrub.

Family : Compositae   **Zone** : 9-10A

Typical Height : 6 Ft.
Drought Tolerance : High
Nutritional Requirements : Low
Light Requirements : High
Leaf Type : Simple
Texture : Medium
Flower Characteristics : Showy

Environmental Problems : None

Gardenia jasminoides

Common Name(s) : Cape Jasmine
Origin : China
Growth Rate : Slow
Salt Tolerance : Low
Soil Requirements : Acid
Plant Type : Evergreen shrub
Foliage Color : Green; variegated
Flowering Season : Spring
Flower Color : White
Propagation : Cuttings; grafting
Human Hazards : None
Common Uses : Foliage plant; flowering shrub; flowering pot plant
Major Problems : Nematodes; iron deficiency; whiteflies; sooty mold
Additional Notes : Use only grafted plants.
Cultivars
'MYSTERY' is medium-sized and has white double flowers; 'AUGUST BEAUTY' has dense foliage with large double flowers; 'VEITCHII' has smaller flowers and is used in the florist trade; 'RADICANS' is a miniature variety with small flowers; 'RADICANS VARIEGATA' is a variegated version of 'RADICANS'; 'PROSTRATA' is a prostrate form.

Family : Rubiaceae   **Zone** : 8-10A

Typical Height : 4 Ft.
Drought Tolerance : Low
Nutritional Requirements : High
Light Requirements : High
Leaf Type : Simple
Texture : Medium
Flower Characteristics : Showy; fragrant

Environmental Problems : None

Gardenia thunbergia

Common Name(s) : Thunbergia Gardenia
Origin : South Africa
Growth Rate : Medium
Salt Tolerance : Low
Soil Requirements : Acid
Plant Type : Evergreen shrub
Foliage Color : Green
Flowering Season : Spring
Flower Color : White
Propagation : Cuttings
Human Hazards : None
Common Uses : Flowering shrub
Major Problems : None

Family : Rutaceae   **Zone** : 10A-11

Typical Height : 10 Ft.
Drought Tolerance : High
Nutritional Requirements : Medium
Light Requirements : High
Leaf Type : Simple
Texture : Medium
Flower Characteristics : Showy; fragrant

Environmental Problems : None

Additional Notes : Often used as a nematode-resistant rootstock for G. jasminoides .

Gaussia maya

Common Name(s) : Maya Palm
Origin : Guatemala
Growth Rate : Medium
Salt Tolerance : n/a
Soil Requirements : Wide
Plant Type : Palm
Foliage Color : Green
Flowering Season : Spring
Flower Color : White
Propagation : Seeds
Human Hazards : None
Common Uses : Palm
Major Problems : None

Family : Palmae   **Zone** : 10B-11

Typical Height : 30 Ft.
Drought Tolerance : High
Nutritional Requirements : Medium
Light Requirements : Medium; high
Leaf Type : Pinnately compound
Texture : Medium
Flower Characteristics : Insignificant

Environmental Problems : None

Additional Notes : This slender palm holds few leaves and may blow over in storms.

Gaylussacia dumosa

Common Name(s) : Huckleberry; Dwarf Huckleberry
Origin : Southeastern United States
Growth Rate : Slow
Salt Tolerance : Low
Soil Requirements : Acid
Plant Type : Evergreen shrub
Foliage Color : Green
Flowering Season : Winter; spring
Flower Color : White
Propagation : Seeds; cuttings
Human Hazards : None
Common Uses : Shrub; edible fruit
Major Problems : None

Family : Ericaceae   **Zone** : 7-9

Typical Height : 6 Ft.
Drought Tolerance : High
Nutritional Requirements : Medium
Light Requirements : Medium
Leaf Type : Simple
Texture : Fine
Flower Characteristics : Insignificant

Environmental Problems : None

Additional Notes : Has attractive, edible black fruits in late spring.

Gazania spp.

Common Name(s) : Gazania
Origin : South Africa
Growth Rate : Medium
Salt Tolerance : Medium
Soil Requirements : Wide
Plant Type : Herbaceous perennial
Foliage Color : Green
Flowering Season : Year-round
Flower Color : Orange; pink; brown & red; yellow
Propagation : Seeds; division; cuttings
Human Hazards : None
Common Uses : Beds; borders
Major Problems : None

Family : Compositae   **Zone** : 8-10B

Typical Height : 1 Ft.
Drought Tolerance : High
Nutritional Requirements : Medium
Light Requirements : High
Leaf Type : Simple
Texture : Medium
Flower Characteristics : Showy

Environmental Problems : None

Additional Notes : Extremely tolerant of dry, high light situations; many cultivars exist.

Gelsemium sempervirens

Common Name(s) : Carolina Yellow Jasmine
Origin : Southeastern North America
Growth Rate : Medium
Salt Tolerance : Low
Soil Requirements : Wide
Plant Type : Evergreen vine
Foliage Color : Green
Flowering Season : Winter; spring
Flower Color : Yellow
Propagation : Cuttings; seeds
Human Hazards : Poisonous
Common Uses : Flowering vine; flowering groundcover
Major Problems : None
Additional Notes : A non-aggressive vine; all parts of plant are poisonous.

Family : Loganiaceae   Zone : 7-9

Typical Height : Not applicable
Drought Tolerance : Medium
Nutritional Requirements : Medium
Light Requirements : Medium; high
Leaf Type : Simple
Texture : Medium
Flower Characteristics : Showy; fragrant

Environmental Problems : None

Gerbera jamesonii

Common Name(s) : Gerbera Daisy
Origin : South Africa
Growth Rate : Medium
Salt Tolerance : Low
Soil Requirements : Wide
Plant Type : Herbaceous perennial
Foliage Color : Green
Flowering Season : Winter; spring
Flower Color : Orange; pink; red; white yellow
Propagation : Tissue culture; seeds; cuttings
Human Hazards : None
Common Uses : Beds; cut flowers; flowering pot plant
Major Problems : None
Additional Notes : Many hybrid cultivars exist. Sometimes treated as an annual.

Family : Compositae   Zone : 8-10B

Typical Height : 1.5 Ft.
Drought Tolerance : Medium
Nutritional Requirements : Medium
Light Requirements : Medium; high
Leaf Type : Simple
Texture : Coarse
Flower Characteristics : Showy

Environmental Problems : None

Ginkgo biloba

Common Name(s) : Maidenhair Tree
Origin : Eastern China
Growth Rate : Slow
Salt Tolerance : Low
Soil Requirements : Wide
Plant Type : Deciduous tree
Foliage Color : Green
Flowering Season : Spring
Flower Color : Brown
Propagation : Seeds; cuttings
Human Hazards : Irritant
Common Uses : Shade tree
Major Problems : None
Additional Notes : Pest and disease free; pollution tolerant; choose male clones only.
Cultivars
'AUTUMN GOLD' is a non-fruiting, upright form with golden fall color; 'PENDULA' is a weeping form;
'PRINCETON SENTRY' is a narrow, columnar male cultivar.

Family : Ginkgoaceae   Zone : 4-9

Typical Height : 70 Ft.
Drought Tolerance : Medium
Nutritional Requirements : Medium
Light Requirements : High
Leaf Type : Simple; two-lobed
Texture : Medium
Flower Characteristics : Insignificant

Environmental Problems : None

Gladiolus spp.

Common Name(s) : Gladiolus
Origin : Africa and Southern Europe; Hybrid
Growth Rate : Medium
Salt Tolerance : Low
Soil Requirements : Wide
Plant Type : Herbaceous perennial
Foliage Color : Green
Flowering Season : Summer; spring
Flower Color : Yellow; red; pink; orange; white; green
Propagation : Division
Human Hazards : None
Common Uses : Beds; borders; cut flowers
Major Problems : Nematodes; thrips
Additional Notes : Lift or protect in north.
Cultivars
Many cultivars exist.

Family : Iridaceae   Zone : 8-10B

Typical Height : 3 Ft.
Drought Tolerance : Medium
Nutritional Requirements : Medium
Light Requirements : High
Leaf Type : Simple; linear
Texture : Coarse
Flower Characteristics : Showy; fragrant

Environmental Problems : None

Gleditsia triacanthos var. inermis

Common Name(s) : Thornless Honey Locust
Origin : Eastern United States
Growth Rate : Fast
Salt Tolerance : Medium
Soil Requirements : Wide
Plant Type : Deciduous tree
Foliage Color : Green
Flowering Season : Spring
Flower Color : Orange
Propagation : Seeds; budding
Human Hazards : None
Common Uses : Shade tree
Major Problems : None

Family : Leguminosae   **Zone** : 3-9

Typical Height : 50 Ft.
Drought Tolerance : High
Nutritional Requirements : Medium
Light Requirements : High
Leaf Type : Pinnately compound
Texture : Fine
Flower Characteristics : Inconspicuous

Environmental Problems : None

Additional Notes : A spineless variety; very tolerant of city conditions.
Cultivars
'SUNBURST' has yellow-green new leaves; 'SHADEMASTER' is a vigorous upright form; 'SKYLINE' has a pyramidal form and upright branches; 'MORAINE' is broad in form and is both thornless and fruitless; 'NANA' is a slow-growing , narrow, upright cultivar; 'MAJESTIC' is a spreading, but upright form.

Globba atrosanguinea

Common Name(s) : Globba
Origin : Borneo
Growth Rate : Medium
Salt Tolerance : n/a
Soil Requirements : Wide
Plant Type : Herbaceous perennial
Foliage Color : Green
Flowering Season : Spring
Flower Color : Red & yellow
Propagation : Division
Human Hazards : None
Common Uses : Specimen plant
Major Problems : None

Family : Zingiberaceae   **Zone** : 10B-11

Typical Height : 3 Ft.
Drought Tolerance : Medium
Nutritional Requirements : Medium
Light Requirements : Medium
Leaf Type : Simple
Texture : Medium
Flower Characteristics : Showy

Environmental Problems : None

Additional Notes : Similar to G. winitti , but with red and yellow flowers.

Globba winitti

Common Name(s) : Globba
Origin : Thailand
Growth Rate : Medium
Salt Tolerance : n/a
Soil Requirements : Wide
Plant Type : Herbaceous perennial
Foliage Color : Green
Flowering Season : Spring
Flower Color : Lavender & yellow
Propagation : Division
Human Hazards : None
Common Uses : Specimen plant
Major Problems : None

Family : Zingiberaceae   **Zone** : 10B-11

Typical Height : 2 Ft.
Drought Tolerance : Medium
Nutritional Requirements : Medium
Light Requirements : Medium
Leaf Type : Simple
Texture : Medium
Flower Characteristics : Showy

Environmental Problems : None

Additional Notes : Has very fine-textured flowers, with long yellow stamens.

Gloriosa rothschildiana *(Photograph p. 211)*

Common Name(s) : Rothschild Gloriosa Lily
Origin : Tropical Africa
Growth Rate : Fast
Salt Tolerance : Low
Soil Requirements : Wide
Plant Type : Perennial vine
Foliage Color : Green
Flowering Season : Spring; summer; fall
Flower Color : Yellow & red
Propagation : Division; seeds
Human Hazards : Poisonous
Common Uses : Flowering vine
Major Problems : Tuber rot

Family : Liliaceae   **Zone** : 8-10B

Typical Height : 5 Ft.
Drought Tolerance : Medium
Nutritional Requirements : Medium
Light Requirements : Medium; high
Leaf Type : Simple
Texture : Medium
Flower Characteristics : Showy

Environmental Problems : None

Additional Notes : All parts of plant are poisonous; tubers rot in wet soil when dormant.

Gloriosa superba

Common Name(s) : Malabar Glory Lily
Origin : Tropical Africa
Growth Rate : Fast
Salt Tolerance : Low
Soil Requirements : Wide
Plant Type : Perennial vine
Foliage Color : Green
Flowering Season : Spring; summer; fall
Flower Color : Yellow & red
Propagation : Seeds; division
Human Hazards : Poisonous
Common Uses : Flowering vine
Major Problems : None

Family : Liliaceae   **Zone** : 8-10B

Typical Height : 5 Ft.
Drought Tolerance : Medium
Nutritional Requirements : Medium
Light Requirements : High; medium
Leaf Type : Simple
Texture : Medium
Flower Characteristics : Showy

Environmental Problems : None

Additional Notes : All parts poisonous; flowers age yellow to red; provide support to climb.

Gloxinia sylvatica *(Photograph p. 214)*

Common Name(s) : Bolivian Sunset
Origin : Peru and Bolivia
Growth Rate : Medium
Salt Tolerance : Low
Soil Requirements : Wide
Plant Type : Herbaceous perennial
Foliage Color : Green
Flowering Season : Winter
Flower Color : Orange-red
Propagation : Division; cuttings
Human Hazards : None
Common Uses : Groundcover; beds
Major Problems : None

Family : Gesneriaceae   **Zone** : 10B-11

Typical Height : 1 Ft.
Drought Tolerance : Low
Nutritional Requirements : Medium
Light Requirements : Medium
Leaf Type : Simple
Texture : Medium
Flower Characteristics : Showy

Environmental Problems : None

Additional Notes : This very showy winter flowering plant tends to go dormant in the spring.

Gordonia lasianthus *(Photograph p. 161)*

Common Name(s) : Loblolly Bay
Origin : Southeastern United States
Growth Rate : Medium
Salt Tolerance : Low
Soil Requirements : Acid
Plant Type : Evergreen tree
Foliage Color : Green
Flowering Season : Summer; fall
Flower Color : White
Propagation : Seeds
Human Hazards : None
Common Uses : Flowering tree
Major Problems : Borers

Family : Theaceae   **Zone** : 8-10A

Typical Height : 35 Ft.
Drought Tolerance : Low
Nutritional Requirements : Medium
Light Requirements : High
Leaf Type : Simple
Texture : Medium
Flower Characteristics : Showy; fragrant

Environmental Problems : None

Additional Notes : A good native for wet areas in southeastern United States.

Gossypium hirsutum

Common Name(s) : Wild Cotton
Origin : Florida and Caribbean Region
Growth Rate : Fast
Salt Tolerance : High
Soil Requirements : Wide
Plant Type : Evergreen shrub
Foliage Color : Green
Flowering Season : Spring; summer
Flower Color : White
Propagation : Seeds
Human Hazards : Poisonous
Common Uses : Flowering shrub
Major Problems : None

Family : Malvaceae   **Zone** : 10A-11

Typical Height : 8 Ft.
Drought Tolerance : High
Nutritional Requirements : Medium
Light Requirements : High
Leaf Type : Simple
Texture : Coarse
Flower Characteristics : Showy

Environmental Problems : None

Additional Notes : Can be trained as a small tree. Seeds can be poisonous to livestock.

Graptophyllum pictum *(Photograph p. 179)*

Common Name(s) : Caricature Plant
Origin : New Guinea
Growth Rate : Fast
Salt Tolerance : Low
Soil Requirements : Wide
Plant Type : Evergreen shrub
Foliage Color : Variegated; purple
Flowering Season : Summer
Flower Color : Red
Propagation : Cuttings
Human Hazards : None
Common Uses : Shrub; foliage plant
Major Problems : Aphids; mealybugs
Additional Notes : Requires pruning to maintain shape. Many different leaf colors and shapes.

Family : Acanthaceae   Zone : 10B-11

Typical Height : 5 Ft.
Drought Tolerance : Low
Nutritional Requirements : Medium
Light Requirements : Medium; high
Leaf Type : Simple
Texture : Coarse
Flower Characteristics : Showy

Environmental Problems : None

Grevillea robusta *(Photograph p. 161)*

Common Name(s) : Silk Oak
Origin : Australia
Growth Rate : Fast
Salt Tolerance : Medium
Soil Requirements : Wide
Plant Type : Evergreen tree
Foliage Color : Green
Flowering Season : Spring
Flower Color : Orange
Propagation : Seeds
Human Hazards : Irritant
Common Uses : Flowering tree
Major Problems : Mushroom root rot
Additional Notes : Weak-wooded.

Family : Proteaceae   Zone : 9-10B

Typical Height : 50 Ft.
Drought Tolerance : Medium
Nutritional Requirements : Medium
Light Requirements : High
Leaf Type : Pinnately compound
Texture : Fine
Flower Characteristics : Showy

Environmental Problems : Weak

Grewia caffra

Common Name(s) : Lavender Star Flower
Origin : South Africa
Growth Rate : Medium
Salt Tolerance : Low
Soil Requirements : Wide
Plant Type : Evergreen shrub
Foliage Color : Green
Flowering Season : Spring; summer
Flower Color : Lavender
Propagation : Seeds; cuttings
Human Hazards : None
Common Uses : Flowering shrub
Major Problems : None
Additional Notes : Has attractive star-shaped lavender flowers.

Family : Tiliaceae   Zone : 10B-11

Typical Height : 8 Ft.
Drought Tolerance : Medium
Nutritional Requirements : Medium
Light Requirements : High
Leaf Type : Simple
Texture : Medium
Flower Characteristics : Showy

Environmental Problems : None

Grewia occidentalis

Common Name(s) : Star Flower
Origin : Africa
Growth Rate : Medium
Salt Tolerance : Medium
Soil Requirements : Wide
Plant Type : Evergreen shrub
Foliage Color : Green
Flowering Season : Spring; summer
Flower Color : Lavender
Propagation : Seeds; cuttings
Human Hazards : None
Common Uses : Flowering shrub
Major Problems : None
Additional Notes : Similar to G. caffra , with attractive star-shaped lavender flowers.

Family : Tiliaceae   Zone : 10B-11

Typical Height : 8 Ft.
Drought Tolerance : Medium
Nutritional Requirements : Medium
Light Requirements : High
Leaf Type : Simple
Texture : Medium
Flower Characteristics : Showy

Environmental Problems : None

Guaiacum officinale

Common Name(s) : Lignum-vitae
Origin : Caribbean Region
Growth Rate : Slow
Salt Tolerance : High
Soil Requirements : Wide
Plant Type : Evergreen tree or shrub
Foliage Color : Green
Flowering Season : Year-round
Flower Color : Blue
Propagation : Seeds
Human Hazards : Irritant
Common Uses : Small flowering tree; flowering shrub
Major Problems : None
Additional Notes : A small, slow-growing hard-wooded flowering tree.

Family : Zygophyllaceae   **Zone** : 10B-11

Typical Height : 15 Ft.
Drought Tolerance : High
Nutritional Requirements : Low
Light Requirements : High
Leaf Type : Pinnately compound
Texture : Fine
Flower Characteristics : Showy

Environmental Problems : None

Guaiacum sanctum *(Photograph p. 161)*

Common Name(s) : Lignum-vitae
Origin : Caribbean Region
Growth Rate : Slow
Salt Tolerance : High
Soil Requirements : Wide
Plant Type : Evergreen tree or shrub
Foliage Color : Green
Flowering Season : Year-round
Flower Color : Blue
Propagation : Seeds
Human Hazards : Irritant
Common Uses : Small flowering tree; flowering shrub
Major Problems : None
Additional Notes : A small, slow growing native tree.

Family : Zygophyllaceae   **Zone** : 10B-11

Typical Height : 15 Ft.
Drought Tolerance : High
Nutritional Requirements : Low
Light Requirements : High
Leaf Type : Pinnately compound
Texture : Fine
Flower Characteristics : Showy

Environmental Problems : None

Guapira discolor

Common Name(s) : Blolly
Origin : Caribbean Region
Growth Rate : Medium
Salt Tolerance : Medium
Soil Requirements : Wide
Plant Type : Evergreen tree
Foliage Color : Green
Flowering Season : Spring; summer
Flower Color : Green-yellow
Propagation : Seeds
Human Hazards : None
Common Uses : Shade tree
Major Problems : None
Additional Notes : A drought tolerant native tree.

Family : Nyctaginaceae   **Zone** : 10B-11

Typical Height : 30 Ft.
Drought Tolerance : High
Nutritional Requirements : Low
Light Requirements : High
Leaf Type : Simple
Texture : Medium
Flower Characteristics : Insignificant

Environmental Problems : None

Guapira longifolia

Common Name(s) : Long-leaved Blolly
Origin : South Florida to Brazil
Growth Rate : Medium
Salt Tolerance : High
Soil Requirements : Wide
Plant Type : Evergreen tree
Foliage Color : Green
Flowering Season : Spring
Flower Color : Green
Propagation : Seeds
Human Hazards : None
Common Uses : Small tree
Major Problems : None
Additional Notes : A good native tree for south Florida.

Family : Nyctaginaceae   **Zone** : 10B-11

Typical Height : 30 Ft.
Drought Tolerance : High
Nutritional Requirements : Medium
Light Requirements : High
Leaf Type : Simple
Texture : Fine
Flower Characteristics : Insignificant

Environmental Problems : None

Guettarda elliptica

Common Name(s) : Everglades Velvetseed
Origin : South Florida and Tropical America
Growth Rate : Medium
Salt Tolerance : Medium
Soil Requirements : Wide
Plant Type : Evergreen shrub or tree
Foliage Color : Green
Flowering Season : Year-round
Flower Color : Pink; white
Propagation : Seeds
Human Hazards : None
Common Uses : Flowering shrub; small flowering tree
Major Problems : None
Additional Notes : A small tropical hammock tree with some shade tolerance.

Family : Rubiaceae   Zone : 10B-11

Typical Height : 15 Ft.
Drought Tolerance : Medium
Nutritional Requirements : Medium
Light Requirements : Medium
Leaf Type : Simple
Texture : Medium
Flower Characteristics : Showy

Environmental Problems : None

Guettarda scabra

Common Name(s) : Rough Velvetseed
Origin : South Florida and Tropical America
Growth Rate : Medium
Salt Tolerance : High
Soil Requirements : Wide
Plant Type : Evergreen shrub or tree
Foliage Color : Green & brown
Flowering Season : Year-round
Flower Color : White
Propagation : Seeds
Human Hazards : None
Common Uses : Flowering shrub; small flowering tree
Major Problems : None
Additional Notes : An attractive, salt-tolerant coastal native for south Florida.

Family : Rubiaceae   Zone : 10B-11

Typical Height : 20 Ft.
Drought Tolerance : High
Nutritional Requirements : Low
Light Requirements : High
Leaf Type : Simple
Texture : Medium
Flower Characteristics : Showy

Environmental Problems : None

Guzmania lingulata

Common Name(s) : Orange Star
Origin : Tropical America
Growth Rate : Slow
Salt Tolerance : Low
Soil Requirements : Wide
Plant Type : Epiphyte
Foliage Color : Yellow-green
Flowering Season : n/a
Flower Color : Orange-red; purple-red
Propagation : Tissue culture; seeds; division
Human Hazards : None
Common Uses : Specimen plant; epiphyte
Major Problems : None
Additional Notes : Has brilliant colored bracts.
Cultivars
Several cultivars exist.

Family : Bromeliaceae   Zone : 10B-11

Typical Height : 1 Ft.
Drought Tolerance : Low
Nutritional Requirements : Low
Light Requirements : Medium
Leaf Type : Simple; linear
Texture : Medium
Flower Characteristics : Showy

Environmental Problems : None

Gymnanthes lucida

Common Name(s) : Crabwood
Origin : Caribbean Region
Growth Rate : Slow
Salt Tolerance : Medium
Soil Requirements : Wide
Plant Type : Evergreen tree
Foliage Color : Green
Flowering Season : Spring
Flower Color : Red
Propagation : Seeds
Human Hazards : None
Common Uses : Small tree
Major Problems : None
Additional Notes : A small native tree for south Florida.

Family : Euphorbiaceae   Zone : 10B-11

Typical Height : 20 Ft.
Drought Tolerance : High
Nutritional Requirements : Low
Light Requirements : High
Leaf Type : Simple
Texture : Medium
Flower Characteristics : Insignificant

Environmental Problems : None

Gynura aurantiaca

Common Name(s) : Purple Passion Vine
Origin : Java
Growth Rate : Fast
Salt Tolerance : Medium
Soil Requirements : Wide
Plant Type : Herbaceous perennial
Foliage Color : Purple
Flowering Season : Summer; fall
Flower Color : Yellow; orange
Propagation : Cuttings
Human Hazards : None
Common Uses : Foliage plant; hanging basket
Major Problems : Mealybugs
Additional Notes : Green leaves covered with purple hairs. Plant rambles.
Cultivars
'PURPLE PASSION' is a more prostrate form.

Family : Compositae   **Zone** : 10B-11

Typical Height : 1.5 Ft.
Drought Tolerance : Medium
Nutritional Requirements : Medium
Light Requirements : Medium; high
Leaf Type : Simple
Texture : Medium
Flower Characteristics : Insignificant

Environmental Problems : None

Habranthus spp. *(Photograph p. 214)*

Common Name(s) : Rain Lilies
Origin : Western Hemisphere
Growth Rate : Medium
Salt Tolerance : Medium
Soil Requirements : Wide
Plant Type : Herbaceous perennial
Foliage Color : Green; gray-green
Flowering Season : Spring; summer
Flower Color : White; pink; red; yellow
Propagation : Division; seed
Human Hazards : None
Common Uses : Beds; rock gardens
Major Problems : None
Additional Notes : Similar to <u>Zephyranthes</u> but flowers usually nodding.
Cultivars
<u>H.</u> <u>brachyandrus</u> and <u>H.</u> <u>robustus</u> are most common.

Family : Amaryllidaceae   **Zone** : 8-10B

Typical Height : .8 Ft.
Drought Tolerance : High
Nutritional Requirements : Medium
Light Requirements : High
Leaf Type : Simple; linear
Texture : Fine
Flower Characteristics : Showy

Environmental Problems : None

Halesia carolina *(Photograph p. 161)*

Common Name(s) : Silverbell
Origin : Southeastern United States
Growth Rate : Medium
Salt Tolerance : Low
Soil Requirements : Acid
Plant Type : Deciduous tree
Foliage Color : Green
Flowering Season : Spring
Flower Color : White
Propagation : Seeds; cuttings; root cuttings
Human Hazards : None
Common Uses : Small flowering tree
Major Problems : None
Additional Notes : Pretty flowering tree for partial shade. <u>H.</u> <u>diptera</u> also native.

Family : Styracaceae   **Zone** : 5-9

Typical Height : 25 Ft.
Drought Tolerance : Low
Nutritional Requirements : Medium
Light Requirements : Medium
Leaf Type : Simple
Texture : Medium
Flower Characteristics : Showy

Environmental Problems : None

Hamamelis virginiana

Common Name(s) : Witch Hazel
Origin : Eastern North America
Growth Rate : Medium
Salt Tolerance : Low
Soil Requirements : Wide
Plant Type : Deciduous shrub or tree
Foliage Color : Green
Flowering Season : Winter
Flower Color : Yellow
Propagation : Seeds
Human Hazards : None
Common Uses : Shrub; small tree
Major Problems : None
Additional Notes : A deciduous, winter flowering shrub for north and central Florida.

Family : Hamamelidaceae   **Zone** : 4-10A

Typical Height : 20 Ft.
Drought Tolerance : Medium
Nutritional Requirements : Low
Light Requirements : Medium; high
Leaf Type : Simple
Texture : Medium
Flower Characteristics : Insignificant

Environmental Problems : None

Hamelia patens (*Photograph p. 179*)

Common Name(s) : Firebush; Scarletbush
Origin : Caribbean Region
Growth Rate : Fast
Salt Tolerance : Medium
Soil Requirements : Wide
Plant Type : Evergreen shrub
Foliage Color : Green
Flowering Season : Year-round
Flower Color : Red
Propagation : Seeds; cuttings; air layers
Human Hazards : None
Common Uses : Flowering shrub
Major Problems : None
Additional Notes : Tubular red flowers attract butterflies and hummingbirds.

Family : Rubiaceae   **Zone** : 10A-11

Typical Height : 10 Ft.
Drought Tolerance : High
Nutritional Requirements : Medium
Light Requirements : High; medium
Leaf Type : Simple
Texture : Medium
Flower Characteristics : Showy

Environmental Problems : None

Harpephyllum caffrum

Common Name(s) : Kaffir Plum
Origin : South Africa
Growth Rate : Medium
Salt Tolerance : Medium
Soil Requirements : Wide
Plant Type : Evergreen tree
Foliage Color : Green
Flowering Season : Spring
Flower Color : White
Propagation : Seeds; cuttings
Human Hazards : None
Common Uses : Edible fruit; shade tree
Major Problems : None
Additional Notes : Has attractive glossy green foliage. Only female tree bears fruit.

Family : Anacardiaceae   **Zone** : 10B-11

Typical Height : 30 Ft.
Drought Tolerance : Medium
Nutritional Requirements : Medium
Light Requirements : High
Leaf Type : Pinnately compound
Texture : Medium
Flower Characteristics : Insignificant

Environmental Problems : None

Harpulia arborea

Common Name(s) : Tulipwood
Origin : Asia and East Indies
Growth Rate : Slow
Salt Tolerance : Low
Soil Requirements : Wide
Plant Type : Evergreen tree
Foliage Color : Green
Flowering Season : Year-round
Flower Color : Yellow
Propagation : Seeds
Human Hazards : None
Common Uses : Shade tree
Major Problems : None
Additional Notes : A medium size tree with attractive orange fruit. Can be weak wooded.

Family : Sapindaceae   **Zone** : 10B-11

Typical Height : 40 Ft.
Drought Tolerance : High
Nutritional Requirements : Low
Light Requirements : High
Leaf Type : Pinnately compound
Texture : Medium
Flower Characteristics : Insignificant

Environmental Problems : None

Haworthia fasciata

Common Name(s) : Zebra Haworthia
Origin : South Africa
Growth Rate : Slow
Salt Tolerance : Low
Soil Requirements : Wide; well drained
Plant Type : Succulent perennial
Foliage Color : Green
Flowering Season : n/a
Flower Color : White
Propagation : Seeds; division; cuttings
Human Hazards : None
Common Uses : Rock gardens; specimen plant; foliage plant
Major Problems : None
Additional Notes : Grow only in well drained soils. Other species are also cultivated.

Family : Liliaceae   **Zone** : 10B-11

Typical Height : .5 Ft.
Drought Tolerance : High
Nutritional Requirements : Low
Light Requirements : Medium; high
Leaf Type : Simple
Texture : Medium
Flower Characteristics : Showy

Environmental Problems : None

Hedera canariensis *(Photograph p. 214)*

Common Name(s) : Algerian Ivy
Origin : North Africa
Growth Rate : Fast
Salt Tolerance : Medium
Soil Requirements : Wide
Plant Type : Evergreen vine
Foliage Color : Green; variegated
Flowering Season : Spring; summer
Flower Color : White
Propagation : Cuttings
Human Hazards : Irritant; poisonous
Common Uses : Hanging baskets; groundcover; vine; foliage plant
Major Problems : Scales; sooty mold
Additional Notes : Numerous varieties with many leaf patterns and shapes are cultivated.
Cultivars
'VARIEGATA' has variegated foliage.

Family : Araliaceae   **Zone** : 8-10B

Typical Height : Not applicable
Drought Tolerance : Medium
Nutritional Requirements : Medium
Light Requirements : Low; medium; high
Leaf Type : Simple
Texture : Medium
Flower Characteristics : Insignificant

Environmental Problems : None

Hedera helix

Common Name(s) : English Ivy
Origin : Europe, Western Asia, and Africa
Growth Rate : Fast
Salt Tolerance : Medium
Soil Requirements : Wide
Plant Type : Evergreen vine or shrub
Foliage Color : Green
Flowering Season : Summer
Flower Color : White
Propagation : Cuttings
Human Hazards : Irritant; poisonous
Common Uses : Hanging baskets; vine; groundcover; foliage plant
Major Problems : Scales; bacterial leafspot; sooty mold
Additional Notes : Hundreds of cultivars exist.

Family : Araliaceae   **Zone** : 5-9

Typical Height : Not applicable
Drought Tolerance : Medium
Nutritional Requirements : Low
Light Requirements : Low; medium; high
Leaf Type : Simple
Texture : Medium
Flower Characteristics : Insignificant

Environmental Problems : None

Hedychium aureum

Common Name(s) : Dwarf Ginger
Origin : India
Growth Rate : Medium
Salt Tolerance : Medium
Soil Requirements : Wide
Plant Type : Herbaceous perennial
Foliage Color : Green
Flowering Season : Spring
Flower Color : Yellow
Propagation : Division
Human Hazards : None
Common Uses : Flowering perennial
Major Problems : None
Additional Notes : A small <u>Hedychium</u> with yellow-gold flowers.

Family : Zingiberaceae   **Zone** : 10A-11

Typical Height : 2 Ft.
Drought Tolerance : Medium
Nutritional Requirements : Medium
Light Requirements : Medium
Leaf Type : Simple
Texture : Coarse
Flower Characteristics : Showy

Environmental Problems : None

Hedychium coccineum *(Photograph p. 195)*

Common Name(s) : Scarlet Ginger Lily
Origin : India
Growth Rate : Medium
Salt Tolerance : Medium
Soil Requirements : Wide
Plant Type : Herbaceous perennial
Foliage Color : Green
Flowering Season : Spring
Flower Color : Orange-red
Propagation : Division
Human Hazards : None
Common Uses : Flowering perennial
Major Problems : None
Additional Notes : Fine-textured light red flowers only last a few days.

Family : Zingiberaceae   **Zone** : 10A-11

Typical Height : 6 Ft.
Drought Tolerance : Medium
Nutritional Requirements : Medium
Light Requirements : Medium
Leaf Type : Simple
Texture : Coarse
Flower Characteristics : Showy

Environmental Problems : None

Hedychium coronarium

Family : Zingiberaceae   Zone : 9-11

Common Name(s) : Butterfly Ginger
Origin : Tropical Asia
Growth Rate : Fast
Salt Tolerance : Medium
Soil Requirements : Wide
Plant Type : Herbaceous perennial
Foliage Color : Green
Flowering Season : Spring
Flower Color : White
Propagation : Division
Human Hazards : None
Common Uses : Flowering perennial
Major Problems : None
Additional Notes : Multiple stemmed plants with fragrant white flowers.

Typical Height : 5 Ft.
Drought Tolerance : Medium
Nutritional Requirements : Medium
Light Requirements : Medium; high
Leaf Type : Simple
Texture : Coarse
Flower Characteristics : Showy; fragrant

Environmental Problems : None

Hedychium flavum

Family : Zingiberaceae   Zone : 10A-11

Common Name(s) : Yellow Ginger
Origin : India
Growth Rate : Medium
Salt Tolerance : Medium
Soil Requirements : Wide
Plant Type : Herbaceous perennial
Foliage Color : Green
Flowering Season : Spring
Flower Color : Yellow
Propagation : Division
Human Hazards : None
Common Uses : Flowering perennial
Major Problems : None
Additional Notes : Similar to H. coronarium , but with yellow flowers.

Typical Height : 5 Ft.
Drought Tolerance : Medium
Nutritional Requirements : Medium
Light Requirements : Medium
Leaf Type : Simple
Texture : Coarse
Flower Characteristics : Showy; fragrant

Environmental Problems : None

Hedychium gardnerianum

Family : Zingiberaceae   Zone : 10A-11

Common Name(s) : Kahili Lily
Origin : India
Growth Rate : Medium
Salt Tolerance : Medium
Soil Requirements : Wide
Plant Type : Herbaceous perennial
Foliage Color : Green
Flowering Season : Spring
Flower Color : Yellow & red
Propagation : Division
Human Hazards : None
Common Uses : Flowering perennial
Major Problems : None
Additional Notes : Similar to H. coccineum , but with short-lived light yellow flowers.

Typical Height : 6 Ft.
Drought Tolerance : Medium
Nutritional Requirements : Medium
Light Requirements : Medium
Leaf Type : Simple
Texture : Coarse
Flower Characteristics : Showy; fragrant

Environmental Problems : None

Hedychium greenei *(Photograph p. 196)*

Family : Zingiberaceae   Zone : 10A-11

Common Name(s) : Ginger Lily
Origin : India
Growth Rate : Medium
Salt Tolerance : Medium
Soil Requirements : Wide
Plant Type : Herbaceous perennial
Foliage Color : Green & red
Flowering Season : Spring
Flower Color : Red
Propagation : Division
Human Hazards : None
Common Uses : Flowering perennial
Major Problems : None
Additional Notes : Similar to H. flavum , but with red flowers. Undersides of leaves are red.

Typical Height : 6 Ft.
Drought Tolerance : Medium
Nutritional Requirements : Medium
Light Requirements : Medium
Leaf Type : Simple
Texture : Coarse
Flower Characteristics : Showy

Environmental Problems : None

Helenium autumnale

Family : Compositae   **Zone** : 3-10B

Common Name(s) : Sneezeweed
Origin : Southeastern United States
Growth Rate : Medium
Salt Tolerance : Low
Soil Requirements : Wide
Plant Type : Herbaceous perennial
Foliage Color : Green
Flowering Season : Summer; fall
Flower Color : Orange; yellow
Propagation : Division
Human Hazards : Poisonous
Common Uses : Borders; cut flowers
Major Problems : None
Additional Notes : Does not cause sneezing. Pinch stalks in early summer to force shoots.

Typical Height : 4 Ft.
Drought Tolerance : Medium
Nutritional Requirements : Medium
Light Requirements : High
Leaf Type : Simple
Texture : Medium
Flower Characteristics : Showy

Environmental Problems : None

Helianthus debilis *(Photograph p. 214)*

Family : Compositae   **Zone** : 8-10B

Common Name(s) : Beach Sunflower
Origin : Florida
Growth Rate : Fast
Salt Tolerance : High
Soil Requirements : Wide
Plant Type : Herbaceous annual
Foliage Color : Green
Flowering Season : Year-round
Flower Color : Yellow
Propagation : Seeds; cuttings
Human Hazards : None
Common Uses : Flowering groundcover; seasides
Major Problems : None
Additional Notes : Prefers sandy coastal areas.

Typical Height : 1.5 Ft.
Drought Tolerance : High
Nutritional Requirements : Low
Light Requirements : High
Leaf Type : Simple
Texture : Medium
Flower Characteristics : Showy

Environmental Problems : None

Helianthus decapetalus

Family : Compositae   **Zone** : 3-10B

Common Name(s) : Thin-leaved Sunflower
Origin : Northeastern United States
Growth Rate : Fast
Salt Tolerance : Low
Soil Requirements : Wide
Plant Type : Herbaceous perennial
Foliage Color : Green
Flowering Season : Summer
Flower Color : Yellow
Propagation : Seeds; division
Human Hazards : None
Common Uses : Borders
Major Problems : None
Additional Notes : Double and single flowering forms exist. Divide every other year.

Typical Height : 4 Ft.
Drought Tolerance : Medium
Nutritional Requirements : Medium
Light Requirements : High
Leaf Type : Simple
Texture : Coarse
Flower Characteristics : Showy

Environmental Problems : None

Heliconia angusta

Family : Heliconiaceae   **Zone** : 10B-11

Common Name(s) : Holiday Heliconia
Origin : Brazil
Growth Rate : Medium
Salt Tolerance : Low
Soil Requirements : Acid
Plant Type : Herbaceous perennial
Foliage Color : Green
Flowering Season : Fall; winter
Flower Color : Red & white
Propagation : Division
Human Hazards : None
Common Uses : Specimen plant; flowering pot plant
Major Problems : K deficiency
Additional Notes : Flowers around Christmas time on second year shoots. Short peduncles.

Typical Height : 2.5 Ft.
Drought Tolerance : Medium
Nutritional Requirements : Medium
Light Requirements : Medium
Leaf Type : Simple
Texture : Coarse
Flower Characteristics : Showy

Environmental Problems : None

Heliconia bihai

Common Name(s) : Lobster Claw
Origin : West Indies & Northern South America
Growth Rate : Fast
Salt Tolerance : Medium
Soil Requirements : Wide
Plant Type : Herbaceous perennial
Foliage Color : Green
Flowering Season : Spring; summer
Flower Color : Red; yellow; green; red & yellow
Propagation : Division
Human Hazards : None
Common Uses : Cut flowers; flowering perennial
Major Problems : None
Additional Notes : Tall clumping with bold foliage and massive flowers on second year stalks.
Cultivars
'HUMILIS' has red bracts; many other cultivars also exist.

Family : Heliconiaceae   **Zone** : 10B-11

Typical Height : 10 Ft.
Drought Tolerance : Medium
Nutritional Requirements : Medium
Light Requirements : Medium; high
Leaf Type : Simple
Texture : Very coarse
Flower Characteristics : Showy

Environmental Problems : None

Heliconia caribaea *(Photograph p. 196)*

Common Name(s) : Caribbean Heliconia
Origin : West Indies
Growth Rate : Fast
Salt Tolerance : Medium
Soil Requirements : Wide
Plant Type : Herbaceous perennial
Foliage Color : Green
Flowering Season : Spring; summer
Flower Color : Red; yellow; green
Propagation : Division
Human Hazards : None
Common Uses : Cut flowers; flowering perennial
Major Problems : None
Additional Notes : Tall clumping with bold foliage and massive flowers on second year stalks.
Cultivars
'PURPUREA' has red bracts; 'CREME' has yellow bracts.

Family : Heliconiaceae   **Zone** : 10B-11

Typical Height : 12 Ft.
Drought Tolerance : Medium
Nutritional Requirements : Medium
Light Requirements : Medium; high
Leaf Type : Simple
Texture : Very coarse
Flower Characteristics : Showy

Environmental Problems : None

Heliconia collinsiana

Common Name(s) : Waxy-leaved Heliconia
Origin : Central America
Growth Rate : Fast
Salt Tolerance : Medium
Soil Requirements : Wide
Plant Type : Herbaceous perennial
Foliage Color : Green
Flowering Season : Summer
Flower Color : Red
Propagation : Division
Human Hazards : None
Common Uses : Specimen plant
Major Problems : None
Additional Notes : All parts of this plant are covered with a waxy bloom. Pendulous flowers.

Family : Heliconiaceae   **Zone** : 10B-11

Typical Height : 7 Ft.
Drought Tolerance : Medium
Nutritional Requirements : Medium
Light Requirements : Medium; high
Leaf Type : Simple
Texture : Coarse
Flower Characteristics : Showy

Environmental Problems : None

Heliconia latispatha *(Photograph p. 196)*

Common Name(s) : Parrot Flower
Origin : Central America
Growth Rate : Fast
Salt Tolerance : Medium
Soil Requirements : Wide
Plant Type : Herbaceous perennial
Foliage Color : Green
Flowering Season : Summer; fall
Flower Color : Orange; yellow
Propagation : Division
Human Hazards : None
Common Uses : Flowering perennial
Major Problems : None
Additional Notes : An aggressive clumping heliconia with erect flowers; many color forms.

Family : Heliconiaceae   **Zone** : 10B-11

Typical Height : 6 Ft.
Drought Tolerance : Medium
Nutritional Requirements : Medium
Light Requirements : Medium; high
Leaf Type : Simple
Texture : Very coarse
Flower Characteristics : Showy

Environmental Problems : Invasive

Heliconia psittacorum *(Photograph p. 196)*

Common Name(s) : Parakeet Flower
Origin : Northern South America
Growth Rate : Fast
Salt Tolerance : Medium
Soil Requirements : Acid
Plant Type : Herbaceous perennial
Foliage Color : Green
Flowering Season : Year-round
Flower Color : Orange; pink; red; yellow
Propagation : Division
Human Hazards : None
Common Uses : Cut flowers; flowering perennial
Major Problems : Fe and Mn deficiencies
Additional Notes : An aggressive spreading species not recommended for landscape use.
Cultivars

Family : Heliconiaceae   **Zone** : 11

Typical Height : 5 Ft.
Drought Tolerance : Low
Nutritional Requirements : High
Light Requirements : High
Leaf Type : Simple
Texture : Coarse
Flower Characteristics : Showy

Environmental Problems : Invasive

'ANDROMEDA' has light red and orange flowers; 'KALEIDOSCOPE' has pink, green, and orange flowers; 'ST.VINCENT RED' has red and orange flowers; 'PARAKEET' has pink and light yellow flowers; 'CHOCONIANA' has light orange flowers.

Heliconia rostrata *(Photograph p. 196)*

Common Name(s) : Lobster Claw
Origin : Argentina to Peru
Growth Rate : Fast
Salt Tolerance : Low
Soil Requirements : Acid
Plant Type : Herbaceous perennial
Foliage Color : Green
Flowering Season : Summer
Flower Color : Red & yellow
Propagation : Division
Human Hazards : None
Common Uses : Cut flowers; flowering perennial
Major Problems : None
Additional Notes : Foliage often tattered by wind. Pendulous flowers on second year stalks.

Family : Heliconiaceae   **Zone** : 10B-11

Typical Height : 5 Ft.
Drought Tolerance : Medium
Nutritional Requirements : Medium
Light Requirements : Medium
Leaf Type : Simple
Texture : Coarse
Flower Characteristics : Showy

Environmental Problems : None

Heliconia stricta *(Photograph p. 197)*

Common Name(s) : Stricta Heliconia
Origin : West Indies & Northern South America
Growth Rate : Medium
Salt Tolerance : Medium
Soil Requirements : Wide
Plant Type : Herbaceous perennial
Foliage Color : Green; green & red
Flowering Season : Fall; winter
Flower Color : Red
Propagation : Division
Human Hazards : None
Common Uses : Cut flowers; flowering perennial
Major Problems : None
Additional Notes : Many varieties of shorter clumping heliconias. Shoots flower second year.
Cultivars

Family : Heliconiaceae   **Zone** : 10B-11

Typical Height : 3 Ft.
Drought Tolerance : Medium
Nutritional Requirements : Medium
Light Requirements : Medium
Leaf Type : Simple
Texture : Very coarse
Flower Characteristics : Showy

Environmental Problems : None

'SHARONII' has dark green leaves with purple midveins and undersides.

Heliconia wagnerana *(Photograph p. 197)*

Common Name(s) : Wagner Heliconia
Origin : Central America
Growth Rate : Medium
Salt Tolerance : Medium
Soil Requirements : Wide
Plant Type : Herbaceous perennial
Foliage Color : Green
Flowering Season : Winter; spring
Flower Color : Pink and cream
Propagation : Division
Human Hazards : None
Common Uses : Cut flowers; flowering perennial
Major Problems : None
Additional Notes : Upright light red bracts have cream-colored edges. Flowers second year.

Family : Heliconiaceae   **Zone** : 10B-11

Typical Height : 5 Ft.
Drought Tolerance : Medium
Nutritional Requirements : Medium
Light Requirements : Medium
Leaf Type : Simple
Texture : Very coarse
Flower Characteristics : Showy

Environmental Problems : None

Heliconia X 'Golden Torch' *(Photograph p. 196)*

Family : Heliconiaceae   **Zone** : 11

Common Name(s) : Golden Torch Heliconia
Origin : Northern South America
Growth Rate : Fast
Salt Tolerance : Medium
Soil Requirements : Acid
Plant Type : Herbaceous perennial
Foliage Color : Green
Flowering Season : Year-round
Flower Color : Orange-yellow
Propagation : Division
Human Hazards : None
Common Uses : Cut flower; flowering perennial
Major Problems : Fe and Mn deficiencies

Typical Height : 6 Ft.
Drought Tolerance : Low
Nutritional Requirements : High
Light Requirements : High
Leaf Type : Simple
Texture : Coarse
Flower Characteristics : Showy

Environmental Problems : Invasive

Additional Notes : An aggressive spreading plant not recommended for landscape use.

Heliotropium spp.

Family : Boraginaceae   **Zone** : 10B-11

Common Name(s) : Heliotrope
Origin : New World Tropics
Growth Rate : Medium
Salt Tolerance : Medium
Soil Requirements : Wide
Plant Type : Herbaceous perennial
Foliage Color : Green
Flowering Season : Fall; winter
Flower Color : Blue; purple; white
Propagation : Cuttings; seeds
Human Hazards : None
Common Uses : Cut flowers; flowering perennial
Major Problems : None

Typical Height : 1.5 Ft.
Drought Tolerance : Medium
Nutritional Requirements : Medium
Light Requirements : High
Leaf Type : Simple
Texture : Medium
Flower Characteristics : Showy; fragrant

Environmental Problems : None

Additional Notes : Often grown for the fragrant flowers. Can be grown in containers.

Hemerocallis spp. *(Photograph p. 197)*

Family : Liliaceae   **Zone** : 5-10B

Common Name(s) : Day Lily
Origin : Eurasia
Growth Rate : Medium
Salt Tolerance : High
Soil Requirements : Wide
Plant Type : Herbaceous perennial
Foliage Color : Green
Flowering Season : Spring; summer; fall
Flower Color : Yellow; pink; orange; red-brown
Propagation : Division
Human Hazards : None
Common Uses : Flowering perennial; seasides
Major Problems : None

Typical Height : 2 Ft.
Drought Tolerance : High
Nutritional Requirements : Medium
Light Requirements : High
Leaf Type : Simple; linear
Texture : Medium
Flower Characteristics : Showy

Environmental Problems : None

Additional Notes : Only certain cultivars suitable for south Florida.
Cultivars
Hundreds of cultivars exist.

Heterospathe elata

Family : Palmae   **Zone** : 10B-11

Common Name(s) : Sagisi Palm
Origin : Philippines
Growth Rate : Slow
Salt Tolerance : Low
Soil Requirements : Wide
Plant Type : Palm
Foliage Color : Green
Flowering Season : Summer
Flower Color : White
Propagation : Seeds
Human Hazards : None
Common Uses : Tree; palm
Major Problems : None

Typical Height : 40 Ft.
Drought Tolerance : High
Nutritional Requirements : Medium
Light Requirements : High
Leaf Type : Pinnately compound
Texture : Medium
Flower Characteristics : Insignificant

Environmental Problems : None

Additional Notes : A medium sized palm, not widely available.

Hibiscus coccineus

Common Name(s) : Swamp Mallow
Origin : Georgia and Florida
Growth Rate : Medium
Salt Tolerance : Low
Soil Requirements : Acid
Plant Type : Herbaceous perennial
Foliage Color : Green
Flowering Season : Spring; summer
Flower Color : Red
Propagation : Seeds; cuttings
Human Hazards : None
Common Uses : Borders; aquatic
Major Problems : None
Additional Notes : A showy native hibiscus for wet areas.

Family : Malvaceae   **Zone** : 8-10B

Typical Height : 6 Ft.
Drought Tolerance : Low
Nutritional Requirements : Medium
Light Requirements : Medium
Leaf Type : Simple
Texture : Medium
Flower Characteristics : Showy

Environmental Problems : None

Hibiscus moscheutos

Common Name(s) : Rose Mallow
Origin : Eastern United States
Growth Rate : Fast
Salt Tolerance : Low
Soil Requirements : Wide
Plant Type : Herbaceous perennial
Foliage Color : Green
Flowering Season : Summer
Flower Color : Pink; red; white
Propagation : Seeds
Human Hazards : None
Common Uses : Specimen plant; borders
Major Problems : None
Additional Notes : This perennial is often grown as an annual in northern states.
Cultivars
Popular cultivar series include: 'SOUTHERN BELLE', 'AVALON', 'DIXIE BELLE', and 'FRISBEE' series.

Family : Malvaceae   **Zone** : 4-10A

Typical Height : 5 Ft.
Drought Tolerance : Low
Nutritional Requirements : Medium
Light Requirements : Medium; high
Leaf Type : Simple
Texture : Coarse
Flower Characteristics : Showy

Environmental Problems : None

Hibiscus rosa-sinensis *(Photograph p. 179)*

Common Name(s) : Hibiscus; Chinese Hibiscus
Origin : China
Growth Rate : Fast
Salt Tolerance : Medium
Soil Requirements : Wide
Plant Type : Evergreen shrub
Foliage Color : Green; variegated
Flowering Season : Year-round
Flower Color : Red; yellow; orange; white; pink
Propagation : Cuttings
Human Hazards : None
Common Uses : Flowering shrub; hedge; flowering pot plant
Major Problems : Nematodes; scales; aphids. Fe deficiency.
Additional Notes : Hundreds of cultivars exist.

Family : Malvaceae   **Zone** : 10A-11

Typical Height : 7 Ft.
Drought Tolerance : Low
Nutritional Requirements : High
Light Requirements : High
Leaf Type : Simple
Texture : Coarse
Flower Characteristics : Showy

Environmental Problems : None

Hibiscus schizopetalus *(Photograph p. 179)*

Common Name(s) : Fringed Hibiscus
Origin : Tropical East Africa
Growth Rate : Fast
Salt Tolerance : Medium
Soil Requirements : Wide
Plant Type : Evergreen shrub
Foliage Color : Green
Flowering Season : Spring; summer; fall
Flower Color : Red; pink
Propagation : Cuttings
Human Hazards : None
Common Uses : Flowering shrub
Major Problems : Nematodes; scales; aphids
Additional Notes : Weeping habit, fringed pendent flowers.

Family : Malvaceae   **Zone** : 10B-11

Typical Height : 10 Ft.
Drought Tolerance : Medium
Nutritional Requirements : Medium
Light Requirements : High
Leaf Type : Simple
Texture : Medium
Flower Characteristics : Showy

Environmental Problems : None

Hibiscus syriacus

Common Name(s) : Rose of Sharon	Family : Malvaceae Zone : 5-9
Origin : China and India	Typical Height : 10 Ft.
Growth Rate : Fast	Drought Tolerance : Low
Salt Tolerance : Low	Nutritional Requirements : High
Soil Requirements : Wide	Light Requirements : High
Plant Type : Deciduous shrub	Leaf Type : Simple
Foliage Color : Green	Texture : Medium
Flowering Season : Summer; fall	Flower Characteristics : Showy

Flower Color : Blue; lavender; pink; white
Propagation : Cuttings
Human Hazards : None   Environmental Problems : None
Common Uses : Flowering shrub; hedge
Major Problems : Nematodes; scales; mites
Additional Notes : Flowers on new growth, prune in winter.
Cultivars
Hundreds of cultivars exist.

Hibiscus tiliaceus *(Photograph p. 162)*

Common Name(s) : Mahoe; Sea Hibiscus   Family : Malvaceae   Zone : 10A-11
Origin : Caribbean Region   Typical Height : 40 Ft.
Growth Rate : Fast   Drought Tolerance : High
Salt Tolerance : High   Nutritional Requirements : Low
Soil Requirements : Wide   Light Requirements : High
Plant Type : Evergreen tree or shrub   Leaf Type : Simple
Foliage Color : Green   Texture : Coarse
Flowering Season : Year-round   Flower Characteristics : Showy
Flower Color : Yellow; red
Propagation : Seeds; cuttings
Human Hazards : None   Environmental Problems : Invasive; weak
Common Uses : Flowering tree; large flowering shrub
Major Problems : None
Additional Notes : Can be weak wooded. Requires shaping to be tree-like.

Hippeastrum X hybridum *(Photograph p. 198)*

Common Name(s) : Amaryllis   Family : Amaryllidaceae   Zone : 8-10B
Origin : Hybrid   Typical Height : 2 Ft.
Growth Rate : Medium   Drought Tolerance : Medium
Salt Tolerance : Low   Nutritional Requirements : Medium
Soil Requirements : Wide   Light Requirements : Medium
Plant Type : Herbaceous perennial   Leaf Type : Simple; linear
Foliage Color : Green   Texture : Coarse
Flowering Season : Spring   Flower Characteristics : Showy
Flower Color : Red; pink; orange; white
Propagation : Division; seed
Human Hazards : Poisonous   Environmental Problems : None
Common Uses : Beds; borders; specimen plant; flowering pot plant
Major Problems : Bulb rots; fungal leafspots; grasshoppers; thrips; virus
Additional Notes : Best to purchase Florida-grown bulbs; plant just below soil surface.

Holmskioldia sanguinea

Common Name(s) : Chinese Hat Plant   Family : Verbenaceae   Zone : 10B-11
Origin : Himalayas   Typical Height : 7 Ft.
Growth Rate : Medium   Drought Tolerance : Low
Salt Tolerance : Medium   Nutritional Requirements : Medium
Soil Requirements : Wide   Light Requirements : Medium; high
Plant Type : Evergreen shrub   Leaf Type : Simple
Foliage Color : Green   Texture : Medium
Flowering Season : Year-round   Flower Characteristics : Showy
Flower Color : Orange; yellow
Propagation : Cuttings
Human Hazards : None   Environmental Problems : None
Common Uses : Flowering shrub
Major Problems : Nematodes
Additional Notes : Unusual shaped flowers; straggly growth habit.

Homalocladium platycladum

Common Name(s) : Ribbonbush
Origin : Solomon Islands
Growth Rate : Medium
Salt Tolerance : Medium
Soil Requirements : Wide
Plant Type : Evergreen shrub
Foliage Color : Green
Flowering Season : n/a
Flower Color : Green
Propagation : Cuttings; division
Human Hazards : None
Common Uses : Shrub
Major Problems : None
Additional Notes : Has flat ribbon-like branches.

Family : Polygonaceae   **Zone** : 10B-11

Typical Height : 5 Ft.
Drought Tolerance : Medium
Nutritional Requirements : Medium
Light Requirements : High
Leaf Type : Simple
Texture : Fine
Flower Characteristics : Insignificant

Environmental Problems : None

Hosta spp.

Common Name(s) : Plantain Lily
Origin : Japan, China, Korea
Growth Rate : Medium
Salt Tolerance : Low
Soil Requirements : Wide
Plant Type : Herbaceous perennial
Foliage Color : Green; variegated
Flowering Season : Spring; summer; fall
Flower Color : Lavender; white; purple
Propagation : Division
Human Hazards : None
Common Uses : Beds
Major Problems : None
Additional Notes : Many cultivars. Best suited for north Florida.

Family : Lilaceae   **Zone** : 3-9

Typical Height : 1.5 Ft.
Drought Tolerance : Medium
Nutritional Requirements : Medium
Light Requirements : Low; medium
Leaf Type : Simple
Texture : Coarse
Flower Characteristics : Showy; fragrant

Environmental Problems : None

Howea forsterana *(Photograph p. 204)*

Common Name(s) : Sentry Palm; Kentia Palm
Origin : Lord Howe Islands
Growth Rate : Slow
Salt Tolerance : Medium
Soil Requirements : Wide
Plant Type : Palm
Foliage Color : Green
Flowering Season : n/a
Flower Color : White
Propagation : Seeds
Human Hazards : None
Common Uses : Foliage plant; tree; palm
Major Problems : Phythophthora bud rot
Additional Notes : This slow-growing graceful palm is excellent for interiorscape use.

Family : Palmae   **Zone** : 9-11

Typical Height : 30 Ft.
Drought Tolerance : Medium
Nutritional Requirements : Low
Light Requirements : Low; medium
Leaf Type : Pinnately compound
Texture : Medium
Flower Characteristics : Insignificant

Environmental Problems : None

Hoya spp.

Common Name(s) : Wax Plant
Origin : Australia, Asia
Growth Rate : Medium
Salt Tolerance : Low
Soil Requirements : Wide
Plant Type : Evergreen vine
Foliage Color : Green; yellow; red; pink
Flowering Season : Spring; summer; fall
Flower Color : White; pink; red
Propagation : Cuttings
Human Hazards : None
Common Uses : Hanging baskets; vine; foliage plant
Major Problems : Scales; mealybugs
Additional Notes : An attractive twining vine often used in hanging baskets.
Cultivars

H. purpurea-fusca 'SILVER PINK' has green leaves with silver-pink spots.

Family : Asclepiadaceae   **Zone** : 10B-11

Typical Height : Not applicable
Drought Tolerance : High
Nutritional Requirements : Medium
Light Requirements : Medium
Leaf Type : Simple
Texture : Medium
Flower Characteristics : Showy; fragrant

Environmental Problems : None

Hura crepitans

Family : Euphorbiaceae   **Zone** : 10B-11

Common Name(s) : Sandbox Tree
Origin : Caribbean Region
Growth Rate : Fast
Salt Tolerance : Low
Soil Requirements : Wide
Plant Type : Deciduous tree
Foliage Color : Green
Flowering Season : n/a
Flower Color : Red
Propagation : Seeds; cuttings
Human Hazards : Spiny; poisonous
Common Uses : Shade tree; flowering tree
Major Problems : None
Additional Notes : Unwisely cultivated in home landscapes. Poisonous seeds and sap.

Typical Height : 60 Ft.
Drought Tolerance : Medium
Nutritional Requirements : Medium
Light Requirements : High
Leaf Type : Simple
Texture : Medium
Flower Characteristics : Showy

Environmental Problems : None

Hydrangea macrophylla *(Photograph p. 180)*

Family : Saxifragaceae   **Zone** : 6-9

Common Name(s) : Hydrangea
Origin : Japan
Growth Rate : Fast
Salt Tolerance : Low
Soil Requirements : Acid
Plant Type : Deciduous shrub
Foliage Color : Green
Flowering Season : Spring; summer
Flower Color : Blue; lavender; pink; white
Propagation : Cuttings
Human Hazards : None
Common Uses : Flowering shrub; hedge; flowering pot plant
Major Problems : Scales; nematodes; chewing insects
Additional Notes : Flowers change color with soil pH; prune hard in late winter.
Cultivars
'BLUE PRINCE', 'BLUE WAVE', 'COERULEA', 'MANDSHURICA', 'MARIESII', 'NIKKO BLUE', and 'OTAKSA'
recommended.

Typical Height : 5 Ft.
Drought Tolerance : Low
Nutritional Requirements : High
Light Requirements : Medium; high
Leaf Type : Simple
Texture : Coarse
Flower Characteristics : Showy

Environmental Problems : None

Hydrangea quercifolia

Family : Saxifragaceae   **Zone** : 5-9

Common Name(s) : Oakleaf Hydrangea
Origin : Southeastern United States
Growth Rate : Medium
Salt Tolerance : Low
Soil Requirements : Acid
Plant Type : Deciduous shrub
Foliage Color : Green
Flowering Season : Spring
Flower Color : White
Propagation : Cuttings
Human Hazards : None
Common Uses : Flowering shrub
Major Problems : Scales
Additional Notes : Best in woodland or informal setting; red-purple fall color.

Typical Height : 6 Ft.
Drought Tolerance : Low
Nutritional Requirements : High
Light Requirements : Medium; high
Leaf Type : Simple; pinnately lobed
Texture : Coarse
Flower Characteristics : Showy

Environmental Problems : None

Hydrocleys nymphoides

Family : Butomaceae   **Zone** : 10A-11

Common Name(s) : Water Poppy
Origin : Tropical America
Growth Rate : Medium
Salt Tolerance : Low
Soil Requirements : n/a
Plant Type : Aquatic perennial
Foliage Color : Green
Flowering Season : Summer
Flower Color : Yellow
Propagation : Division
Human Hazards : None
Common Uses : Aquatic; specimen plant
Major Problems : None
Additional Notes : This small aquatic plant is well-suited for small ponds or tubs.

Typical Height : .8 Ft.
Drought Tolerance : Low
Nutritional Requirements : Medium
Light Requirements : High
Leaf Type : Simple
Texture : Medium
Flower Characteristics : Showy

Environmental Problems : None

Trees

Acer rubrum
Red Maple

Araucaria heterophylla
Norfolk Island Pine

Albizia julibrissin
Mimosa

Annona muricata
Soursop

Beaucarnea recurvata
Ponytail

Bixa orellena
Annatto

153

Trees

Blighia sapida
Akee

Bauhinia variegata
Orchid Tree

Bulnesia arborea
Bulnesia

Bursera simaruba
Gumbo Limbo

Brachychiton acerifolius
Flame Bottle Tree

Caesalpinia granadillo
Bridalveil Tree

Trees

Butea monosperma
Flame of the Forest

Caesalpinia granadillo
Bridalveil Tree

Callistemon rigidus
Erect Bottlebrush

Callistemon viminalis
Weeping Bottlebrush

Calophyllum inophyllum
Mastwood

Cananga odorata
Ylang Ylang

Trees

Carica papaya
Papaya

Cassia fistula
Golden Shower

Cassia javanica
Pink and White Shower

Cecropia palmata
Snakewood

Cedrus atlantica
Atlas Cedar

Ceiba pentandra
Silk-Cotton Tree

156

Trees

Cercis canadensis
Redbud

Chrysophyllum oliviforme
Satin Leaf

Chionanthus virginicus
Fringe Tree

Chorisia speciosa
Floss-Silk Tree

Cinnamomum camphora
Camphor Tree

Clusia rosea
Pitch Apple

Trees

Coccoloba diversifolia
Pigeon Plum

Coccoloba uvifera
Sea Grape

Conocarpus erectus var. *sericeus*
Silver Buttonwood

Cordia boissieri
Texas Wild Olive

Cordia sebestena
Geiger Tree

Cornus florida
Flowering Dogwood

Trees

Delonix regia
Royal Poinciana

Delonix regia
Royal Poinciana

Dracaena draco
Dragon Tree

Eriobotrya japonica
Loquat

Erythrina variegata
Coral Tree

Eugenia brasiliensis
Grumichama

159

Trees

Erythrina variegata var. *orientalis*
Coral Tree

Euphoria longan
Longan

Ficus aspera
Clown Fig

Ficus benghalensis
Banyan Tree

Ficus carica
Edible Fig

Ficus rubiginosa
Rusty Fig

Trees

Ficus lyrata
Fiddleleaf Fig

Ficus retusa 'Green Gem'
Indian Laurel

Gordonia lasianthus
Loblolly Bay

Grevillea robusta
Silk Oak

Guaiacum sanctum
Lignum-Vitae

Halesia carolina
Silverbell

161

Trees

Hibiscus tiliaceus
Mahoe

Illicium anisatum
Anise Tree

Illicium floridanum
Florida Anise

Jacaranda mimosifolia
Jacaranda

Juniperus chinensis 'Torulosa'
Chinese Juniper

Juniperus silicicola
Southern Red Cedar

162

Trees

Kigelia pinnata
Sausage Tree

Koelreuteria elegans
Golden Shower Tree

Krugiodendron ferreum
Black Ironwood

Lagerstroemia indica
Crape Myrtle

Lagerstroemia speciosa
Queen's Crape Myrtle

Licaria triandra
Gulf Licaria

163

Trees

Liriodendron tulipifera
Tulip Tree

Magnolia grandiflora
Southern Magnolia

Magnolia virginiana
Sweetbay

Manilkara zapota
Sapodilla

Mangifera indica
Mango

Millettia ovalifolia
Millettia

Trees

Myrciaria cauliflora
Jaboticaba

Nectandra coriacea
Lancewood

Ochrosia elliptica
Ochrosia

Ostrya virginiana
American Hophornbeam

Parkinsonia aculeata
Jerusalem Thorn

Peltophorum pterocarpum
Copperpod

Trees

Pandanus utilis
Screwpine

Parmentiera cereifera
Candlefruit

Pinus elliottii
Slash Pine

Plumeria alba
White Frangipani

Phyllanthus acidus
Otaheite Gooseberry

Podocarpus gracilior
Weeping Podocarpus

166

Trees

Plumeria rubra
Frangipani

Podocarpus macrophyllus
Yew Podocarpus

Podocarpus nagi
Nagi Podocarpus

Pongamia pinnata
Pongam

Pouteria sapota
Mammee Sapote

Prunus caroliniana
Cherry Laurel

167

Trees

Pseudobombax ellipticum
Shavingbrush Tree

Psidium guajava
Guava

Psidium littorale
Cattley Guava

Quercus laevis
Turkey Oak

Quercus virginiana
Live Oak

Samanea saman
Rain Tree

Trees

Ravenala madagascariensis
Travelers Tree

Sphaeropteris cooperi
Australian Tree Fern

Simarouba glauca
Paradise Tree

Spathodea campanulata
African Tulip Tree

Stenocarpus sinuatus
Firewheel Tree

Styrax grandifolius
Snowbell

Trees

Swietenia mahagoni
Mahogany

Tabebuia caraiba
Silver Trumpet Tree

Syzygium jambos
Rose Apple

Tabebuia chrysotricha
Golden Tabebuia

Tabebuia heterophylla
Pink Trumpet Tree

Tamarindus indica
Tamarind

Trees

Tabebuia impetiginosa
Purple Tabebuia

Taxodium distichum
Bald Cypress

Tecoma stans
Yellow Elder

Terminalia catappa
Tropical Almond

Ulmus alata
Winged Elm

Ulmus parvifolia
Chinese Elm

171

Shrubs

Acalypha hispida
Chenille Plant

Acalypha wilkesiana
Copperleaf

Acer palmatum 'Dissectum'
Japanese Maple

Adenium obesum
Desert Rose

Aesculus pavia
Red Buckeye

Agave sp.
Century Plant

Shrubs

Ardisia crenata
Coral Ardisia

Bauhinia punctata
Red Bauhinia

Bambusa vulgaris
Common Bamboo

Berberis julianae
Wintergreen Barberry

Berberis thunbergii 'Atropurpurea'
Japanese Barberry

Bougainvillea glabra
Lesser Bougainvillea

Shrubs

Brassaia actinophylla
Schefflera

Breynia disticha
Snowbush

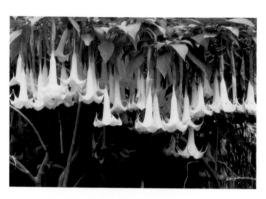

Brugmansia X candida
Angel's - Trumpet

Caesalpinia pulcherrima var. *flava*
Dwarf Poinciana

Brunfelsia australis
Yesterday-Today-and-Tomorrow

Calyptranthes pallens
Spicewood

Shrubs

Calliandra haematocephala
Red Powderpuff

Camellia japonica
Common Camellia

Carissa macrocarpa
Natal Plum

Cassia alata
Candle Bush

Chrysobalanus icaco
Cocoplum

Codiaeum variegatum var. *pictum*
Croton

175

Shrubs

Clerodendrum paniculatum
Pagoda Flower

Cordyline terminalis
Ti Plant

Crassula argentea
Jade Plant

Cuphea ignea
Cigar Plant

Cycas circinalis
Queen Sago

Cycas revoluta
King Sago

Shrubs

Dioon spinulosum
Spiny Dioon

Dombeya wallichii
Tropical Snowball

Dracaena deremensis 'Warneckii'
Warneck Dracaena

Dracaena fragrans 'Massangeana'
Fragrant Dracaena

Dracaena reflexa 'Song of India'
Reflexed Dracaena

Dracaena sanderana
Ribbon Plant

177

Shrubs

Duranta repens
Golden Dewdrop

Euphorbia pulcherrima
Poinsettia

Eugenia uniflora
Surinam Cherry

Euphorbia cotinifolia
Red Spurge

Euphorbia trigona
Cathedral Cactus

Feijoa sellowiana
Feijoa

Shrubs

Fatsia japonica
Fatsia

Galphimia glauca
Shower-of-Gold

Graptophyllum pictum
Caricature Plant

Hamelia patens
Firebush

Hibiscus rosa-sinensis
Hibiscus

Hibiscus schizopetalus
Fringed Hibiscus

Shrubs

Hydrangea macrophylla
Hydrangea

Ilex cornuta
Chinese Holly

Ilex rotunda
Ground Holly

Ixora 'Nora Grant'
Hybrid Ixora

Ixora 'Petite'
Dwarf Hybrid Ixora

Jasminum nitidum
Shining Jasmine

Shrubs

Jatropha integerrima
Peregrina

Justicia carnea
Flamingo Plant

Juniperus chinensis 'Blue Vase'
Chinese Juniper

Mahonia bealei
Leatherleaf Mahonia

Kalmia latifolia
Mountain Laurel

Leucophyllum frutescens
Texas Sage

181

Shrubs

Mallotonia gnaphalodes
Sea Lavender

Malpighia glabra
Barbados Cherry

Malvaviscus arboreus
Turk's Cap

Medinella magnifica
Medinella

Michelia figo
Banana Shrub

Nerium oleander
Oleander

Shrubs

Noronhia emarginata
Madagascar Olive

Pachystachys lutea
Golden Shrimp Plant

Opuntia sp.
Prickly Pear

Pandanus sanderi
Sander Screwpine

Pedilanthus tithymaloides
Redbird Flower

Philodendron selloum
Tree Philodendron

183

Shrubs

Pittosporum tobira
Japanese Pittosporum

Pittosporum tobira 'Wheeler's Dwarf '
Japanese Pittosporum

Platycladus orientalis
Oriental Arborvitae

Plumbago auriculata
Plumbago

Polyscias filicifolia
Fernleaf Aralia

Polyscias fruticosa
Ming Aralia

Shrubs

Polyscias obtusa
Oakleaf Aralia

Polyscias pinnata 'Marginata'
Balfour Aralia

Pseuderanthemum reticulatum
Reticulated Pseuderanthemum

Pyracantha coccinea
Red Firethorn

Rhododendron austrinum
Florida Flame Azalea

Rhododendron hybrids
Azalea

Shrubs

Rhododendron canescens
Pink Pinxter Azalea

Rhodoleia championii
Rhodoleia

Russelia equisetiformis
Firecracker Plant

Scaevola taccada
Beach Naupaka

Schefflera arboricola
Dwarf Schefflera

Severinia buxifolia
Boxthorn

Shrubs

Strelitzia nicolai
White Bird of Paradise

Thevetia peruviana
Yellow Oleander

Tibouchina granulosa
Purple Glory Tree

Triphasia trifolia
Limeberry

Tetrazygia bicolor
Florida Tetrazygia

Viburnum tinus
Laurestinus

187

Shrubs

Turnera ulmifolia
Yellow Alder

Vitex agnus-castus
Chaste Tree

Vitex trifolia 'Variegata'
Vitex

Yucca aloifolia
Spanish Bayonet

Zamia furfuracea
Cardboard Palm

Zamia pumila
Coontie

Herbaceous Perennials

Adiantum sp.
Maidenhair Fern

Aechmea fasciata 'Variegata'
Silver Vase

Agapanthus africanus
Lily-of-the-Nile

Aglaonema commutatum 'Silver Queen'
Aglaonema

Achimenes longiflora
Achimenes

Aloe barbadensis
Barbados Aloe

Herbaceous Perennials

Alocasia cucullata
Chinese Taro

Alocasia X amazonica
Amazon Elephant's Ear

Alpinia purpurata 'Eileen McDonald'
Pink Ginger

Alpinia zerumbet
Shellflower

Alpinia zerumbet 'Variegata'
Variegated Shellflower

Ananas comosus 'Variegatus'
Variegated Pineapple

Herbaceous Perennials

Anthurium 'Lady Jane'
Lady Jane Anthurium

Anthurium andraeanum
Flamingo Flower

Anthurium clarinervium
Anthurium

Anthurium salviniae
Birdsnest Anthurium

Asplenium nidus
Birdsnest Fern

Begonia X rex-cultorum
Rex Begonia

Herbaceous Perennials

Burbidgea schizocheila
Burbidgea

Caladium X hortulanum
Fancy-Leaved Caladium

Calathea lancifolia
Rattlesnake Plant

Calathea makoyana
Peacock Plant

Calathea zebrina
Zebra Calathea

Canna X generalis
Garden Canna

Herbaceous Perennials

Cattleya sp.
Cattleya Orchid

Clivia miniata
Kaffir Lily

Cortaderia selloana
Pampas Grass

Crinum asiaticum
Tree Crinum

Costus speciosus
Crepe Ginger

Crinum X amabile
Giant Spider Lily

Herbaceous Perennials

Crinum jagus
Saint Christopher Lily

Crinum zeylanicum
Milk and Wine Lily

Crossandra infundibuliformis
Crossandra

Cryptanthus sp.
Earth Star

Cyperus alternifolius
Umbrella Sedge

Dichorisandra thyrsiflora
Blue Ginger

Herbaceous Perennials

Cyperus papyrus
Papyrus

Dieffenbachia maculata 'Exotica'
Spotted Dumbcane

Epidendrum ibaguense
Reed-Stem Epidendrum

Etlingera elatior
Torch Ginger

Hedychium coccineum
Scarlet Ginger Lily

Eucharis amazonica
Amazon Lily

Herbaceous Perennials

Hedychium greenei
Ginger Lily

Heliconia caribaea
Caribbean Heliconia

Heliconia X 'Golden Torch'
Golden Torch Heliconia

Heliconia latispatha
Parrot Flower

Heliconia psittacorum 'Andromeda'
Parakeet Flower

Heliconia rostrata
Lobster Claw

Herbaceous Perennials

Heliconia stricta
Stricta Heliconia

Heliconia stricta 'Sharonii'
Stricta Heliconia

Heliconia wagnerana
Wagner Heliconia

Hemerocallis sp.
Day Lily

Hymenocallis floridana
Spider Lily

Hymenocallis narcissiflora
Ismene

Herbaceous Perennials

Hippeastrum X hybridum
Amaryllis

Iris hexagona var. *savannarum*
Blue Flag

Musa coccinea
Red Flowering Banana

Musa ornata
Lavender Flowering Banana

Musa velutina
Pink Banana

Neomarica gracilis
Walking Iris

Herbaceous Perennials

Neoregelia carolinae
Blushing Bromeliad

Phaius tankervilliae
Nun's Orchid

Phlox divaricata
Blue Phlox

Pontederia cordata
Pickerel Weed

Platycerium bifurcatum
Staghorn Fern

Salvia farinacea
Blue Sage

199

Herbaceous Perennials

Sabatia grandiflora
Marsh Pinks

Scadoxus multiflorus
Blood Lily

Sprekelia formosissima
Aztec Lily

Spathiphyllum 'Mauna Loa'
Peace Lily

Strelitzia reginae
Bird of Paradise

Strobilanthes dyeranus
Persian Shield

Herbaceous Perennials

Tillandsia lindenii
Air Plant

Xanthosoma lindenii
Indian Kale

Uniola paniculata
Sea Oats

Zantedeschia elliottiana
Calla Lily

Zephyranthes treatiae
Zephyr Lily

Zingiber spectabile
Blushing Ginger

201

Palms

Acoelorrhaphe wrightii - Paurotis Palm

Archontophoenix alexandrae - Alexandra Palm

Bismarckia nobilis - Bismarck Palm

Butia capitata - Pindo Palm

Carpentaria acuminata- Carpentaria Palm

Caryota urens - Toddy Fishtail Palm

Palms

Chamaedorea cataractarum - Cat Palm

Chamaerops humilis - European Fan Palm

Chrysalidocarpus lutescens - Areca Palm

Coccothrinax crinita - Old Man Palm

Cocos nucifera - Coconut Palm

Copernicia hospita - Hospita Copernicia

203

Palms

Corypha elata - Gebang Palm

Cyrtostachys renda - Sealing Wax Palm

Dictyosperma album var. *furfuraceum*
Hurricane Palm

Elaeis guineensis
African Oil Palm

Howea forsterana - Sentry Palm

Hyophorbe lagenicaulis - Bottle Palm

Palms

Latania lontaroides
Red Latan Palm

Licuala grandis
Licuala Palm

Licuala spinosa
Spiny Licuala

Livistona decipiens
Cut-Leaved Fan Palm

Livistona chinensis
Chinese Fan Palm

Livistona rotundifolia
Roundleaf Livistona

205

Palms

Phoenix canariensis - Canary Island Date Palm

Phoenix dactylifera - Date Palm

Phoenix reclinata - Senegal Date Palm

Phoenix roebelenii - Pygmy Date Palm

Phoenix sylvestris - Wild Date Palm

Pritchardia pacifica - Pritchardia Palm

Palms

Pseudophoenix sargentii
Buccaneer Palm

Ptychosperma elegans
Solitaire Palm

Ravenea rivularis
Majesty Palm

Rhapis excelsa
Lady Palm

Rhapis humilis
Slender Lady Palm

Rhapidophyllum hystrix
Needle Palm

207

Palms

Roystonea regia
Cuban Royal Palm

Serenoa repens
Saw Palmetto

Sabal palmetto
Sabal Palm

Syagrus romanzoffiana
Queen Palm

Thrinax morrisii
Key Thatch Palm

Trachycarpus fortunei
Windmill Palm

Palms

Trithrinax acanthocoma
Spiny Fiber Palm

Veitchia joannis
Joannis Palm

Veitchia mcdanielsii
Sunshine Palm

Wodyetia bifurcata
Foxtail Palm

Veitchia merrillii
Adonidia Palm

Washingtonia filifera (front)-Desert Fan Palm
W. robusta (rear)-Washington Palm

209

Vines

Allamanda violacea
Purple Allamanda

Antigonon leptopus
Coral Vine

Aristolochia grandiflora
Pelican Flower

Congea tomentosa
Wooly Congea

Cryptostegia madagascariensis
Madagascar Rubber Vine

Cydista aequinoctialis
Garlic Vine

Vines

Gloriosa rothschildiana
Rothschild Gloriosa Lily

Hylocereus undatus
Night-Blooming Cereus

Epipremnum aureum
Pothos

Petrea volubilis
Queen's Wreath

Ficus pumila
Creeping Fig

Passiflora coccinea
Red Passion Flower

Vines

Pyrostegia venusta
Flame Vine

Stephanotis floribunda
Madagascar jasmine

Senecio confusus
Mexican Flame Vine

Tecomanthe venusta
Tecomanthe

Thunbergia alata
Black-Eyed Susan Vine

Thunbergia grandiflora
Bengal Clock Vine

Groundcovers

Asparagus densiflorus 'Sprengeri'
Asparagus Fern

Callisia fragrans 'Melnickoff'
Fragrant Callisia

Dietes vegeta
African Iris

Evolvulus glomeratus
Blue Daze

Cuphea hyssopifolia 'Allyson'
False Heather

Fittonia verschaffeltii
Nerve Plant

Groundcovers

Gaillardia X grandiflora
Blanket Flower

Gloxinia sylvatica
Bolivian Sunset

Habranthus robustus
Rain Lily

Hedera canariensis
Algerian Ivy

Helianthus debilis
Beach Sunflower

Juniperus horizontalis 'Plumosa'
Creeping Juniper

Groundcovers

Kaempferia pulchra
Pretty Resurrection Lily

Lantana camara
Yellow Sage

Lantana montevidensis
Trailing Lantana

Nephrolepis exaltata
Boston Fern

Pilea serpyllifolia (left)-Stoplight Pilea
P. microphylla (right)-Artillery Plant

Peperomia magnoliifolia
Desert Privet

Groundcovers

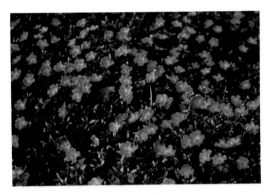

Portulaca grandiflora
Purslane

Rhoeo spathacea
Oyster Plant

Rumohra adiantiformis
Leatherleaf Fern

Selaginella sp.
Spikemoss

Setcreasea pallida
Purple-Heart

Zephyranthes rosea
Rain Lily

Hylocereus undatus *(Photograph p. 211)*

Common Name(s) : Night-blooming Cereus
Origin : Tropical America
Growth Rate : Medium
Salt Tolerance : High
Soil Requirements : Wide
Plant Type : Succulent vine
Foliage Color : Green
Flowering Season : Summer
Flower Color : White & yellow
Propagation : Cuttings
Human Hazards : None
Common Uses : Flowering vine; edible fruit
Major Problems : Scales
Additional Notes : Strap-like stems are heavy and ungainly. Fragrant flowers open at night.

Family : Cactaceae   **Zone** : 10B-11
Typical Height : Not applicable
Drought Tolerance : High
Nutritional Requirements : Low
Light Requirements : Medium; high
Leaf Type : None
Texture : Coarse
Flower Characteristics : Showy; fragrant

Environmental Problems : None

Hymenocallis caroliniana

Common Name(s) : Spider Lily
Origin : Southeastern United States
Growth Rate : Medium
Salt Tolerance : Low
Soil Requirements : Acid
Plant Type : Herbaceous perennial
Foliage Color : Green
Flowering Season : Summer
Flower Color : White
Propagation : Seeds; division
Human Hazards : Poisonous
Common Uses : Beds; borders
Major Problems : Leafspots
Additional Notes : A hardy spider lily for part shade; good in woodland setting.

Family : Amaryllidaceae   **Zone** : 7-9
Typical Height : 2 Ft.
Drought Tolerance : Medium
Nutritional Requirements : Medium
Light Requirements : Medium
Leaf Type : Simple; linear
Texture : Coarse
Flower Characteristics : Showy; fragrant

Environmental Problems : None

Hymenocallis floridana *(Photograph p. 197)*

Common Name(s) : Spider Lily
Origin : Florida
Growth Rate : Medium
Salt Tolerance : Low
Soil Requirements : Wide
Plant Type : Herbaceous perennial
Foliage Color : Green
Flowering Season : Summer
Flower Color : White
Propagation : Seeds; division
Human Hazards : Poisonous
Common Uses : Groundcover; specimen plant
Major Problems : None
Additional Notes : Variable throughout range; sometimes grows as emergent aquatic.

Family : Amaryllidaceae   **Zone** : 8-11
Typical Height : 2 Ft.
Drought Tolerance : Medium
Nutritional Requirements : Medium
Light Requirements : Medium; high
Leaf Type : Simple; linear
Texture : Coarse
Flower Characteristics : Showy; fragrant

Environmental Problems : None

Hymenocallis latifolia

Common Name(s) : Spider Lily
Origin : Florida and West Indies
Growth Rate : Medium
Salt Tolerance : High
Soil Requirements : Alkaline
Plant Type : Herbaceous perennial
Foliage Color : Green
Flowering Season : Summer
Flower Color : White
Propagation : Seeds; division
Human Hazards : Poisonous
Common Uses : Beds; flowering perennial
Major Problems : Leafspots
Additional Notes : Bulbs may need division every few years.

Family : Amaryllidaceae   **Zone** : 10A-11
Typical Height : 3 Ft.
Drought Tolerance : High
Nutritional Requirements : Medium
Light Requirements : High
Leaf Type : Simple
Texture : Coarse
Flower Characteristics : Fragrant; showy

Environmental Problems : None

Hymenocallis narcissiflora *(Photograph p. 197)*   Family : Amaryllidaceae   Zone : 9-10B

Common Name(s) : Ismene; Basket Flower; Peruvian Daffodil
Origin : Andes of Peru and Bolivia
Growth Rate : Medium
Salt Tolerance : Low
Soil Requirements : Wide
Plant Type : Herbaceous perennial
Foliage Color : Green
Flowering Season : Summer
Flower Color : White
Propagation : Division
Human Hazards : Poisonous
Common Uses : Beds; borders; specimen plant
Major Problems : None
Additional Notes : May rot in winter if kept wet.
Cultivars
'SULPHUR QUEEN' is similar but yellow.

Typical Height : 3 Ft.
Drought Tolerance : Medium
Nutritional Requirements : Medium
Light Requirements : Medium
Leaf Type : Simple; linear
Texture : Coarse
Flower Characteristics : Fragrant; showy

Environmental Problems : None

Hymenocallis palmeri   Family : Amaryllidaceae   Zone : 10A-11

Common Name(s) : Alligator Lily
Origin : Florida
Growth Rate : Medium
Salt Tolerance : Low
Soil Requirements : Acid
Plant Type : Herbaceous perennial
Foliage Color : Green
Flowering Season : Summer
Flower Color : White; green
Propagation : Division
Human Hazards : Poisonous
Common Uses : Beds; flowering perennial
Major Problems : None
Additional Notes : Useful in sites that flood but grows well with good drainage as well.

Typical Height : 1 Ft.
Drought Tolerance : Medium
Nutritional Requirements : Low
Light Requirements : Medium
Leaf Type : Simple
Texture : Medium
Flower Characteristics : Showy; fragrant

Environmental Problems : None

Hyophorbe lagenicaulis *(Photograph p. 204)*   Family : Palmae   Zone : 10B-11

Common Name(s) : Bottle Palm
Origin : Mauritius
Growth Rate : Slow
Salt Tolerance : High
Soil Requirements : Wide
Plant Type : Palm
Foliage Color : Green
Flowering Season : Summer
Flower Color : White
Propagation : Seeds
Human Hazards : None
Common Uses : Small tree; palm
Major Problems : K deficiency
Additional Notes : Has a short swollen trunk and a bottle-like appearance.

Typical Height : 12 Ft.
Drought Tolerance : High
Nutritional Requirements : Medium
Light Requirements : Medium; high
Leaf Type : Pinnately compound
Texture : Medium
Flower Characteristics : Insignificant

Environmental Problems : None

Hyophorbe verschaffeltii   Family : Palmae   Zone : 10B-11

Common Name(s) : Spindle Palm
Origin : Rodriguez Island
Growth Rate : Slow
Salt Tolerance : High
Soil Requirements : Wide
Plant Type : Palm
Foliage Color : Green
Flowering Season : Summer
Flower Color : White
Propagation : Seeds
Human Hazards : None
Common Uses : Small tree; palm
Major Problems : K deficiency.
Additional Notes : Has triangular leaf arrangement on a swollen trunk.

Typical Height : 20 Ft.
Drought Tolerance : High
Nutritional Requirements : High
Light Requirements : High
Leaf Type : Pinnately compound
Texture : Medium
Flower Characteristics : Insignificant

Environmental Problems : None

Hypelate trifoliata

Common Name(s) : White Ironwood
Origin : Lower Florida Keys & West Indies
Growth Rate : Slow
Salt Tolerance : High
Soil Requirements : Wide
Plant Type : Evergreen tree
Foliage Color : Green
Flowering Season : Spring; summer
Flower Color : White
Propagation : Seeds
Human Hazards : None
Common Uses : Small tree
Major Problems : None

Family : Sapindaceae   **Zone** : 10B-11

Typical Height : 30 Ft.
Drought Tolerance : High
Nutritional Requirements : Low
Light Requirements : High
Leaf Type : Trifoliate
Texture : Medium
Flower Characteristics : Insignificant

Environmental Problems : None

Additional Notes : A small native tree with very hard dense wood.

Hypericum X moserianum

Common Name(s) : Goldflower; St. Johns Wort
Origin : Hybrid
Growth Rate : Medium
Salt Tolerance : Low
Soil Requirements : Wide
Plant Type : Evergreen shrub
Foliage Color : Green
Flowering Season : Summer; fall
Flower Color : Yellow
Propagation : Seeds; cuttings; division
Human Hazards : None
Common Uses : Flowering shrub; rock gardens
Major Problems : None

Family : Hypericaceae   **Zone** : 7-10A

Typical Height : 2.5 Ft.
Drought Tolerance : Medium
Nutritional Requirements : Medium
Light Requirements : Medium; high
Leaf Type : Simple
Texture : Medium
Flower Characteristics : Showy

Environmental Problems : None

Additional Notes : Cut back to the ground each year to force healthy new growth.

Hyphaene spp.

Common Name(s) : Gingerbread Palm
Origin : North Africa
Growth Rate : Slow
Salt Tolerance : High
Soil Requirements : Wide
Plant Type : Palm
Foliage Color : Silver
Flowering Season : Summer
Flower Color : Brown
Propagation : Seeds
Human Hazards : None
Common Uses : Palm
Major Problems : None

Family : Palmae   **Zone** : 10B-11

Typical Height : 20 Ft.
Drought Tolerance : High
Nutritional Requirements : Low
Light Requirements : High
Leaf Type : Simple; palmately lobed
Texture : Very coarse
Flower Characteristics : Insignificant

Environmental Problems : None

Additional Notes : This drought-tolerant palm is unusual in that it regularly branches.

Hypoestes phyllostachya

Common Name(s) : Polka-dot Plant
Origin : Madagascar
Growth Rate : Fast
Salt Tolerance : Low
Soil Requirements : Wide
Plant Type : Herbaceous perennial
Foliage Color : Green & pink
Flowering Season : Spring; summer; fall
Flower Color : Lavender
Propagation : Cuttings
Human Hazards : None
Common Uses : Foliage plant; specimen plant; beds; groundcover
Major Problems : Aphids
Additional Notes : This plant has green leaves with pink spots.
Cultivars
'PINK SPLASH' is a more compact variety with larger pink spots; 'WHITE SPLASH' is compact with white spots on the leaves.

Family : Acanthaceae   **Zone** : 10B-11

Typical Height : 2 Ft.
Drought Tolerance : Low
Nutritional Requirements : Medium
Light Requirements : Low; medium
Leaf Type : Simple
Texture : Medium
Flower Characteristics : Insignificant

Environmental Problems : None

Ilex X attenuata

Common Name(s) : Attenuate Holly
Origin : Hybrid
Growth Rate : Medium
Salt Tolerance : Medium
Soil Requirements : Acid
Plant Type : Evergreen tree or shrub
Foliage Color : Green; variegated
Flowering Season : Spring
Flower Color : White
Propagation : Cuttings; grafting
Human Hazards : Spiny
Common Uses : Small tree; hedge; shrub
Major Problems : None
Additional Notes : A red-berried hybrid between I. cassine and I. opaca . Pyramidal form.
Cultivars
'FOSTERI' has dark blue-green foliage; 'EAST PALATKA' has flat yellow- green leaves; 'SAVANNAH' has wavy spiny leaves; 'HUME #2' has dense dark green foliage and fruits heavily; 'SUNNY FOSTER' has variegated foliage.

Family : Aquifoliaceae   Zone : 7-10B

Typical Height : 30 Ft.
Drought Tolerance : Medium
Nutritional Requirements : Low
Light Requirements : High
Leaf Type : Simple
Texture : Medium
Flower Characteristics : Insignificant

Environmental Problems : None

Ilex cassine

Common Name(s) : Dahoon Holly
Origin : Southeastern United States, Cuba
Growth Rate : Medium
Salt Tolerance : Medium
Soil Requirements : Acid
Plant Type : Evergreen tree
Foliage Color : Green
Flowering Season : Spring
Flower Color : White
Propagation : Seeds; cuttings; grafting
Human Hazards : None
Common Uses : Small tree; hedge
Major Problems : None
Additional Notes : Red-berried native holly. Grows in boggy sites.

Family : Aquifoliaceae   Zone : 7-10B

Typical Height : 30 Ft.
Drought Tolerance : High
Nutritional Requirements : Low
Light Requirements : High
Leaf Type : Simple
Texture : Medium
Flower Characteristics : Insignificant

Environmental Problems : None

Ilex cornuta *(Photograph p. 180)*

Common Name(s) : Chinese Holly
Origin : Eastern China
Growth Rate : Medium
Salt Tolerance : Low
Soil Requirements : Wide
Plant Type : Evergreen shrub
Foliage Color : Green
Flowering Season : Spring
Flower Color : White
Propagation : Cuttings
Human Hazards : Spiny
Common Uses : Shrub; hedge
Major Problems : Scales
Additional Notes : Good border plant with attractive red fruit.
Cultivars
'BURFORDII' has entire leaves with a single spine at the tip; 'ROTUNDA' is globe-shaped with very spiny yellow-green foliage; 'DAZZLER' has large bright red berries; 'BURFORDII NANA' is a slightly smaller selection of 'BURFORDII'; 'O-SPRING' is a variegated form of 'BURFORDII'.

Family : Aquifoliaceae   Zone : 7-9

Typical Height : 6 Ft.
Drought Tolerance : Medium
Nutritional Requirements : Medium
Light Requirements : Medium; high
Leaf Type : Simple
Texture : Medium
Flower Characteristics : Insignificant

Environmental Problems : None

Ilex crenata

Common Name(s) : Japanese Holly
Origin : Japan
Growth Rate : Slow
Salt Tolerance : Low
Soil Requirements : Acid
Plant Type : Evergreen shrub
Foliage Color : Green
Flowering Season : Spring
Flower Color : White
Propagation : Cuttings
Human Hazards : None
Common Uses : Shrub; hedge
Major Problems : Scales; nematodes
Additional Notes : Many cultivars exist; some are dwarf.
Cultivars
Dwarf cultivars include: 'COMPACTA', 'HELLERI', 'CONVEXA', 'MARIESII', 'HETZII', 'PETITE POINT', and 'TINY TIM'.

Family : Aquifoliaceae   Zone : 6B-9

Typical Height : 6 Ft.
Drought Tolerance : Low
Nutritional Requirements : Medium
Light Requirements : Medium; high
Leaf Type : Simple
Texture : Medium
Flower Characteristics : Insignificant

Environmental Problems : None

Ilex glabra

Common Name(s) : Gallberry
Origin : Eastern North America
Growth Rate : Slow
Salt Tolerance : Medium
Soil Requirements : Acid
Plant Type : Evergreen shrub
Foliage Color : Green
Flowering Season : Spring
Flower Color : White
Propagation : Cuttings
Human Hazards : None
Common Uses : Shrub
Major Problems : None

Family : Aquifoliaceae   **Zone** : 5-10A

Typical Height : 8 Ft.
Drought Tolerance : Medium
Nutritional Requirements : Low
Light Requirements : Medium; high
Leaf Type : Simple
Texture : Medium
Flower Characteristics : Insignificant

Environmental Problems : None

Additional Notes : Clump-forming native shrub. Black fruits in winter.
Cultivars
'VIRIDIS' has leaves green in winter; 'NIGRA' has purple leaves in winter; 'IVORY QUEEN' and 'LEUCOCARPA' have white fruits.

Ilex krugiana

Common Name(s) : Krug Holly; Tawnyberry Holly
Origin : South Florida and Caribbean
Growth Rate : Medium
Salt Tolerance : High
Soil Requirements : Wide
Plant Type : Evergreen tree
Foliage Color : Green
Flowering Season : Spring
Flower Color : White
Propagation : Seeds
Human Hazards : None
Common Uses : Small tree
Major Problems : None

Family : Aquifoliaceae   **Zone** : 10B-11

Typical Height : 30 Ft.
Drought Tolerance : High
Nutritional Requirements : Medium
Light Requirements : Medium
Leaf Type : Simple
Texture : Medium
Flower Characteristics : Insignificant

Environmental Problems : None

Additional Notes : A native tropical holly with dark purple fruits.

Ilex latifolia

Common Name(s) : Lusterleaf Holly
Origin : China and Japan
Growth Rate : Medium
Salt Tolerance : Low
Soil Requirements : Wide
Plant Type : Evergreen tree
Foliage Color : Green
Flowering Season : Spring
Flower Color : White
Propagation : Seeds; cuttings
Human Hazards : None
Common Uses : Shade tree
Major Problems : None

Family : Aquifoliaceae   **Zone** : 7-10B

Typical Height : 35 Ft.
Drought Tolerance : Low
Nutritional Requirements : High
Light Requirements : Medium
Leaf Type : Simple
Texture : Medium
Flower Characteristics : Insignificant

Environmental Problems : None

Additional Notes : Generally pest-free; difficult to propagate.

Ilex opaca

Common Name(s) : American Holly
Origin : Eastern United States
Growth Rate : Slow
Salt Tolerance : Medium
Soil Requirements : Acid
Plant Type : Evergreen tree
Foliage Color : Green; variegated
Flowering Season : Summer
Flower Color : White
Propagation : Seeds; grafting; cuttings
Human Hazards : None
Common Uses : Small tree
Major Problems : Scales

Family : Aquifoliaceae   **Zone** : 5-9

Typical Height : 35 Ft.
Drought Tolerance : High
Nutritional Requirements : Medium
Light Requirements : Medium; high
Leaf Type : Simple
Texture : Medium
Flower Characteristics : Insignificant

Environmental Problems : None

Additional Notes : Showy red berries in winter. Hundreds of cultivars exist.

Ilex rotunda *(Photograph p. 180)*
Common Name(s) : Round Holly
Origin : Korea to Vietnam
Growth Rate : Slow
Salt Tolerance : Low
Soil Requirements : Wide
Plant Type : Evergreen tree
Foliage Color : Green
Flowering Season : Spring
Flower Color : White
Propagation : Seeds; cuttings
Human Hazards : None
Common Uses : Small tree
Major Problems : None
Additional Notes : Showy fruit display; few problems; difficult to propagate.

Family : Aquifoliaceae   Zone : 8-10B

Typical Height : 20 Ft.
Drought Tolerance : Medium
Nutritional Requirements : High
Light Requirements : Medium
Leaf Type : Simple
Texture : Medium
Flower Characteristics : Insignificant

Environmental Problems : None

Ilex vomitoria
Common Name(s) : Yaupon Holly
Origin : Southeastern United States
Growth Rate : Medium
Salt Tolerance : High
Soil Requirements : Wide
Plant Type : Evergreen tree or shrub
Foliage Color : Green
Flowering Season : Spring; summer
Flower Color : White
Propagation : Seeds; cuttings
Human Hazards : None
Common Uses : Small tree; shrub
Major Problems : None
Additional Notes : Many cultivars exist.
Cultivars

Family : Aquifoliaceae   Zone : 7-10A

Typical Height : 20 Ft.
Drought Tolerance : High
Nutritional Requirements : Low
Light Requirements : Medium; high
Leaf Type : Simple
Texture : Fine
Flower Characteristics : Insignificant

Environmental Problems : None

'NANA' is a dwarf form that does not set fruit; 'JEWEL' is grown for its heavy fruit set; 'OTIS MILEY' and 'YAWKEYII' have yellow fruits; 'PENDULA' is a weeping form; 'SCHELLINGS DWARF' is a very compact form with red new leaves.

Illicium anisatum *(Photograph p. 162)*
Common Name(s) : Anise Tree; Chinese Anise
Origin : Japan and Korea
Growth Rate : Medium
Salt Tolerance : Low
Soil Requirements : Wide
Plant Type : Evergreen shrub or tree
Foliage Color : Green
Flowering Season : Spring
Flower Color : Yellow-green
Propagation : Seeds; cuttings
Human Hazards : None
Common Uses : Shrub; hedge
Major Problems : Scales
Additional Notes : Fragrant anise-scented foliage.

Family : Illiciaceae   Zone : 8-10B

Typical Height : 20 Ft.
Drought Tolerance : Medium
Nutritional Requirements : Medium
Light Requirements : Medium; high
Leaf Type : Simple
Texture : Medium
Flower Characteristics : Insignificant

Environmental Problems : None

Illicium floridanum *(Photograph p. 162)*
Common Name(s) : Florida Anise; Purple Anise
Origin : Southeastern United States
Growth Rate : Medium
Salt Tolerance : Low
Soil Requirements : Wide
Plant Type : Evergreen shrub
Foliage Color : Green
Flowering Season : Spring
Flower Color : Red-purple
Propagation : Seeds; cuttings
Human Hazards : None
Common Uses : Shrub
Major Problems : Scales
Additional Notes : This native has aromatic anise-scented leaves.

Family : Illiciaceae   Zone : 8-10A

Typical Height : 15 Ft.
Drought Tolerance : Medium
Nutritional Requirements : Medium
Light Requirements : Medium; high
Leaf Type : Simple
Texture : Medium
Flower Characteristics : Showy

Environmental Problems : None

Ipomoea fistulosa

Common Name(s) : Morning-glory
Origin : Florida and Tropical America
Growth Rate : Fast
Salt Tolerance : Medium
Soil Requirements : Wide
Plant Type : Perennial vine
Foliage Color : Green
Flowering Season : Winter; spring
Flower Color : Purple
Propagation : Seeds; cuttings
Human Hazards : None
Common Uses : Flowering vine; flowering groundcover
Major Problems : None
Additional Notes : Can be grown as groundcover or will climb up a support.

Family : Convolvulaceae   **Zone** : 9-11

Typical Height : Not applicable
Drought Tolerance : Medium
Nutritional Requirements : Medium
Light Requirements : High
Leaf Type : Simple
Texture : Medium
Flower Characteristics : Showy

Environmental Problems : None

Ipomoea pes-caprae

Common Name(s) : Railroad Vine
Origin : South Florida
Growth Rate : Fast
Salt Tolerance : High
Soil Requirements : Wide
Plant Type : Perennial vine
Foliage Color : Green
Flowering Season : Summer; fall
Flower Color : Purple
Propagation : Cuttings; division
Human Hazards : Poisonous
Common Uses : Flowering groundcover; seasides
Major Problems : None
Additional Notes : A native vine well adapted to beaches and coastal dunes.

Family : Convolvulaceae   **Zone** : 10B-11

Typical Height : .5 Ft.
Drought Tolerance : High
Nutritional Requirements : Low
Light Requirements : High
Leaf Type : Simple
Texture : Coarse
Flower Characteristics : Showy

Environmental Problems : None

Ipomoea spp.

Common Name(s) : Morning-glory
Origin : n/a
Growth Rate : Fast
Salt Tolerance : Medium
Soil Requirements : Wide
Plant Type : Perennial vine
Foliage Color : Green
Flowering Season : Summer; fall
Flower Color : Blue; pink; purple; red; white
Propagation : Cuttings; division
Human Hazards : None
Common Uses : Flowering vine; vine; groundcover
Major Problems : None
Additional Notes : Some native, some fragrant. Can become weedy. Best as annuals.

Family : Convolvulaceae   **Zone** : 9-11

Typical Height : Not applicable
Drought Tolerance : Medium
Nutritional Requirements : Medium
Light Requirements : High
Leaf Type : Simple
Texture : Medium
Flower Characteristics : Showy

Environmental Problems : Invasive

Ipomoea stolonifera

Common Name(s) : Morning Glory
Origin : Southeastern United States
Growth Rate : Fast
Salt Tolerance : Medium
Soil Requirements : Wide
Plant Type : Perennial vine
Foliage Color : Green
Flowering Season : Spring; summer; fall
Flower Color : White & purple
Propagation : Cuttings; division
Human Hazards : Poisonous
Common Uses : Flowering groundcover
Major Problems : None
Additional Notes : A native vine well adapted to dry sandy soils.

Family : Convolvulaceae   **Zone** : 8-10B

Typical Height : .5 Ft.
Drought Tolerance : High
Nutritional Requirements : Low
Light Requirements : High
Leaf Type : Simple
Texture : Coarse
Flower Characteristics : Showy

Environmental Problems : None

Iresine spp.

Common Name(s) : Blood Leaf
Origin : South America
Growth Rate : Fast
Salt Tolerance : Medium
Soil Requirements : Wide
Plant Type : Herbaceous perennial
Foliage Color : Red; variegated
Flowering Season : Summer
Flower Color : Green
Propagation : Cuttings
Human Hazards : None
Common Uses : Beds; borders; specimen plant; foliage plant
Major Problems : Mites
Additional Notes : I. herbstii has notched leaves. I. lindenii has pointed leaves.

Family : Amaranthaceae   Zone : 10B-11

Typical Height : 3 Ft.
Drought Tolerance : Low
Nutritional Requirements : Medium
Light Requirements : Medium; high
Leaf Type : Simple
Texture : Medium
Flower Characteristics : Insignificant

Environmental Problems : None

Iris 'Louisiana Hybrids'

Common Name(s) : Louisiana Iris
Origin : Hybrid
Growth Rate : Medium
Salt Tolerance : Low
Soil Requirements : Acid
Plant Type : Herbaceous perennial
Foliage Color : Green
Flowering Season : Spring; summer
Flower Color : Red; yellow; blue; white; purple
Propagation : Division
Human Hazards : Irritant
Common Uses : Beds; borders; specimen plant
Major Problems : Iris borers
Additional Notes : Good perennials for wet areas. Many cultivars exist.

Family : Iridaceae   Zone : 7-10B

Typical Height : 2.5 Ft.
Drought Tolerance : Low
Nutritional Requirements : Medium
Light Requirements : High
Leaf Type : Simple; linear
Texture : Coarse
Flower Characteristics : Showy

Environmental Problems : None

Iris hexagona var. savannarum *(Photo. p. 198)*

Common Name(s) : Prairie Iris; Blue Flag
Origin : Southeastern United States
Growth Rate : Medium
Salt Tolerance : Low
Soil Requirements : Acid
Plant Type : Herbaceous perennial
Foliage Color : Green
Flowering Season : Spring
Flower Color : Lavender; white
Propagation : Division
Human Hazards : Irritant
Common Uses : Beds; flowering perennial
Major Problems : None
Additional Notes : Useful in wet areas.

Family : Iridaceae   Zone : 8-10B

Typical Height : 5 Ft.
Drought Tolerance : Low
Nutritional Requirements : Medium
Light Requirements : High
Leaf Type : Simple; linear
Texture : Coarse
Flower Characteristics : Showy

Environmental Problems : None

Iris kaempferi

Common Name(s) : Japanese Iris
Origin : Japan
Growth Rate : Medium
Salt Tolerance : Low
Soil Requirements : Wide
Plant Type : Herbaceous perennial
Foliage Color : Green
Flowering Season : Spring
Flower Color : Purple
Propagation : Division
Human Hazards : Irritant
Common Uses : Beds
Major Problems : Thrips; virus
Additional Notes : The japanese iris has rather flat reddish-purple blooms.

Family : Iridaceae   Zone : 5-9

Typical Height : 2 Ft.
Drought Tolerance : Medium
Nutritional Requirements : Low
Light Requirements : High
Leaf Type : Simple; linear
Texture : Medium
Flower Characteristics : Showy

Environmental Problems : None

Iris virginica

Common Name(s) : Southern Blue Flag; Blue Flag
Origin : Southeastern United States
Growth Rate : Medium
Salt Tolerance : Low
Soil Requirements : Acid
Plant Type : Herbaceous perennial
Foliage Color : Green
Flowering Season : Spring
Flower Color : Lavender; white
Propagation : Division
Human Hazards : Irritant
Common Uses : Beds; flowering perennial
Major Problems : None
Additional Notes : Useful in wet areas.

Family : Iridaceae   **Zone** : 8-10B

Typical Height : 3 Ft.
Drought Tolerance : Low
Nutritional Requirements : Medium
Light Requirements : High
Leaf Type : Simple; linear
Texture : Coarse
Flower Characteristics : Showy

Environmental Problems : None

Iva frutescens

Common Name(s) : Marsh Elder
Origin : Southeastern United States
Growth Rate : Medium
Salt Tolerance : High
Soil Requirements : Alkaline
Plant Type : Evergreen shrub
Foliage Color : Green
Flowering Season : Spring; summer
Flower Color : Green
Propagation : Seeds
Human Hazards : None
Common Uses : Shrub
Major Problems : None
Additional Notes : Useful native where brackish water accumulates.

Family : Compositae   **Zone** : 8-10B

Typical Height : 4 Ft.
Drought Tolerance : High
Nutritional Requirements : Low
Light Requirements : High
Leaf Type : Simple
Texture : Medium
Flower Characteristics : Insignificant

Environmental Problems : None

Iva imbricata

Common Name(s) : Seacoast Beach Elder
Origin : Southeastern United States
Growth Rate : Fast
Salt Tolerance : High
Soil Requirements : Alkaline
Plant Type : Herbaceous perennial
Foliage Color : Green
Flowering Season : Spring; summer
Flower Color : Green
Propagation : Seeds
Human Hazards : None
Common Uses : Seasides
Major Problems : None
Additional Notes : Sand binder; roots along stems.

Family : Compositae   **Zone** : 9-10B

Typical Height : 2 Ft.
Drought Tolerance : High
Nutritional Requirements : Low
Light Requirements : High
Leaf Type : Simple
Texture : Medium
Flower Characteristics : Inconspicuous

Environmental Problems : None

Ixora chinensis

Common Name(s) : Chinese Ixora
Origin : Malay Peninsula and China
Growth Rate : Medium
Salt Tolerance : Medium
Soil Requirements : Acid
Plant Type : Evergreen shrub
Foliage Color : Green
Flowering Season : Year-round
Flower Color : Orange-red; yellow; white
Propagation : Cuttings
Human Hazards : None
Common Uses : Flowering shrub; flowering pot plant
Major Problems : Nematodes; Fe deficiency; scales
Additional Notes : Despite its problems, an excellent flowering shrub for south Florida.
Cultivars
'DIXIANA' has dark orange flowers.

Family : Rubiaceae   **Zone** : 10B-11

Typical Height : 3 Ft.
Drought Tolerance : Medium
Nutritional Requirements : High
Light Requirements : High
Leaf Type : Simple
Texture : Medium
Flower Characteristics : Showy

Environmental Problems : None

Ixora coccinea

Common Name(s) : Flame of The Woods; Red Ixora
Origin : Southern Asia
Growth Rate : Medium
Salt Tolerance : Medium
Soil Requirements : Acid
Plant Type : Evergreen shrub
Foliage Color : Green
Flowering Season : Year-round
Flower Color : Yellow; red; pink
Propagation : Cuttings
Human Hazards : None
Common Uses : Hedge; flowering shrub; flowering pot plant
Major Problems : Nematodes; Fe deficiency; scales; root rots
Additional Notes : Several cultivars exist;
Cultivars
'MAGEE'S YELLOW' has yellow flowers.

Family : Rubiaceae   **Zone** : 10B-11

Typical Height : 5 Ft.
Drought Tolerance : Medium
Nutritional Requirements : High
Light Requirements : High
Leaf Type : Simple
Texture : Medium
Flower Characteristics : Showy

Environmental Problems : None

Ixora duffii

Common Name(s) : Ixora
Origin : Southern Asia
Growth Rate : Medium
Salt Tolerance : Medium
Soil Requirements : Acid
Plant Type : Evergreen shrub
Foliage Color : Green
Flowering Season : Year-round
Flower Color : Orange-red
Propagation : Cuttings
Human Hazards : None
Common Uses : Hedge; flowering shrub; flowering pot plant
Major Problems : Nematodes; scales; Fe deficiency; root rots
Additional Notes : A free flowering species with large leathery leaves.
Cultivars
'SUPER KING' has large round balls of bright red flowers.

Family : Rubiaceae   **Zone** : 10B-11

Typical Height : 5 Ft.
Drought Tolerance : Medium
Nutritional Requirements : High
Light Requirements : High
Leaf Type : Simple
Texture : Medium
Flower Characteristics : Showy

Environmental Problems : None

Ixora hybrids *(Photograph p. 180)*

Common Name(s) : Hybrid Ixora
Origin : Hybrid
Growth Rate : Medium
Salt Tolerance : Medium
Soil Requirements : Acid
Plant Type : Evergreen shrub
Foliage Color : Green
Flowering Season : Year-round
Flower Color : Orange-red; yellow; red; pink
Propagation : Cuttings
Human Hazards : None
Common Uses : Flowering shrub; flowering pot plant
Major Problems : Nematodes; scales; Fe deficiency; root rots
Cultivars
'PETITES' are small-leaved, compact orange-red, red, yellow, or pink flowering varieties; 'NORA GRANT' is a nematode-resistant pink flowering cultivar; 'MAUI' has large leaves and orange-red flowers.

Family : Rubiaceae   **Zone** : 10B-11

Typical Height : 2.5 Ft.
Drought Tolerance : Medium
Nutritional Requirements : High
Light Requirements : High
Leaf Type : Simple
Texture : Medium
Flower Characteristics : Showy

Environmental Problems : None

Jacaranda mimosifolia *(Photograph p. 162)*

Common Name(s) : Jacaranda
Origin : Brazil and Argentina
Growth Rate : Fast
Salt Tolerance : Low
Soil Requirements : Wide
Plant Type : Deciduous tree
Foliage Color : Green
Flowering Season : Spring; summer
Flower Color : Blue
Propagation : Seeds
Human Hazards : None
Common Uses : Flowering tree
Major Problems : Mushroom root rot
Additional Notes : Attractive flowering tree with very fine-textured foliage.

Family : Bignoniaceae   **Zone** : 10A-11

Typical Height : 45 Ft.
Drought Tolerance : High
Nutritional Requirements : Medium
Light Requirements : High
Leaf Type : Bipinnately compound
Texture : Fine
Flower Characteristics : Showy

Environmental Problems : None

Jacquemontia spp.

Common Name(s) : Jacquemontia
Origin : Tropical America
Growth Rate : Medium
Salt Tolerance : Low
Soil Requirements : Acid
Plant Type : Herbaceous vine
Foliage Color : Green
Flowering Season : Spring; summer; fall
Flower Color : White; blue
Propagation : Cuttings
Human Hazards : None
Common Uses : Flowering vine
Major Problems : None
Additional Notes : Several species are cultivated. <u>J. tamnifolia</u> is the hardiest.

Family : Convolvulaceae   **Zone** : 10B-11

Typical Height : Not applicable
Drought Tolerance : High
Nutritional Requirements : Medium
Light Requirements : Medium; high
Leaf Type : Simple
Texture : Medium
Flower Characteristics : Showy

Environmental Problems : None

Jacquinia keyensis

Common Name(s) : Joewood
Origin : South Florida and West Indies
Growth Rate : Slow
Salt Tolerance : High
Soil Requirements : Alkaline
Plant Type : Evergreen shrub or tree
Foliage Color : Green
Flowering Season : Year-round
Flower Color : White
Propagation : Seeds
Human Hazards : None
Common Uses : Flowering shrub; small flowering tree; seasides
Major Problems : None
Additional Notes : Seldom used native of south Florida.

Family : Theophrastaceae   **Zone** : 10B-11

Typical Height : 15 Ft.
Drought Tolerance : High
Nutritional Requirements : Low
Light Requirements : High; medium
Leaf Type : Simple
Texture : Medium
Flower Characteristics : Showy; fragrant

Environmental Problems : None

Jasminum dichotomum

Common Name(s) : Gold Coast Jasmine
Origin : Tropical Africa
Growth Rate : Medium
Salt Tolerance : Low
Soil Requirements : Wide
Plant Type : Evergreen vine
Foliage Color : Green
Flowering Season : Year-round
Flower Color : White
Propagation : Cuttings
Human Hazards : None
Common Uses : Flowering vine
Major Problems : Scales
Additional Notes : Closed flower buds are red. Can become weedy.

Family : Oleaceae   **Zone** : 10B-11

Typical Height : Not applicable
Drought Tolerance : Medium
Nutritional Requirements : Medium
Light Requirements : Medium; high
Leaf Type : Simple
Texture : Medium
Flower Characteristics : Showy; fragrant

Environmental Problems : Weedy

Jasminum fluminense

Common Name(s) : Azores Jasmine
Origin : Tropical Africa
Growth Rate : Medium
Salt Tolerance : Low
Soil Requirements : Wide
Plant Type : Evergreen vine
Foliage Color : Green
Flowering Season : Year-round
Flower Color : White
Propagation : Cuttings; seeds
Human Hazards : None
Common Uses : Flowering vine
Major Problems : Scales
Additional Notes : Seeds self-sow, can become a weed.

Family : Oleaceae   **Zone** : 10B-11

Typical Height : Not applicable
Drought Tolerance : Medium
Nutritional Requirements : Medium
Light Requirements : Medium; high
Leaf Type : Trifoliate
Texture : Medium
Flower Characteristics : Showy; fragrant

Environmental Problems : Weedy

Jasminum humile

Family : Oleaceae   **Zone** : 7-9

Common Name(s) : Yellow Jasmine
Origin : Himalayas
Growth Rate : Medium
Salt Tolerance : Low
Soil Requirements : Wide
Plant Type : Evergreen shrub
Foliage Color : Green
Flowering Season : Spring; summer
Flower Color : Yellow
Propagation : Cuttings
Human Hazards : None
Common Uses : Flowering shrub
Major Problems : Scales
Additional Notes : Best suited for central and north Florida.

Typical Height : 15 Ft.
Drought Tolerance : Medium
Nutritional Requirements : Medium
Light Requirements : Medium; high
Leaf Type : Pinnately compound
Texture : Medium
Flower Characteristics : Showy; fragrant

Environmental Problems : None

Jasminum mesnyi

Family : Oleaceae   **Zone** : 8-10A

Common Name(s) : Primrose Jasmine
Origin : Western China
Growth Rate : Medium
Salt Tolerance : Low
Soil Requirements : Wide
Plant Type : Evergreen shrub
Foliage Color : Green
Flowering Season : Winter; spring
Flower Color : Yellow
Propagation : Cuttings
Human Hazards : None
Common Uses : Flowering shrub; hedge; flowering groundcover
Major Problems : Scales
Additional Notes : Sprawling shrub best suited for central and northern Florida.

Typical Height : 8 Ft.
Drought Tolerance : Medium
Nutritional Requirements : Medium
Light Requirements : High
Leaf Type : Pinnately compound
Texture : Medium
Flower Characteristics : Showy

Environmental Problems : None

Jasminum multiflorum

Family : Oleaceae   **Zone** : 10B-11

Common Name(s) : Downy Jasmine
Origin : India
Growth Rate : Medium
Salt Tolerance : Low
Soil Requirements : Wide
Plant Type : Evergreen shrub or vine
Foliage Color : Green
Flowering Season : Spring; summer; fall
Flower Color : White
Propagation : Cuttings
Human Hazards : None
Common Uses : Flowering shrub; hedge; flowering vine
Major Problems : Scales
Additional Notes : Sprawling growth habit, downy leaf surface.

Typical Height : 5 Ft.
Drought Tolerance : Medium
Nutritional Requirements : Medium
Light Requirements : Medium; high
Leaf Type : Pinnately compound
Texture : Medium
Flower Characteristics : Showy

Environmental Problems : None

Jasminum nitidum *(Photograph p. 180)*

Family : Oleaceae   **Zone** : 10B-11

Common Name(s) : Shining Jasmine
Origin : Admiralty Islands
Growth Rate : Medium
Salt Tolerance : Medium
Soil Requirements : Wide
Plant Type : Evergreen shrub
Foliage Color : Green
Flowering Season : Spring; summer
Flower Color : White
Propagation : Cuttings
Human Hazards : None
Common Uses : Flowering shrub; hedge
Major Problems : Scales
Additional Notes : Shiny leaves.

Typical Height : 5 Ft.
Drought Tolerance : Medium
Nutritional Requirements : Medium
Light Requirements : Medium; high
Leaf Type : Pinnately compound
Texture : Medium
Flower Characteristics : Showy; fragrant

Environmental Problems : None

Jasminum officinale

Common Name(s) : Poet's Jasmine
Origin : Iran to Western China
Growth Rate : Medium
Salt Tolerance : Low
Soil Requirements : Wide
Plant Type : Deciduous vine
Foliage Color : Green
Flowering Season : Spring; summer; fall
Flower Color : White
Propagation : Cuttings
Human Hazards : None
Common Uses : Flowering vine
Major Problems : Scales
Additional Notes : Fragrant flowers contain essential oil used in perfumes.
Cultivars
'GRANDIFLORUM' has large purple-tinted flowers. 'AUREO-VARIEGATUM' has variegated foliage.

Family : Oleaceae   **Zone** : 7-10B

Typical Height : Not applicable
Drought Tolerance : Medium
Nutritional Requirements : Medium
Light Requirements : Medium; high
Leaf Type : Pinnately compound
Texture : Medium
Flower Characteristics : Showy; fragrant

Environmental Problems : None

Jasminum sambac

Common Name(s) : Arabian Jasmine
Origin : India
Growth Rate : Medium
Salt Tolerance : Low
Soil Requirements : Wide
Plant Type : Evergreen vine or shrub
Foliage Color : Green
Flowering Season : Summer; fall
Flower Color : White
Propagation : Cuttings
Human Hazards : None
Common Uses : Flowering vine; flowering shrub
Major Problems : Scales
Additional Notes : Flowers are used to flavor tea.
Cultivars
'GRAND DUKE' has double flowers.

Family : Oleaceae   **Zone** : 10A-11

Typical Height : 5 Ft.
Drought Tolerance : Medium
Nutritional Requirements : Medium
Light Requirements : Medium; high
Leaf Type : Simple
Texture : Medium
Flower Characteristics : Showy; fragrant

Environmental Problems : None

Jasminum volubile

Common Name(s) : Wax Jasmine
Origin : Australia
Growth Rate : Medium
Salt Tolerance : Medium
Soil Requirements : Wide
Plant Type : Evergreen shrub or vine
Foliage Color : Green
Flowering Season : Year-round
Flower Color : White
Propagation : Cuttings
Human Hazards : None
Common Uses : Hedge; flowering shrub
Major Problems : Scales
Additional Notes : Tends to vine if not sheared.

Family : Oleaceae   **Zone** : 10B-11

Typical Height : 3 Ft.
Drought Tolerance : Medium
Nutritional Requirements : Medium
Light Requirements : High; medium
Leaf Type : Simple
Texture : Medium
Flower Characteristics : Showy; fragrant

Environmental Problems : None

Jatropha gossypifolia

Common Name(s) : Cotton-leaved Jatropha
Origin : Tropical America
Growth Rate : Medium
Salt Tolerance : Medium
Soil Requirements : Wide
Plant Type : Evergreen shrub
Foliage Color : Red-green
Flowering Season : Year-round
Flower Color : Red
Propagation : Cuttings
Human Hazards : Poisonous
Common Uses : Shrub
Major Problems : None
Additional Notes : Leaves are coppery-green with red veins. Tolerant of poor soil conditions.

Family : Euphorbiaceae   **Zone** : 10B-11

Typical Height : 5 Ft.
Drought Tolerance : High
Nutritional Requirements : Low
Light Requirements : High
Leaf Type : Simple; lobed
Texture : Medium
Flower Characteristics : Insignificant

Environmental Problems : Weedy

Jatropha integerrima *(Photograph p. 181)*

Common Name(s) : Peregrina
Origin : Cuba
Growth Rate : Medium
Salt Tolerance : Medium
Soil Requirements : Wide
Plant Type : Evergreen shrub
Foliage Color : Green
Flowering Season : Year-round
Flower Color : Red
Propagation : Cuttings
Human Hazards : Poisonous
Common Uses : Flowering shrub
Major Problems : Leafminers; mites; scales
Additional Notes : Tolerant of poor soil conditions; leaf shape is highly variable.
Cultivars
'COMPACTA' is a more compact cultivar.

Family : Euphorbiaceae   Zone : 10B-11

Typical Height : 8 Ft.
Drought Tolerance : High
Nutritional Requirements : Low
Light Requirements : High
Leaf Type : Simple; lobed
Texture : Medium
Flower Characteristics : Showy

Environmental Problems : None

Jatropha multifida

Common Name(s) : Coral Plant
Origin : Tropical America
Growth Rate : Medium
Salt Tolerance : Medium
Soil Requirements : Wide
Plant Type : Evergreen shrub
Foliage Color : Green
Flowering Season : Spring; summer; fall
Flower Color : Red
Propagation : Seeds; cuttings
Human Hazards : Poisonous
Common Uses : Flowering shrub
Major Problems : Mites; scales
Additional Notes : Fine textured specimen plant. Seed toxic to humans.

Family : Euphorbiaceae   Zone : 10A-11

Typical Height : 15 Ft.
Drought Tolerance : High
Nutritional Requirements : Low
Light Requirements : High
Leaf Type : Simple; finely divided
Texture : Fine
Flower Characteristics : Showy

Environmental Problems : None

Jatropha podagrica

Common Name(s) : Gout Plant
Origin : Central America
Growth Rate : Medium
Salt Tolerance : Medium
Soil Requirements : Wide
Plant Type : Evergreen shrub
Foliage Color : Green
Flowering Season : Spring; fall
Flower Color : Red
Propagation : Seeds
Human Hazards : Poisonous
Common Uses : Flowering shrub
Major Problems : Mites; scales
Additional Notes : Has swollen base; leaves are very deeply lobed.

Family : Euphorbiaceae   Zone : 10B-11

Typical Height : 3 Ft.
Drought Tolerance : High
Nutritional Requirements : Low
Light Requirements : High
Leaf Type : Simple; palmately lobed
Texture : Fine
Flower Characteristics : Showy

Environmental Problems : None

Juncus effusus

Common Name(s) : Soft Rush
Origin : Eurasia, North America, Australia
Growth Rate : Medium
Salt Tolerance : Medium
Soil Requirements : Wet
Plant Type : Herbaceous perennial
Foliage Color : Green
Flowering Season : Summer
Flower Color : Brown
Propagation : Division
Human Hazards : None
Common Uses : Aquatic
Major Problems : None
Additional Notes : Good for wet sites.

Family : Juncaceae   Zone : 4-10B

Typical Height : 4 Ft.
Drought Tolerance : Low
Nutritional Requirements : Low
Light Requirements : High
Leaf Type : Simple; linear
Texture : Fine
Flower Characteristics : Insignificant

Environmental Problems : None

Juniperus chinensis *(Photograph p. 162, 181)*

Common Name(s) : Chinese Juniper
Origin : Eastern Asia
Growth Rate : Medium
Salt Tolerance : Medium
Soil Requirements : Wide
Plant Type : Evergreen shrub or tree
Foliage Color : Green
Flowering Season : Spring
Flower Color : n/a
Propagation : Cuttings
Human Hazards : None
Common Uses : Shrub; hedge; groundcover; tree
Major Problems : Mites; bacterial blight
Additional Notes : Many cultivars, prostrate or upright. Does not tolerate severe pruning.
Cultivars

Family : Cupressaceae   **Zone** : 3-10B

Typical Height : 6 Ft.
Drought Tolerance : High
Nutritional Requirements : Low
Light Requirements : High
Leaf Type : Scale-like
Texture : Fine
Flower Characteristics : Cone

Environmental Problems : None

'HETZII' grows to about 10 ft and has a vase-shape and blue-green foliage; 'PFTIZERANA' is a broad spreading cultivar 6 ft tall; 'PARSONII' is low-growing with gray-green foliage; 'TORULOSA' is a taller variety with twisted branches; 'BLUE VASE' is a broad spreading variety with blue-green foliage; 'MINT JULEP' is a smaller mint green foliage spreading variety.

Juniperus chinensis var. procumbens

Common Name(s) : Japanese Garden Juniper
Origin : Japan
Growth Rate : Medium
Salt Tolerance : Medium
Soil Requirements : Wide
Plant Type : Evergreen shrub
Foliage Color : Blue-green; variegated
Flowering Season : Spring
Flower Color : n/a
Propagation : Cuttings
Human Hazards : None
Common Uses : Groundcover
Major Problems : Mites; bacterial blight
Additional Notes : A low creeping, sometimes mounding groundcover.
Cultivars

Family : Cupressaceae   **Zone** : 5-10B

Typical Height : 2 Ft.
Drought Tolerance : High
Nutritional Requirements : Low
Light Requirements : High
Leaf Type : Scale-like
Texture : Fine
Flower Characteristics : Cone

Environmental Problems : None

'NANA' is a slow-growing dwarf variety; 'VARIEGATA' has yellow and green foliage.

Juniperus chinensis var. sargentii

Common Name(s) : Sargent Juniper
Origin : Japan
Growth Rate : Medium
Salt Tolerance : Medium
Soil Requirements : Wide
Plant Type : Evergreen shrub
Foliage Color : Blue-green
Flowering Season : Spring
Flower Color : n/a
Propagation : Cuttings
Human Hazards : None
Common Uses : Shrub; groundcover
Major Problems : Mites; bacterial blight
Additional Notes : A creeping or spreading variety.
Cultivars

Family : Cupressaceae   **Zone** : 4-10A

Typical Height : 2.5 Ft.
Drought Tolerance : High
Nutritional Requirements : Low
Light Requirements : High
Leaf Type : Scale-like
Texture : Fine
Flower Characteristics : Cone

Environmental Problems : None

'GLAUCA' and 'MANEY' have blue-green foliage; 'VIRIDIS' has green new leaves.

Juniperus conferta

Common Name(s) : Shore Juniper
Origin : Sakhalin and Japan
Growth Rate : Medium
Salt Tolerance : High
Soil Requirements : Wide
Plant Type : Evergreen shrub
Foliage Color : Blue-green
Flowering Season : Spring
Flower Color : n/a
Propagation : Cuttings; seeds
Human Hazards : None
Common Uses : Shrub; groundcover; seasides
Major Problems : Mites; bacterial blight
Additional Notes : This salt-tolerant juniper has many cultivars.
Cultivars

Family : Cupressaceae   **Zone** : 6-10A

Typical Height : 2 Ft.
Drought Tolerance : High
Nutritional Requirements : Low
Light Requirements : High
Leaf Type : Scale-like
Texture : Fine
Flower Characteristics : Cone

Environmental Problems : None

'BLUE PACIFIC' is a blue-green trailing juniper; 'COMPACTA' is a more compact cultivar.

Juniperus horizontalis *(Photograph p. 214)*

Common Name(s) : Creeping Juniper
Origin : North America
Growth Rate : Medium
Salt Tolerance : Medium
Soil Requirements : Wide
Plant Type : Evergreen shrub
Foliage Color : Green; blue-green
Flowering Season : Spring
Flower Color : n/a
Propagation : Cuttings
Human Hazards : None
Common Uses : Groundcover
Major Problems : Mites; bacterial blight
Additional Notes : Many cultivars of creeping juniper exist.

Family : Cupressaceae   **Zone** : 3-9
Typical Height : 1 Ft.
Drought Tolerance : High
Nutritional Requirements : Medium
Light Requirements : High
Leaf Type : Scale-like
Texture : Fine
Flower Characteristics : Cone

Environmental Problems : None

Cultivars
'ANDORRA COMPACTA' is a compact variety with purplish foliage in winter; 'BAR HARBOR' is a slow growing variety with silver-blue foliage that turns purple in winter; 'PLUMOSA' is a more vigorous variety with green foliage turning purple in winter; 'WILTONII' is very low growing with blue-green foliage.

Juniperus silicicola *(Photograph p. 162)*

Common Name(s) : Southern Red Cedar
Origin : Southeastern United States
Growth Rate : Medium
Salt Tolerance : High
Soil Requirements : Wide
Plant Type : Evergreen tree
Foliage Color : Green
Flowering Season : Spring
Flower Color : n/a
Propagation : Seeds; cuttings
Human Hazards : None
Common Uses : Small tree; shrub
Major Problems : Mites
Additional Notes : A native pyramidal juniper.

Family : Cupressaceae   **Zone** : 8-10B
Typical Height : 25 Ft.
Drought Tolerance : High
Nutritional Requirements : Low
Light Requirements : High
Leaf Type : Scale-like
Texture : Fine
Flower Characteristics : Cone

Environmental Problems : None

Juniperus virginiana

Common Name(s) : Eastern Red Cedar
Origin : Eastern United States
Growth Rate : Fast
Salt Tolerance : Medium
Soil Requirements : Wide
Plant Type : Evergreen tree or shrub
Foliage Color : Blue-green
Flowering Season : Spring
Flower Color : n/a
Propagation : Cuttings
Human Hazards : None
Common Uses : Tree; shrub
Major Problems : Mites
Additional Notes : Many cultivars exist.

Family : Cupressaceae   **Zone** : 2-9
Typical Height : 30 Ft.
Drought Tolerance : High
Nutritional Requirements : Low
Light Requirements : High
Leaf Type : Scale-like
Texture : Fine
Flower Characteristics : Cone

Environmental Problems : None

Cultivars
'SKY ROCKET' is a narrow columnar cultivar; 'CANAERTII' is a more compact pyramidal cultivar with dark green foliage; 'GLAUCA' is a dense pyramidal form with grayish foliage; 'BURKII' is a fast-growing pyramidal form with blue-green foliage that turns purplish in winter.

Justicia brandegeana

Common Name(s) : Shrimp Plant
Origin : Mexico
Growth Rate : Fast
Salt Tolerance : Low
Soil Requirements : Wide
Plant Type : Evergreen shrub
Foliage Color : Green
Flowering Season : Spring; summer
Flower Color : Red-brown
Propagation : Cuttings
Human Hazards : None
Common Uses : Beds; flowering perennial; flowering pot plant; flowering shrub
Major Problems : None
Additional Notes : Frost kills back to the ground.

Family : Acanthaceae   **Zone** : 9-11
Typical Height : 4 Ft.
Drought Tolerance : Low
Nutritional Requirements : Medium
Light Requirements : Medium; high
Leaf Type : Simple
Texture : Medium
Flower Characteristics : Showy

Environmental Problems : Weedy

Justicia carnea *(Photograph p. 181)*
Common Name(s) : Flamingo Plant
Origin : Northern South America
Growth Rate : Medium
Salt Tolerance : Low
Soil Requirements : Wide
Plant Type : Evergreen shrub
Foliage Color : Green
Flowering Season : Spring; summer
Flower Color : Pink
Propagation : Cuttings
Human Hazards : None
Common Uses : Flowering shrub
Major Problems : Scales
Additional Notes : Prune hard after blooming to maintain compactness.

Family : Acanthaceae   Zone : 10B-11

Typical Height : 4 Ft.
Drought Tolerance : Low
Nutritional Requirements : Medium
Light Requirements : Medium
Leaf Type : Simple
Texture : Coarse
Flower Characteristics : Showy

Environmental Problems : None

Justicia spicegera
Common Name(s) : Mohintli
Origin : Mexico to Colombia
Growth Rate : Fast
Salt Tolerance : Low
Soil Requirements : Wide
Plant Type : Evergreen shrub
Foliage Color : Green
Flowering Season : Summer
Flower Color : Orange
Propagation : Cuttings
Human Hazards : None
Common Uses : Flowering shrub
Major Problems : None
Additional Notes : Should be cut back regularly to maintain shape.

Family : Acanthaceae   Zone : 10B-11

Typical Height : 5 Ft.
Drought Tolerance : Low
Nutritional Requirements : Medium
Light Requirements : High
Leaf Type : Simple
Texture : Medium
Flower Characteristics : Showy

Environmental Problems : None

Kaempferia pulchra *(Photograph p. 215)*
Common Name(s) : Pretty Resurrection Lily
Origin : Thailand and Malay Archipelego
Growth Rate : Medium
Salt Tolerance : Low
Soil Requirements : Wide
Plant Type : Herbaceous perennial
Foliage Color : Green
Flowering Season : Spring; summer; fall
Flower Color : Lavender
Propagation : Division
Human Hazards : None
Common Uses : Groundcover; specimen plant; foliage plant
Major Problems : Chewing insects
Additional Notes : Attractive banded foliage is deciduous in winter.

Family : Zingiberaceae   Zone : 10B-11

Typical Height : .5 Ft.
Drought Tolerance : Medium
Nutritional Requirements : Low
Light Requirements : Low; medium
Leaf Type : Simple
Texture : Coarse
Flower Characteristics : Showy

Environmental Problems : None

Kaempferia roscoeana
Common Name(s) : Peacock Lily; Dwarf Ginger Lily
Origin : Burma
Growth Rate : Medium
Salt Tolerance : Low
Soil Requirements : Wide
Plant Type : Herbaceous perennial
Foliage Color : Green
Flowering Season : Spring; summer; fall
Flower Color : White
Propagation : Division
Human Hazards : None
Common Uses : Groundcover; specimen plant; foliage plant
Major Problems : Chewing insects.
Additional Notes : Attractive banded foliage is deciduous in winter. Similar to K. pulchra .

Family : Zingiberaceae   Zone : 10B-11

Typical Height : .5 Ft.
Drought Tolerance : Medium
Nutritional Requirements : Low
Light Requirements : Low; medium
Leaf Type : Simple
Texture : Coarse
Flower Characteristics : Showy

Environmental Problems : None

Kalanchoe blossfeldiana

Common Name(s) : Kalanchoe
Origin : Madagascar
Growth Rate : Medium
Salt Tolerance : Medium
Soil Requirements : Wide
Plant Type : Succulent perennial
Foliage Color : Blue-green; green
Flowering Season : Winter
Flower Color : Pink; yellow; red; orange; white
Propagation : Cuttings
Human Hazards : None
Common Uses : Flowering groundcover; flowering pot plant
Major Problems : Crown rot
Additional Notes : A very drought tolerant succulent. May become weedy.
Cultivars
Many cultivars exist.

Family : Crassulaceae   **Zone** : 10A-11

Typical Height : 1 Ft.
Drought Tolerance : High
Nutritional Requirements : Low
Light Requirements : High
Leaf Type : Simple
Texture : Medium
Flower Characteristics : Showy

Environmental Problems : None

Kalanchoe gastonis-bonnieri

Common Name(s) : Life Plant
Origin : Madagascar
Growth Rate : Medium
Salt Tolerance : Medium
Soil Requirements : Wide
Plant Type : Succulent perennial
Foliage Color : Blue-green
Flowering Season : n/a
Flower Color : Red; yellow
Propagation : Cuttings; plantlets
Human Hazards : None
Common Uses : Foliage plant; rock garden
Major Problems : None
Additional Notes : A very drought tolerant succulent. Produces plantlets at leaf tips.

Family : Crassulaceae   **Zone** : 10A-11

Typical Height : 2.5 Ft.
Drought Tolerance : High
Nutritional Requirements : Low
Light Requirements : High
Leaf Type : Simple
Texture : Coarse
Flower Characteristics : Showy

Environmental Problems : None

Kalanchoe pinnata

Common Name(s) : Live-forever; Curtain Plant
Origin : Pantropical
Growth Rate : Medium
Salt Tolerance : Medium
Soil Requirements : Wide
Plant Type : Succulent perennial
Foliage Color : Green
Flowering Season : Spring; summer
Flower Color : Red
Propagation : Cuttings; plantlets
Human Hazards : None
Common Uses : Rock gardens; specimen plant
Major Problems : None
Additional Notes : Plantlets develop on leaf margins of this succulent.

Family : Crassulaceae   **Zone** : 10B-11

Typical Height : 4 Ft.
Drought Tolerance : High
Nutritional Requirements : Low
Light Requirements : Medium; high
Leaf Type : Simple
Texture : Medium
Flower Characteristics : Showy

Environmental Problems : Weedy

Kalanchoe tomentosa

Common Name(s) : Panda Plant; Pussy Ears
Origin : Madagascar
Growth Rate : Medium
Salt Tolerance : Medium
Soil Requirements : Wide
Plant Type : Succulent perennial
Foliage Color : Silver
Flowering Season : Spring; summer
Flower Color : Yellow
Propagation : Cuttings
Human Hazards : None
Common Uses : Rock gardens; specimen plant; foliage plant
Major Problems : None
Additional Notes : High humidity in the summer causes disease problems.

Family : Crassulaceae   **Zone** : 10B-11

Typical Height : .8 Ft.
Drought Tolerance : High
Nutritional Requirements : Medium
Light Requirements : Medium; high
Leaf Type : Simple
Texture : Coarse
Flower Characteristics : Showy

Environmental Problems : None

Kalmia hirsuta

Common Name(s) : Sandhill Laurel
Origin : Southeastern United States
Growth Rate : Slow
Salt Tolerance : Low
Soil Requirements : Acid
Plant Type : Evergreen shrub
Foliage Color : Green
Flowering Season : Spring; summer
Flower Color : Pink
Propagation : Seeds; cuttings
Human Hazards : Poisonous
Common Uses : Flowering groundcover; flowering shrub
Major Problems : None
Additional Notes : A low-growing, hairy-leaved relative of mountain laurel.

Family : Ericaceae   **Zone** : 7-10A

Typical Height : 2 Ft.
Drought Tolerance : Medium
Nutritional Requirements : Medium
Light Requirements : Medium; high
Leaf Type : Simple
Texture : Medium
Flower Characteristics : Showy

Environmental Problems : None

Kalmia latifolia *(Photograph p. 181)*

Common Name(s) : Mountain Laurel
Origin : Eastern United States
Growth Rate : Slow
Salt Tolerance : Low
Soil Requirements : Acid
Plant Type : Evergreen shrub
Foliage Color : Green
Flowering Season : Spring
Flower Color : Pink; red; white
Propagation : Seeds; cuttings; grafting
Human Hazards : Poisonous
Common Uses : Flowering shrub
Major Problems : Leafspots; leafminers
Additional Notes : Clones from northern end of range not suitable for Florida.
Cultivars
Many cultivars exist.

Family : Ericaceae   **Zone** : 4-8

Typical Height : 8 Ft.
Drought Tolerance : Low
Nutritional Requirements : High
Light Requirements : Medium; low
Leaf Type : Simple
Texture : Medium
Flower Characteristics : Showy

Environmental Problems : None

Khaya nyasica

Common Name(s) : Nyasaland Mahogany; African Mahogany
Origin : Central Africa
Growth Rate : Fast
Salt Tolerance : Low
Soil Requirements : Wide
Plant Type : Evergreen tree
Foliage Color : Green
Flowering Season : n/a
Flower Color : Green
Propagation : Seeds
Human Hazards : None
Common Uses : Timber; shade tree
Major Problems : None
Additional Notes : Grown primarily for its reddish wood.

Family : Meliaceae   **Zone** : 10B-11

Typical Height : 120 Ft.
Drought Tolerance : High
Nutritional Requirements : Low
Light Requirements : High
Leaf Type : Pinnately compound
Texture : Medium
Flower Characteristics : Insignificant

Environmental Problems : None

Kigelia pinnata *(Photograph p. 163)*

Common Name(s) : Sausage Tree
Origin : Tropical Africa
Growth Rate : Medium
Salt Tolerance : Low
Soil Requirements : Wide
Plant Type : Evergreen tree
Foliage Color : Green
Flowering Season : Year-round
Flower Color : Purple
Propagation : Seeds
Human Hazards : None
Common Uses : Shade tree
Major Problems : Scales; nematodes
Additional Notes : Grown for its curious sausage-shaped inedible hanging fruits.

Family : Bignoniaceae   **Zone** : 10B-11

Typical Height : 40 Ft.
Drought Tolerance : Medium
Nutritional Requirements : Medium
Light Requirements : High
Leaf Type : Pinnately compound
Texture : Medium
Flower Characteristics : Showy; fragrant

Environmental Problems : None

Kniphofia spp.

Family : Liliaceae   **Zone** : 6-10B

Common Name(s) : Tritoma; Torch Lily; Red Hot Poker Plant
Origin : Tropical Africa and Madagascar
Growth Rate : Medium
Salt Tolerance : Medium
Soil Requirements : Wide
Plant Type : Herbaceous perennial
Foliage Color : Green
Flowering Season : Summer
Flower Color : Orange; red; yellow
Propagation : Seeds; division
Human Hazards : None
Common Uses : Borders; specimen plant; cut flowers
Major Problems : None
Additional Notes : <u>K. uvaria</u> is best known; many hybrids exist.

Typical Height : 3 Ft.
Drought Tolerance : Medium
Nutritional Requirements : Medium
Light Requirements : High
Leaf Type : Simple
Texture : Coarse
Flower Characteristics : Showy

Environmental Problems : None

Koelreuteria bipinnata

Family : Sapindaceae   **Zone** : 8-10B

Common Name(s) : Golden Shower Tree
Origin : Southwest China
Growth Rate : Medium
Salt Tolerance : Low
Soil Requirements : Wide
Plant Type : Deciduous tree
Foliage Color : Green
Flowering Season : Summer; fall
Flower Color : Yellow
Propagation : Seeds
Human Hazards : None
Common Uses : Flowering tree
Major Problems : None
Additional Notes : Attractive coppery-colored seed pods in fall & winter.

Typical Height : 45 Ft.
Drought Tolerance : Medium
Nutritional Requirements : Medium
Light Requirements : High
Leaf Type : Bipinnately compound
Texture : Medium
Flower Characteristics : Showy

Environmental Problems : None

Koelreuteria elegans *(Photograph p. 163)*

Family : Sapindaceae   **Zone** : 9-10B

Common Name(s) : Golden Shower Tree
Origin : Taiwan and Japan
Growth Rate : Medium
Salt Tolerance : Low
Soil Requirements : Wide
Plant Type : Deciduous tree
Foliage Color : Green
Flowering Season : Summer; fall
Flower Color : Yellow
Propagation : Seeds
Human Hazards : None
Common Uses : Flowering tree
Major Problems : Scales; mushroom root rot
Additional Notes : Attractive coppery-colored seed pods in fall & winter.

Typical Height : 40 Ft.
Drought Tolerance : Medium
Nutritional Requirements : Medium
Light Requirements : High
Leaf Type : Pinnately compound
Texture : Medium
Flower Characteristics : Showy

Environmental Problems : Weedy

Krugiodendron ferreum *(Photograph p. 163)*

Family : Rhamnaceae   **Zone** : 10B-11

Common Name(s) : Black Ironwood; Leadwood
Origin : Caribbean Region
Growth Rate : Slow
Salt Tolerance : Medium
Soil Requirements : Wide
Plant Type : Evergreen tree
Foliage Color : Green
Flowering Season : Spring
Flower Color : Green-yellow
Propagation : Seeds
Human Hazards : None
Common Uses : Small tree
Major Problems : None
Additional Notes : Slow-growing dense-wooded native tree for south Florida.

Typical Height : 25 Ft.
Drought Tolerance : High
Nutritional Requirements : Low
Light Requirements : High
Leaf Type : Simple
Texture : Fine
Flower Characteristics : Insignificant

Environmental Problems : None

Lachenalia spp.

Common Name(s) : Leopard Lily; Cape Cowslip
Origin : South Africa
Growth Rate : Medium
Salt Tolerance : Medium
Soil Requirements : Well-drained
Plant Type : Herbaceous perennial
Foliage Color : Green; brown
Flowering Season : Winter; spring
Flower Color : Red; white; pink; orange; yellow
Propagation : Division
Human Hazards : None
Common Uses : Beds; borders; rock gardens; cut flowers; flowering pot plant
Major Problems : None
Additional Notes : Good drainage essential; attractive foliage.

Family : Liliaceae   **Zone** : 9-10B

Typical Height : 1 Ft.
Drought Tolerance : Medium
Nutritional Requirements : Medium
Light Requirements : High
Leaf Type : Simple
Texture : Coarse
Flower Characteristics : Showy

Environmental Problems : None

Lagerstroemia indica *(Photograph p. 163)*

Common Name(s) : Crape Myrtle
Origin : Southern Asia and Australia
Growth Rate : Medium
Salt Tolerance : Low
Soil Requirements : Wide
Plant Type : Deciduous tree
Foliage Color : Green
Flowering Season : Summer
Flower Color : Red; pink; white; purple
Propagation : Seeds; cuttings
Human Hazards : None
Common Uses : Small flowering tree; flowering shrub
Major Problems : Powdery mildew; root rot; aphids
Additional Notes : Has attractive bark; many cultivars
Cultivars

Family : Lythraceae   **Zone** : 7-10B

Typical Height : 20 Ft.
Drought Tolerance : High
Nutritional Requirements : Medium
Light Requirements : High
Leaf Type : Simple
Texture : Medium
Flower Characteristics : Showy

Environmental Problems : None

Red flowering cultivars include: 'COUNTRY RED', 'DALLAS RED', 'RUBRA', 'WATERMELON RED', 'VICTOR', 'WILLIAM TOOVEY', 'AMERICA', and 'BATON ROUGE' ; pink cultivars include: 'POTOMAC', 'TUSCARORA', 'SEMINOLE', 'PINK LACE', 'PINK RUFFLES', and 'BASHAM'S PARTY PINK'; white cultivars include: 'ALBA', 'WHITE CLOUD' and 'SNOW LACE'; purples include: 'CATAUBA'.

Lagerstroemia speciosa *(Photograph p. 163)*

Common Name(s) : Queen's Crape Myrtle
Origin : India and East Indies
Growth Rate : Medium
Salt Tolerance : Low
Soil Requirements : Wide
Plant Type : Deciduous tree
Foliage Color : Green
Flowering Season : Summer
Flower Color : Purple
Propagation : Seeds; cuttings
Human Hazards : Poisonous
Common Uses : Flowering tree
Major Problems : Scales; aphids; sooty mold
Additional Notes : A more tropical, larger crape myrtle.

Family : Lythraceae   **Zone** : 10B-11

Typical Height : 35 Ft.
Drought Tolerance : High
Nutritional Requirements : Medium
Light Requirements : High
Leaf Type : Simple
Texture : Coarse
Flower Characteristics : Showy

Environmental Problems : None

Laguncularia racemosa

Common Name(s) : White Mangrove; White Buttonwood
Origin : Caribbean Region and South America
Growth Rate : Medium
Salt Tolerance : High
Soil Requirements : Wide
Plant Type : Evergreen tree
Foliage Color : Green
Flowering Season : Spring
Flower Color : Green-white
Propagation : Seeds
Human Hazards : None
Common Uses : Shade tree
Major Problems : None
Additional Notes : Grows best in warm coastal areas.

Family : Combretaceae   **Zone** : 10B-11

Typical Height : 50 Ft.
Drought Tolerance : Low
Nutritional Requirements : Low
Light Requirements : High
Leaf Type : Simple
Texture : Medium
Flower Characteristics : Insignificant; fragrant

Environmental Problems : None

Lantana camara *(Photograph p. 215)*

Common Name(s) : Yellow Sage; Common Lantana
Origin : Tropical America
Growth Rate : Medium
Salt Tolerance : High
Soil Requirements : Wide
Plant Type : Evergreen shrub
Foliage Color : Green
Flowering Season : Year-round
Flower Color : Red; pink; yellow; orange
Propagation : Cuttings; seeds
Human Hazards : Poisonous
Common Uses : Flowering shrub; groundcovers
Major Problems : Whiteflies
Additional Notes : Can become weedy in some areas; toxic to livestock; many cultivars.
Cultivars
'BIG GOLD' and 'GOLD MOUND' have yellow-orange flowers; 'CONFETTI' has yellow, pink, and purple flowers; 'CREME' has cream-colored flowers; 'LEMON DROP' and 'NEW GOLD' have yellow flowers; 'PINK caprice' has pink flowers; 'TANGERINE' has orange flowers; 'ZEKE RED' has red flowers.

Family : Verbenaceae   **Zone** : 9-11

Typical Height : 5 Ft.
Drought Tolerance : High
Nutritional Requirements : Low
Light Requirements : High
Leaf Type : Simple
Texture : Medium
Flower Characteristics : Showy

Environmental Problems : Weedy

Lantana montevidensis *(Photograph p. 215)*

Common Name(s) : Trailing Lantana
Origin : South America
Growth Rate : Medium
Salt Tolerance : High
Soil Requirements : Wide
Plant Type : Evergreen shrub
Foliage Color : Green
Flowering Season : Year-round
Flower Color : Lavender
Propagation : Cuttings
Human Hazards : None
Common Uses : Flowering groundcover; hanging basket plant
Major Problems : Whiteflies
Additional Notes : A tough, attractive plant with trailing foliage and abundant flowers.

Family : Verbenaceae   **Zone** : 10B-11

Typical Height : 1 Ft.
Drought Tolerance : Medium
Nutritional Requirements : Low
Light Requirements : High
Leaf Type : Simple
Texture : Medium
Flower Characteristics : Showy

Environmental Problems : None

Lantana ovatifolia var. reclinata

Common Name(s) : Dwarf Lantana
Origin : South Florida
Growth Rate : Fast
Salt Tolerance : Medium
Soil Requirements : Wide
Plant Type : Evergreen shrub
Foliage Color : Green
Flowering Season : Year-round
Flower Color : Yellow
Propagation : Cuttings; seeds
Human Hazards : None
Common Uses : Groundcover
Major Problems : None
Additional Notes : A non-poisonous, non-weedy native lantana.

Family : Verbenaceae   **Zone** : 10B-11

Typical Height : 1 Ft.
Drought Tolerance : High
Nutritional Requirements : Low
Light Requirements : High
Leaf Type : Simple
Texture : Fine
Flower Characteristics : Showy

Environmental Problems : None

Lapeirousia laxa

Common Name(s) : Scarlet Freesia
Origin : South Africa
Growth Rate : Medium
Salt Tolerance : Low
Soil Requirements : Wide
Plant Type : Herbaceous perennial
Foliage Color : Green
Flowering Season : Spring
Flower Color : Red; white
Propagation : Division; seeds
Human Hazards : None
Common Uses : Beds; rock gardens
Major Problems : None
Additional Notes : A dwarf iris relative that increases rapidly; easy and fast from seed.
Cultivars
'ALBA' has white flowers.

Family : Iridaceae   **Zone** : 7-11

Typical Height : .5 Ft.
Drought Tolerance : Low
Nutritional Requirements : Medium
Light Requirements : Medium
Leaf Type : Simple; linear
Texture : Medium
Flower Characteristics : Showy

Environmental Problems : None

Latania loddigesii

Common Name(s) : Blue Latan Palm
Origin : Mauritius Island
Growth Rate : Slow
Salt Tolerance : Medium
Soil Requirements : Wide
Plant Type : Palm
Foliage Color : Blue-green; green
Flowering Season : Summer
Flower Color : White
Propagation : Seeds
Human Hazards : None
Common Uses : Tree; palm
Major Problems : Lethal yellowing (slightly susceptible).
Additional Notes : <u>L. lontaroides</u> has red leaves when young. See photograph page 205.

Family : Palmae   **Zone** : 10B-11

Typical Height : 30 Ft.
Drought Tolerance : High
Nutritional Requirements : Medium
Light Requirements : High
Leaf Type : Simple; palmately lobed
Texture : Very coarse
Flower Characteristics : Insignificant

Environmental Problems : None

Lavandula angustifolia

Common Name(s) : True Lavender
Origin : Mediterranean Region
Growth Rate : Medium
Salt Tolerance : Low
Soil Requirements : Wide
Plant Type : Herbaceous perennial
Foliage Color : Silver
Flowering Season : Summer
Flower Color : Purple
Propagation : Seeds; cuttings
Human Hazards : None
Common Uses : Borders; cut flowers; rock gardens
Major Problems : None
Additional Notes : Dried flowers and foliage used for sweet smelling sachets and potpourris.

Family : Labiatae   **Zone** : 5-10B

Typical Height : 2 Ft.
Drought Tolerance : Medium
Nutritional Requirements : Medium
Light Requirements : High
Leaf Type : Simple; linear
Texture : Medium
Flower Characteristics : Showy; fragrant

Environmental Problems : None

Lawsonia inermis

Common Name(s) : Henna
Origin : North Africa, Asia, and Australia
Growth Rate : Medium
Salt Tolerance : Medium
Soil Requirements : Wide
Plant Type : Evergreen shrub
Foliage Color : Green
Flowering Season : Year-round
Flower Color : White; pink
Propagation : Cuttings; seeds
Human Hazards : None
Common Uses : Shrub; hedge
Major Problems : None
Additional Notes : May be trained into a small tree. A source of orange dye.

Family : Lythraceae   **Zone** : 10B-11

Typical Height : 7 Ft.
Drought Tolerance : Medium
Nutritional Requirements : Medium
Light Requirements : High
Leaf Type : Simple
Texture : Fine
Flower Characteristics : Insignificant; fragrant

Environmental Problems : None

Leea coccinea

Common Name(s) : West Indian Holly
Origin : Burma
Growth Rate : Medium
Salt Tolerance : Medium
Soil Requirements : Wide
Plant Type : Evergreen shrub
Foliage Color : Green; red-purple
Flowering Season : Summer
Flower Color : White
Propagation : Seeds
Human Hazards : Irritant
Common Uses : Shrub; foliage plant
Major Problems : None
Additional Notes : Very cold sensitive; red berries have irritating sap.
Cultivars
'RUBRA' has purple-red foliage.

Family : Leeaceae   **Zone** : 11

Typical Height : 5 Ft.
Drought Tolerance : Low
Nutritional Requirements : Medium
Light Requirements : Medium
Leaf Type : Pinnately compound
Texture : Medium
Flower Characteristics : Insignificant

Environmental Problems : None

Leucojum spp.

Common Name(s) : Snowflake
Origin : Europe
Growth Rate : Medium
Salt Tolerance : Low
Soil Requirements : Wide
Plant Type : Herbaceous perennial
Foliage Color : Green
Flowering Season : Spring
Flower Color : White
Propagation : Division
Human Hazards : None
Common Uses : Beds; borders; rock gardens
Major Problems : None
Additional Notes : May not flower after mild winter.

Family : Amaryllidaceae   **Zone** : 6-8

Typical Height : .5 Ft.
Drought Tolerance : Low
Nutritional Requirements : Medium
Light Requirements : Medium; high
Leaf Type : Simple; linear
Texture : Medium
Flower Characteristics : Showy

Environmental Problems : None

Leucophyllum frutescens *(Photograph p. 181)*

Common Name(s) : Texas Sage
Origin : Texas and Mexico
Growth Rate : Slow
Salt Tolerance : Medium
Soil Requirements : Wide
Plant Type : Evergreen shrub
Foliage Color : Silver-green
Flowering Season : Summer
Flower Color : Lavender
Propagation : Cuttings
Human Hazards : None
Common Uses : Flowering shrub; hedge
Major Problems : None
Additional Notes : Good for rock gardens and other hot, dry locations.

Family : Scrophulariaceae   **Zone** : 8-10B

Typical Height : 5 Ft.
Drought Tolerance : High
Nutritional Requirements : Low
Light Requirements : High
Leaf Type : Simple
Texture : Fine
Flower Characteristics : Showy

Environmental Problems : None

Liatrus spp.

Common Name(s) : Liatrus
Origin : North America
Growth Rate : Medium
Salt Tolerance : Low
Soil Requirements : Wide
Plant Type : Herbaceous perennial
Foliage Color : Green
Flowering Season : Summer; fall
Flower Color : Lavender; pink; white
Propagation : Seeds; division
Human Hazards : None
Common Uses : Borders; cut flowers
Major Problems : None
Additional Notes : Seed to flower in two years. Flowers dry well.

Family : Compositae   **Zone** : 3-10B

Typical Height : 3 Ft.
Drought Tolerance : Medium
Nutritional Requirements : Medium
Light Requirements : Medium; high
Leaf Type : Simple; linear
Texture : Fine
Flower Characteristics : Showy

Environmental Problems : None

Licania michauxii

Common Name(s) : Gopher Apple
Origin : Southeastern United States
Growth Rate : Slow
Salt Tolerance : High
Soil Requirements : Wide
Plant Type : Evergreen shrub
Foliage Color : Green
Flowering Season : Summer
Flower Color : Green
Propagation : Seeds
Human Hazards : None
Common Uses : Groundcover
Major Problems : None
Additional Notes : Difficult to transplant.

Family : Chrysobalanaceae   **Zone** : 8-11

Typical Height : 1 Ft.
Drought Tolerance : High
Nutritional Requirements : Low
Light Requirements : High
Leaf Type : Simple
Texture : Medium
Flower Characteristics : Insignificant

Environmental Problems : None

Licaria triandra *(Photograph p. 163)*

Common Name(s) : Gulf Licaria
Origin : South Florida and The Caribbean
Growth Rate : Medium
Salt Tolerance : Medium
Soil Requirements : Wide
Plant Type : Evergreen tree
Foliage Color : Green
Flowering Season : Spring; summer
Flower Color : Purple; white
Propagation : Seeds
Human Hazards : None
Common Uses : Tree
Major Problems : None
Additional Notes : Attractive small tree for south Florida.

Family : Lauraceae   **Zone** : 10B-11

Typical Height : 25 Ft.
Drought Tolerance : High
Nutritional Requirements : Low
Light Requirements : High
Leaf Type : Simple
Texture : Medium
Flower Characteristics : Insignficant

Environmental Problems : None

Licuala grandis *(Photograph p. 205)*

Common Name(s) : Licuala Palm
Origin : New Hebrides Islands
Growth Rate : Slow
Salt Tolerance : Low
Soil Requirements : Wide
Plant Type : Palm
Foliage Color : Green
Flowering Season : Summer
Flower Color : White
Propagation : Seeds
Human Hazards : Spiny
Common Uses : Small tree; palm
Major Problems : None
Additional Notes : A very beautiful slow growing small palm with large round leaves.

Family : Palmae   **Zone** : 10B-11

Typical Height : 8 Ft.
Drought Tolerance : Medium
Nutritional Requirements : High
Light Requirements : Medium
Leaf Type : Simple
Texture : Very coarse
Flower Characteristics : Insignificant

Environmental Problems : None

Licuala spinosa *(Photograph p. 205)*

Common Name(s) : Spiny Licuala
Origin : Malaysia, Philippines, Indonesia
Growth Rate : Slow
Salt Tolerance : Low
Soil Requirements : Wide
Plant Type : Palm
Foliage Color : Green
Flowering Season : Summer
Flower Color : White
Propagation : Seeds
Human Hazards : Spiny
Common Uses : Shrub; palm
Major Problems : None
Additional Notes : Leaves of this suckering palm have spiny petioles.

Family : Palmae   **Zone** : 10B-11

Typical Height : 12 Ft.
Drought Tolerance : Medium
Nutritional Requirements : Medium
Light Requirements : Medium
Leaf Type : Palmately compound
Texture : Coarse
Flower Characteristics : Insignificant

Environmental Problems : None

Ligustrum japonicum

Common Name(s) : Japanese Privet
Origin : Japan
Growth Rate : Medium
Salt Tolerance : Medium
Soil Requirements : Wide
Plant Type : Evergreen tree or shrub
Foliage Color : Green; variegated
Flowering Season : Spring
Flower Color : White
Propagation : Cuttings
Human Hazards : None
Common Uses : Small tree; shrub; hedge
Major Problems : Scales; whiteflies; sooty mold
Additional Notes : A shrub that can be shaped into a small tree. Rarely flowers.
Cultivars
'ROTUNDIFOLIUM' has rounded leaves; 'HOWARDI' and 'FRASIERI' have yellow and green variegated foliage; 'JACK FROST' has white-margined green leaves.

Family : Oleaceae   **Zone** : 7-10B

Typical Height : 12 Ft.
Drought Tolerance : High
Nutritional Requirements : Medium
Light Requirements : Medium; high
Leaf Type : Simple
Texture : Medium
Flower Characteristics : Showy; fragrant

Environmental Problems : None

Ligustrum lucidum

Common Name(s) : Glossy Privet
Origin : China, Korea, Japan
Growth Rate : Medium
Salt Tolerance : Low
Soil Requirements : Wide
Plant Type : Evergreen tree or shrub
Foliage Color : Green
Flowering Season : Spring
Flower Color : White
Propagation : Cuttings
Human Hazards : None
Common Uses : Small tree; shrub
Major Problems : Whiteflies; scales; sooty mold
Additional Notes : Usually grown as a shrub, but can be trained into a small tree.

Family : Oleaceae   **Zone** : 7-10B

Typical Height : 30 Ft.
Drought Tolerance : Low
Nutritional Requirements : Medium
Light Requirements : Medium; high
Leaf Type : Simple
Texture : Medium
Flower Characteristics : Insignificant

Environmental Problems : None

Ligustrum sinense

Common Name(s) : Chinese Privet
Origin : China and Korea
Growth Rate : Medium
Salt Tolerance : Low
Soil Requirements : Wide
Plant Type : Deciduous shrub
Foliage Color : Green; variegated
Flowering Season : Spring
Flower Color : White
Propagation : Cuttings; air layers
Human Hazards : None
Common Uses : Shrub; hedge
Major Problems : None
Additional Notes : Fine textured foliage.
Cultivars
'VARIEGATUM' has variegated foliage.

Family : Oleaceae   **Zone** : 7-10B

Typical Height : 5 Ft.
Drought Tolerance : Medium
Nutritional Requirements : Medium
Light Requirements : Medium; high
Leaf Type : Simple
Texture : Medium
Flower Characteristics : Showy; fragrant

Environmental Problems : None

Lilium catesbaei

Common Name(s) : Catesby Lily; Pine Lily
Origin : Southeastern United States
Growth Rate : Medium
Salt Tolerance : Low
Soil Requirements : Acid
Plant Type : Herbaceous perennial
Foliage Color : Green
Flowering Season : Summer; fall
Flower Color : Red
Propagation : Division
Human Hazards : None
Common Uses : Beds; specimen plant
Major Problems : None
Additional Notes : A dwarf late-flowering native lily.

Family : Liliaceae   **Zone** : 8-10B

Typical Height : 1 Ft.
Drought Tolerance : Low
Nutritional Requirements : Medium
Light Requirements : Medium
Leaf Type : Simple; linear
Texture : Medium
Flower Characteristics : Showy

Environmental Problems : None

Lilium spp.

Common Name(s) : Lily
Origin : Temperate Northern Hemisphere
Growth Rate : Medium
Salt Tolerance : Low
Soil Requirements : Acid
Plant Type : Herbaceous perennial
Foliage Color : Green
Flowering Season : Summer
Flower Color : Yellow; orange; white; red; pink
Propagation : Division
Human Hazards : None
Common Uses : Beds; borders; cut flowers
Major Problems : Virus; nematodes; bulb rots
Additional Notes : Only some varieties adaptable to Florida.

Family : Lilaceae   **Zone** : 3-9

Typical Height : 4 Ft.
Drought Tolerance : Low
Nutritional Requirements : High
Light Requirements : Medium
Leaf Type : Simple; linear
Texture : Medium
Flower Characteristics : Showy; fragrant

Environmental Problems : None

Limonium latifolium

Common Name(s) : Hardy Statice
Origin : Eastern Europe and Western Russia
Growth Rate : Medium
Salt Tolerance : High
Soil Requirements : Wide
Plant Type : Herbaceous perennial
Foliage Color : Green
Flowering Season : Summer
Flower Color : Blue; pink
Propagation : Seeds
Human Hazards : None
Common Uses : Borders; cut flowers
Major Problems : None
Additional Notes : Good for seaside plantings. Excellent cut or dried flower.

Family : Plumbaginaceae   **Zone** : 3-10B

Typical Height : 1.5 Ft.
Drought Tolerance : High
Nutritional Requirements : Medium
Light Requirements : High
Leaf Type : Simple
Texture : Medium
Flower Characteristics : Showy

Environmental Problems : None

Lippia nodiflora

Common Name(s) : Matchweed
Origin : Southeastern USA and Tropical America
Growth Rate : Fast
Salt Tolerance : High
Soil Requirements : Wide
Plant Type : Herbaceous perennial
Foliage Color : Green
Flowering Season : Year-round
Flower Color : Pink
Propagation : Cuttings; division
Human Hazards : None
Common Uses : Groundcover
Major Problems : None
Additional Notes : Tolerates foot traffic, but generally considered a weed.

Family : Verbenaceae   **Zone** : 8-11

Typical Height : .3 Ft.
Drought Tolerance : High
Nutritional Requirements : Low
Light Requirements : High
Leaf Type : Simple
Texture : Fine
Flower Characteristics : Insignificant

Environmental Problems : Weedy

Liquidambar formosana

Common Name(s) : Formosan Gum
Origin : Southern China and Taiwan
Growth Rate : Fast
Salt Tolerance : Low
Soil Requirements : Wide
Plant Type : Deciduous tree
Foliage Color : Green
Flowering Season : Spring
Flower Color : White
Propagation : Seeds; grafting; cuttings
Human Hazards : None
Common Uses : Shade tree
Major Problems : None
Additional Notes : Pyramidal shape with attractive red fall color.

Family : Hamamelidaceae   **Zone** : 7-10A

Typical Height : 100 Ft.
Drought Tolerance : High
Nutritional Requirements : Medium
Light Requirements : High
Leaf Type : Simple; palmately lobed
Texture : Medium
Flower Characteristics : Insignificant

Environmental Problems : None

Liquidambar orientalis

Common Name(s) : Oriental Sweetgum
Origin : Asia Minor
Growth Rate : Slow
Salt Tolerance : Low
Soil Requirements : Wide
Plant Type : Deciduous tree
Foliage Color : Green
Flowering Season : Spring
Flower Color : White
Propagation : Seeds; cuttings
Human Hazards : None
Common Uses : Small tree
Major Problems : None
Additional Notes : Pyramidal shape with attractive red fall color.

Family : Hamamelidaceae   **Zone** : 7-10A

Typical Height : 35 Ft.
Drought Tolerance : High
Nutritional Requirements : Medium
Light Requirements : High
Leaf Type : Simple; palmately lobed
Texture : Medium
Flower Characteristics : Insignificant

Environmental Problems : None

Liquidambar styraciflua

Common Name(s) : Sweetgum
Origin : Eastern United States
Growth Rate : Fast
Salt Tolerance : Low
Soil Requirements : Wide
Plant Type : Deciduous tree
Foliage Color : Green
Flowering Season : Spring
Flower Color : White
Propagation : Seeds; grafting; cuttings
Human Hazards : None
Common Uses : Shade tree
Major Problems : Borers; caterpillars

Family : Hamamelidaceae   Zone : 5-10A

Typical Height : 50 Ft.
Drought Tolerance : High
Nutritional Requirements : Medium
Light Requirements : High
Leaf Type : Simple; palmately lobed
Texture : Medium
Flower Characteristics : Insignificant

Environmental Problems : None

Additional Notes : Pyramidal with attractive fall color. Large plants do not transplant well.
Cultivars
'PURPLE MAJESTY' has excellent purple fall color; 'FESTIVAL' has a columnar form and red fall color; 'BURGUNDY' has wine-red leaves in the fall; 'MORAINE' is an upright oval form with bright red fall color; 'VARIEGATA' has yellow and green variegated foliage;

Liriodendron tulipifera *(Photograph p. 164)*

Common Name(s) : Tulip Tree
Origin : Eastern United States
Growth Rate : Fast
Salt Tolerance : Low
Soil Requirements : Wide
Plant Type : Deciduous tree
Foliage Color : Green
Flowering Season : Spring
Flower Color : Green-yellow
Propagation : Seeds; cuttings
Human Hazards : None
Common Uses : Shade tree
Major Problems : Borers

Family : Magnoliaceae   Zone : 4-10A

Typical Height : 75 Ft.
Drought Tolerance : Low
Nutritional Requirements : Medium
Light Requirements : High
Leaf Type : Simple; palmately lobed
Texture : Medium
Flower Characteristics : Showy

Environmental Problems : None

Additional Notes : A large pest resistant tree; intolerant of soil flooding.

Liriope muscari

Common Name(s) : Lilyturf
Origin : Japan, China
Growth Rate : Medium
Salt Tolerance : Medium
Soil Requirements : Wide
Plant Type : Herbaceous perennial
Foliage Color : Green; variegated
Flowering Season : Summer
Flower Color : Pink; lavender; blue; white; purple
Propagation : Division; tissue culture
Human Hazards : None
Common Uses : Groundcover
Major Problems : Scales

Family : Liliaceae   Zone : 6-10B

Typical Height : 1 Ft.
Drought Tolerance : High
Nutritional Requirements : Medium
Light Requirements : Medium; high
Leaf Type : Simple; linear
Texture : Fine
Flower Characteristics : Showy

Environmental Problems : None

Additional Notes : Forms dense clumps, but will not tolerate foot traffic. Many cultivars.
Cultivars
'MONROE WHITE' has white flowers; 'SAMANTHA' has rosy-pink flowers; 'SILVER MIDGET', 'SILVERY SUNPROOF', 'JOHN BURCH', and 'VARIEGATA' hav variegated foliage; 'GOLD-BANDED' has narrow gold bands on the leaves; 'MAJESTIC', 'BIG BLUE', and 'EVERGREEN GIANT' are tall varieties; 'GRANDIFLORA' has lavender flowers; 'LILAC BEAUTY' has purple flowers.

Liriope spicata

Common Name(s) : Creeping Lilyturf
Origin : China, Vietnam
Growth Rate : Medium
Salt Tolerance : High
Soil Requirements : Wide
Plant Type : Herbaceous perennial
Foliage Color : Green
Flowering Season : Summer
Flower Color : Purple
Propagation : Division
Human Hazards : None
Common Uses : Groundcover
Major Problems : Scales

Family : Liliaceae   Zone : 7-10B

Typical Height : 1 Ft.
Drought Tolerance : High
Nutritional Requirements : Medium
Light Requirements : Medium
Leaf Type : Simple; linear
Texture : Fine
Flower Characteristics : Showy

Environmental Problems : None

Additional Notes : Covers faster than L. muscari .

Litchi chinensis

Common Name(s) : Lychee; Litchi
Origin : Souhteast Asia
Growth Rate : Medium
Salt Tolerance : Low
Soil Requirements : Wide
Plant Type : Evergreen tree
Foliage Color : Green
Flowering Season : Spring
Flower Color : White
Propagation : Seeds; air layers; grafting
Human Hazards : None
Common Uses : Shade tree; edible fruit
Major Problems : Mushroom root rot
Additional Notes : Beautiful shade tree with delicious fruit.
Cultivars
'BREWSTER', 'BENGAL', 'MAURITIUS', and 'SWEETCLIFF' are popular cultivars.

Family : Sapindaceae   **Zone** : 10A-11

Typical Height : 35 Ft.
Drought Tolerance : Medium
Nutritional Requirements : Medium
Light Requirements : High
Leaf Type : Pinnately compound
Texture : Medium
Flower Characteristics : Insignificant

Environmental Problems : None

Livistona australis

Common Name(s) : Australian Fan Palm
Origin : Australia
Growth Rate : Slow
Salt Tolerance : Medium
Soil Requirements : Wide
Plant Type : Palm
Foliage Color : Green
Flowering Season : Spring
Flower Color : Yellow
Propagation : Seeds
Human Hazards : Spiny
Common Uses : Tree; foliage plant; palm
Major Problems : K deficiency
Additional Notes : Good foliage plant when young.

Family : Palmae   **Zone** : 9-11

Typical Height : 40 Ft.
Drought Tolerance : High
Nutritional Requirements : Medium
Light Requirements : Medium; high
Leaf Type : Simple; palmately lobed
Texture : Very coarse
Flower Characteristics : Insignificant

Environmental Problems : None

Livistona chinensis *(Photograph p. 205)*

Common Name(s) : Chinese Fan Palm
Origin : China
Growth Rate : Slow
Salt Tolerance : Medium
Soil Requirements : Wide
Plant Type : Palm
Foliage Color : Green
Flowering Season : Summer
Flower Color : White
Propagation : Seeds
Human Hazards : Spiny
Common Uses : Tree; foliage plant; palm
Major Problems : Lethal yellowing (moderately susceptible)
Additional Notes : Leaflet tips often droop in this species.

Family : Palmae   **Zone** : 9-11

Typical Height : 25 Ft.
Drought Tolerance : High
Nutritional Requirements : Medium
Light Requirements : Medium; high
Leaf Type : Simple; palmately lobed
Texture : Very coarse
Flower Characteristics : Insignificant

Environmental Problems : None

Livistona decipiens *(Photograph p. 205)*

Common Name(s) : Cut-leaved Fan Palm
Origin : Australia
Growth Rate : Slow
Salt Tolerance : Medium
Soil Requirements : Wide
Plant Type : Palm
Foliage Color : Green
Flowering Season : Spring
Flower Color : Yellow
Propagation : Seeds
Human Hazards : Spiny
Common Uses : Tree; palm
Major Problems : None
Additional Notes : Has deeply divided leaves that become tattered in the wind.

Family : Palmae   **Zone** : 9-11

Typical Height : 30 Ft.
Drought Tolerance : High
Nutritional Requirements : Medium
Light Requirements : Medium; high
Leaf Type : Simple; palmately lobed
Texture : Coarse
Flower Characteristics : Insignificant

Environmental Problems : None

Livistona mariae

Common Name(s) : n/a
Origin : Australia
Growth Rate : Slow
Salt Tolerance : Medium
Soil Requirements : Wide
Plant Type : Palm
Foliage Color : Green
Flowering Season : Summer
Flower Color : Yellow
Propagation : Seeds
Human Hazards : Spiny
Common Uses : Palm
Major Problems : K deficiency
Additional Notes : Young leaves have reddish tint; has open habit.

Family : Palmae   Zone : 10A-10B

Typical Height : 40 Ft.
Drought Tolerance : High
Nutritional Requirements : Medium
Light Requirements : High
Leaf Type : Simple; palmately lobed
Texture : Very coarse
Flower Characteristics : Insignificant

Environmental Problems : None

Livistona rotundifolia *(Photograph p. 205)*

Common Name(s) : Roundleaf Livistona
Origin : Philippines, Indonesia
Growth Rate : Medium
Salt Tolerance : Low
Soil Requirements : Wide
Plant Type : Palm
Foliage Color : Green
Flowering Season : Summer
Flower Color : Yellow
Propagation : Seeds
Human Hazards : Spiny
Common Uses : Shade tree; foliage plant; palm
Major Problems : Lethal yellowing (slightly susceptible).
Additional Notes : Beautiful, bamboo-like trunk; less cold hardy than other species.

Family : Palmae   Zone : 10B-11

Typical Height : 35 Ft.
Drought Tolerance : High
Nutritional Requirements : Medium
Light Requirements : Medium; high
Leaf Type : Simple; palmately lobed
Texture : Very coarse
Flower Characteristics : Insignificant

Environmental Problems : None

Livistona saribus

Common Name(s) : Fan Palm
Origin : Southeast Asia, Indonesia, Philippines
Growth Rate : Medium
Salt Tolerance : Medium
Soil Requirements : Wide
Plant Type : Palm
Foliage Color : Green
Flowering Season : Spring
Flower Color : Yellow
Propagation : Seeds
Human Hazards : None
Common Uses : Tree; palm
Major Problems : None
Additional Notes : Has deeply divided leaves with smaller divisions in leaflets.

Family : Palmae   Zone : 9-11

Typical Height : 60 Ft.
Drought Tolerance : High
Nutritional Requirements : Medium
Light Requirements : Medium; high
Leaf Type : Simple; palmately lobed
Texture : Coarse
Flower Characteristics : Insignificant

Environmental Problems : None

Lobelia cardinalis

Common Name(s) : Cardinal Flower
Origin : Eastern North America
Growth Rate : Medium
Salt Tolerance : Low
Soil Requirements : Wide
Plant Type : Herbaceous perennial
Foliage Color : Green
Flowering Season : Summer; fall
Flower Color : Red; pink; white
Propagation : Seeds; cuttings; division
Human Hazards : None
Common Uses : Aquatic; specimen plant
Major Problems : None
Additional Notes : Best grown in damp soil near stream banks. Spreads rapidly.
Cultivars
'ALBA' has white flowers; 'ROSEA' has pink flowers.

Family : Lobeliaceae   Zone : 3-10A

Typical Height : 3 Ft.
Drought Tolerance : Low
Nutritional Requirements : Medium
Light Requirements : Medium; high
Leaf Type : Simple
Texture : Medium
Flower Characteristics : Showy

Environmental Problems : None

Lonchocarpus sp.

Common Name(s) : Florida Lilac
Origin : New World Tropics
Growth Rate : Fast
Salt Tolerance : Low
Soil Requirements : Acid
Plant Type : Evergreen tree
Foliage Color : Green
Flowering Season : Summer
Flower Color : Pink; lavender
Propagation : Seeds
Human Hazards : None
Common Uses : Flowering tree
Major Problems : Mg and Fe deficiencies; caterpillars
Additional Notes : Several species in trade.

Family : Leguminosae   **Zone** : 10B-11

Typical Height : 40 Ft.
Drought Tolerance : Medium
Nutritional Requirements : Medium
Light Requirements : High
Leaf Type : Pinnately compound
Texture : Medium
Flower Characteristics : Showy

Environmental Problems : None

Lonicera japonica

Common Name(s) : Japanese Honeysuckle
Origin : Eastern Asia
Growth Rate : Fast
Salt Tolerance : Medium
Soil Requirements : Wide
Plant Type : Evergreen vine
Foliage Color : Green
Flowering Season : Summer
Flower Color : White; yellow
Propagation : Seeds; cuttings
Human Hazards : None
Common Uses : Flowering vine; groundcover
Major Problems : None
Additional Notes : Flowers fade to yellow. Aggressive. Best in central and north Florida.
Cultivars
'HALLIANA' is less vigorous than species and has white flowers turning to yellow; 'PURPUREA' is a vigorous variety with purple-tinted foliage; 'VARIEGATA' has variegated foliage.

Family : Caprifoliaceae   **Zone** : 5-10B

Typical Height : Not applicable
Drought Tolerance : Medium
Nutritional Requirements : Low
Light Requirements : Medium; high
Leaf Type : Simple
Texture : Medium
Flower Characteristics : Showy; fragrant

Environmental Problems : Invasive

Lonicera nitida

Common Name(s) : Box Honeysuckle
Origin : China
Growth Rate : Medium
Salt Tolerance : High
Soil Requirements : Wide
Plant Type : Evergreen shrub
Foliage Color : Green
Flowering Season : Summer
Flower Color : White
Propagation : Cuttings; seeds
Human Hazards : None
Common Uses : Shrub; hedge
Major Problems : None
Additional Notes : Withstands shearing.

Family : Caprifoliaceae   **Zone** : 7-10A

Typical Height : 6 Ft.
Drought Tolerance : High
Nutritional Requirements : Low
Light Requirements : High
Leaf Type : Simple
Texture : Fine
Flower Characteristics : Showy; fragrant

Environmental Problems : None

Lonicera sempervirens

Common Name(s) : Trumpet Honeysuckle; Coral Honeysuckle
Origin : Eastern United States
Growth Rate : Low
Salt Tolerance : Medium
Soil Requirements : Wide
Plant Type : Evergreen vine
Foliage Color : Green
Flowering Season : Spring; summer
Flower Color : Red & yellow
Propagation : Cuttings
Human Hazards : None
Common Uses : Flowering vine
Major Problems : None
Additional Notes : Does not make a dense covering; many cultivars exist.
Cultivars
'SULPHUREA' has yellow flowers; 'SUPERBA' and 'MAGNIFICA' have bright red flowers;

Family : Caprifoliaceae   **Zone** : 4-10A

Typical Height : Not applicable
Drought Tolerance : Medium
Nutritional Requirements : Low
Light Requirements : Medium; high
Leaf Type : Simple
Texture : Medium
Flower Characteristics : Showy; fragrant

Environmental Problems : None

Loropetalum chinense

Common Name(s) : Loropetalum
Origin : Japan, China, and Himalayas
Growth Rate : Medium
Salt Tolerance : Low
Soil Requirements : Acid
Plant Type : Evergreen shrub
Foliage Color : Green
Flowering Season : Spring
Flower Color : White
Propagation : Seeds; grafting
Human Hazards : None
Common Uses : Shrub
Major Problems : Mites; nematodes; root rots. Fe deficiency
Additional Notes : Grows best in north Florida.

Family : Hamamelidaceae   Zone : 8-10A

Typical Height : 10 Ft.
Drought Tolerance : Medium
Nutritional Requirements : Medium
Light Requirements : High
Leaf Type : Simple
Texture : Medium
Flower Characteristics : Insignificant

Environmental Problems : None

Lycium carolinianum

Common Name(s) : Christmas Berry
Origin : Southeastern United States
Growth Rate : Medium
Salt Tolerance : High
Soil Requirements : Wide
Plant Type : Evergreen shrub
Foliage Color : Green
Flowering Season : Summer
Flower Color : White; lavender
Propagation : Cuttings; seeds; suckers
Human Hazards : None
Common Uses : Shrub
Major Problems : None
Additional Notes : This Florida native is good for coastal landscapes. Red berries in winter.

Family : Solanaceae   Zone : 7-11

Typical Height : 7 Ft.
Drought Tolerance : High
Nutritional Requirements : Low
Light Requirements : Medium; high
Leaf Type : Simple
Texture : Fine
Flower Characteristics : Insignificant

Environmental Problems : Invasive

Lycoris spp.

Common Name(s) : Hurricane Lilies
Origin : Eastern Asia
Growth Rate : Medium
Salt Tolerance : Low
Soil Requirements : Wide
Plant Type : Herbaceous perennial
Foliage Color : Green
Flowering Season : Fall
Flower Color : Red; yellow; white; pink
Propagation : Division
Human Hazards : None
Common Uses : Beds; borders; specimen plant
Major Problems : None
Additional Notes : L. radiata naturalizes in north Florida; excellent fall flowers.

Family : Amaryllidaceae   Zone : 8-10B

Typical Height : 1.5 Ft.
Drought Tolerance : Medium
Nutritional Requirements : Medium
Light Requirements : Medium
Leaf Type : Simple
Texture : Medium
Flower Characteristics : Showy

Environmental Problems : None

Lyonia ferruginea

Common Name(s) : Rusty Lyonia
Origin : Southeastern United States
Growth Rate : Slow
Salt Tolerance : Low
Soil Requirements : Acid
Plant Type : Evergreen shrub or tree
Foliage Color : Green
Flowering Season : Spring
Flower Color : White
Propagation : Seeds
Human Hazards : None
Common Uses : Shrub; small tree
Major Problems : None
Additional Notes : Two other native species are also infrequently cultivated.

Family : Ericaceae   Zone : 8-10B

Typical Height : 15 Ft.
Drought Tolerance : High
Nutritional Requirements : Low
Light Requirements : High
Leaf Type : Simple
Texture : Medium
Flower Characteristics : Insignificant

Environmental Problems : None

Lysiloma latisiliqua

Common Name(s) : Wild Tamarind
Origin : South Florida and West Indies
Growth Rate : Medium
Salt Tolerance : High
Soil Requirements : Wide
Plant Type : Evergreen tree
Foliage Color : Green
Flowering Season : Spring; summer
Flower Color : White
Propagation : Seeds
Human Hazards : None
Common Uses : Shade tree
Major Problems : None
Additional Notes : This outstanding tree has a weeping habit.

Family : Leguminosae   **Zone** : 10B-11

Typical Height : 45 Ft.
Drought Tolerance : High
Nutritional Requirements : Medium
Light Requirements : High
Leaf Type : Pinnately compound
Texture : Fine
Flower Characteristics : Insignificant; fragrant

Environmental Problems : None

Lysiloma sabicu

Common Name(s) : Sabicu
Origin : Bahamas and West Indies
Growth Rate : Medium
Salt Tolerance : High
Soil Requirements : Wide
Plant Type : Evergreen tree
Foliage Color : Green
Flowering Season : Spring; summer
Flower Color : White
Propagation : Seeds
Human Hazards : None
Common Uses : Shade tree
Major Problems : None
Additional Notes : An excellent small weeping tree for south Florida.

Family : Leguminosae   **Zone** : 10B-11

Typical Height : 25 Ft.
Drought Tolerance : High
Nutritional Requirements : Low
Light Requirements : High
Leaf Type : Pinnately compound
Texture : Fine
Flower Characteristics : Insignificant

Environmental Problems : None

Macadamia integrifolia

Common Name(s) : Macadamia Nut
Origin : Australia
Growth Rate : Slow
Salt Tolerance : Low
Soil Requirements : Wide
Plant Type : Evergreen tree
Foliage Color : Green
Flowering Season : Spring
Flower Color : White
Propagation : Seed; grafting
Human Hazards : Poisonous
Common Uses : Shade tree; edible fruit
Major Problems : None
Additional Notes : Does not fruit dependably in Florida. Poisonous leaves and nutshells.

Family : Proteaceae   **Zone** : 10A-11

Typical Height : 20 Ft.
Drought Tolerance : Medium
Nutritional Requirements : Medium
Light Requirements : High
Leaf Type : Simple
Texture : Medium
Flower Characteristics : Insignificant

Environmental Problems : None

Macrozamia moorei

Common Name(s) : Moore's Macrozamia
Origin : Australia
Growth Rate : Slow
Salt Tolerance : Low
Soil Requirements : Wide
Plant Type : Evergreen shrub (cycad)
Foliage Color : Green
Flowering Season : Spring
Flower Color : n/a
Propagation : Seeds
Human Hazards : None
Common Uses : Shrub
Major Problems : None
Additional Notes : A large graceful cycad.

Family : Zamiaceae   **Zone** : 10B-11

Typical Height : 10 Ft.
Drought Tolerance : High
Nutritional Requirements : Low
Light Requirements : Medium; high
Leaf Type : Pinnately compound
Texture : Medium
Flower Characteristics : Insignificant

Environmental Problems : None

Magnolia fraseri

Common Name(s) : Fraser Magnolia
Origin : Eastern United States
Growth Rate : Medium
Salt Tolerance : Low
Soil Requirements : Acid
Plant Type : Deciduous tree
Foliage Color : Green
Flowering Season : Spring
Flower Color : White
Propagation : Seeds; cuttings
Human Hazards : None
Common Uses : Shade tree; flowering tree
Major Problems : None

Family : Magnoliaceae   **Zone** : 5-8

Typical Height : 45 Ft.
Drought Tolerance : Low
Nutritional Requirements : High
Light Requirements : Medium; high
Leaf Type : Simple
Texture : Coarse
Flower Characteristics : Fragrant; showy

Environmental Problems : None

Additional Notes : Has large fragrant white flowers and cucumber-shaped fruits in fall.

Magnolia grandiflora *(Photograph p. 164)*

Common Name(s) : Southern Magnolia
Origin : Southeastern United States
Growth Rate : Medium
Salt Tolerance : High
Soil Requirements : Acid
Plant Type : Evergreen tree
Foliage Color : Green & brown
Flowering Season : Spring
Flower Color : White
Propagation : Seeds; grafting; air layers
Human Hazards : None
Common Uses : Flowering tree
Major Problems : Scales

Family : Magnoliaceae   **Zone** : 7-10B

Typical Height : 65 Ft.
Drought Tolerance : Medium
Nutritional Requirements : Medium
Light Requirements : High
Leaf Type : Simple
Texture : Coarse
Flower Characteristics : Showy; fragrant

Environmental Problems : None

Additional Notes : This hardy tree has large leathery leaves and showy flowers.
Cultivars
'ST. MARY' is a compact, early flowering variety with bronze foliage; 'MAJESTIC BEAUTY' has a pyramidal form and larger flowers; 'SAMUEL SOMMER' has very large fragrant flowers; 'LITTLE GEM' is a very compact variety.

Magnolia stellata

Common Name(s) : Star Magnolia
Origin : Japan
Growth Rate : Slow
Salt Tolerance : Low
Soil Requirements : Acid
Plant Type : Deciduous shrub or tree
Foliage Color : Green
Flowering Season : Winter; spring
Flower Color : Pink; white
Propagation : Seeds; cuttings
Human Hazards : None
Common Uses : Flowering shrub; small flowering tree
Major Problems : Leafspots; nematodes

Family : Magnoliaceae   **Zone** : 5-8

Typical Height : 8 Ft.
Drought Tolerance : Low
Nutritional Requirements : High
Light Requirements : Medium; high
Leaf Type : Simple
Texture : Coarse
Flower Characteristics : Showy; fragrant

Environmental Problems : None

Additional Notes : Best treated as a shrub.
Cultivars
'DR. MERRILL' has much larger flowers than species; 'ROYAL STAR' has double, nearly white flowers; 'CENTENNIAL', 'ROSEA', and 'WATERLILY' have pink buds with flowers fading to white; 'RUBRA' has dark rose colored flowers.

Magnolia virginiana *(Photograph p. 164)*

Common Name(s) : Sweetbay
Origin : Southeastern United States
Growth Rate : Medium
Salt Tolerance : Low
Soil Requirements : Wide
Plant Type : Deciduous tree
Foliage Color : Green
Flowering Season : Summer
Flower Color : White
Propagation : Seeds
Human Hazards : None
Common Uses : Flowering tree
Major Problems : Scales; borers

Family : Magnoliaceae   **Zone** : 5-10B

Typical Height : 50 Ft.
Drought Tolerance : Low
Nutritional Requirements : Medium
Light Requirements : High; medium
Leaf Type : Simple
Texture : Medium
Flower Characteristics : Showy; fragrant

Environmental Problems : None

Additional Notes : Good for wet sites in southeastern United States.
Cultivars
Var. <u>australis</u> is more evergreen.

Magnolia X soulangiana

Common Name(s) : Saucer Magnolia
Origin : Hybrid
Growth Rate : Medium
Salt Tolerance : Low
Soil Requirements : Acid
Plant Type : Deciduous tree
Foliage Color : Green
Flowering Season : Winter; spring
Flower Color : Pink; white; purple
Propagation : Cuttings
Human Hazards : None
Common Uses : Flowering tree
Major Problems : Leafspots
Additional Notes : Spectacular flowers are sometimes killed by frosts.
Cultivars
'SAN JOSE' has large rosy-purple flowers; 'ALEXANDRINA', 'ANDRE LEROY', 'BROZZONI', 'GRACE MCDADE' 'LOMBARDY RODE' and 'RUSTICA RUBRA' have pink to purple on the outside of the flowers and white inside; 'BURGUNDY' has deep purple flowers.

Family : Magnoliaceae   **Zone** : 5-8

Typical Height : 25 Ft.
Drought Tolerance : Low
Nutritional Requirements : High
Light Requirements : Medium
Leaf Type : Simple
Texture : Coarse
Flower Characteristics : Showy

Environmental Problems : None

Mahonia bealei *(Photograph p. 181)*

Common Name(s) : Leatherleaf Mahonia
Origin : China
Growth Rate : Slow
Salt Tolerance : Medium
Soil Requirements : Wide
Plant Type : Evergreen shrub
Foliage Color : Green
Flowering Season : Spring; summer
Flower Color : Yellow
Propagation : Seeds; cuttings
Human Hazards : Spiny
Common Uses : Shrub; hedge
Major Problems : None
Additional Notes : A spiny-leaved shrub with blue-black fruits.

Family : Berberidaceae   **Zone** : 6-9

Typical Height : 6 Ft.
Drought Tolerance : Medium
Nutritional Requirements : Medium
Light Requirements : Medium; high
Leaf Type : Pinnately compound
Texture : Coarse
Flower Characteristics : Insignificant

Environmental Problems : None

Mahonia fortunei

Common Name(s) : Holly Grape
Origin : China
Growth Rate : Slow
Salt Tolerance : Medium
Soil Requirements : Wide
Plant Type : Evergreen shrub
Foliage Color : Green
Flowering Season : Fall
Flower Color : Yellow
Propagation : Seeds; cuttings
Human Hazards : Spiny
Common Uses : Shrub; hedge
Major Problems : None
Additional Notes : A spiny-leaved shrub with blue-black fruits.

Family : Berberidaceae   **Zone** : 8-9

Typical Height : 5 Ft.
Drought Tolerance : Medium
Nutritional Requirements : Medium
Light Requirements : Medium; high
Leaf Type : Pinnately compound
Texture : Medium
Flower Characteristics : Insignificant

Environmental Problems : None

Mallotonia gnaphalodes *(Photograph p. 182)*

Common Name(s) : Sea Lavender
Origin : Caribbean Region
Growth Rate : Slow
Salt Tolerance : High
Soil Requirements : Wide
Plant Type : Evergreen shrub
Foliage Color : Silver
Flowering Season : Year-round
Flower Color : White
Propagation : Layers; seeds; cuttings
Human Hazards : None
Common Uses : Shrub; seasides
Major Problems : Root rot
Additional Notes : This Florida native is well adapted for beach landscapes.

Family : Boraginaceae   **Zone** : 10B-11

Typical Height : 5 Ft.
Drought Tolerance : High
Nutritional Requirements : Low
Light Requirements : High
Leaf Type : Simple
Texture : Fine
Flower Characteristics : Insignificant

Environmental Problems : None

Malpighia coccigera

Common Name(s) : Singapore Holly
Origin : West Indies
Growth Rate : Slow
Salt Tolerance : Medium
Soil Requirements : Wide
Plant Type : Evergreen shrub
Foliage Color : Green
Flowering Season : Summer
Flower Color : Pink
Propagation : Seeds; cuttings
Human Hazards : Spiny
Common Uses : Shrub; groundcover
Major Problems : Nematodes; scales
Additional Notes : Some forms more prostrate than others.

Family : Malpighiaceae   **Zone** : 10B-11

Typical Height : 3 Ft.
Drought Tolerance : Medium
Nutritional Requirements : Medium
Light Requirements : Medium
Leaf Type : Simple
Texture : Fine
Flower Characteristics : Showy

Environmental Problems : None

Malpighia glabra *(Photograph p. 182)*

Common Name(s) : Barbados Cherry
Origin : Tropical America
Growth Rate : Fast
Salt Tolerance : High
Soil Requirements : Wide
Plant Type : Evergreen shrub or tree
Foliage Color : Green
Flowering Season : Year-round
Flower Color : Pink
Propagation : Cuttings; seeds
Human Hazards : None
Common Uses : Flowering shrub; hedge; edible fruit; small flowering tree
Major Problems : Nematodes; scales; whiteflies
Additional Notes : Edible red fruit high in vitamin C.

Family : Malpighiaceae   **Zone** : 10A-11

Typical Height : 12 Ft.
Drought Tolerance : High
Nutritional Requirements : Low
Light Requirements : Medium; high
Leaf Type : Simple
Texture : Medium
Flower Characteristics : Showy

Environmental Problems : None

Malus angustifolia

Common Name(s) : Southern Crab Apple
Origin : Southeastern United States
Growth Rate : Medium
Salt Tolerance : Low
Soil Requirements : Wide
Plant Type : Deciduous tree
Foliage Color : Green
Flowering Season : Spring
Flower Color : Pink
Propagation : Seeds; suckers
Human Hazards : None
Common Uses : Edible fruit; small flowering tree
Major Problems : Tent caterpillars; cedar-apple rust
Additional Notes : Short-lived.

Family : Rosaceae   **Zone** : 5-9

Typical Height : 20 Ft.
Drought Tolerance : Medium
Nutritional Requirements : Medium
Light Requirements : High
Leaf Type : Simple
Texture : Medium
Flower Characteristics : Showy

Environmental Problems : Invasive

Malvaviscus arboreus *(Photograph p. 182)*

Common Name(s) : Turk's Cap; Wax Mallow
Origin : Mexico to Colombia
Growth Rate : Fast
Salt Tolerance : Low
Soil Requirements : Wide
Plant Type : Evergreen shrub
Foliage Color : Green
Flowering Season : Spring; summer; fall
Flower Color : Red
Propagation : Cuttings
Human Hazards : None
Common Uses : Flowering shrub
Major Problems : None
Additional Notes : A spreading, sprawling shrub with straggly growth.

Family : Malvaceae   **Zone** : 9-11

Typical Height : 7 Ft.
Drought Tolerance : High
Nutritional Requirements : Medium
Light Requirements : High
Leaf Type : Simple
Texture : Medium
Flower Characteristics : Showy

Environmental Problems : None

Mammea americana

Common Name(s) : Mammee Apple
Origin : West Indies
Growth Rate : Fast
Salt Tolerance : Medium
Soil Requirements : Wide
Plant Type : Evergreen tree
Foliage Color : Green
Flowering Season : Spring
Flower Color : White
Propagation : Seeds
Human Hazards : Poisonous
Common Uses : Tree; edible fruit
Major Problems : None

Family : Guttiferae   **Zone** : 10B-11

Typical Height : 50 Ft.
Drought Tolerance : High
Nutritional Requirements : Medium
Light Requirements : High
Leaf Type : Simple
Texture : Coarse
Flower Characteristics : Showy; fragrant

Environmental Problems : None

Additional Notes : Produces large edible fruits with an apricot-like flavor. Poisonous seeds.

Mandevilla sanderi

Common Name(s) : Mandevilla
Origin : Brazil
Growth Rate : Fast
Salt Tolerance : Medium
Soil Requirements : Wide
Plant Type : Evergreen vine
Foliage Color : Green
Flowering Season : Summer
Flower Color : Pink; red
Propagation : Cuttings
Human Hazards : None
Common Uses : Flowering vine
Major Problems : Nematodes; mealybugs; scales

Family : Apocynaceae   **Zone** : 10A-11

Typical Height : Not applicable
Drought Tolerance : High
Nutritional Requirements : Medium
Light Requirements : High
Leaf Type : Simple
Texture : Medium
Flower Characteristics : Showy

Environmental Problems : None

Additional Notes : Numerous hybrids exist.
Cultivars
'ROSEA' has lighter pink flowers;

Mandevilla splendens

Common Name(s) : Pink Allamanda
Origin : Southeastern Brazil
Growth Rate : Fast
Salt Tolerance : Medium
Soil Requirements : Wide
Plant Type : Evergreen vine
Foliage Color : Green
Flowering Season : Summer
Flower Color : Pink
Propagation : Cuttings
Human Hazards : None
Common Uses : Flowering vine; flowering pot plant
Major Problems : Nematodes; mealybugs; scales

Family : Apocynaceae   **Zone** : 10A-11

Typical Height : Not applicable
Drought Tolerance : High
Nutritional Requirements : Medium
Light Requirements : High
Leaf Type : Simple
Texture : Medium
Flower Characteristics : Showy

Environmental Problems : None

Additional Notes : Numerous hybrids available.

Mangifera indica *(Photograph p. 164)*

Common Name(s) : Mango
Origin : Southern Asia
Growth Rate : Medium
Salt Tolerance : Medium
Soil Requirements : Wide
Plant Type : Evergreen tree
Foliage Color : Green
Flowering Season : Winter
Flower Color : Pink-white
Propagation : Seeds; grafting
Human Hazards : Irritant
Common Uses : Edible fruit; shade tree; flowering tree
Major Problems : Anthracnose; scales

Family : Anacardiaceae   **Zone** : 10B-11

Typical Height : 60 Ft.
Drought Tolerance : Medium
Nutritional Requirements : Medium
Light Requirements : High
Leaf Type : Simple
Texture : Coarse
Flower Characteristics : Showy

Environmental Problems : Messy

Additional Notes : Many varieties of mango exist. Excellent fruit.
Cultivars
Popular cultivars include: 'KEITT', 'KENT', 'EDWARD', 'GLENN', 'TOMMY ATKINS', 'IRWIN', and 'HADEN'.

Manilkara bahamensis

Common Name(s) : Wild Dilly; Wild Sapodilla
Origin : South Florida and West Indies
Growth Rate : Medium
Salt Tolerance : Medium
Soil Requirements : Wide
Plant Type : Evergreen tree or shrub
Foliage Color : Green
Flowering Season : Spring
Flower Color : Yellow
Propagation : Seeds
Human Hazards : None
Common Uses : Small tree; shrub; edible
Major Problems : None
Additional Notes : Has white milky sap; brown scurfy fruit is edible.

Family : Sapotaceae   Zone : 10B-11

Typical Height : 30 Ft.
Drought Tolerance : High
Nutritional Requirements : Low
Light Requirements : High
Leaf Type : Simple
Texture : Coarse
Flower Characteristics : Insignificant

Environmental Problems : None

Manilkara kauki

Common Name(s) : n/a
Origin : Asia
Growth Rate : Medium
Salt Tolerance : Medium
Soil Requirements : Wide
Plant Type : Evergreen tree
Foliage Color : Green & white
Flowering Season : n/a
Flower Color : White
Propagation : Seeds; cuttings
Human Hazards : None
Common Uses : Tree
Major Problems : None
Additional Notes : Undersides of leaves are covered with dense white hairs. Fruits are red.

Family : Sapotaceae   Zone : 10B-11

Typical Height : 60 Ft.
Drought Tolerance : Medium
Nutritional Requirements : Medium
Light Requirements : High
Leaf Type : Simple
Texture : Medium
Flower Characteristics : Showy

Environmental Problems : None

Manilkara roxburghiana

Common Name(s) : Mimusops
Origin : India
Growth Rate : Medium
Salt Tolerance : High
Soil Requirements : Wide
Plant Type : Evergreen tree
Foliage Color : Green
Flowering Season : Summer
Flower Color : White
Propagation : Seeds
Human Hazards : None
Common Uses : Shade tree
Major Problems : None
Additional Notes : Good for coastal landscapes.

Family : Sapotaceae   Zone : 10B-11

Typical Height : 35 Ft.
Drought Tolerance : High
Nutritional Requirements : Low
Light Requirements : High
Leaf Type : Simple
Texture : Coarse
Flower Characteristics : Insignificant

Environmental Problems : None

Manilkara zapota (Photograph p. 164)

Common Name(s) : Sapodilla
Origin : Mexico and Central America
Growth Rate : Slow
Salt Tolerance : High
Soil Requirements : Wide
Plant Type : Evergreen tree
Foliage Color : Green
Flowering Season : Summer
Flower Color : White
Propagation : Seeds; grafting
Human Hazards : None
Common Uses : Edible fruit; shade tree
Major Problems : Scales
Additional Notes : A well adapted slow-growing shade tree naturalized in south Florida.

Family : Sapotaceae   Zone : 10B-11

Typical Height : 45 Ft.
Drought Tolerance : High
Nutritional Requirements : Low
Light Requirements : High
Leaf Type : Simple
Texture : Medium
Flower Characteristics : Insignificant; fragrant

Environmental Problems : None

Maranta arundinacea

Common Name(s) : Arrowroot; Obedience Plant
Origin : Tropical America
Growth Rate : Medium
Salt Tolerance : Low
Soil Requirements : Wide
Plant Type : Herbaceous perrennial
Foliage Color : Green; variegated
Flowering Season : Spring; summer
Flower Color : White
Propagation : Division
Human Hazards : None
Common Uses : Specimen plant
Major Problems : None

Family : Marantaceae   **Zone** : 10B-11

Typical Height : 5 Ft.
Drought Tolerance : Medium
Nutritional Requirements : Medium
Light Requirements : Medium
Leaf Type : Simple
Texture : Coarse
Flower Characteristics : Insignificant

Environmental Problems : None

Additional Notes : Variegated form makes an attractive specimen plant. Deciduous in winter.
Cultivars
'VARIEGATA' has yellow-green and green variegated foliage.

Maranta leuconeura

Common Name(s) : Prayer Plant
Origin : Brazil
Growth Rate : Medium
Salt Tolerance : Low
Soil Requirements : Wide
Plant Type : Herbaceous perennial
Foliage Color : Green & pink; variegated
Flowering Season : Spring; summer
Flower Color : White
Propagation : Cuttings; division
Human Hazards : None
Common Uses : Beds; specimen plant; foliage plant
Major Problems : Nematodes

Family : Marantaceae   **Zone** : 10B-11

Typical Height : 1 Ft.
Drought Tolerance : Low
Nutritional Requirements : Medium
Light Requirements : Low; medium
Leaf Type : Simple
Texture : Coarse
Flower Characteristics : Insignificant

Environmental Problems : None

Additional Notes : Several cultivars with varying leaf patterns. Leaves fold at night.
Cultivars
Var. erythroneura has silver and dark green upper leaf surfaces with red veins; var. kerchoviana has silvery leaves with 2 rows of dark green spots along the midvein.

Mastichodendron foetidissimum

Common Name(s) : Mastic
Origin : Caribbean Region
Growth Rate : Medium
Salt Tolerance : High
Soil Requirements : Wide
Plant Type : Evergreen tree
Foliage Color : Green
Flowering Season : Spring; summer; fall
Flower Color : Green-yellow
Propagation : Seeds
Human Hazards : None
Common Uses : Shade tree; edible fruit
Major Problems : None

Family : Sapotaceae   **Zone** : 10B-11

Typical Height : 50 Ft.
Drought Tolerance : High
Nutritional Requirements : Low
Light Requirements : High
Leaf Type : Simple
Texture : Medium
Flower Characteristics : Insignificant

Environmental Problems : None

Additional Notes : Female trees have edible messy fruit.

Maytenus phyllanthoides

Common Name(s) : Florida Mayten
Origin : Southern United States
Growth Rate : Medium
Salt Tolerance : Medium
Soil Requirements : Wide
Plant Type : Evergreen shrub or tree
Foliage Color : Green
Flowering Season : Summer
Flower Color : White
Propagation : Seeds; cuttings
Human Hazards : None
Common Uses : Shrub; small tree
Major Problems : None
Additional Notes : An uncommon native shrub.

Family : Celastraceae   **Zone** : 10B-11

Typical Height : 15 Ft.
Drought Tolerance : High
Nutritional Requirements : Low
Light Requirements : Medium; high
Leaf Type : Simple
Texture : Medium
Flower Characteristics : Insignificant

Environmental Problems : None

Maytenus undatus

Common Name(s) : Maytenus
Origin : n/a
Growth Rate : Medium
Salt Tolerance : High
Soil Requirements : Wide
Plant Type : Evergreen shrub
Foliage Color : Green
Flowering Season : Summer
Flower Color : White
Propagation : Cuttings
Human Hazards : None
Common Uses : Hedge; shrub
Major Problems : None
Additional Notes : A durable, but seldom-used landscape plant.

Family : Celastraceae   **Zone** : 10B-11

Typical Height : 6 Ft.
Drought Tolerance : High
Nutritional Requirements : Low
Light Requirements : Medium; high
Leaf Type : Simple
Texture : Medium
Flower Characteristics : Insignificant

Environmental Problems : None

Medinella magnifica *(Photograph p. 182)*

Common Name(s) : Medinella
Origin : Philippines
Growth Rate : Medium
Salt Tolerance : Low
Soil Requirements : Acid
Plant Type : Evergreen shrub
Foliage Color : Green
Flowering Season : Spring; summer; fall
Flower Color : Pink
Propagation : Cuttings
Human Hazards : None
Common Uses : Flowering shrub
Major Problems : None
Additional Notes : Has spectacular pink flowers and attractive lavender fruit.

Family : Melastomataceae   **Zone** : 11

Typical Height : 6 Ft.
Drought Tolerance : Low
Nutritional Requirements : Medium
Light Requirements : Medium
Leaf Type : Simple
Texture : Coarse
Flower Characteristics : Showy

Environmental Problems : None

Melaleuca decora

Common Name(s) : Snow In Summer
Origin : Australia
Growth Rate : Medium
Salt Tolerance : Medium
Soil Requirements : Wide
Plant Type : Evergreen tree
Foliage Color : Green
Flowering Season : Summer
Flower Color : White
Propagation : Seeds; cuttings
Human Hazards : None
Common Uses : Small tree
Major Problems : None
Additional Notes : A relatively scarce, non-weedy melaleuca.

Family : Myrtaceae   **Zone** : 10B-11

Typical Height : 30 Ft.
Drought Tolerance : High
Nutritional Requirements : Low
Light Requirements : High
Leaf Type : Simple
Texture : Fine
Flower Characteristics : Showy

Environmental Problems : None

Melia azedarach

Common Name(s) : Chinaberry
Origin : Southern Asia
Growth Rate : Fast
Salt Tolerance : High
Soil Requirements : Wide
Plant Type : Evergreen tree
Foliage Color : Green
Flowering Season : Spring
Flower Color : Lavender
Propagation : Seeds; cuttings
Human Hazards : Poisonous
Common Uses : Shade tree
Major Problems : Scales; whiteflies; sooty mold
Additional Notes : Often poorly shaped and weak wooded. Fruit is poisonous.

Family : Meliaceae   **Zone** : 7-10B

Typical Height : 55 Ft.
Drought Tolerance : High
Nutritional Requirements : Low
Light Requirements : High
Leaf Type : Pinnately compound
Texture : Fine
Flower Characteristics : Showy; fragrant

Environmental Problems : Weak; weedy

Melicoccus bijugatus

Common Name(s) : Spanish Lime; Genip
Origin : Caribbean Region
Growth Rate : Slow
Salt Tolerance : Medium
Soil Requirements : Wide
Plant Type : Evergreen tree
Foliage Color : Green
Flowering Season : Spring
Flower Color : White
Propagation : Seeds
Human Hazards : None
Common Uses : Shade tree; edible fruit
Major Problems : None
Additional Notes : Generally planted in the Keys.

Family : Sapindaceae   **Zone** : 10B-11

Typical Height : 45 Ft.
Drought Tolerance : High
Nutritional Requirements : Medium
Light Requirements : High
Leaf Type : Simple
Texture : Medium
Flower Characteristics : Insignificant

Environmental Problems : None

Merremia dissecta

Common Name(s) : Cutleaf Morning Glory
Origin : Tropical America
Growth Rate : Fast
Salt Tolerance : Medium
Soil Requirements : Wide
Plant Type : Evergreen vine
Foliage Color : Green
Flowering Season : Spring; summer; fall
Flower Color : White
Propagation : Seeds; cuttings
Human Hazards : None
Common Uses : Flowering vine
Major Problems : None
Additional Notes : Capsules ornamental; can be weedy. M. tuberosa , the woodrose, also grown.

Family : Convolvulaceae   **Zone** : 9-10B

Typical Height : Not applicable
Drought Tolerance : Medium
Nutritional Requirements : Medium
Light Requirements : High
Leaf Type : Simple
Texture : Fine
Flower Characteristics : Showy

Environmental Problems : Weedy

Metasequoia glyptostroboides

Common Name(s) : Dawn Redwood
Origin : China
Growth Rate : Fast
Salt Tolerance : Low
Soil Requirements : Wide
Plant Type : Deciduous tree
Foliage Color : Green
Flowering Season : Spring
Flower Color : n/a
Propagation : Seeds; cuttings
Human Hazards : None
Common Uses : Shade tree
Major Problems : None
Additional Notes : Has an attractive pyramidal form and brown fall color.

Family : Taxodiaceae   **Zone** : 5-9

Typical Height : 100 Ft.
Drought Tolerance : Medium
Nutritional Requirements : Low
Light Requirements : High
Leaf Type : Needle
Texture : Fine
Flower Characteristics : Insignificant

Environmental Problems : None

Michelia figo *(Photograph p. 182)*

Common Name(s) : Banana Shrub
Origin : China
Growth Rate : Medium
Salt Tolerance : Low
Soil Requirements : Wide
Plant Type : Evergreen shrub
Foliage Color : Green
Flowering Season : Spring
Flower Color : Yellow
Propagation : Cuttings
Human Hazards : None
Common Uses : Flowering shrub
Major Problems : Scales
Additional Notes : Formal shrub; flowers have banana fragrance.

Family : Magnoliaceae   **Zone** : 7-9

Typical Height : 8 Ft.
Drought Tolerance : Low
Nutritional Requirements : High
Light Requirements : Medium
Leaf Type : Simple
Texture : Medium
Flower Characteristics : Showy; fragrant

Environmental Problems : None

Millettia ovalifolia *(Photograph p. 164)*

Common Name(s) : Millettia
Origin : Burma
Growth Rate : Medium
Salt Tolerance : Low
Soil Requirements : Wide
Plant Type : Evergreen tree
Foliage Color : Green
Flowering Season : Spring
Flower Color : Pink
Propagation : Seeds
Human Hazards : None
Common Uses : Small flowering tree
Major Problems : Nutritional deficiencies
Additional Notes : Resembles a redbud when in bloom.

Family : Leguminosae   **Zone** : 10B-11

Typical Height : 25 Ft.
Drought Tolerance : High
Nutritional Requirements : Medium
Light Requirements : High
Leaf Type : Pinnately compound
Texture : Fine
Flower Characteristics : Showy

Environmental Problems : None

Mimusops elengi

Common Name(s) : Spanish Cherry
Origin : India to Malay Peninsula
Growth Rate : Medium
Salt Tolerance : Medium
Soil Requirements : Wide
Plant Type : Evergreen tree
Foliage Color : Green
Flowering Season : n/a
Flower Color : White
Propagation : Seeds; cuttings
Human Hazards : None
Common Uses : Tree; edible fruit
Major Problems : None
Additional Notes : New growth is covered with reddish hairs. Astringent fruit is edible.

Family : Sapotaceae   **Zone** : 10B-11

Typical Height : 30 Ft.
Drought Tolerance : Medium
Nutritional Requirements : Medium
Light Requirements : High
Leaf Type : Simple
Texture : Medium
Flower Characteristics : Insignificant; fragrant

Environmental Problems : None

Mitchella repens

Common Name(s) : Twinberry
Origin : Southeastern United States
Growth Rate : Medium
Salt Tolerance : Low
Soil Requirements : Acid
Plant Type : Evergreen shrub
Foliage Color : Green
Flowering Season : Spring
Flower Color : White
Propagation : Seeds; cuttings
Human Hazards : None
Common Uses : Groundcover
Major Problems : None
Additional Notes : Best in a woodland setting; has attractive red fruit.

Family : Rubiaceae   **Zone** : 5-8

Typical Height : .2 Ft.
Drought Tolerance : Low
Nutritional Requirements : Medium
Light Requirements : Low
Leaf Type : Simple
Texture : Fine
Flower Characteristics : Insignificant

Environmental Problems : None

Monarda didyma

Common Name(s) : Bee Balm
Origin : Eastern United States
Growth Rate : Fast
Salt Tolerance : Low
Soil Requirements : Wide
Plant Type : Herbaceous perennial
Foliage Color : Green
Flowering Season : Summer
Flower Color : Pink; red; white
Propagation : Seeds; division
Human Hazards : None
Common Uses : Borders; specimen plant
Major Problems : None
Additional Notes : Early settlers made tea out of the leaves.

Family : Labiatae   **Zone** : 4-9

Typical Height : 2.5 Ft.
Drought Tolerance : Medium
Nutritional Requirements : Medium
Light Requirements : Medium; high
Leaf Type : Simple
Texture : Medium
Flower Characteristics : Showy

Environmental Problems : None

Monstera deliciosa

Common Name(s) : Ceriman; Swiss Cheese Plant
Origin : Mexico and Central America
Growth Rate : Medium
Salt Tolerance : Low
Soil Requirements : Wide
Plant Type : Evergreen vine
Foliage Color : Green; variegated
Flowering Season : Summer
Flower Color : White
Propagation : Cuttings; seeds
Human Hazards : Irritant
Common Uses : Vine; foliage plant; edible fruit; epiphyte
Major Problems : None
Additional Notes : Ripe fruit edible, but contains calcium oxalate crystals.
Cultivars
'VARIEGATA' has variegated foliage.

Family : Araceae   **Zone** : 10B-11

Typical Height : Not applicable
Drought Tolerance : Medium
Nutritional Requirements : Medium
Light Requirements : Low; medium
Leaf Type : Simple; pinnately lobed
Texture : Coarse
Flower Characteristics : Insignificant

Environmental Problems : None

Moringa pterygosperma

Common Name(s) : Horseradish Tree
Origin : India
Growth Rate : Fast
Salt Tolerance : Low
Soil Requirements : Wide
Plant Type : Evergreen tree
Foliage Color : Green
Flowering Season : Year-round
Flower Color : White
Propagation : Seeds; cuttings
Human Hazards : None
Common Uses : Shade tree; edible
Major Problems : None
Additional Notes : All parts of this tree, including the roots, are edible.

Family : Moringaceae   **Zone** : 10B-11

Typical Height : 25 Ft.
Drought Tolerance : High
Nutritional Requirements : Medium
Light Requirements : High
Leaf Type : Bipinnately compound
Texture : Fine
Flower Characteristics : Showy; fragrant

Environmental Problems : None

Morus alba

Common Name(s) : White Mulberry; Common Mulberry
Origin : China
Growth Rate : Fast
Salt Tolerance : Low
Soil Requirements : Wide
Plant Type : Deciduous tree
Foliage Color : Green
Flowering Season : Spring
Flower Color : Green
Propagation : Seeds; cuttings
Human Hazards : None
Common Uses : Tree; edible fruit
Major Problems : Bacterial blight; leafspots
Additional Notes : Variable shaped leaves. Edible fruits attract wildlife.
Cultivars
'CHAPARRAL' and 'URBANA' are fruitless weeping forms; 'STRIBLING' and 'KINGAN' are fast-growing fruitless clones; 'PYRAMIDALIS' is an upright clone; 'PENDULA' is a fruiting weeping variety.

Family : Moraceae   **Zone** : 4-10B

Typical Height : 60 Ft.
Drought Tolerance : High
Nutritional Requirements : Low
Light Requirements : High
Leaf Type : Simple
Texture : Medium
Flower Characteristics : Insignificant

Environmental Problems : Messy

Morus rubra

Common Name(s) : Red Mulberry
Origin : Eastern North America
Growth Rate : Fast
Salt Tolerance : Low
Soil Requirements : Wide
Plant Type : Deciduous tree
Foliage Color : Green
Flowering Season : Spring
Flower Color : White
Propagation : Seeds; cuttings
Human Hazards : None
Common Uses : Shade tree; edible fruit; windbreak
Major Problems : Bacterial blight; leafspots
Additional Notes : Fruit messy in a patio setting.

Family : Moraceae   **Zone** : 4-10B

Typical Height : 40 Ft.
Drought Tolerance : High
Nutritional Requirements : Low
Light Requirements : High
Leaf Type : Simple
Texture : Medium
Flower Characteristics : Insignificant

Environmental Problems : Messy

Muntingia calabura

Common Name(s) : Capulin; Cotton Candy Tree
Origin : Tropical America
Growth Rate : Fast
Salt Tolerance : Low
Soil Requirements : Wide
Plant Type : Evergreen tree
Foliage Color : Green
Flowering Season : Spring; summer; fall
Flower Color : White
Propagation : Seeds; cuttings
Human Hazards : None
Common Uses : Small tree; edible fruit
Major Problems : None
Additional Notes : Fast growing, weak wooded tree with messy sweet fruit.

Family : Elaeocarpaceae   Zone : 10B-11

Typical Height : 25 Ft.
Drought Tolerance : Medium
Nutritional Requirements : Medium
Light Requirements : High
Leaf Type : Simple
Texture : Medium
Flower Characteristics : Insignificant

Environmental Problems : Weak; messy

Murraya paniculata

Common Name(s) : Orange Jessamine; Orange Jasmine
Origin : Southern Asia, Australia, Pacific Isl.
Growth Rate : Medium
Salt Tolerance : Medium
Soil Requirements : Wide
Plant Type : Evergreen tree or shrub
Foliage Color : Green
Flowering Season : Summer; spring
Flower Color : White
Propagation : Cuttings; seeds
Human Hazards : None
Common Uses : Small flowering tree; flowering shrub
Major Problems : Scales; whiteflies; nematodes; sooty mold
Additional Notes : A shrub that can be shaped into a small tree.
Cultivars
'LAKEVIEW' is an improved variety.

Family : Rutaceae   Zone : 9-11

Typical Height : 15 Ft.
Drought Tolerance : High
Nutritional Requirements : Medium
Light Requirements : Medium; high
Leaf Type : Pinnately compound
Texture : Fine
Flower Characteristics : Showy; fragrant

Environmental Problems : None

Musa acuminata

Common Name(s) : Edible Banana
Origin : Southeast Asia and Pacific Islands
Growth Rate : Fast
Salt Tolerance : Low
Soil Requirements : Wide
Plant Type : Herbaceous perennial
Foliage Color : Green; green & red
Flowering Season : Year-round
Flower Color : Purple & yellow
Propagation : Division; tissue culture
Human Hazards : None
Common Uses : Edible fruit
Major Problems : Nematodes; sigatoka leafspot; K deficiency
Additional Notes : Many cultivars, some dwarf. Killed to ground by frost.
Cultivars
Popular cultivars include: 'CAVENDISH', 'DWARF CAVENDISH', 'GRAND NAIN', and 'RIO'.

Family : Musaceae   Zone : 10B-11

Typical Height : 15 Ft.
Drought Tolerance : Low
Nutritional Requirements : High
Light Requirements : High
Leaf Type : Simple
Texture : Very coarse
Flower Characteristics : Showy

Environmental Problems : Messy

Musa coccinea *(Photograph p. 198)*

Common Name(s) : Red Flowering Banana
Origin : Indochina
Growth Rate : Fast
Salt Tolerance : Low
Soil Requirements : Wide
Plant Type : Herbaceous perennial
Foliage Color : Green
Flowering Season : Year-round
Flower Color : Orange-red
Propagation : Division; seeds
Human Hazards : None
Common Uses : Cut flowers; specimen plant
Major Problems : Deightoniella stem rot. K deficiency
Additional Notes : Spectacular erect flowers are excellent cut flowers. Frost sensitive.

Family : Musaceae   Zone : 11

Typical Height : 7 Ft.
Drought Tolerance : Low
Nutritional Requirements : High
Light Requirements : Medium; high
Leaf Type : Simple
Texture : Very coarse
Flower Characteristics : Showy

Environmental Problems : None

Musa ornata *(Photograph p. 198)*
Common Name(s) : Lavender Flowering Banana
Origin : Bangladesh to Burma
Growth Rate : Fast
Salt Tolerance : Low
Soil Requirements : Wide
Plant Type : Herbaceous perennial
Foliage Color : Green & red
Flowering Season : Year-round
Flower Color : Lavender
Propagation : Division; seeds
Human Hazards : None
Common Uses : Cut flowers; specimen plant
Major Problems : None
Additional Notes : A large inedible banana with attractive upright flowers.

Family : Musaceae   Zone : 10B-11

Typical Height : 10 Ft.
Drought Tolerance : Medium
Nutritional Requirements : High
Light Requirements : Medium; high
Leaf Type : Simple
Texture : Very coarse
Flower Characteristics : Showy

Environmental Problems : None

Musa velutina *(Photograph p. 198)*
Common Name(s) : Pink Banana
Origin : Assam
Growth Rate : Fast
Salt Tolerance : Low
Soil Requirements : Wide
Plant Type : Herbaceous perennial
Foliage Color : Green
Flowering Season : Year-round
Flower Color : Lavender
Propagation : Division; seeds
Human Hazards : None
Common Uses : Shrub
Major Problems : K deficiency
Additional Notes : Small banana grown for its attractive seedy pink fruits.

Family : Musaceae   Zone : 10B-11

Typical Height : 4 Ft.
Drought Tolerance : Low
Nutritional Requirements : Medium
Light Requirements : Medium; high
Leaf Type : Simple
Texture : Coarse
Flower Characteristics : Showy

Environmental Problems : None

Musa X paradisiaca
Common Name(s) : Plantain; Edible Banana
Origin : Hybrid
Growth Rate : Fast
Salt Tolerance : Low
Soil Requirements : Wide
Plant Type : Herbaceous perennial
Foliage Color : Green
Flowering Season : Year-round
Flower Color : Lavender & yellow
Propagation : Division; tissue culture
Human Hazards : None
Common Uses : Edible fruit
Major Problems : Sigatoka leafspot; nematodes. K deficiency
Additional Notes : Many cultivars, some dwarf. Killed to ground by frost.

Family : Musaceae   Zone : 10A-11

Typical Height : 20 Ft.
Drought Tolerance : Low
Nutritional Requirements : High
Light Requirements : High
Leaf Type : Simple
Texture : Very coarse
Flower Characteristics : Showy

Environmental Problems : None

Musa zebrina
Common Name(s) : Red Banana
Origin : Java
Growth Rate : Fast
Salt Tolerance : Medium
Soil Requirements : Wide
Plant Type : Herbaceous perennial
Foliage Color : Blue-green & red
Flowering Season : Spring; summer; fall
Flower Color : Purple & yellow
Propagation : Division
Human Hazards : None
Common Uses : Edible fruit; shrub
Major Problems : Sigatoka leafspot. K deficiency
Additional Notes : Has attractive blue-green leaves with red undersides and red spots on top.

Family : Musaceae   Zone : 11

Typical Height : 12 Ft.
Drought Tolerance : Low
Nutritional Requirements : High
Light Requirements : High
Leaf Type : Simple
Texture : Very coarse
Flower Characteristics : Insignificant

Environmental Problems : Messy

Myrcianthes fragrans

Common Name(s) : Simpson's Stopper; Twinberry
Origin : South Florida
Growth Rate : Slow
Salt Tolerance : High
Soil Requirements : Wide
Plant Type : Evergreen tree or shrub
Foliage Color : Green
Flowering Season : Year-round
Flower Color : White
Propagation : Seeds
Human Hazards : None
Common Uses : Small tree; shrub
Major Problems : None
Additional Notes : Orange fruit attracts mockingbirds.

Family : Myrtaceae   **Zone** : 10A-11

Typical Height : 25 Ft.
Drought Tolerance : High
Nutritional Requirements : Low
Light Requirements : Medium; high
Leaf Type : Simple
Texture : Medium
Flower Characteristics : Insignificant; fragrant

Environmental Problems : None

Myrciaria cauliflora *(Photograph p. 165)*

Common Name(s) : Jaboticaba
Origin : Southern Brazil
Growth Rate : Slow
Salt Tolerance : Low
Soil Requirements : Wide
Plant Type : Evergreen tree or shrub
Foliage Color : Green
Flowering Season : Year-round
Flower Color : White
Propagation : Seeds; grafting
Human Hazards : None
Common Uses : Edible fruit; shrub; small tree
Major Problems : None
Additional Notes : A large shrub or small tree with attractive bark and delicious fruit.

Family : Myrtaceae   **Zone** : 10B-11

Typical Height : 15 Ft.
Drought Tolerance : Medium
Nutritional Requirements : Medium
Light Requirements : Medium; high
Leaf Type : Simple
Texture : Fine
Flower Characteristics : Insignificant

Environmental Problems : None

Myrica cerifera

Common Name(s) : Wax Myrtle
Origin : Southeastern United States
Growth Rate : Medium
Salt Tolerance : High
Soil Requirements : Wide
Plant Type : Evergreen shrub or tree
Foliage Color : Green
Flowering Season : Summer;spring
Flower Color : White
Propagation : Seeds; root suckers
Human Hazards : None
Common Uses : Shrub; small tree
Major Problems : None
Additional Notes : Can be weedy; root suckers profusely; leaves stain masonry.

Family : Myricaceae   **Zone** : 6-11

Typical Height : 20 Ft.
Drought Tolerance : High
Nutritional Requirements : Low
Light Requirements : High
Leaf Type : Simple
Texture : Fine
Flower Characteristics : Insignificant

Environmental Problems : Invasive

Myrica pusilla

Common Name(s) : Dwarf Wax Myrtle
Origin : Southeastern United States
Growth Rate : Medium
Salt Tolerance : High
Soil Requirements : Wide
Plant Type : Evergreen shrub
Foliage Color : Green
Flowering Season : Summer; spring
Flower Color : White
Propagation : Seeds; root suckers
Human Hazards : None
Common Uses : Shrub
Major Problems : None
Additional Notes : Similar to M. cerifera , but much smaller.

Family : Myricaceae   **Zone** : 6-10B

Typical Height : 2 Ft.
Drought Tolerance : High
Nutritional Requirements : Low
Light Requirements : High
Leaf Type : Simple
Texture : Fine
Flower Characteristics : Insignificant

Environmental Problems : Invasive

Myrsine guianensis

Common Name(s) : Rapanea
Origin : South Florida
Growth Rate : Medium
Salt Tolerance : High
Soil Requirements : Wide
Plant Type : Evergreen shrub
Foliage Color : Green
Flowering Season : Year-round
Flower Color : White
Propagation : Seeds
Human Hazards : None
Common Uses : Shrub
Major Problems : None
Additional Notes : This Florida native can be trained into a small tree.

Family : Myrsinaceae   Zone : 10B-11

Typical Height : 18 Ft.
Drought Tolerance : High
Nutritional Requirements : Low
Light Requirements : Medium; low
Leaf Type : Simple
Texture : Medium
Flower Characteristics : Insignificant

Environmental Problems : None

Myrtus communis

Common Name(s) : Dwarf Myrtle
Origin : Southern Europe
Growth Rate : Medium
Salt Tolerance : Low
Soil Requirements : Wide
Plant Type : Evergreen shrub
Foliage Color : Green
Flowering Season : Spring
Flower Color : White
Propagation : Cuttings; seeds
Human Hazards : None
Common Uses : Shrub; hedge
Major Problems : None
Additional Notes : Attractive evergreen leaves scented when crushed.
Cultivars
'COMPACTA' is a more compact form; 'MICROPHYLLA' is a compact form with small leaves.

Family : Myrtaceae   Zone : 8-9

Typical Height : 8 Ft.
Drought Tolerance : High
Nutritional Requirements : Medium
Light Requirements : High
Leaf Type : Simple
Texture : Fine
Flower Characteristics : Showy; fragrant

Environmental Problems : None

Nandina domestica

Common Name(s) : Heavenly Bamboo; Nandina
Origin : Japan, China, and India
Growth Rate : Medium
Salt Tolerance : Low
Soil Requirements : Wide
Plant Type : Evergreen shrub
Foliage Color : Green; red
Flowering Season : Spring
Flower Color : White
Propagation : Seeds
Human Hazards : Poisonous
Common Uses : Groundcover; shrub; hedge
Major Problems : Scales; root rot
Additional Notes : Has poisonous red berries and reddish foliage in fall and winter.
Cultivars
'ALBA' has white berries; 'COMPACTA' is a more compact form; 'NANA', 'PYGMAEA', and 'HARBOR DWARF' are dwarf varieties.

Family : Nandinaceae   Zone : 7-10B

Typical Height : 8 Ft.
Drought Tolerance : Medium
Nutritional Requirements : Medium
Light Requirements : Medium
Leaf Type : Pinnately compound
Texture : Fine
Flower Characteristics : Insignificant

Environmental Problems : None

Narcissus tazetta

Common Name(s) : Paper-white Narcissus
Origin : Mediterranean Region
Growth Rate : Medium
Salt Tolerance : Low
Soil Requirements : Wide
Plant Type : Herbaceous perenial
Foliage Color : Green
Flowering Season : Spring
Flower Color : Yellow; white
Propagation : Division
Human Hazards : Poisonous
Common Uses : Beds; borders; cut flowers
Major Problems : Narcissus bulb fly; bulb mites; bacterial rots
Additional Notes : Will sometimes flower in fall or winter.

Family : Amaryllidaceae   Zone : 8-9

Typical Height : 1 Ft.
Drought Tolerance : Low
Nutritional Requirements : High
Light Requirements : Medium; high
Leaf Type : Simple; linear
Texture : Medium
Flower Characteristics : Showy; fragrant

Environmental Problems : None

Nectandra coriacea *(Photograph p. 165)*

Common Name(s) : Lancewood
Origin : South Florida and West Indies
Growth Rate : Medium
Salt Tolerance : Medium
Soil Requirements : Wide
Plant Type : Evergreen tree
Foliage Color : Green
Flowering Season : Summer; fall
Flower Color : White
Propagation : Seeds
Human Hazards : None
Common Uses : Shade tree
Major Problems : None
Additional Notes : A small native tree of the Florida Keys.

Family : Lauraceae   **Zone** : 10A-11

Typical Height : 35 Ft.
Drought Tolerance : High
Nutritional Requirements : Medium
Light Requirements : High
Leaf Type : Simple
Texture : Medium
Flower Characteristics : Insignificant

Environmental Problems : None

Nelumbo nucifera

Common Name(s) : Sacred Lotus; East Indian Lotus
Origin : Southern Asia to Australia
Growth Rate : Medium
Salt Tolerance : Low
Soil Requirements : n/a
Plant Type : Aquatic perennial
Foliage Color : Green
Flowering Season : Summer
Flower Color : Pink; red; white; yellow
Propagation : Division; seeds
Human Hazards : None
Common Uses : Aquatic; cut flowers; specimen plant
Major Problems : None
Additional Notes : A large aquatic plant with 12 inch flowers. Seedheads use as dried flowers.
Cultivars
Many cultivars with varying flower colors exist.

Family : Nymphaeaceae   **Zone** : 4-10B

Typical Height : 5 Ft.
Drought Tolerance : Low
Nutritional Requirements : Medium
Light Requirements : High
Leaf Type : Simple
Texture : Coarse
Flower Characteristics : Showy; fragrant

Environmental Problems : None

Neodypsis decaryi

Common Name(s) : Triangle Palm
Origin : Madagascar
Growth Rate : Medium
Salt Tolerance : Low
Soil Requirements : Wide
Plant Type : Palm
Foliage Color : Blue-green
Flowering Season : Spring
Flower Color : White
Propagation : Seeds
Human Hazards : None
Common Uses : Tree; palm
Major Problems : K deficiency
Additional Notes : Leaves arranged in three planes.

Family : Palmae   **Zone** : 10B-11

Typical Height : 25 Ft.
Drought Tolerance : High
Nutritional Requirements : Medium
Light Requirements : Medium; high
Leaf Type : Pinnately compound
Texture : Medium
Flower Characteristics : Insignificant

Environmental Problems : None

Neodypsis lastelliana

Common Name(s) : Teddy Bear Palm
Origin : Madagascar
Growth Rate : Medium
Salt Tolerance : Low
Soil Requirements : Wide
Plant Type : Palm
Foliage Color : Green
Flowering Season : Spring
Flower Color : White
Propagation : Seeds
Human Hazards : None
Common Uses : Tree; palm
Major Problems : None
Additional Notes : Has red crownshaft and leaflets at right angles to rachis.

Family : Palmae   **Zone** : 10B-11

Typical Height : 30 Ft.
Drought Tolerance : High
Nutritional Requirements : Medium
Light Requirements : High
Leaf Type : Pinnately compound
Texture : Medium
Flower Characteristics : Insignificant

Environmental Problems : None

Neomarica spp. *(Photograph p. 198)*

Common Name(s) : Walking Iris; Twelve Apostles
Origin : Tropical America
Growth Rate : Medium
Salt Tolerance : Low
Soil Requirements : Wide
Plant Type : Herbaceous perennial
Foliage Color : Green
Flowering Season : Summer
Flower Color : Blue; yellow; white
Propagation : Division
Human Hazards : None
Common Uses : Beds; borders
Major Problems : None
Additional Notes : Each flower lasts one day.
Cultivars
N. caerulea has large blue flowers; N. gracilis has white flowers with blue markings;
N. longifolia has yellow flowers.

Family : Iridaceae   **Zone** : 10B-11

Typical Height : 3 Ft.
Drought Tolerance : Low
Nutritional Requirements : Medium
Light Requirements : Medium
Leaf Type : Simple; linear
Texture : Coarse
Flower Characteristics : Showy

Environmental Problems : None

Neoregelia carolinae *(Photograph p. 199)*

Common Name(s) : Blushing Bromeliad
Origin : Brazil
Growth Rate : Slow
Salt Tolerance : Low
Soil Requirements : Well-drained
Plant Type : Epiphyte
Foliage Color : Green & red; variegated
Flowering Season : Spring; summer; fall
Flower Color : Purple; lavender
Propagation : Division; seeds
Human Hazards : Spiny
Common Uses : Foliage plant; specimen plant; epiphyte
Major Problems : Scales
Additional Notes : Green foliage has red bracts and purplish inflorescence.
Cultivars
'MEYENDORFII' has deeper red bracts; 'TRICOLOR' has leaves with a yellow central stripe; 'PINWHEEL',
'FLANDRIA' 'INFERNO', and 'ARGENTA' have yellow leaf margins.

Family : Bromeliaceae   **Zone** : 10B-11

Typical Height : 1 Ft.
Drought Tolerance : Medium
Nutritional Requirements : Low
Light Requirements : Medium; high
Leaf Type : Simple; linear
Texture : Medium
Flower Characteristics : Showy

Environmental Problems : None

Neoregelia spectabilis

Common Name(s) : Painted Fingernail
Origin : Brazil
Growth Rate : Slow
Salt Tolerance : Medium
Soil Requirements : Wide
Plant Type : Epiphyte
Foliage Color : Green, gray, and red
Flowering Season : n/a
Flower Color : Blue
Propagation : Seeds; division
Human Hazards : None
Common Uses : Epiphyte; beds; borders; specimen plant
Major Problems : Scales
Additional Notes : Has green leaves with gray-striped undersides and red tips.

Family : Bromeliaceae   **Zone** : 10A-11

Typical Height : 1.5 Ft.
Drought Tolerance : Medium
Nutritional Requirements : Low
Light Requirements : Medium; high
Leaf Type : Simple; linear
Texture : Coarse
Flower Characteristics : Insignificant

Environmental Problems : None

Nephrolepis biserrata

Common Name(s) : Sword Fern
Origin : Tropics
Growth Rate : Medium
Salt Tolerance : Low
Soil Requirements : Wide
Plant Type : Herbaceous perennial
Foliage Color : Green
Flowering Season : n/a
Flower Color : n/a
Propagation : Spores; division
Human Hazards : None
Common Uses : Foliage plant; specimen plant
Major Problems : None
Additional Notes : Similar to N. exaltata , but leaflets not notched.
Cultivars
'FURCANS' has leaflets with split tips.

Family : Davalliaceae   **Zone** : 10B-11

Typical Height : 4 Ft.
Drought Tolerance : Low
Nutritional Requirements : Medium
Light Requirements : Medium; low
Leaf Type : Pinnately compound
Texture : Medium
Flower Characteristics : n/a

Environmental Problems : None

Nephrolepis cordifolia

Common Name(s) : Erect Sword Fern
Origin : Tropics
Growth Rate : Medium
Salt Tolerance : Low
Soil Requirements : Wide
Plant Type : Herbaceous perennial
Foliage Color : Green
Flowering Season : n/a
Flower Color : n/a
Propagation : Spores; division
Human Hazards : None
Common Uses : Foliage plant; specimen plant
Major Problems : None
Additional Notes : Has erect leaves with toothed leaflets.

Family : Davalliaceae   **Zone** : 10B-11

Typical Height : 2 Ft.
Drought Tolerance : Low
Nutritional Requirements : Medium
Light Requirements : Medium; low
Leaf Type : Pinnately compound
Texture : Medium
Flower Characteristics : n/a

Environmental Problems : None

Nephrolepis exaltata *(Photograph p. 215)*

Common Name(s) : Boston Fern
Origin : Tropics
Growth Rate : Fast
Salt Tolerance : Low
Soil Requirements : Wide
Plant Type : Herbaceous perennial
Foliage Color : Green
Flowering Season : n/a
Flower Color : n/a
Propagation : Spores; tissue culture; division
Human Hazards : None
Common Uses : Beds; specimen plant; foliage plant; hanging baskets; epiphyte
Major Problems : Scales; mites; mealybugs; fungal blight
Additional Notes : An excellent foliage plant for hanging baskets; many cultivars exist.
Cultivars
Popular cultivars include: 'ROOSEVELT', 'PETTICOAT', 'FLUFFY RUFFLES', 'COMPACTA', 'DALLAS', 'MAASII', 'WHITMANII', and 'BOSTONIENSIS'.

Family : Davalliaceae   **Zone** : 10A-11

Typical Height : 3 Ft.
Drought Tolerance : Medium
Nutritional Requirements : Medium
Light Requirements : Low; medium; high
Leaf Type : Pinnately compound
Texture : Medium
Flower Characteristics : n/a

Environmental Problems : None

Nerium oleander *(Photograph p. 182)*

Common Name(s) : Oleander
Origin : Eurasia
Growth Rate : Medium
Salt Tolerance : High
Soil Requirements : Wide
Plant Type : Evergreen shrub
Foliage Color : Green; variegated
Flowering Season : Spring; summer; fall
Flower Color : White; pink; red; yellow
Propagation : Cuttings
Human Hazards : Poisonous
Common Uses : Flowering shrub; hedge
Major Problems : Scales; caterpillars; witch's broom
Additional Notes : Excellent seaside plant. Poisonous. Many insect and disease pests.
Cultivars
'PETITE SALMON' is compact with salmon flowers; 'PETITE PINK' is compact with pink flowers; 'HAWAII' has single salmon-pink flowers; 'SISTER AGNES' has single white flowers; 'HARDY RED' has single red flowers; 'CALYPSO' has single rosy red flowers; 'MRS ROEDING' has double salmon-pink flowers.

Family : Apocynaceae   **Zone** : 8-11

Typical Height : 12 Ft.
Drought Tolerance : High
Nutritional Requirements : Low
Light Requirements : High
Leaf Type : Simple
Texture : Medium
Flower Characteristics : Showy; fragrant

Environmental Problems : None

Newbouldia laevis

Common Name(s) : Boundary Tree
Origin : Tropical West Africa
Growth Rate : Medium
Salt Tolerance : Medium
Soil Requirements : Wide
Plant Type : Evergreen tree
Foliage Color : Green
Flowering Season : Summer
Flower Color : Pink; purple; purple & white
Propagation : Seeds
Human Hazards : None
Common Uses : Tree
Major Problems : None
Additional Notes : Extremely columnar growth habit.

Family : Bignoniaceae   **Zone** : 10B-11

Typical Height : 30 Ft.
Drought Tolerance : Medium
Nutritional Requirements : Medium
Light Requirements : High
Leaf Type : Pinnately compound
Texture : Coarse
Flower Characteristics : Insignificant; fragrant

Environmental Problems : None

Noronhia emarginata *(Photograph p. 183)*

Common Name(s) : Madagascar Olive
Origin : Madagascar
Growth Rate : Medium
Salt Tolerance : High
Soil Requirements : Wide
Plant Type : Evergreen tree
Foliage Color : Green
Flowering Season : Spring
Flower Color : Yellow
Propagation : Seeds
Human Hazards : None
Common Uses : Tree
Major Problems : None
Additional Notes : Excellent small tree for coastal areas.

Family : Oleaceae   **Zone** : 10B-11

Typical Height : 25 Ft.
Drought Tolerance : High
Nutritional Requirements : Low
Light Requirements : High
Leaf Type : Simple
Texture : Medium
Flower Characteristics : Insignificant

Environmental Problems : None

Nuphar luteum

Common Name(s) : Yellow Pond Lily; Spatterdock
Origin : Northern Hemisphere
Growth Rate : Fast
Salt Tolerance : Low
Soil Requirements : n/a
Plant Type : Aquatic perennial
Foliage Color : Green
Flowering Season : Summer; fall
Flower Color : Yellow
Propagation : Division
Human Hazards : None
Common Uses : Aquatic
Major Problems : None
Additional Notes : Common native waterlily with cup-like flowers.

Family : Nymphaeaceae   **Zone** : 3-10B

Typical Height : 3 Ft.
Drought Tolerance : Low
Nutritional Requirements : Medium
Light Requirements : High
Leaf Type : Simple
Texture : Coarse
Flower Characteristics : Showy

Environmental Problems : None

Nymphaea hybrids

Common Name(s) : Waterlily
Origin : Hybrid
Growth Rate : Medium
Salt Tolerance : Low
Soil Requirements : n/a
Plant Type : Aquatic perennial
Foliage Color : Green; purple
Flowering Season : Summer; fall
Flower Color : Blue; lavender; pink; purple; red; white; yellow
Propagation : Division
Human Hazards : None
Common Uses : Aquatic; cut flowers
Major Problems : None
Additional Notes : Tropical and hardy types available. May be day or evening bloomers.
Cultivars
Many cultivars exist.

Family : Nymphaeaceae   **Zone** : 3-11

Typical Height : 3 Ft.
Drought Tolerance : Low
Nutritional Requirements : Medium
Light Requirements : Medium; high
Leaf Type : Simple
Texture : Coarse
Flower Characteristics : Showy; fragrant

Environmental Problems : None

Nymphaea odorata

Common Name(s) : Fragrant Waterlily
Origin : Southeastern United States
Growth Rate : Medium
Salt Tolerance : Low
Soil Requirements : n/a
Plant Type : Aquatic perennial
Foliage Color : Green & purple
Flowering Season : Summer; fall
Flower Color : Pink; purple; white; yellow
Propagation : Division
Human Hazards : None
Common Uses : Aquatic; cut flowers
Major Problems : None
Additional Notes : Many cultivars exist.

Family : Nymphaeaceae   **Zone** : 3-11

Typical Height : 1 Ft.
Drought Tolerance : Low
Nutritional Requirements : Medium
Light Requirements : Medium; high
Leaf Type : Simple
Texture : Coarse
Flower Characteristics : Showy; fragrant

Environmental Problems : None

Nymphoides spp.

Common Name(s) : Floating Hearts; Banana Plant
Origin : Worldwide
Growth Rate : Medium
Salt Tolerance : Low
Soil Requirements : n/a
Plant Type : Aquatic perennial
Foliage Color : Green; purple; red
Flowering Season : Summer
Flower Color : White; yellow
Propagation : Division
Human Hazards : None
Common Uses : Aquatic
Major Problems : None
Additional Notes : Native and exotic spp.; floating aquatic; combines well with water lilies.

Family : Menyanthaceae   Zone : 7-10B

Typical Height : .25 Ft.
Drought Tolerance : Low
Nutritional Requirements : Medium
Light Requirements : High
Leaf Type : Simple
Texture : Medium
Flower Characteristics : Showy

Environmental Problems : None

Nyssa aquatica

Common Name(s) : Water Tupelo
Origin : Southeastern United States
Growth Rate : Slow
Salt Tolerance : Low
Soil Requirements : Acid
Plant Type : Deciduous tree
Foliage Color : Green
Flowering Season : Spring
Flower Color : Green
Propagation : Seeds
Human Hazards : None
Common Uses : Shade tree
Major Problems : None
Additional Notes : An excellent tree for waterlogged sites.

Family : Nyssaceae   Zone : 7-10A

Typical Height : 40 Ft.
Drought Tolerance : Low
Nutritional Requirements : Medium
Light Requirements : High
Leaf Type : Simple
Texture : Medium
Flower Characteristics : Insignificant

Environmental Problems : None

Nyssa sylvatica

Common Name(s) : Black Tupelo
Origin : Southeastern United States
Growth Rate : Medium
Salt Tolerance : Low
Soil Requirements : Wide
Plant Type : Deciduous tree
Foliage Color : Green
Flowering Season : Spring
Flower Color : White
Propagation : Seeds
Human Hazards : None
Common Uses : Shade tree
Major Problems : None
Additional Notes : Best suited for wet sites in southeastern United States.

Family : Nyssaceae   Zone : 4-9

Typical Height : 65 Ft.
Drought Tolerance : Low
Nutritional Requirements : Low
Light Requirements : High
Leaf Type : Simple
Texture : Medium
Flower Characteristics : Insignificant

Environmental Problems : None

Ochna serrulata

Common Name(s) : Mickey Mouse Plant; Bird's-eye Bush
Origin : South Africa
Growth Rate : Fast
Salt Tolerance : Low
Soil Requirements : Acid
Plant Type : Evergreen shrub
Foliage Color : Green
Flowering Season : Spring; summer
Flower Color : Yellow
Propagation : Cuttings; seeds
Human Hazards : None
Common Uses : Flowering shrub
Major Problems : None
Additional Notes : Persistent red sepals and black fruit showy, resemble Mickey Mouse ears.

Family : Ochnaceae   Zone : 10B-11

Typical Height : 5 Ft.
Drought Tolerance : Medium
Nutritional Requirements : Medium
Light Requirements : Medium; high
Leaf Type : Simple
Texture : Medium
Flower Characteristics : Showy

Environmental Problems : None

Ochrosia elliptica *(Photograph p. 165)*
Common Name(s) : Ochrosia
Origin : Oceania
Growth Rate : Medium
Salt Tolerance : High
Soil Requirements : Wide
Plant Type : Evergreen tree or shrub
Foliage Color : Green
Flowering Season : Summer
Flower Color : Yellow-white
Propagation : Seeds
Human Hazards : Poisonous
Common Uses : Small tree; shrub
Major Problems : Scales
Additional Notes : A shrub that can be pruned as a small tree.

Family : Apocynaceae   **Zone** : 10B-11

Typical Height : 15 Ft.
Drought Tolerance : High
Nutritional Requirements : Medium
Light Requirements : Medium; high
Leaf Type : Simple
Texture : Medium
Flower Characteristics : Insignificant; fragrant

Environmental Problems : None

Ochrosia parviflora
Common Name(s) : Kopsia
Origin : Australia
Growth Rate : Slow
Salt Tolerance : High
Soil Requirements : Wide
Plant Type : Evergreen shrub
Foliage Color : Green
Flowering Season : Summer
Flower Color : White
Propagation : Cuttings; seeds
Human Hazards : Poisonous
Common Uses : Flowering shrub; hedge
Major Problems : Scales
Additional Notes : Poisonous fruit. Withstands heavy pruning and shearing.

Family : Apocynaceae   **Zone** : 10B-11

Typical Height : 10 Ft.
Drought Tolerance : High
Nutritional Requirements : Low
Light Requirements : High
Leaf Type : Simple
Texture : Coarse
Flower Characteristics : Showy; fragrant

Environmental Problems : None

Oenothera spp.
Common Name(s) : Sundrops; Evening Primrose
Origin : Western Hemisphere
Growth Rate : Medium
Salt Tolerance : Low
Soil Requirements : Wide
Plant Type : Herbaceous perennial
Foliage Color : Green
Flowering Season : Summer
Flower Color : Yellow; white; pink
Propagation : Seeds; division
Human Hazards : None
Common Uses : Specimen plant; borders; rock gardens
Major Problems : None
Additional Notes : Both day and night blooming species exist.

Family : Onagraceae   **Zone** : 4-10B

Typical Height : .9 Ft.
Drought Tolerance : High
Nutritional Requirements : Medium
Light Requirements : High
Leaf Type : Simple
Texture : Medium
Flower Characteristics : Showy; fragrant

Environmental Problems : None

Oncidium spp.
Common Name(s) : Dancing Lady Orchid
Origin : Tropical America
Growth Rate : Slow
Salt Tolerance : Low
Soil Requirements : Well-drained
Plant Type : Epiphyte
Foliage Color : Green
Flowering Season : Spring; summer
Flower Color : Yellow; brown; red; pink; white; orange
Propagation : Division; tissue culture
Human Hazards : None
Common Uses : Flowering pot plant; epiphyte
Major Problems : Virus
Additional Notes : Most species have showy sprays of yellow and brown flowers.

Family : Orchidaceae   **Zone** : 10B-11

Typical Height : 1 Ft.
Drought Tolerance : High
Nutritional Requirements : Low
Light Requirements : Medium
Leaf Type : Simple
Texture : Medium
Flower Characteristics : Showy

Environmental Problems : None

Ophiopogon jaburan

Family : Liliaceae   **Zone** : 8-10B

Common Name(s) : Jaburan Lilyturf; White Lilyturf; Snakebeard

Origin : Japan	**Typical Height** : 1.5 Ft.
Growth Rate : Medium	**Drought Tolerance** : Medium
Salt Tolerance : Medium	**Nutritional Requirements** : Medium
Soil Requirements : Wide	**Light Requirements** : Medium; low
Plant Type : Herbaceous perennial	**Leaf Type** : Simple; linear
Foliage Color : Green; variegated	**Texture** : Fine
Flowering Season : Summer	**Flower Characteristics** : Insignificant
Flower Color : White	
Propagation : Division	
Human Hazards : None	**Environmental Problems** : None
Common Uses : Groundcover	
Major Problems : None	

Additional Notes : Excellent ground cover for shady areas. Damaged by foot traffic.

Cultivars

'VARIEGATUS' and 'VITTATUS' have variegated foliage.

Ophiopogon japonicus

Family : Liliaceae   **Zone** : 8-10B

Common Name(s) : Mondo Grass; Monkey Grass; Dwarf Lilyturf; Border Grass

Origin : Japan and Korea	**Typical Height** : .7 Ft.
Growth Rate : Medium	**Drought Tolerance** : Medium
Salt Tolerance : Medium	**Nutritional Requirements** : Medium
Soil Requirements : Wide	**Light Requirements** : Medium; low
Plant Type : Herbaceous perennial	**Leaf Type** : Simple; linear
Foliage Color : Green	**Texture** : Fine
Flowering Season : Summer	**Flower Characteristics** : Insignificant
Flower Color : Lavender; white	
Propagation : Division	
Human Hazards : None	**Environmental Problems** : None
Common Uses : Groundcover	
Major Problems : None	

Additional Notes : Excellent ground cover for shady areas. Damaged by foot traffic.

Cultivars

'NANA' is a dwarf variety;

Opuntia spp. *(Photograph p. 183)*

Family : Cactaceae   **Zone** : 3-11

Common Name(s) : Prickly Pear; Cholla Cactus

Origin : New World	**Typical Height** : 8 Ft.
Growth Rate : Medium	**Drought Tolerance** : High
Salt Tolerance : High	**Nutritional Requirements** : Low
Soil Requirements : Wide	**Light Requirements** : High
Plant Type : Succulent perennial	**Leaf Type** : None
Foliage Color : Green	**Texture** : Coarse
Flowering Season : Spring	**Flower Characteristics** : Showy
Flower Color : Purple; red; white; yellow	
Propagation : Seeds; cuttings	
Human Hazards : None	**Environmental Problems** : None
Common Uses : Rock gardens	
Major Problems : Mealybugs	

Additional Notes : Spiny or spineless cacti, some with edible fruit. Many species.

Ornithogalum umbellatum

Family : Liliaceae   **Zone** : 4-10B

Common Name(s) : Star of Bethlehem

Origin : Europe and Northern Africa	**Typical Height** : 1 Ft.
Growth Rate : Medium	**Drought Tolerance** : Medium
Salt Tolerance : Medium	**Nutritional Requirements** : Medium
Soil Requirements : Wide	**Light Requirements** : High
Plant Type : Herbaceous perennial	**Leaf Type** : Simple; linear
Foliage Color : Green	**Texture** : Medium
Flowering Season : Spring	**Flower Characteristics** : Showy
Flower Color : White	
Propagation : Division	
Human Hazards : None	**Environmental Problems** : None
Common Uses : Beds; borders; cut flowers	
Major Problems : None	

Additional Notes : Easy and adaptable; increases rapidly. Other species sometimes available.

Orontium aquaticum

Common Name(s) : Golden Club
Origin : Eastern United States
Growth Rate : Medium
Salt Tolerance : Low
Soil Requirements : Acid
Plant Type : Herbaceous perennial
Foliage Color : Green
Flowering Season : Spring; summer
Flower Color : Yellow
Propagation : Seeds; division
Human Hazards : None
Common Uses : Aquatic
Major Problems : None
Additional Notes : A good foliage plant for the perimeter of a bog or water garden.

Family : Araceae   **Zone** : 5-10A

Typical Height : 1 Ft.
Drought Tolerance : Low
Nutritional Requirements : High
Light Requirements : Low
Leaf Type : Simple
Texture : Coarse
Flower Characteristics : Showy

Environmental Problems : None

Osmanthus fragrans

Common Name(s) : Sweet Osmanthus
Origin : Eastern Asia
Growth Rate : Medium
Salt Tolerance : Low
Soil Requirements : Well-drained
Plant Type : Evergreen shrub
Foliage Color : Green
Flowering Season : Fall; winter
Flower Color : White
Propagation : Cuttings
Human Hazards : None
Common Uses : Hedge; shrub
Major Problems : Scales
Additional Notes : Intensely fragrant flowers; good drainage necessary.
Cultivars
  O. americana is native to Florida and has larger untoothed leaves.

Family : Oleaceae   **Zone** : 7-9

Typical Height : 20 Ft.
Drought Tolerance : Medium
Nutritional Requirements : Medium
Light Requirements : Medium
Leaf Type : Simple
Texture : Medium
Flower Characteristics : Insignificant; fragrant

Environmental Problems : None

Osmanthus heterophyllus

Common Name(s) : Holly Osmanthus; Holly Olive
Origin : Japan and Taiwan
Growth Rate : Medium
Salt Tolerance : Low
Soil Requirements : Well-drained
Plant Type : Evergreen shrub
Foliage Color : Green; variegated
Flowering Season : Fall
Flower Color : White
Propagation : Cuttings
Human Hazards : Spiny
Common Uses : Hedge; shrub
Major Problems : Scales
Additional Notes : Spiny leaves; withstands shearing well.
Cultivars
'AUREUS' has yellow-margined leaves; 'ROTUNDIFOLIUS' is a dwarf variety with entire leaves;
'VARIEGATUS' has white-margined leaves; 'PURPUREUS' has purplish young leaves.

Family : Oleaceae   **Zone** : 7-9

Typical Height : 12 Ft.
Drought Tolerance : Medium
Nutritional Requirements : Medium
Light Requirements : Medium
Leaf Type : Simple
Texture : Medium
Flower Characteristics : Insignificant; fragrant

Environmental Problems : None

Osmanthus X fortunei

Common Name(s) : Fortune Osmanthus
Origin : Hybrid
Growth Rate : Medium
Salt Tolerance : Low
Soil Requirements : Wide
Plant Type : Evergreen shrub
Foliage Color : Green
Flowering Season : Winter
Flower Color : White
Propagation : Cuttings
Human Hazards : Spiny
Common Uses : Shrub; hedge
Major Problems : Scales
Additional Notes : Spiny leaves; very fragrant flowers; takes clipping well.

Family : Oleaceae   **Zone** : 7-9

Typical Height : 18 Ft.
Drought Tolerance : Medium
Nutritional Requirements : Medium
Light Requirements : Medium; high
Leaf Type : Simple
Texture : Medium
Flower Characteristics : Insignificant; fragrant

Environmental Problems : None

Osmunda regalis

Common Name(s) : Royal Fern; Cinnamon Fern
Origin : Western Hemisphere
Growth Rate : Medium
Salt Tolerance : Low
Soil Requirements : Acid
Plant Type : Herbaceous perennial
Foliage Color : Green
Flowering Season : n/a
Flower Color : n/a
Propagation : Division; spores
Human Hazards : None
Common Uses : Beds; groundcover
Major Problems : None
Additional Notes : Native fern useful as background in moist shady borders and beds.

Family : Osmundaceae   **Zone** : 3-10B

Typical Height : 5 Ft.
Drought Tolerance : Low
Nutritional Requirements : Medium
Light Requirements : Medium
Leaf Type : Bipinnately compound
Texture : Medium
Flower Characteristics : n/a

Environmental Problems : None

Ostrya virginiana *(Photograph p. 165)*

Common Name(s) : American Hophornbeam
Origin : Eastern North America
Growth Rate : Medium
Salt Tolerance : Low
Soil Requirements : Wide
Plant Type : Deciduous tree
Foliage Color : Green
Flowering Season : Winter; spring
Flower Color : Green
Propagation : Seeds
Human Hazards : None
Common Uses : Small tree
Major Problems : None
Additional Notes : Intolerant of wet soils; grows well on poor, dry soils; few pests.

Family : Betulaceae   **Zone** : 4-10A

Typical Height : 25 Ft.
Drought Tolerance : High
Nutritional Requirements : Low
Light Requirements : Medium
Leaf Type : Simple
Texture : Medium
Flower Characteristics : Insignificant

Environmental Problems : None

Oxydendrum arboreum

Common Name(s) : Sourwood
Origin : Eastern United States
Growth Rate : Slow
Salt Tolerance : Low
Soil Requirements : Acid
Plant Type : Deciduous tree
Foliage Color : Green
Flowering Season : Spring; summer
Flower Color : White
Propagation : Seeds
Human Hazards : None
Common Uses : Flowering tree
Major Problems : Pollution sensitive
Additional Notes : Good nectar source for honey.

Family : Ericaceae   **Zone** : 6-9

Typical Height : 40 Ft.
Drought Tolerance : Medium
Nutritional Requirements : Medium
Light Requirements : High
Leaf Type : Simple
Texture : Medium
Flower Characteristics : Showy

Environmental Problems : None

Pachira aquatica

Common Name(s) : Guiana Chestnut; Malabar Chestnut
Origin : Tropical America
Growth Rate : Medium
Salt Tolerance : Medium
Soil Requirements : Wide
Plant Type : Deciduous tree
Foliage Color : Green
Flowering Season : Spring; summer
Flower Color : Pink; red
Propagation : Seeds
Human Hazards : None
Common Uses : Flowering tree; edible
Major Problems : Scales; mites
Additional Notes : An attractive tree with edible seed.

Family : Bombacaceae   **Zone** : 10B-11

Typical Height : 30 Ft.
Drought Tolerance : Medium
Nutritional Requirements : Medium
Light Requirements : High
Leaf Type : Palmately compound
Texture : Coarse
Flower Characteristics : Showy; fragrant

Environmental Problems : None

Pachypodium lamerei

Common Name(s) : Madagascar Palm
Origin : Madagascar
Growth Rate : Medium
Salt Tolerance : Medium
Soil Requirements : Wide
Plant Type : Succulent shrub
Foliage Color : Green
Flowering Season : Spring
Flower Color : White
Propagation : Seeds
Human Hazards : Spiny
Common Uses : Rock gardens; foliage plant; specimen plant
Major Problems : Mealybugs; scales
Additional Notes : This spiny unbranched shrub may become deciduous if water stressed.

Family : Apocynaceae   **Zone** : 10B-11

Typical Height : 6 Ft.
Drought Tolerance : High
Nutritional Requirements : Medium
Light Requirements : High
Leaf Type : Simple; linear
Texture : Medium
Flower Characteristics : Showy

Environmental Problems : None

Pachystachys lutea *(Photograph p. 183)*

Common Name(s) : Golden Shrimp Plant
Origin : Peru
Growth Rate : Fast
Salt Tolerance : Low
Soil Requirements : Wide
Plant Type : Evergreen shrub
Foliage Color : Green
Flowering Season : Summer; fall
Flower Color : Yellow & white
Propagation : Cuttings
Human Hazards : None
Common Uses : Flowering shrub; hedge; flowering pot plant
Major Problems : Mites
Additional Notes : Prune hard once each year for compact growth.

Family : Acanthaceae   **Zone** : 10B-11

Typical Height : 3 Ft.
Drought Tolerance : Low
Nutritional Requirements : Medium
Light Requirements : High; medium
Leaf Type : Simple
Texture : Medium
Flower Characteristics : Showy

Environmental Problems : None

Pandanus baptistii

Common Name(s) : Blue Screwpine
Origin : New Britain
Growth Rate : Slow
Salt Tolerance : High
Soil Requirements : Wide
Plant Type : Evergreen shrub
Foliage Color : Blue-green & white
Flowering Season : n/a
Flower Color : n/a
Propagation : Suckers; cuttings
Human Hazards : None
Common Uses : Shrub; foliage plant; rock gardens
Major Problems : None
Additional Notes : This spineless screwpine has blue-green foliage with white stripes.

Family : Pandanaceae   **Zone** : 10B-11

Typical Height : 3 Ft.
Drought Tolerance : High
Nutritional Requirements : Low
Light Requirements : High
Leaf Type : Simple; linear
Texture : Medium
Flower Characteristics : Insignificant

Environmental Problems : None

Pandanus sanderi *(Photograph p. 183)*

Common Name(s) : Sander Screwpine
Origin : Timor
Growth Rate : Medium
Salt Tolerance : High
Soil Requirements : Wide
Plant Type : Evergreen shrub
Foliage Color : Variegated
Flowering Season : n/a
Flower Color : n/a
Propagation : Cuttings; division
Human Hazards : Spiny
Common Uses : Shrub
Major Problems : None
Additional Notes : Spineless or slightly spiny leaves have a broad yellow central stripe.

Family : Pandanaceae   **Zone** : 10B-11

Typical Height : 10 Ft.
Drought Tolerance : High
Nutritional Requirements : Low
Light Requirements : High
Leaf Type : Simple; linear
Texture : Coarse
Flower Characteristics : Insignficant

Environmental Problems : None

Pandanus utilis *(Photograph p. 166)*

Common Name(s) : Screwpine
Origin : Madagascar
Growth Rate : Slow
Salt Tolerance : High
Soil Requirements : Wide
Plant Type : Evergreen tree
Foliage Color : Green
Flowering Season : Year-round
Flower Color : Yellow
Propagation : Seeds; large cuttings
Human Hazards : Spiny
Common Uses : Tree; edible
Major Problems : Lethal yellowing (slightly susceptible); scales. K deficiency
Additional Notes : Spiny leaves, fruit has an edible pulp.

Family : Pandanaceae   Zone : 10B-11

Typical Height : 25 Ft.
Drought Tolerance : High
Nutritional Requirements : Low
Light Requirements : High
Leaf Type : Simple; linear
Texture : Coarse
Flower Characteristics : Insignificant

Environmental Problems : None

Pandanus veitchii

Common Name(s) : Veitch Screwpine
Origin : Polynesia
Growth Rate : Slow
Salt Tolerance : High
Soil Requirements : Wide
Plant Type : Evergreen tree
Foliage Color : Green; variegated
Flowering Season : Year-round
Flower Color : Yellow
Propagation : Suckers; cuttings
Human Hazards : None
Common Uses : Tree
Major Problems : Scales
Additional Notes : Spineless varieties exist.

Family : Pandanaceae   Zone : 10B-11

Typical Height : 25 Ft.
Drought Tolerance : High
Nutritional Requirements : Low
Light Requirements : High
Leaf Type : Simple; linear
Texture : Coarse
Flower Characteristics : Insignificant

Environmental Problems : None

Pandorea jasminoides

Common Name(s) : Bower Plant
Origin : Australia
Growth Rate : Medium
Salt Tolerance : Low
Soil Requirements : Wide
Plant Type : Evergreen vine
Foliage Color : Green
Flowering Season : Spring; summer
Flower Color : White; pink
Propagation : Cuttings
Human Hazards : None
Common Uses : Flowering vine
Major Problems : None
Additional Notes : Not as vigorous as the similar pink trumpet vine (Podranea ricasoliana).

Family : Bignoniaceae   Zone : 10B-11

Typical Height : Not applicable
Drought Tolerance : Medium
Nutritional Requirements : Medium
Light Requirements : High
Leaf Type : Pinnately compound
Texture : Fine
Flower Characteristics : Showy

Environmental Problems : None

Parkinsonia aculeata *(Photograph p. 165)*

Common Name(s) : Jerusalem Thorn; Palo Verde
Origin : Subtropical America
Growth Rate : Fast
Salt Tolerance : High
Soil Requirements : Wide
Plant Type : Deciduous tree
Foliage Color : Green
Flowering Season : Spring; summer
Flower Color : Yellow
Propagation : Seeds
Human Hazards : Spiny
Common Uses : Flowering tree
Major Problems : Scales; root rot
Additional Notes : A small spiny tree with open growth habit. Blows over easily.

Family : Leguminosae   Zone : 8-11

Typical Height : 25 Ft.
Drought Tolerance : High
Nutritional Requirements : Low
Light Requirements : High
Leaf Type : Pinnately compound
Texture : Fine
Flower Characteristics : Showy; fragrant

Environmental Problems : Weak

Parmentiera cereifera *(Photograph p. 166)*
Common Name(s) : Candlefruit
Origin : Panama
Growth Rate : Medium
Salt Tolerance : Medium
Soil Requirements : Wide
Plant Type : Evergreen tree
Foliage Color : Green
Flowering Season : Spring
Flower Color : White
Propagation : Seeds
Human Hazards : None
Common Uses : Flowering tree; edible fruit
Major Problems : None
Additional Notes : A novelty tree with long waxy fruits that hang directly from the trunk.

Family : Bignoniaceae   Zone : 10B-11

Typical Height : 30 Ft.
Drought Tolerance : Medium
Nutritional Requirements : Medium
Light Requirements : High
Leaf Type : Pinnately compound
Texture : Medium
Flower Characteristics : Showy

Environmental Problems : None

Parthenocissus quinquefolia
Common Name(s) : Virginia Creeper
Origin : Eastern United States
Growth Rate : Fast
Salt Tolerance : Low
Soil Requirements : Wide
Plant Type : Deciduous vine
Foliage Color : Green
Flowering Season : Summer
Flower Color : White
Propagation : Seeds; cuttings
Human Hazards : Poisonous
Common Uses : Vine; groundcover
Major Problems : None
Additional Notes : Poisonous fruits; a good native vine, but can become weedy.

Family : Vitaceae   Zone : 4-10B

Typical Height : Not applicable
Drought Tolerance : High
Nutritional Requirements : Low
Light Requirements : Medium; high
Leaf Type : Palmately compound
Texture : Medium
Flower Characteristics : Insignificant

Environmental Problems : Invasive; weedy

Passiflora caerulea
Common Name(s) : Blue Passion Flower
Origin : South America
Growth Rate : Fast
Salt Tolerance : Medium
Soil Requirements : Wide
Plant Type : Evergreen vine
Foliage Color : Green
Flowering Season : Summer
Flower Color : Blue; white
Propagation : Seeds; cuttings
Human Hazards : None
Common Uses : Flowering vine; edible fruit
Major Problems : Caterpillars
Additional Notes : One of the hardiest tropical passifloras.
Cultivars
'GRANDIFLORA' has flowers 5-6 inches across; 'CONSTANCE ELLIOTT' has white flowers.

Family : Passifloraceae   Zone : 9-11

Typical Height : Not applicable
Drought Tolerance : Medium
Nutritional Requirements : Medium
Light Requirements : High
Leaf Type : Simple
Texture : Medium
Flower Characteristics : Showy; fragrant

Environmental Problems : None

Passiflora coccinea *(Photograph p. 211)*
Common Name(s) : Red Passion Flower
Origin : Venezuela to Bolivia
Growth Rate : Fast
Salt Tolerance : Low
Soil Requirements : Wide
Plant Type : Evergreen vine
Foliage Color : Green
Flowering Season : Summer; fall
Flower Color : Red
Propagation : Seeds; cuttings
Human Hazards : None
Common Uses : Flowering vine
Major Problems : Caterpillars
Additional Notes : Flowers to 5 inches wide, last only one day.

Family : Passifloraceae   Zone : 10B-11

Typical Height : Not applicable
Drought Tolerance : Medium
Nutritional Requirements : Medium
Light Requirements : High
Leaf Type : Simple
Texture : Medium
Flower Characteristics : Showy

Environmental Problems : None

Passiflora edulis

Family : Passifloraceae   **Zone** : 10A-11

Common Name(s) : Passion Fruit; Purple Granadilla
Origin : Brazil
Growth Rate : Fast
Salt Tolerance : Low
Soil Requirements : Wide
Plant Type : Evergreen vine
Foliage Color : Green
Flowering Season : Year-round
Flower Color : Purple & white
Propagation : Seeds; cuttings
Human Hazards : None
Common Uses : Flowering vine; edible fruit
Major Problems : Caterpillars; nematodes
Additional Notes : Many cultivars available, fruit pulp is often used in juices.

Typical Height : Not applicable
Drought Tolerance : Medium
Nutritional Requirements : Medium
Light Requirements : High
Leaf Type : Simple
Texture : Medium
Flower Characteristics : Showy; fragrant

Environmental Problems : None

Passiflora quadrangularis

Family : Passifloraceae   **Zone** : 10B-11

Common Name(s) : Granadillo
Origin : South America
Growth Rate : Fast
Salt Tolerance : Low
Soil Requirements : Wide
Plant Type : Evergreen vine
Foliage Color : Green
Flowering Season : Summer
Flower Color : Purple
Propagation : Cuttings; seeds
Human Hazards : None
Common Uses : Flowering vine; edible fruit
Major Problems : Caterpillars
Additional Notes : This square-stemmed passiflora has outstanding large fruits.
Cultivars
Several cultivars exist.

Typical Height : Not applicable
Drought Tolerance : Medium
Nutritional Requirements : Medium
Light Requirements : High
Leaf Type : Simple
Texture : Coarse
Flower Characteristics : Showy; fragrant

Environmental Problems : None

Pedilanthus tithymaloides *(Photograph p. 183)*

Family : Euphorbiaceae   **Zone** : 10A-11

Common Name(s) : Redbird Flower
Origin : Caribbean Region
Growth Rate : Medium
Salt Tolerance : Medium
Soil Requirements : Wide
Plant Type : Evergreen succulent shrub
Foliage Color : Green; variegated
Flowering Season : n/a
Flower Color : Red
Propagation : Cuttings
Human Hazards : Irritant; poisonous
Common Uses : Rock gardens; specimen plant
Major Problems : Scales
Additional Notes : Upright zigzag stems with red slipper shaped flowers. Milky sap.
Cultivars
'VARIEGATUS' has red, white, and green foliage; 'NANA COMPACTA' has very short internodes and dark green foliage.

Typical Height : 4 Ft.
Drought Tolerance : High
Nutritional Requirements : Medium
Light Requirements : High
Leaf Type : Simple
Texture : Medium
Flower Characteristics : Showy

Environmental Problems : None

Pellionia daveauana

Family : Urticaceae   **Zone** : 10B-11

Common Name(s) : Trailing Watermelon Begonia
Origin : Southeast Asia
Growth Rate : Medium
Salt Tolerance : Low
Soil Requirements : Wide
Plant Type : Herbaceous perennial
Foliage Color : Green; gray-green
Flowering Season : Fall
Flower Color : White
Propagation : Cuttings
Human Hazards : None
Common Uses : Groundcover; hanging baskets
Major Problems : None
Additional Notes : Excellent succulent groundcover with attractive foliage for shady areas.

Typical Height : 1 Ft.
Drought Tolerance : Medium
Nutritional Requirements : Low
Light Requirements : Low; medium
Leaf Type : Simple
Texture : Medium
Flower Characteristics : Insignificant

Environmental Problems : None

Peltandra virginica

Common Name(s) : Arrow Arum
Origin : Eastern United States
Growth Rate : Medium
Salt Tolerance : Low
Soil Requirements : Acid
Plant Type : Herbaceous perennial
Foliage Color : Green
Flowering Season : Fall; spring; summer
Flower Color : Green
Propagation : Seeds; division
Human Hazards : None
Common Uses : Aquatic
Major Problems : None
Additional Notes : A good companion plant for the water garden.

Family : Araceae   **Zone** : 3-10B

Typical Height : 2.5 Ft.
Drought Tolerance : Low
Nutritional Requirements : Medium
Light Requirements : Low
Leaf Type : Simple
Texture : Coarse
Flower Characteristics : Insignificant

Environmental Problems : None

Peltophorum dubium

Common Name(s) : Copperpod
Origin : Brazil
Growth Rate : Fast
Salt Tolerance : Medium
Soil Requirements : Wide
Plant Type : Evergreen tree
Foliage Color : Green
Flowering Season : Spring; summer
Flower Color : Yellow
Propagation : Seeds
Human Hazards : None
Common Uses : Flowering tree
Major Problems : None
Additional Notes : Similar to P. pterocarpum , but with smaller leaflets.

Family : Leguminosae   **Zone** : 10B-11

Typical Height : 45 Ft.
Drought Tolerance : High
Nutritional Requirements : Medium
Light Requirements : High
Leaf Type : Bipinnately compound
Texture : Fine
Flower Characteristics : Showy; fragrant

Environmental Problems : Weak

Peltophorum pterocarpum *(Photograph p. 165)*

Common Name(s) : Yellow Poinciana; Copperpod
Origin : India to Australia
Growth Rate : Fast
Salt Tolerance : Medium
Soil Requirements : Wide
Plant Type : Evergreen tree
Foliage Color : Green
Flowering Season : Spring; summer
Flower Color : Yellow
Propagation : Seeds
Human Hazards : None
Common Uses : Flowering tree
Major Problems : None
Additional Notes : Shallow rooted, easily blown over in windstorms.

Family : Leguminosae   **Zone** : 9-11

Typical Height : 45 Ft.
Drought Tolerance : High
Nutritional Requirements : Medium
Light Requirements : High
Leaf Type : Bipinnately compound
Texture : Fine
Flower Characteristics : Showy; fragrant

Environmental Problems : Weak

Pennisetum setaceum

Common Name(s) : Fountain Grass
Origin : Ethiopia
Growth Rate : Medium
Salt Tolerance : Low
Soil Requirements : Wide
Plant Type : Herbaceous perennial
Foliage Color : Green; purple
Flowering Season : Fall; winter
Flower Color : Pink; purple
Propagation : Seed; division
Human Hazards : None
Common Uses : Flowering perennial; cut flowers
Major Problems : None
Additional Notes : Several cultivars mostly grown as annuals or cut back hard twice a year.
Cultivars
'ATROSANGUINEUM' has purple foliage and seed heads; 'CUPREUM' has reddish foliage and seed heads; 'RUBRUM' has rosy colored foliage and copper colored seed heads.

Family : Gramineae   **Zone** : N/A

Typical Height : 3 Ft.
Drought Tolerance : Medium
Nutritional Requirements : Medium
Light Requirements : High
Leaf Type : Simple; linear
Texture : Fine
Flower Characteristics : Showy

Environmental Problems : None

Pentas lanceolata

Common Name(s) : Pentas
Origin : Tropical East Africa
Growth Rate : Medium
Salt Tolerance : Low
Soil Requirements : Wide
Plant Type : Herbaceous perennial
Foliage Color : Green
Flowering Season : Year-round
Flower Color : Pink; red; white
Propagation : Cuttings
Human Hazards : None
Common Uses : Beds; flowering perennial
Major Problems : Mites
Additional Notes : Flowers attract butterflies. Cut back occasionally.

Family : Rubiaceae   **Zone** : 9-11

Typical Height : 3.5 Ft.
Drought Tolerance : Low
Nutritional Requirements : Medium
Light Requirements : High
Leaf Type : Simple
Texture : Medium
Flower Characteristics : Showy

Environmental Problems : None

Peperomia dahlstedtii

Common Name(s) : Vining Peperomia
Origin : Southern Brazil
Growth Rate : Medium
Salt Tolerance : Low
Soil Requirements : Wide
Plant Type : Herbaceous perennial
Foliage Color : Green
Flowering Season : Summer
Flower Color : Green
Propagation : Cuttings
Human Hazards : None
Common Uses : Groundcover; foliage plant; hanging basket
Major Problems : Leafspots; rots
Additional Notes : Has thick green leaves with lighter green veins on red stems.

Family : Piperaceae   **Zone** : 10B-11

Typical Height : .3 Ft.
Drought Tolerance : Medium
Nutritional Requirements : Medium
Light Requirements : Low; medium
Leaf Type : Simple
Texture : Medium
Flower Characteristics : Insignificant

Environmental Problems : None

Peperomia fraseri

Common Name(s) : Flowering Peperomia
Origin : Ecuador
Growth Rate : Medium
Salt Tolerance : Low
Soil Requirements : Wide
Plant Type : Herbaceous perennial
Foliage Color : Green
Flowering Season : Summer
Flower Color : White
Propagation : Cuttings
Human Hazards : None
Common Uses : Groundcover; foliage plant; hanging basket
Major Problems : Leafspots; rots
Additional Notes : Has white puffy flowers on long stalk.

Family : Piperaceae   **Zone** : 10B-11

Typical Height : 2 Ft.
Drought Tolerance : Medium
Nutritional Requirements : Medium
Light Requirements : Low; medium
Leaf Type : Simple
Texture : Medium
Flower Characteristics : Insignificant

Environmental Problems : None

Peperomia glabella

Common Name(s) : Wax Privet
Origin : Tropical America
Growth Rate : Medium
Salt Tolerance : Low
Soil Requirements : Wide
Plant Type : Herbaceous perennial
Foliage Color : Green; variegated
Flowering Season : Summer
Flower Color : Green
Propagation : Cuttings
Human Hazards : None
Common Uses : Groundcover; foliage plant; hanging basket
Major Problems : Leafspots; rots
Additional Notes : Has fairly broad, but pointed succulent leaves.
Cultivars
'VARIEGATA' has broad white margins on the leaves.

Family : Piperaceae   **Zone** : 10B-11

Typical Height : .5 Ft.
Drought Tolerance : Medium
Nutritional Requirements : Medium
Light Requirements : Low; medium
Leaf Type : Simple
Texture : Medium
Flower Characteristics : Insignificant

Environmental Problems : None

Peperomia hirta

Common Name(s) : n/a
Origin : Cuba
Growth Rate : Medium
Salt Tolerance : Low
Soil Requirements : Wide
Plant Type : Herbaceous perennial
Foliage Color : Green
Flowering Season : Summer
Flower Color : Green
Propagation : Cuttings
Human Hazards : None
Common Uses : Groundcover; foliage plant; hanging basket
Major Problems : Leafspots; rots
Additional Notes : Pubescent leaves have lighter colored undersides. Rambling habit.

Family : Piperaceae   Zone : 10B-11

Typical Height : 1 Ft.
Drought Tolerance : Medium
Nutritional Requirements : Medium
Light Requirements : Low; medium
Leaf Type : Simple
Texture : Medium
Flower Characteristics : Insignificant

Environmental Problems : None

Peperomia maculosa

Common Name(s) : Radiator Plant
Origin : Caribbean Region
Growth Rate : Medium
Salt Tolerance : Low
Soil Requirements : Wide
Plant Type : Herbaceous perennial
Foliage Color : Green
Flowering Season : Summer
Flower Color : Red-green
Propagation : Cuttings
Human Hazards : None
Common Uses : Groundcover; foliage plant; hanging basket
Major Problems : Leafspots; rots
Additional Notes : Petioles have reddish spots. Leaves are longer than many species.

Family : Piperaceae   Zone : 10B-11

Typical Height : 1 Ft.
Drought Tolerance : Medium
Nutritional Requirements : Medium
Light Requirements : Low; medium
Leaf Type : Simple
Texture : Medium
Flower Characteristics : Insignificant

Environmental Problems : None

Peperomia magnoliifolia *(Photograph p. 215)*

Common Name(s) : Desert Privet
Origin : Caribbean Region
Growth Rate : Medium
Salt Tolerance : Low
Soil Requirements : Wide
Plant Type : Herbaceous perennial
Foliage Color : Green
Flowering Season : Summer
Flower Color : Green
Propagation : Cuttings
Human Hazards : None
Common Uses : Groundcover; foliage plant; hanging basket
Major Problems : Leafspots; rots
Additional Notes : Very similar to P. obtusifolia , but leaves more elongated.

Family : Piperaceae   Zone : 10B-11

Typical Height : 1 Ft.
Drought Tolerance : Medium
Nutritional Requirements : Medium
Light Requirements : Low; medium
Leaf Type : Simple
Texture : Medium
Flower Characteristics : Insignificant

Environmental Problems : None

Peperomia obtusifolia

Common Name(s) : Baby Rubber Plant
Origin : Tropical America
Growth Rate : Medium
Salt Tolerance : Low
Soil Requirements : Wide
Plant Type : Herbaceous perennial
Foliage Color : Green; variegated
Flowering Season : Summer
Flower Color : Green
Propagation : Cuttings
Human Hazards : None
Common Uses : Groundcover; foliage plant; hanging basket
Major Problems : Leafspots; rots
Additional Notes : Excellent ground cover for shady areas. Damaged by foot traffic.
Cultivars
'ALBA' has white new leaves with red markings; 'ALBO-MARGINATA' has narrow white leaf margins; 'VARIEGATA' has white, gray-green, and green foliage.

Family : Piperaceae   Zone : 10B-11

Typical Height : 1.5 Ft.
Drought Tolerance : Medium
Nutritional Requirements : Medium
Light Requirements : Low; medium
Leaf Type : Simple
Texture : Medium
Flower Characteristics : Insignificant

Environmental Problems : None

Peperomia scandens

Common Name(s) : Philodendron Peperomia
Origin : Peru
Growth Rate : Medium
Salt Tolerance : Low
Soil Requirements : Wide
Plant Type : Herbaceous perennial
Foliage Color : Green; variegated
Flowering Season : Summer
Flower Color : Green
Propagation : Cuttings
Human Hazards : None
Common Uses : Groundcover; foliage plant; hanging basket
Major Problems : Leafspots; rots
Additional Notes : A succulent trailing species with pointed foliage.
Cultivars
'VARIEGATA' has variegated foliage.

Family : Piperaceae   Zone : 10B-11

Typical Height : .5 Ft.
Drought Tolerance : Medium
Nutritional Requirements : Medium
Light Requirements : Low; medium
Leaf Type : Simple
Texture : Medium
Flower Characteristics : Insignificant

Environmental Problems : None

Pereskia aculeata

Common Name(s) : Barbados Gooseberry; Lemon Vine
Origin : Tropical America
Growth Rate : Medium
Salt Tolerance : High
Soil Requirements : Wide
Plant Type : Evergreen vine
Foliage Color : Green
Flowering Season : Summer; spring
Flower Color : Yellow
Propagation : Cuttings
Human Hazards : Spiny
Common Uses : Flowering vine; edible fruit
Major Problems : None
Additional Notes : Very spiny leafy vine in the cactus family.

Family : Cactaceae   Zone : 10B-11

Typical Height : Not applicable
Drought Tolerance : High
Nutritional Requirements : Low
Light Requirements : High
Leaf Type : Simple
Texture : Medium
Flower Characteristics : Showy

Environmental Problems : None

Persea americana

Common Name(s) : Avocado; Alligator Pear
Origin : Tropical America
Growth Rate : Fast
Salt Tolerance : Low
Soil Requirements : Wide
Plant Type : Evergreen tree
Foliage Color : Green
Flowering Season : Winter
Flower Color : Green
Propagation : Seeds; grafting
Human Hazards : None
Common Uses : Edible fruit; shade tree
Major Problems : Phytophthora root rot; scales
Additional Notes : Many selected varieties exist; brittle wood.

Family : Lauraceae   Zone : 10A-11

Typical Height : 45 Ft.
Drought Tolerance : High
Nutritional Requirements : Medium
Light Requirements : High
Leaf Type : Simple
Texture : Coarse
Flower Characteristics : Insignificant

Environmental Problems : Weak; messy

Persea borbonia

Common Name(s) : Red Bay
Origin : Southeastern United States
Growth Rate : Medium
Salt Tolerance : High
Soil Requirements : Wide
Plant Type : Evergreen tree
Foliage Color : Green
Flowering Season : Spring
Flower Color : Green
Propagation : Seeds
Human Hazards : None
Common Uses : Shade tree
Major Problems : Galls
Additional Notes : Good for wet sites.
Cultivars
Var. humilis remains somewhat dwarf.

Family : Lauraceae   Zone : 7-10B

Typical Height : 55 Ft.
Drought Tolerance : High
Nutritional Requirements : Low
Light Requirements : High
Leaf Type : Simple
Texture : Fine
Flower Characteristics : Insignificant

Environmental Problems : None

Petrea volubilis *(Photograph p. 211)*

Common Name(s) : Queen's Wreath
Origin : Caribbean Region
Growth Rate : Medium
Salt Tolerance : Medium
Soil Requirements : Wide
Plant Type : Evergreen vine
Foliage Color : Green
Flowering Season : Spring; summer
Flower Color : Purple; white
Propagation : Layering; suckers
Human Hazards : None
Common Uses : Flowering vine
Major Problems : None
Additional Notes : Sandpaper-like leaves, pendulous flower resemble wisteria.

Family : Verbenaceae   **Zone** : 10B-11

Typical Height : Not applicable
Drought Tolerance : Medium
Nutritional Requirements : Medium
Light Requirements : High; medium
Leaf Type : Simple
Texture : Medium
Flower Characteristics : Showy

Environmental Problems : None

Phaius tankervilliae *(Photograph p. 199)*

Common Name(s) : Nun's Orchid
Origin : Himalayas
Growth Rate : Medium
Salt Tolerance : Low
Soil Requirements : Acid
Plant Type : Herbaceous perennial
Foliage Color : Green
Flowering Season : Spring
Flower Color : Pink, white, & brown
Propagation : Division; flower stems
Human Hazards : None
Common Uses : Beds; flowering perennial
Major Problems : Nematodes. Mg deficiency.
Additional Notes : A showy terrestrial orchid that is easy to grow.

Family : Orchidaceae   **Zone** : 10B-11

Typical Height : 3 Ft.
Drought Tolerance : Medium
Nutritional Requirements : Medium
Light Requirements : Medium
Leaf Type : Simple
Texture : Coarse
Flower Characteristics : Showy

Environmental Problems : None

Phalaenopsis spp.

Common Name(s) : Moth Orchid
Origin : Tropical Asia and Oceania
Growth Rate : Slow
Salt Tolerance : Low
Soil Requirements : Well-drained
Plant Type : Epiphyte
Foliage Color : Green; green & purple
Flowering Season : Winter; spring; summer
Flower Color : White; pink; purple; lavender; yellow
Propagation : Cuttings; tissue culture; division
Human Hazards : None
Common Uses : Flowering pot plant; epiphyte; cut flower
Major Problems : Virus; bacterial and fungal rots
Additional Notes : Many species and hybrids exist. Flowers are very long lasting.

Family : Orchidaceae   **Zone** : 10B-11

Typical Height : .5 Ft.
Drought Tolerance : Low
Nutritional Requirements : Low
Light Requirements : Medium
Leaf Type : Simple
Texture : Medium
Flower Characteristics : Showy

Environmental Problems : None

Philodendron domesticum

Common Name(s) : Spade-leaf Philodendron
Origin : Brazil
Growth Rate : Fast
Salt Tolerance : Medium
Soil Requirements : Wide
Plant Type : Epiphytic vine
Foliage Color : Green
Flowering Season : n/a
Flower Color : Green & red
Propagation : Cuttings
Human Hazards : None
Common Uses : Foliage plant; vine
Major Problems : Mites; scales
Additional Notes : Large leaves are spade shaped.

Family : Araceae   **Zone** : 10B-11

Typical Height : Not applicable
Drought Tolerance : High
Nutritional Requirements : Low
Light Requirements : Low; medium
Leaf Type : Simple
Texture : Coarse
Flower Characteristics : Insignificant

Environmental Problems : None

Philodendron goeldii

Family : Araceae   **Zone** : 10B-11

Common Name(s) : Philodendron Schefflera
Origin : Brazil
Growth Rate : Medium
Salt Tolerance : Medium
Soil Requirements : Wide
Plant Type : Evergreen shrub
Foliage Color : Green
Flowering Season : n/a
Flower Color : Green
Propagation : Cuttings
Human Hazards : None
Common Uses : Foliage plant; shrub
Major Problems : Mites; scales

Typical Height : 2.5 Ft.
Drought Tolerance : High
Nutritional Requirements : Low
Light Requirements : Low; medium
Leaf Type : Compound
Texture : Coarse
Flower Characteristics : Insignificant

Environmental Problems : None

Additional Notes : Curious leaflets are arranged in a spiral & resemble those ofSchefflera.

Philodendron scandens var. oxycardium

Family : Araceae   **Zone** : 10B-11

Common Name(s) : Heart-leaf Philodendron
Origin : Tropical America
Growth Rate : Fast
Salt Tolerance : Medium
Soil Requirements : Wide
Plant Type : Epiphytic vine
Foliage Color : Green
Flowering Season : n/a
Flower Color : n/a
Propagation : Cuttings
Human Hazards : None
Common Uses : Hanging baskets; foliage plant; vine; totem pole
Major Problems : Mites; scales

Typical Height : Not applicable
Drought Tolerance : High
Nutritional Requirements : Low
Light Requirements : Low; medium
Leaf Type : Simple
Texture : Coarse
Flower Characteristics : Insignificant

Environmental Problems : None

Additional Notes : This rambling vine has heart-shaped leaves.
Cultivars
Var. _micans_ is similar, except that juvenile leaves have reddish undersides ; 'LEMON LIME' has yellow-green foliage; 'VARIEGATUM' is variegated.

Philodendron selloum _(Photograph p. 183)_

Family : Araceae   **Zone** : 10A-11

Common Name(s) : Tree Philodendron
Origin : Southern Brazil
Growth Rate : Fast
Salt Tolerance : Low
Soil Requirements : Wide
Plant Type : Evergreen shrub
Foliage Color : Green
Flowering Season : Spring; summer
Flower Color : Green & white
Propagation : Seeds; tissue culture
Human Hazards : Irritant
Common Uses : Shrub; foliage plant; hedge
Major Problems : Mites; scales; K deficiency

Typical Height : 8 Ft.
Drought Tolerance : Medium
Nutritional Requirements : Medium
Light Requirements : Low; medium; high
Leaf Type : Simple; pinnately lobed
Texture : Very coarse
Flower Characteristics : Insignificant

Environmental Problems : None

Additional Notes : Sap stains clothes and may irritate skin; has deeply lobed leaves.

Philodendron speciosum

Family : Araceae   **Zone** : 10A-11

Common Name(s) : Imperial Philodendron
Origin : Southern Brazil
Growth Rate : Fast
Salt Tolerance : Low
Soil Requirements : Wide
Plant Type : Evergreen shrub
Foliage Color : Green
Flowering Season : Spring; summer
Flower Color : Green & white
Propagation : Seeds; cuttings
Human Hazards : Irritant
Common Uses : Shrub
Major Problems : Mites; scales

Typical Height : 8 Ft.
Drought Tolerance : Medium
Nutritional Requirements : Medium
Light Requirements : Low; medium; high
Leaf Type : Simple
Texture : Very coarse
Flower Characteristics : Insignificant

Environmental Problems : None

Additional Notes : A self-heading species with huge arrowhead-shaped leaves.

Philodendron spp.

Family : Araceae   **Zone** : 10B-11

Common Name(s) : Philodendron
Origin : New World Tropics
Growth Rate : Medium
Salt Tolerance : Low
Soil Requirements : Wide
Plant Type : Herbaceous perennial
Foliage Color : Green
Flowering Season : Summer
Flower Color : White
Propagation : Cuttings; seeds
Human Hazards : Irritant
Common Uses : Foliage plant; specimen plant; vine
Major Problems : Mites; scales; mealybugs; leafspots; bacterial rots
Additional Notes : Many hybrids and species with various foliage colors and shapes.

Typical Height : 3 Ft.
Drought Tolerance : Medium
Nutritional Requirements : Medium
Light Requirements : Medium; low
Leaf Type : Simple
Texture : Coarse
Flower Characteristics : Insignificant

Environmental Problems : None

Cultivars
'LYNETTE' is a compact self-heading hybrid with prominent depressed veins; 'PLUTO' has oval leaves with undulating lobed margins; 'RED EMERALD' has green arrowhead-shaped leaves with red petioles and veins; 'WEND-IMBE' is a self-heading hybrid with arrowhead-shaped leaves; 'EVANSII' is a hybrid between P. speciosus and P. selloum .

Philodendron wendlandii

Family : Araceae   **Zone** : 10B-11

Common Name(s) : Birdsnest Philodendron
Origin : Central America
Growth Rate : Slow
Salt Tolerance : Low
Soil Requirements : Wide
Plant Type : Herbaceous perennial
Foliage Color : Green
Flowering Season : Summer
Flower Color : White
Propagation : Cuttings; seeds
Human Hazards : Irritant
Common Uses : Foliage plant; specimen plant
Major Problems : Mites; scales
Additional Notes : A compact self-heading species with thick spongy petioles.

Typical Height : 3 Ft.
Drought Tolerance : Medium
Nutritional Requirements : Medium
Light Requirements : Medium; low
Leaf Type : Simple
Texture : Coarse
Flower Characteristics : Insignificant

Environmental Problems : None

Philodendron williamsii

Family : Araceae   **Zone** : 10B-11

Common Name(s) : Philodendron
Origin : Brazil
Growth Rate : Slow
Salt Tolerance : Low
Soil Requirements : Wide
Plant Type : Evergreen shrub
Foliage Color : Green
Flowering Season : Summer
Flower Color : White
Propagation : Cuttings; seeds
Human Hazards : Irritant
Common Uses : Shrub
Major Problems : Mites; scales
Additional Notes : A striking, self heading, narrow leaf philodendron.

Typical Height : 5 Ft.
Drought Tolerance : Medium
Nutritional Requirements : Medium
Light Requirements : Medium; low
Leaf Type : Simple
Texture : Coarse
Flower Characteristics : Insignificant

Environmental Problems : None

Phlox divaricata *(Photograph p. 199)*

Family : Polemoniaceae   **Zone** : 5-9

Common Name(s) : Blue Phlox
Origin : Eastern North America
Growth Rate : Medium
Salt Tolerance : Low
Soil Requirements : Acid
Plant Type : Herbaceous perennial
Foliage Color : Green
Flowering Season : Spring
Flower Color : Blue
Propagation : Seeds; division
Human Hazards : None
Common Uses : Borders
Major Problems : None
Additional Notes : A lovely native phlox that should be used more widely.

Typical Height : 2 Ft.
Drought Tolerance : Low
Nutritional Requirements : Medium
Light Requirements : Medium
Leaf Type : Simple
Texture : Medium
Flower Characteristics : Showy

Environmental Problems : None

Phoenix canariensis *(Photograph p. 206)*

Common Name(s) : Canary Island Date
Origin : Canary Islands
Growth Rate : Slow
Salt Tolerance : Medium
Soil Requirements : Wide
Plant Type : Palm
Foliage Color : Green
Flowering Season : Spring
Flower Color : White
Propagation : Seeds
Human Hazards : Spiny
Common Uses : Tree; palm
Major Problems : Lethal yellowing (moderately susceptible); weevils. Mg deficiency
Additional Notes : Has attractive trunk pattern. Plants under this name are often hybrids.

Family : Palmae **Zone** : 9-11

Typical Height : 40 Ft.
Drought Tolerance : High
Nutritional Requirements : Medium
Light Requirements : Medium; high
Leaf Type : Pinnately compound
Texture : Coarse
Flower Characteristics : Insignificant

Environmental Problems : None

Phoenix dactylifera *(Photograph p. 206)*

Common Name(s) : Date Palm
Origin : North Africa
Growth Rate : Slow
Salt Tolerance : High
Soil Requirements : Wide
Plant Type : Palm
Foliage Color : Green
Flowering Season : Spring
Flower Color : White
Propagation : Seeds; suckers
Human Hazards : Spiny
Common Uses : Tree; edible fruit; palm
Major Problems : Lethal yellowing (slightly susceptible)
Additional Notes : Has long dangerous spines on the petioles. Fruits poorly in Florida.
Cultivars
Cultivars include 'MEDJOOL', 'ZAHEDII', and 'DEGLET NOOR'.

Family : Palmae **Zone** : 9-11

Typical Height : 70 Ft.
Drought Tolerance : High
Nutritional Requirements : Medium
Light Requirements : High
Leaf Type : Pinnately compound
Texture : Coarse
Flower Characteristics : Insignificant

Environmental Problems : None

Phoenix reclinata *(Photograph p. 206)*

Common Name(s) : Senegal Date; Reclinata Palm
Origin : Africa
Growth Rate : Medium
Salt Tolerance : Medium
Soil Requirements : Wide
Plant Type : Palm
Foliage Color : Green
Flowering Season : Spring
Flower Color : White
Propagation : Seeds; suckers
Human Hazards : Spiny
Common Uses : Multi-trunked tree; palm
Major Problems : None
Additional Notes : A multiple stemmed spiny palm; often hybridizes with other dates.

Family : Palmae **Zone** : 10A-11

Typical Height : 25 Ft.
Drought Tolerance : High
Nutritional Requirements : Medium
Light Requirements : High
Leaf Type : Pinnately compound
Texture : Medium
Flower Characteristics : Insignificant

Environmental Problems : None

Phoenix roebelenii *(Photograph p. 206)*

Common Name(s) : Pygmy Date Palm
Origin : Southeast Asia
Growth Rate : Slow
Salt Tolerance : Low
Soil Requirements : Wide
Plant Type : Palm
Foliage Color : Green
Flowering Season : Spring
Flower Color : White
Propagation : Seeds
Human Hazards : Spiny
Common Uses : Small tree; palm
Major Problems : Mg, Mn, and K deficiencies; pestalotia blight.
Additional Notes : Often planted as multiples.

Family : Palmae **Zone** : 10A-11

Typical Height : 10 Ft.
Drought Tolerance : High
Nutritional Requirements : Medium
Light Requirements : Medium; high
Leaf Type : Pinnately compound
Texture : Medium
Flower Characteristics : Insignificant

Environmental Problems : None

Phoenix rupicola

Common Name(s) : Cliff Date
Origin : India
Growth Rate : Slow
Salt Tolerance : Medium
Soil Requirements : Wide
Plant Type : Palm
Foliage Color : Green
Flowering Season : Spring
Flower Color : White
Propagation : Seeds
Human Hazards : Spiny
Common Uses : Tree; palm
Major Problems : None
Additional Notes : A rare, but desirable and graceful date palm.

Family : Palmae   **Zone** : 10A-11

Typical Height : 25 Ft.
Drought Tolerance : High
Nutritional Requirements : Medium
Light Requirements : High
Leaf Type : Pinnately compound
Texture : Medium
Flower Characteristics : Insignificant

Environmental Problems : None

Phoenix sylvestris *(Photograph p. 206)*

Common Name(s) : Wild Date Palm
Origin : India
Growth Rate : Slow
Salt Tolerance : Medium
Soil Requirements : Wide
Plant Type : Palm
Foliage Color : Blue-green; green;
Flowering Season : Spring
Flower Color : White
Propagation : Seeds
Human Hazards : Spiny
Common Uses : Tree; palm
Major Problems : None
Additional Notes : The bluish-green cast of the leaves is variable.

Family : Palmae   **Zone** : 9-11

Typical Height : 50 Ft.
Drought Tolerance : High
Nutritional Requirements : Medium
Light Requirements : High
Leaf Type : Pinnately compound
Texture : Medium
Flower Characteristics : Insignificant

Environmental Problems : None

Phormium tenax

Common Name(s) : New Zealand Flax
Origin : New Zealand
Growth Rate : Medium
Salt Tolerance : High
Soil Requirements : Wide
Plant Type : Herbaceous perennial
Foliage Color : Red; green; variegated
Flowering Season : Summer
Flower Color : Yellow; red
Propagation : Seeds; division
Human Hazards : None
Common Uses : Specimen plant
Major Problems : Scales
Additional Notes : Dwarf varieties and variegated form exist.
Cultivars
'ATROPURPUREUM' has reddish-purple leaves; 'AUREUM' has broad yellow stripes on leaves; 'RUBRUM' has red leaves; 'VARIEGATUM' has leaves striped with light yellow and white; 'VEITCHIANUM' has broad white stripes on leaves.

Family : Agavaceae   **Zone** : 9-10B

Typical Height : 3 Ft.
Drought Tolerance : High
Nutritional Requirements : Medium
Light Requirements : Medium; high
Leaf Type : Simple; linear
Texture : Coarse
Flower Characteristics : Showy

Environmental Problems : None

Photinia glabra

Common Name(s) : Japanese Photinia; Red Leaf Photinia
Origin : Japan
Growth Rate : Medium
Salt Tolerance : Low
Soil Requirements : Wide
Plant Type : Evergreen shrub
Foliage Color : Green; red
Flowering Season : Spring
Flower Color : White
Propagation : Seeds; cuttings
Human Hazards : None
Common Uses : Shrub; hedge
Major Problems : Scales
Additional Notes : New leaves emerge red.

Family : Rosaceae   **Zone** : 8-9

Typical Height : 8 Ft.
Drought Tolerance : Medium
Nutritional Requirements : Medium
Light Requirements : High
Leaf Type : Simple
Texture : Medium
Flower Characteristics : Insignificant

Environmental Problems : None

Photinia serrulata

Common Name(s) : Chinese Photinia
Origin : China
Growth Rate : Medium
Salt Tolerance : Low
Soil Requirements : Wide
Plant Type : Evergreen shrub
Foliage Color : Green; red
Flowering Season : Spring
Flower Color : White
Propagation : Seeds; cuttings
Human Hazards : None
Common Uses : Shrub; hedge
Major Problems : Scales; fireblight

Family : Rosaceae   **Zone** : 8-9

Typical Height : 30 Ft.
Drought Tolerance : Medium
Nutritional Requirements : Medium
Light Requirements : High
Leaf Type : Simple
Texture : Coarse
Flower Characteristics : Insignificant

Environmental Problems : None

Additional Notes : New leaves emerge red and turn red again prior to dropping in spring.
Cultivars
'ACULEATA' has red twigs and is more compact than species; 'NOVA' is compact, but spreading.

Photinia X fraseri

Common Name(s) : Fraser Photinia; Redleaf Photinia
Origin : Hybrid
Growth Rate : Medium
Salt Tolerance : Low
Soil Requirements : Wide
Plant Type : Evergreen shrub
Foliage Color : Green; red
Flowering Season : Spring
Flower Color : White
Propagation : Seeds; cuttings
Human Hazards : None
Common Uses : Shrub; hedge
Major Problems : Scales

Family : Rosaceae   **Zone** : 8-9

Typical Height : 8 Ft.
Drought Tolerance : Medium
Nutritional Requirements : Medium
Light Requirements : High
Leaf Type : Simple
Texture : Medium
Flower Characteristics : Insignificant

Environmental Problems : None

Additional Notes : New leaves emerge red. Excellent for espalier.

Phygelius capensis

Common Name(s) : Cape Figwort; Cape Fuchsia
Origin : South Africa
Growth Rate : Medium
Salt Tolerance : Low
Soil Requirements : Wide
Plant Type : Herbaceous perennial
Foliage Color : Green
Flowering Season : Summer; fall
Flower Color : Red; orange
Propagation : Seeds; cuttings
Human Hazards : None
Common Uses : Flowering shrub; borders
Major Problems : None

Family : Scrophulariaceae   **Zone** : 8-10B

Typical Height : 3.5 Ft.
Drought Tolerance : Medium
Nutritional Requirements : Medium
Light Requirements : Medium
Leaf Type : Simple
Texture : Medium
Flower Characteristics : Showy

Environmental Problems : None

Additional Notes : Cut back hard in spring.

Phyllanthus acidus (Photograph p. 166)

Common Name(s) : Otaheite Gooseberry; Star Gooseberry
Origin : India and Madagascar
Growth Rate : Medium
Salt Tolerance : Medium
Soil Requirements : Wide
Plant Type : Evergreen tree
Foliage Color : Green
Flowering Season : Winter; spring
Flower Color : Yellow; red
Propagation : Seeds; cuttings
Human Hazards : None
Common Uses : Edible; small tree
Major Problems : Caterpillars

Family : Euphorbiaceae   **Zone** : 10B-11

Typical Height : 20 Ft.
Drought Tolerance : High
Nutritional Requirements : Low
Light Requirements : High
Leaf Type : Simple
Texture : Medium
Flower Characteristics : Insignificant

Environmental Problems : Weedy

Additional Notes : Edible acid fruits resemble gooseberries. Naturalized in south Florida.

Phyllostachys aurea

Common Name(s) : Golden Bamboo
Origin : China
Growth Rate : Fast
Salt Tolerance : Medium
Soil Requirements : Wide
Plant Type : Evergreen shrub
Foliage Color : Green
Flowering Season : n/a
Flower Color : n/a
Propagation : Division; cuttings
Human Hazards : None
Common Uses : Shrub; edible
Major Problems : None

Family : Gramineae   **Zone** : 8-9

Typical Height : 20 Ft.
Drought Tolerance : High
Nutritional Requirements : Medium
Light Requirements : High
Leaf Type : Simple; linear
Texture : Medium
Flower Characteristics : Insignificant

Environmental Problems : Invasive

Additional Notes : Yellowish canes are often used for fishing poles. A running species.
Cultivars
'ALBO-VARIEGATA' has white-striped leaves; 'FLAVESCENS-INVERSA' has green culms with yellow grooves; 'KOI' has yellow culms with a green stripe.

Phyllostachys aureosulcata

Common Name(s) : Yellow-groove Bamboo
Origin : China
Growth Rate : Fast
Salt Tolerance : Medium
Soil Requirements : Wide
Plant Type : Evergreen shrub
Foliage Color : Green
Flowering Season : n/a
Flower Color : n/a
Propagation : Division; cuttings
Human Hazards : None
Common Uses : Shrub; edible
Major Problems : None

Family : Gramineae   **Zone** : 8-9

Typical Height : 30 Ft.
Drought Tolerance : Medium
Nutritional Requirements : Medium
Light Requirements : High
Leaf Type : Simple; linear
Texture : Medium
Flower Characteristics : Insignificant

Environmental Problems : Invasive

Additional Notes : A running bamboo with yellow and green striped canes. New shoots edible.
Cultivars
'ALATA' has larger, gracefully arching culms.

Phyllostachys bambusioides

Common Name(s) : Giant Timber Bamboo
Origin : China
Growth Rate : Fast
Salt Tolerance : Medium
Soil Requirements : Wide
Plant Type : Evergreen shrub
Foliage Color : Green
Flowering Season : n/a
Flower Color : n/a
Propagation : Division; cuttings
Human Hazards : None
Common Uses : Large shrub; timber; edible
Major Problems : None

Family : Gramineae   **Zone** : 8-9

Typical Height : 60 Ft.
Drought Tolerance : Medium
Nutritional Requirements : Medium
Light Requirements : High
Leaf Type : Simple; linear
Texture : Medium
Flower Characteristics : Insignificant

Environmental Problems : Invasive

Additional Notes : A large running bamboo used for timber in many regions. New shoots edible.
Cultivars
'ALL GOLD' has golden culms with few light green stripes; 'CASTILLONII' has gold culms with green grooves; 'SLENDER CROOKSTEM' has crooked stems.

Phyllostachys nigra

Common Name(s) : Black Bamboo
Origin : China
Growth Rate : Fast
Salt Tolerance : Low
Soil Requirements : Wide
Plant Type : Evergreen shrub
Foliage Color : Green
Flowering Season : n/a
Flower Color : n/a
Propagation : Division; cuttings
Human Hazards : None
Common Uses : Large shrub; foliage plant; edible
Major Problems : None

Family : Gramineae   **Zone** : 8-9

Typical Height : 25 Ft.
Drought Tolerance : Medium
Nutritional Requirements : Medium
Light Requirements : High
Leaf Type : Simple; linear
Texture : Medium
Flower Characteristics : Insignificant

Environmental Problems : Invasive

Additional Notes : A black stemmed running species. New shoots are edible.
Cultivars
'HENON' is larger and has a coating of tawny hairs on new shoots; 'BORY' has purple-brown blotches on the culms.

Phyllostachys viridis

Common Name(s) : Yellow Running Bamboo
Origin : China
Growth Rate : Fast
Salt Tolerance : Medium
Soil Requirements : Wide
Plant Type : Evergreen shrub
Foliage Color : Green
Flowering Season : n/a
Flower Color : n/a
Propagation : Division; cuttings
Human Hazards : None
Common Uses : Large shrub; edible
Major Problems : None
Additional Notes : A running bamboo with golden stems. New shoots edible.
Cultivars
'ROBERT YOUNG' has new light green new stems that become yellow with green stripes as they mature.

Family : Gramineae   **Zone** : 8-9

Typical Height : 40 Ft.
Drought Tolerance : Medium
Nutritional Requirements : Medium
Light Requirements : High
Leaf Type : Simple; linear
Texture : Medium
Flower Characteristics : Insignificant

Environmental Problems : Invasive

Physostegia virginiana

Common Name(s) : False Dragonhead; Obedient Plant
Origin : Northeastern United States
Growth Rate : Medium
Salt Tolerance : Low
Soil Requirements : Wide
Plant Type : Herbaceous perennial
Foliage Color : Green
Flowering Season : Summer
Flower Color : Pink; purple; white
Propagation : Division; seeds
Human Hazards : None
Common Uses : Borders; cut flowers
Major Problems : None
Additional Notes : Can become invasive.

Family : Labiatae   **Zone** : 3-10A

Typical Height : 3 Ft.
Drought Tolerance : Medium
Nutritional Requirements : Medium
Light Requirements : Medium; high
Leaf Type : Simple
Texture : Medium
Flower Characteristics : Showy

Environmental Problems : Invasive

Pilea cadierei

Common Name(s) : Aluminum Plant
Origin : Vietnam
Growth Rate : Fast
Salt Tolerance : Medium
Soil Requirements : Wide
Plant Type : Herbaceous perennial
Foliage Color : Green & silver
Flowering Season : Summer
Flower Color : White
Propagation : Cuttings
Human Hazards : None
Common Uses : Beds; specimen plant; foliage plant
Major Problems : Mites
Additional Notes : An attractive rambling pilea for shady moist sites.

Family : Urticaceae   **Zone** : 10A-11

Typical Height : 1 Ft.
Drought Tolerance : Low
Nutritional Requirements : Medium
Light Requirements : Low; medium
Leaf Type : Simple
Texture : Medium
Flower Characteristics : Insignificant

Environmental Problems : None

Pilea microphylla *(Photograph p. 215)*

Common Name(s) : Artillery Plant
Origin : Tropical America
Growth Rate : Medium
Salt Tolerance : Low
Soil Requirements : Wide
Plant Type : Herbaceous perennial
Foliage Color : Green
Flowering Season : Year-round
Flower Color : Green
Propagation : Cuttings
Human Hazards : None
Common Uses : Groundcover; foliage plant
Major Problems : Rhizoctonia blight
Additional Notes : Light green foliage; some varieties may be weedy.

Family : Urticaceae   **Zone** : 10B-11

Typical Height : 1 Ft.
Drought Tolerance : Medium
Nutritional Requirements : Medium
Light Requirements : Low; medium; high
Leaf Type : Simple
Texture : Fine
Flower Characteristics : Insignificant

Environmental Problems : Weedy

Pilea serpyllifolia *(Photograph p. 215)*

Common Name(s) : Stoplight Pilea
Origin : West Indies
Growth Rate : Medium
Salt Tolerance : Low
Soil Requirements : Wide
Plant Type : Herbaceous perennial
Foliage Color : Green
Flowering Season : Year-round
Flower Color : Red
Propagation : Cuttings
Human Hazards : None
Common Uses : Beds; groundcover; foliage plant
Major Problems : Rhizoctonia blight
Additional Notes : Similar to P. microphylla , but has larger leaves and red flowers.
Cultivars
'STOPLIGHT' is a select variety.

Family : Urticaceae   Zone : 10B-11

Typical Height : 1 Ft.
Drought Tolerance : Medium
Nutritional Requirements : Medium
Light Requirements : Low; medium; high
Leaf Type : Simple
Texture : Fine
Flower Characteristics : Insignificant

Environmental Problems : None

Pimenta dioica

Common Name(s) : Allspice
Origin : Caribbean Region
Growth Rate : Slow
Salt Tolerance : Low
Soil Requirements : Wide
Plant Type : Evergreen tree
Foliage Color : Green
Flowering Season : Spring
Flower Color : White
Propagation : Seeds
Human Hazards : None
Common Uses : Small tree; edible fruit
Major Problems : None
Additional Notes : A beautiful small tree with exfoliating bark. Source of allspice.

Family : Myrtaceae   Zone : 10B-11

Typical Height : 20 Ft.
Drought Tolerance : High
Nutritional Requirements : Medium
Light Requirements : High
Leaf Type : Simple
Texture : Medium
Flower Characteristics : Insignificant

Environmental Problems : None

Pinanga kuhlii

Common Name(s) : Pinanga Palm
Origin : Java and Sumatra
Growth Rate : Medium
Salt Tolerance : Low
Soil Requirements : Wide
Plant Type : Palm
Foliage Color : Green
Flowering Season : Spring; summer
Flower Color : Yellow
Propagation : Seeds
Human Hazards : None
Common Uses : Foliage plant; shrub; palm
Major Problems : None
Additional Notes : This is the hardiest of pinangas. A clumping species for moderate shade.

Family : Palmae   Zone : 10B-11

Typical Height : 12 Ft.
Drought Tolerance : Low
Nutritional Requirements : Medium
Light Requirements : Medium
Leaf Type : Pinnately compound
Texture : Coarse
Flower Characteristics : Insignificant

Environmental Problems : None

Pinckneya pubens

Common Name(s) : Fevertree; Pinckneya
Origin : Southeastern United States
Growth Rate : Medium
Salt Tolerance : Low
Soil Requirements : Acid
Plant Type : Deciduous tree
Foliage Color : Green
Flowering Season : Spring
Flower Color : Pink; yellow
Propagation : Seeds
Human Hazards : None
Common Uses : Small flowering tree
Major Problems : None
Additional Notes : Showiest part of flower is enlarged pink sepal; needs moist soil.

Family : Rubiaceae   Zone : 7-9

Typical Height : 15 Ft.
Drought Tolerance : Low
Nutritional Requirements : Medium
Light Requirements : Medium
Leaf Type : Simple
Texture : Medium
Flower Characteristics : Showy

Environmental Problems : None

Pinus caribaea

Common Name(s) : Cuban Pine
Origin : West Indies
Growth Rate : Medium
Salt Tolerance : Medium
Soil Requirements : Wide
Plant Type : Evergreen tree
Foliage Color : Green
Flowering Season : Spring
Flower Color : Brown
Propagation : Seeds
Human Hazards : None
Common Uses : Timber; tree
Major Problems : None
Additional Notes : An important timber tree in the Caribbean. Has 3 or 4 needles/ fascicle.

Family : Pinaceae   Zone : 10A-11

Typical Height : 100 Ft.
Drought Tolerance : High
Nutritional Requirements : Low
Light Requirements : High
Leaf Type : Needle
Texture : Fine
Flower Characteristics : Insignificant

Environmental Problems : None

Pinus clausa

Common Name(s) : Sand Pine
Origin : Southeastern United States
Growth Rate : Slow
Salt Tolerance : High
Soil Requirements : Wide
Plant Type : Evergreen tree
Foliage Color : Green
Flowering Season : Spring
Flower Color : Brown
Propagation : Seeds
Human Hazards : None
Common Uses : Tree
Major Problems : None
Additional Notes : Very tolerant of dry, sandy soils.

Family : Pinaceae   Zone : 7-10B

Typical Height : 40 Ft.
Drought Tolerance : High
Nutritional Requirements : Low
Light Requirements : High
Leaf Type : Needle
Texture : Fine
Flower Characteristics : Cone

Environmental Problems : None

Pinus elliottii *(Photograph p. 166)*

Common Name(s) : Slash Pine
Origin : Southeastern United States
Growth Rate : Fast
Salt Tolerance : High
Soil Requirements : Wide
Plant Type : Evergreen tree
Foliage Color : Green
Flowering Season : Spring
Flower Color : Brown
Propagation : Seeds
Human Hazards : None
Common Uses : Timber; shade tree
Major Problems : Borers; pine blister rust
Additional Notes : Very sensitive to grade changes and soil compaction.
Cultivars
Var. densa has extremely dense, rot-resistant wood.

Family : Pinaceae   Zone : 8-10B

Typical Height : 75 Ft.
Drought Tolerance : High
Nutritional Requirements : Low
Light Requirements : High
Leaf Type : Needle
Texture : Fine
Flower Characteristics : Insignificant

Environmental Problems : None

Pinus glabra

Common Name(s) : Spruce Pine
Origin : Southeastern United States
Growth Rate : Medium
Salt Tolerance : Low
Soil Requirements : Acid
Plant Type : Evergreen tree
Foliage Color : Green
Flowering Season : Spring
Flower Color : Brown
Propagation : Seeds
Human Hazards : None
Common Uses : Tree
Major Problems : Pine blister rust; borers
Additional Notes : Has attractive texture.

Family : Pinaceae   Zone : 8-9

Typical Height : 40 Ft.
Drought Tolerance : Low
Nutritional Requirements : Medium
Light Requirements : High
Leaf Type : Needle
Texture : Fine
Flower Characteristics : Insignificant

Environmental Problems : None

Pinus palustris

Common Name(s) : Longleaf Pine
Origin : Southeastern United States
Growth Rate : Medium
Salt Tolerance : Low
Soil Requirements : Wide
Plant Type : Evergreen tree
Foliage Color : Green
Flowering Season : Spring
Flower Color : Brown
Propagation : Seeds
Human Hazards : None
Common Uses : Tree
Major Problems : Borers; pine bark beetles
Additional Notes : A common timber tree in central and north Florida.

Family : Pinaceae   **Zone** : 7-10A

Typical Height : 70 Ft.
Drought Tolerance : High
Nutritional Requirements : Low
Light Requirements : High
Leaf Type : Needle
Texture : Fine
Flower Characteristics : Cone

Environmental Problems : None

Pinus taeda

Common Name(s) : Loblolly Pine
Origin : Southeastern United States
Growth Rate : Medium
Salt Tolerance : Low
Soil Requirements : Wide
Plant Type : Evergreen tree
Foliage Color : Green
Flowering Season : Spring
Flower Color : Brown
Propagation : Seeds
Human Hazards : None
Common Uses : Tree
Major Problems : Pine bark beetles; borers
Additional Notes : A tree used for lumber and pulpwood.

Family : Pinaceae   **Zone** : 7-10A

Typical Height : 70 Ft.
Drought Tolerance : High
Nutritional Requirements : Low
Light Requirements : High
Leaf Type : Needle
Texture : Fine
Flower Characteristics : Cone

Environmental Problems : None

Pinus thunbergiana

Common Name(s) : Japanese Black Pine
Origin : Japan
Growth Rate : Medium
Salt Tolerance : High
Soil Requirements : Wide
Plant Type : Evergreen tree
Foliage Color : Green
Flowering Season : Spring
Flower Color : Brown
Propagation : Seeds
Human Hazards : None
Common Uses : Tree
Major Problems : None
Additional Notes : Has 2 sharp needles per fascicle. Good for coastal areas.

Family : Pinaceae   **Zone** : 5-9

Typical Height : 60 Ft.
Drought Tolerance : High
Nutritional Requirements : Low
Light Requirements : High
Leaf Type : Needle
Texture : Fine
Flower Characteristics : Insignificant

Environmental Problems : None

Pinus virginiana

Common Name(s) : Virginia Pine; Scrub Pine
Origin : Eastern United States
Growth Rate : Slow
Salt Tolerance : Medium
Soil Requirements : Wide
Plant Type : Evergreen tree
Foliage Color : Green
Flowering Season : Spring
Flower Color : Brown
Propagation : Seeds
Human Hazards : None
Common Uses : Tree
Major Problems : Borers; pine bark beetles
Additional Notes : Has 2 short needles per fascicle. Good for dry sandy sites.

Family : Pinaceae   **Zone** : 4-9

Typical Height : 35 Ft.
Drought Tolerance : High
Nutritional Requirements : Low
Light Requirements : High
Leaf Type : Needle
Texture : Fine
Flower Characteristics : Insignificant

Environmental Problems : None

Piscidia piscipula

Common Name(s) : Jamaican Dogwood; Fish-poison Tree
Origin : Florida Keys and West Indies
Growth Rate : Fast
Salt Tolerance : High
Soil Requirements : Wide
Plant Type : Evergreen tree
Foliage Color : Green
Flowering Season : Spring
Flower Color : White; lavender
Propagation : Seeds
Human Hazards : Poisonous
Common Uses : Tree
Major Problems : None

Family : Leguminosae   **Zone** : 11

Typical Height : 40 Ft.
Drought Tolerance : High
Nutritional Requirements : Low
Light Requirements : High
Leaf Type : Pinnately compound
Texture : Medium
Flower Characteristics : Showy

Environmental Problems : None

Additional Notes : Bark & other tree parts used to stupefy fish. Native to the Florida Keys.

Pistacia chinensis

Common Name(s) : Chinese Pistache
Origin : China and Taiwan
Growth Rate : Medium
Salt Tolerance : Low
Soil Requirements : Wide
Plant Type : Deciduous tree
Foliage Color : Green
Flowering Season : Spring
Flower Color : White
Propagation : Seeds; grafting
Human Hazards : None
Common Uses : Shade tree
Major Problems : Oak root fungus

Family : Anacardiaceae   **Zone** : 8-10A

Typical Height : 40 Ft.
Drought Tolerance : High
Nutritional Requirements : Medium
Light Requirements : Medium
Leaf Type : Pinnately compound
Texture : Medium
Flower Characteristics : Insignificant

Environmental Problems : Messy

Additional Notes : Fruits showy but messy; root rot on wet soils. Red & orange fall color.

Pistia stratiotes

Common Name(s) : Water Lettuce
Origin : Pantropical
Growth Rate : Fast
Salt Tolerance : Low
Soil Requirements : n/a
Plant Type : Aquatic perennial
Foliage Color : Green
Flowering Season : n/a
Flower Color : Green
Propagation : Division
Human Hazards : Irritant
Common Uses : Aquatic
Major Problems : None

Family : Araceae   **Zone** : 9-11

Typical Height : .5 Ft.
Drought Tolerance : Low
Nutritional Requirements : Low
Light Requirements : Medium; high
Leaf Type : Simple
Texture : Coarse
Flower Characteristics : Insignificant

Environmental Problems : Invasive

Additional Notes : A floating aquatic plant grown primarily for its unusual foliage.

Pithecellobium dulce

Common Name(s) : Manila Tamarind
Origin : Mexico and Central America
Growth Rate : Medium
Salt Tolerance : Medium
Soil Requirements : Wide
Plant Type : Evergreen tree
Foliage Color : Green
Flowering Season : Summer
Flower Color : White
Propagation : Seeds
Human Hazards : Spiny; irritant
Common Uses : Shade tree
Major Problems : None

Family : Leguminosae   **Zone** : 10B-11

Typical Height : 50 Ft.
Drought Tolerance : Medium
Nutritional Requirements : Medium
Light Requirements : High
Leaf Type : Pinnately compound
Texture : Fine
Flower Characteristics : Showy

Environmental Problems : Weedy; weak

Additional Notes : Susceptible to wind damage. A weedy species not recommended.

Pithecellobium guadalupense

Common Name(s) : Blackbead
Origin : Caribbean Region
Growth Rate : Medium
Salt Tolerance : High
Soil Requirements : Wide
Plant Type : Evergreen tree or shrub
Foliage Color : Green
Flowering Season : Spring; summer
Flower Color : Pink
Propagation : Seeds
Human Hazards : Irritant
Common Uses : Flowering shrub; small flowering tree
Major Problems : None
Additional Notes : This Florida native has lustrous black seeds.

Family : Leguminosae   **Zone** : 10A-11

Typical Height : 18 Ft.
Drought Tolerance : High
Nutritional Requirements : Low
Light Requirements : High
Leaf Type : Pinnately compound
Texture : Medium
Flower Characteristics : Showy

Environmental Problems : None

Pithecellobium unguis-cati

Common Name(s) : Cat's Claw
Origin : Caribbean Region
Growth Rate : Medium
Salt Tolerance : High
Soil Requirements : Wide
Plant Type : Evergreen shrub or tree
Foliage Color : Green
Flowering Season : Summer
Flower Color : Green-yellow
Propagation : Seeds
Human Hazards : Spiny; irritant
Common Uses : Small tree; shrub
Major Problems : None
Additional Notes : A spiny Florida native that can become a small tree.

Family : Leguminosae   **Zone** : 10A-11

Typical Height : 18 Ft.
Drought Tolerance : High
Nutritional Requirements : Low
Light Requirements : High
Leaf Type : Pinnately compound
Texture : Fine
Flower Characteristics : Insignificant

Environmental Problems : None

Pittosporum ferrugineum

Common Name(s) : Rusty Pittosporum
Origin : Australia and Malay Achipeligo
Growth Rate : Medium
Salt Tolerance : Medium
Soil Requirements : Wide
Plant Type : Evergreen tree
Foliage Color : Green
Flowering Season : Spring
Flower Color : White; yellow-white
Propagation : Seeds; cuttings
Human Hazards : None
Common Uses : Small tree
Major Problems : None
Additional Notes : A good small tree with attractive orange fruit.
Cultivars
'FLOYD L. WRAY' is a select clone.

Family : Pittosporaceae   **Zone** : 9-11

Typical Height : 30 Ft.
Drought Tolerance : High
Nutritional Requirements : Medium
Light Requirements : High
Leaf Type : Simple
Texture : Medium
Flower Characteristics : Insignificant

Environmental Problems : None

Pittosporum tobira *(Photograph p. 184)*

Common Name(s) : Japanese Pittosporum
Origin : China and Japan
Growth Rate : Medium
Salt Tolerance : High
Soil Requirements : Wide
Plant Type : Evergreen shrub
Foliage Color : Green
Flowering Season : Summer
Flower Color : White
Propagation : Seeds; cuttings
Human Hazards : None
Common Uses : Hedge; shrub; groundcover
Major Problems : Leafspots; virus; scales; nematodes
Additional Notes : Good for seaside plantings.
Cultivars
'COMPACTA' is a more compact form; 'VARIEGATA' has variegated foliage; 'WHEELER'S DWARF' is a very compact variety with very brittle wood.

Family : Pittosporaceae   **Zone** : 8-11

Typical Height : 8 Ft.
Drought Tolerance : Medium
Nutritional Requirements : Medium
Light Requirements : Medium; high
Leaf Type : Simple
Texture : Medium
Flower Characteristics : Insignificant

Environmental Problems : None

Platanus occidentalis

Common Name(s) : Sycamore
Origin : Eastern United States
Growth Rate : Fast
Salt Tolerance : Low
Soil Requirements : Wide
Plant Type : Deciduous tree
Foliage Color : Green
Flowering Season : Spring
Flower Color : Green
Propagation : Seeds
Human Hazards : None
Common Uses : Shade tree
Major Problems : Antracnose
Additional Notes : Large deciduous tree for moist sites. Exfoliating bark.
Cultivars
Var. glabrata has smaller, but more deeply lobed leaves.

Family : Platanaceae   **Zone** : 4-10B

Typical Height : 100 Ft.
Drought Tolerance : Low
Nutritional Requirements : Medium
Light Requirements : High
Leaf Type : Simple; palmately lobed
Texture : Coarse
Flower Characteristics : Insignificant

Environmental Problems : None

Platycerium bifurcatum *(Photograph p. 199)*

Common Name(s) : Staghorn Fern
Origin : Australia and Polynesia
Growth Rate : Medium
Salt Tolerance : Low
Soil Requirements : Well-drained
Plant Type : Epiphyte
Foliage Color : Green
Flowering Season : n/a
Flower Color : n/a
Propagation : Spores; division; tissue culture
Human Hazards : None
Common Uses : Epiphyte; foliage plant; hanging basket
Major Problems : Scales; mites
Additional Notes : Other similar species are sometimes cultivated; susceptible to fern scale.

Family : Polypodiaceae   **Zone** : 10B-11

Typical Height : 3 Ft.
Drought Tolerance : Medium
Nutritional Requirements : Medium
Light Requirements : Low; medium
Leaf Type : Simple; two-lobed
Texture : Coarse
Flower Characteristics : n/a

Environmental Problems : None

Platycladus orientalis *(Photograph p. 184)*

Common Name(s) : Oriental Arborvitae
Origin : China and Korea
Growth Rate : Medium
Salt Tolerance : Low
Soil Requirements : Wide
Plant Type : Evergreen shrub
Foliage Color : Green
Flowering Season : Spring
Flower Color : Brown
Propagation : Seeds; cuttings; grafting
Human Hazards : None
Common Uses : Shrub; small tree
Major Problems : Mites; bacterial blight
Additional Notes : A large shrub that can be trained into a tree. Susceptible to mites.
Cultivars
'AUREUS' has golden new foliage.

Family : Cupressaceae   **Zone** : 5-10B

Typical Height : 20 Ft.
Drought Tolerance : Medium
Nutritional Requirements : Medium
Light Requirements : Medium; high
Leaf Type : Scale-like
Texture : Fine
Flower Characteristics : Cone

Environmental Problems : None

Platycodon grandiflorus

Common Name(s) : Balloon Flower
Origin : Eastern Asia
Growth Rate : Medium
Salt Tolerance : Low
Soil Requirements : Wide
Plant Type : Herbaceous perennial
Foliage Color : Green
Flowering Season : Summer
Flower Color : Blue; white; pink
Propagation : Seeds; division
Human Hazards : None
Common Uses : Specimen plant; beds; borders.
Major Problems : None
Additional Notes : Carefree; flowers the second year from seed; seldom needs dividing.

Family : Campanulaceae   **Zone** : 3-9

Typical Height : 2 Ft.
Drought Tolerance : Medium
Nutritional Requirements : Medium
Light Requirements : High
Leaf Type : Simple
Texture : Medium
Flower Characteristics : Showy

Environmental Problems : None

Plumbago auriculata *(Photograph p. 184)*

Common Name(s) : Plumbago
Origin : South Africa
Growth Rate : Medium
Salt Tolerance : Medium
Soil Requirements : Wide
Plant Type : Evergreen shrub
Foliage Color : Green
Flowering Season : Spring; summer; fall
Flower Color : Blue; white
Propagation : Cuttings
Human Hazards : Irritant
Common Uses : Flowering shrub; hedge; flowering groundcover
Major Problems : Cottony cushion scale; mites
Additional Notes : Straggly growth if unpruned.
Cultivars
'ALBA' has white flowers.

Family : Plumbaginaceae   **Zone** : 10A-11

Typical Height : 5 Ft.
Drought Tolerance : Medium
Nutritional Requirements : Medium
Light Requirements : High
Leaf Type : Simple
Texture : Medium
Flower Characteristics : Showy; fragrant

Environmental Problems : None

Plumbago indica

Common Name(s) : Scarlet Leadwort
Origin : Southeast Asia
Growth Rate : Medium
Salt Tolerance : Medium
Soil Requirements : Wide
Plant Type : Evergreen shrub
Foliage Color : Green
Flowering Season : Spring; summer; fall
Flower Color : Red
Propagation : Cuttings
Human Hazards : Irritant
Common Uses : Flowering shrub
Major Problems : None
Additional Notes : A rambling plant that may require pruning to maintain any shape.

Family : Plumbaginaceae   **Zone** : 10B-11

Typical Height : 5 Ft.
Drought Tolerance : Medium
Nutritional Requirements : Medium
Light Requirements : High
Leaf Type : Simple
Texture : Medium
Flower Characteristics : Showy

Environmental Problems : None

Plumeria alba *(Photograph p. 166)*

Common Name(s) : White Frangipani
Origin : West Indies
Growth Rate : Slow
Salt Tolerance : High
Soil Requirements : Wide
Plant Type : Deciduous tree
Foliage Color : Green
Flowering Season : Summer
Flower Color : White & yellow
Propagation : Large cuttings
Human Hazards : Irritant
Common Uses : Small flowering tree
Major Problems : Rust; scales
Additional Notes : Fragant flowers used in Hawaiian leis.

Family : Apocynaceae   **Zone** : 10B-11

Typical Height : 20 Ft.
Drought Tolerance : High
Nutritional Requirements : Low
Light Requirements : High
Leaf Type : Simple
Texture : Coarse
Flower Characteristics : Showy; fragrant

Environmental Problems : None

Plumeria rubra *(Photograph p. 167)*

Common Name(s) : Frangipani
Origin : Mexico, Caribbean Region
Growth Rate : Slow
Salt Tolerance : High
Soil Requirements : Wide
Plant Type : Deciduous tree
Foliage Color : Green
Flowering Season : Spring; summer
Flower Color : Pink; red
Propagation : Large cuttings
Human Hazards : Irritant
Common Uses : Small flowering tree
Major Problems : Rust; scales
Additional Notes : Thick succulent stems root easily.

Family : Apocynaceae   **Zone** : 10B-11

Typical Height : 20 Ft.
Drought Tolerance : High
Nutritional Requirements : Low
Light Requirements : High
Leaf Type : Simple
Texture : Coarse
Flower Characteristics : Showy; fragrant

Environmental Problems : None

Podocarpus gracilior *(Photograph p. 166)*

Common Name(s) : Weeping Podocarpus
Origin : East Africa
Growth Rate : Medium
Salt Tolerance : Medium
Soil Requirements : Wide
Plant Type : Evergreen tree
Foliage Color : Green
Flowering Season : Summer
Flower Color : n/a
Propagation : Seeds; cuttings; air layers
Human Hazards : None
Common Uses : Shade tree
Major Problems : None
Additional Notes : Fine textured leaves, pendulous branches.

Family : Podocarpaceae   **Zone** : 10A-11

Typical Height : 50 Ft.
Drought Tolerance : Medium
Nutritional Requirements : Medium
Light Requirements : Medium; high
Leaf Type : Simple; linear
Texture : Fine
Flower Characteristics : n/a

Environmental Problems : None

Podocarpus macrophyllus *(Photograph p. 167)*

Common Name(s) : Yew Podocarpus
Origin : Japan
Growth Rate : Medium
Salt Tolerance : Medium
Soil Requirements : Wide
Plant Type : Evergreen tree
Foliage Color : Green
Flowering Season : Summer
Flower Color : n/a
Propagation : Seeds; cuttings
Human Hazards : None
Common Uses : Tree; shrub; hedge
Major Problems : Scales; sooty mold
Additional Notes : Often sheared into a tall screen or columnar tree.
Cultivars
Var. maki is more shrublike than species.

Family : Podocarpaceae   **Zone** : 7-11

Typical Height : 35 Ft.
Drought Tolerance : Medium
Nutritional Requirements : Low
Light Requirements : Medium; high
Leaf Type : Simple; linear
Texture : Fine
Flower Characteristics : n/a

Environmental Problems : None

Podocarpus nagi *(Photograph p. 167)*

Common Name(s) : Nagi Podocarpus
Origin : Japan, Ryukyu Islands
Growth Rate : Medium
Salt Tolerance : Medium
Soil Requirements : Wide
Plant Type : Evergreen tree
Foliage Color : Green
Flowering Season : Summer
Flower Color : n/a
Propagation : Seeds
Human Hazards : None
Common Uses : Tree
Major Problems : Scales; sooty mold
Additional Notes : Cut foliage is good for flower arrangements.

Family : Podocarpaceae   **Zone** : 9-10B

Typical Height : 50 Ft.
Drought Tolerance : Medium
Nutritional Requirements : Medium
Light Requirements : Medium; high
Leaf Type : Simple
Texture : Fine
Flower Characteristics : n/a

Environmental Problems : None

Podocarpus neriifolius

Common Name(s) : Podocarpus
Origin : China to New Guinea
Growth Rate : Medium
Salt Tolerance : Medium
Soil Requirements : Wide
Plant Type : Evergreen tree
Foliage Color : Green
Flowering Season : Summer
Flower Color : n/a
Propagation : Seeds; cuttings
Human Hazards : None
Common Uses : Tree
Major Problems : Scales; sooty mold
Additional Notes : Similar to P. macrophyllus , but has longer leaves.

Family : Podocarpaceae   **Zone** : 9-11

Typical Height : 70 Ft.
Drought Tolerance : Medium
Nutritional Requirements : Low
Light Requirements : High
Leaf Type : Simple; linear
Texture : Medium
Flower Characteristics : n/a

Environmental Problems : None

Podranea ricasoliana

Common Name(s) : Pink Trumpet Vine
Origin : South Africa
Growth Rate : Fast
Salt Tolerance : Low
Soil Requirements : Wide
Plant Type : Evergreen vine
Foliage Color : Green
Flowering Season : Spring; winter
Flower Color : Pink
Propagation : Cuttings; layers
Human Hazards : None
Common Uses : Flowering vine
Major Problems : Nematodes; mites; scales; caterpillars
Additional Notes : Flowers pink, striped with red.

Family : Bignoniaceae   **Zone** : 10A-11

Typical Height : Not applicable
Drought Tolerance : Medium
Nutritional Requirements : Medium
Light Requirements : High; medium
Leaf Type : Pinnately compound
Texture : Medium
Flower Characteristics : Showy

Environmental Problems : None

Polianthes geminiflora

Common Name(s) : Twin Flower
Origin : Mexico
Growth Rate : Medium
Salt Tolerance : Medium
Soil Requirements : Alkaline
Plant Type : Herbaceous perennial
Foliage Color : Green
Flowering Season : Summer; fall
Flower Color : Red
Propagation : Seeds; division
Human Hazards : None
Common Uses : Beds; borders; cut flowers
Major Problems : None
Additional Notes : Related to tuberose; should be used more widely.

Family : Agavaceae   **Zone** : 9-10B

Typical Height : 2.5 Ft.
Drought Tolerance : Medium
Nutritional Requirements : Medium
Light Requirements : High
Leaf Type : Simple; linear
Texture : Fine
Flower Characteristics : Showy

Environmental Problems : None

Polianthes tuberosa

Common Name(s) : Tuberose
Origin : Mexico
Growth Rate : Medium
Salt Tolerance : Low
Soil Requirements : Wide
Plant Type : Herbaceous perennial
Foliage Color : Green
Flowering Season : Summer; fall
Flower Color : White
Propagation : Division
Human Hazards : None
Common Uses : Beds; borders; cut flowers
Major Problems : Nematodes
Additional Notes : Single-flowered variety most fragrant.

Family : Agavaceae   **Zone** : 9-10A

Typical Height : 2.5 Ft.
Drought Tolerance : Low
Nutritional Requirements : High
Light Requirements : Medium
Leaf Type : Simple; linear
Texture : Medium
Flower Characteristics : Fragrant; showy.

Environmental Problems : None

Polypodium grandiceps

Common Name(s) : Elkhorn Fern
Origin : n/a
Growth Rate : Medium
Salt Tolerance : Low
Soil Requirements : Wide
Plant Type : Herbaceous perennial
Foliage Color : Green
Flowering Season : n/a
Flower Color : n/a
Propagation : Division; spores
Human Hazards : None
Common Uses : Specimen plant; foliage plant; cut foliage
Major Problems : None
Additional Notes : Lance-shaped fronds have divided tips.

Family : Polypodiaceae   **Zone** : 10B-11

Typical Height : 2 Ft.
Drought Tolerance : Medium
Nutritional Requirements : Low
Light Requirements : Low; medium
Leaf Type : Simple; lobed
Texture : Medium
Flower Characteristics : n/a

Environmental Problems : None

Polypodium scolopendria

Family : Polypodiaceae   **Zone** : 10B-11

Common Name(s) : Wart Fern
Origin : Old World Tropics
Growth Rate : Medium
Salt Tolerance : Low
Soil Requirements : Wide
Plant Type : Herbaceous perennial
Foliage Color : Green
Flowering Season : n/a
Flower Color : n/a
Propagation : Division; spores
Human Hazards : None
Common Uses : Specimen plant; foliage plant
Major Problems : None
Additional Notes : Has upright fronds with oakleaf shape.

Typical Height : 2 Ft.
Drought Tolerance : Medium
Nutritional Requirements : Low
Light Requirements : Low; medium
Leaf Type : Simple; pinnately lobed
Texture : Medium
Flower Characteristics : n/a

Environmental Problems : None

Polypodium spp.

Family : Polypodiaceae   **Zone** : N/A

Common Name(s) : Polypody Fern
Origin : Worldwide
Growth Rate : Medium
Salt Tolerance : Low
Soil Requirements : Wide
Plant Type : Herbaceous perennial
Foliage Color : Green
Flowering Season : n/a
Flower Color : n/a
Propagation : Spores; division
Human Hazards : None
Common Uses : Beds; groundcover; specimen plant; foliage plant
Major Problems : Fern scale
Additional Notes : Many species spreading by rhizomes. Some are native.

Typical Height : 2 Ft.
Drought Tolerance : Low
Nutritional Requirements : Low
Light Requirements : Low; medium
Leaf Type : Simple; pinnately lobed
Texture : Medium
Flower Characteristics : n/a

Environmental Problems : None

Polyscias crispata

Family : Araliaceae   **Zone** : 10B-11

Common Name(s) : Chicken Gizzard Aralia
Origin : South Pacific Islands
Growth Rate : Medium
Salt Tolerance : Medium
Soil Requirements : Wide
Plant Type : Evergreen shrub
Foliage Color : Green; variegated
Flowering Season : Year-round
Flower Color : White
Propagation : Cuttings
Human Hazards : Irritant
Common Uses : Shrub; hedge; foliage plant
Major Problems : Aphids; thrips; mites
Additional Notes : Many cultivars, all of which have 2 primary lobes per leaflet.
Cultivars
'PALA PALA' is a variegated form with large leaflets; 'CHICKEN GIZZARD' is a green-leaved form with large leaflets; 'CELERY' is a green-leaved form with small leaflets.

Typical Height : 7 Ft.
Drought Tolerance : High
Nutritional Requirements : Medium
Light Requirements : Low; medium; high
Leaf Type : Pinnately compound
Texture : Medium
Flower Characteristics : Insignificant

Environmental Problems : None

Polyscias filicifolia *(Photograph p. 184)*

Family : Araliaceae   **Zone** : 10B-11

Common Name(s) : Fernleaf Aralia
Origin : South Pacific Islands
Growth Rate : Medium
Salt Tolerance : Medium
Soil Requirements : Wide
Plant Type : Evergreen shrub
Foliage Color : Green
Flowering Season : Year-round
Flower Color : White
Propagation : Cuttings
Human Hazards : Irritant
Common Uses : Shrub; hedge; foliage plant
Major Problems : Aphids; thrips; mites
Additional Notes : Some cultivars have toothed leaflets. Golden foliage in full sun.

Typical Height : 10 Ft.
Drought Tolerance : High
Nutritional Requirements : Medium
Light Requirements : Low; medium; high
Leaf Type : Pinnately compound
Texture : Medium
Flower Characteristics : Insignificant

Environmental Problems : None

Polyscias fruticosa *(Photograph p. 184)*

Common Name(s) : Ming Aralia
Origin : South Pacific Islands
Growth Rate : Medium
Salt Tolerance : Medium
Soil Requirements : Wide
Plant Type : Evergreen shrub
Foliage Color : Green
Flowering Season : Year-round
Flower Color : White
Propagation : Cuttings
Human Hazards : Irritant
Common Uses : Shrub; hedge; foliage plant
Major Problems : Aphids; thrips; mites
Additional Notes : Many cultivars with finely divided foliage.
Cultivars
'ELEGANS' has parsley-like foliage; 'IMPROVED MING' has very fine light green foliage.

Family : Araliaceae   **Zone** : 10B-11

Typical Height : 6 Ft.
Drought Tolerance : High
Nutritional Requirements : Medium
Light Requirements : Low; medium; high
Leaf Type : Bipinnately compound
Texture : Fine
Flower Characteristics : Insignificant

Environmental Problems : None

Polyscias guilfoylei

Common Name(s) : Roseleaf Aralia
Origin : South Pacific Islands
Growth Rate : Medium
Salt Tolerance : Medium
Soil Requirements : Wide
Plant Type : Evergreen shrub
Foliage Color : Green; variegated
Flowering Season : Year-round
Flower Color : White
Propagation : Cuttings
Human Hazards : Irritant
Common Uses : Shrub; hedge; foliage plant
Major Problems : Aphids; thrips; mites
Additional Notes : Has highly variable leaf shape and color. Rarely flowers in S. Florida.
Cultivars
'BLACKIE' has very dark green puckered, crisp foliage; 'VICTORIAE' is variegated with finely divided leaflets; 'FISHTAIL' has leaflets resembling a tattered fishtail; 'VARIEGATA' has green and yellow-green foliage; 'MARGINATA' has white margined green leaves; 'ROSELEAF MING' has very finely divided leaflets.

Family : Araliaceae   **Zone** : 10B-11

Typical Height : 10 Ft.
Drought Tolerance : High
Nutritional Requirements : Medium
Light Requirements : Low; medium; high
Leaf Type : Pinnately compound
Texture : Medium
Flower Characteristics : Insignificant

Environmental Problems : None

Polyscias obtusa *(Photograph p. 185)*

Common Name(s) : Oakleaf Aralia
Origin : South Pacific Islands
Growth Rate : Medium
Salt Tolerance : Medium
Soil Requirements : Wide
Plant Type : Evergreen shrub
Foliage Color : Green
Flowering Season : Year round
Flower Color : White
Propagation : Cuttings
Human Hazards : Irritant
Common Uses : Shrub; hedge; foliage plant
Major Problems : Aphids; thrips; mites
Additional Notes : Has oak-shaped leaves.

Family : Araliaceae   **Zone** : 10B-11

Typical Height : 6 Ft.
Drought Tolerance : High
Nutritional Requirements : Medium
Light Requirements : Low; medium; high
Leaf Type : Pinnately compound
Texture : Coarse
Flower Characteristics : Insignificant

Environmental Problems : None

Polyscias pinnata *(Photograph p. 185)*

Common Name(s) : Balfour Aralia
Origin : South Pacific Islands
Growth Rate : Medium
Salt Tolerance : Medium
Soil Requirements : Wide
Plant Type : Evergreen shrub
Foliage Color : Green; variegated
Flowering Season : Year-round
Flower Color : White
Propagation : Cuttings
Human Hazards : Irritant
Common Uses : Shrub; hedge; foliage plant
Major Problems : Aphids; thrips; mites
Additional Notes : This species has 3 to 5 large round leaflets per leaf.
Cultivars
'DINNER PLATE' has very large round leaves; 'MARGINATA' has smaller white-margined green leaves; 'PENNOCKII' has green and yellow-green foliage.

Family : Araliaceae   **Zone** : 10B-11

Typical Height : 6 Ft.
Drought Tolerance : High
Nutritional Requirements : Medium
Light Requirements : Low; medium; high
Leaf Type : Pinnately compound
Texture : Coarse
Flower Characteristics : Insignificant

Environmental Problems : None

Polyscias scutellaria

Common Name(s) : Cup-leaved Aralia
Origin : South Pacific Islands
Growth Rate : Medium
Salt Tolerance : Medium
Soil Requirements : Wide
Plant Type : Evergreen shrub
Foliage Color : Purple-green; green
Flowering Season : Year-round
Flower Color : White
Propagation : Cuttings
Human Hazards : Irritant
Common Uses : Shrub; hedge; foliage plant
Major Problems : Aphids; thrips; mites
Additional Notes : This species usually has simple cupped leaves.
Cultivars
'FABIAN' has purple-green foliage.

Family : Araliaceae   **Zone** : 10B-11

Typical Height : 6 Ft.
Drought Tolerance : High
Nutritional Requirements : Medium
Light Requirements : Low; medium; high
Leaf Type : Simple
Texture : Medium
Flower Characteristics : Insignificant

Environmental Problems : None

Pongamia pinnata *(Photograph p. 167)*

Common Name(s) : Pongam
Origin : Tropical Asia, Africa, & Australia
Growth Rate : Fast
Salt Tolerance : Medium
Soil Requirements : Wide
Plant Type : Evergreen tree
Foliage Color : Green
Flowering Season : Spring
Flower Color : Pink
Propagation : Seeds
Human Hazards : None
Common Uses : Shade tree; flowering tree
Major Problems : Nutritional deficiencies; caterpillars
Additional Notes : Very resistant to wind.

Family : Leguminosae   **Zone** : 10B-11

Typical Height : 35 Ft.
Drought Tolerance : High
Nutritional Requirements : Medium
Light Requirements : High
Leaf Type : Pinnately compound
Texture : Medium
Flower Characteristics : Showy; fragrant

Environmental Problems : None

Pontederia cordata *(Photograph p. 199)*

Common Name(s) : Pickerel Weed
Origin : Eastern North America
Growth Rate : Medium
Salt Tolerance : Low
Soil Requirements : Wet
Plant Type : Herbaceous perennial
Foliage Color : Green
Flowering Season : Summer; fall
Flower Color : Purple
Propagation : Division
Human Hazards : None
Common Uses : Aquatic
Major Problems : None
Additional Notes : Use in contained pools or in littoral zone of ponds. Spreads rapidly.

Family : Pontederiaceae   **Zone** : 3-10B

Typical Height : 3 Ft.
Drought Tolerance : Low
Nutritional Requirements : Low
Light Requirements : High
Leaf Type : Simple
Texture : Coarse
Flower Characteristics : Showy

Environmental Problems : None

Portulaca grandiflora *(Photograph p. 216)*

Common Name(s) : Purslane; Moss Rose
Origin : South America
Growth Rate : Fast
Salt Tolerance : High
Soil Requirements : Wide
Plant Type : Herbaceous perennial
Foliage Color : Green
Flowering Season : Year round
Flower Color : Red; yellow; orange; pink; white
Propagation : Seed; cuttings
Human Hazards : None
Common Uses : Grouncover
Major Problems : None
Additional Notes : As groundcover needs replacement every few years.

Family : Portulacacae   **Zone** : 10B-11

Typical Height : .5 Ft.
Drought Tolerance : High
Nutritional Requirements : Low
Light Requirements : High
Leaf Type : Simple
Texture : Fine
Flower Characteristics : Showy

Environmental Problems : None

Portulacaria afra

Family : Portulacaceae   Zone : 10A-11

Common Name(s) : Elephant Bush
Origin : South Africa
Growth Rate : Medium
Salt Tolerance : High
Soil Requirements : Wide
Plant Type : Succulent shrub
Foliage Color : Green
Flowering Season : n/a
Flower Color : Pink
Propagation : Cuttings
Human Hazards : None
Common Uses : Foliage plant; rock gardens
Major Problems : Stem rots
Additional Notes : This succulent shrub looks somewhat like Crassula argentea .

Typical Height : 10 Ft.
Drought Tolerance : High
Nutritional Requirements : Medium
Light Requirements : High
Leaf Type : Simple
Texture : Fine
Flower Characteristics : Insignificant

Environmental Problems : None

Pouteria campechiana

Family : Sapotaceae   Zone : 10B-11

Common Name(s) : Eggfruit; Canistel
Origin : Cuba, Mexico and Central America
Growth Rate : Fast
Salt Tolerance : Medium
Soil Requirements : Wide
Plant Type : Evergreen tree
Foliage Color : Green
Flowering Season : Spring; summer
Flower Color : White
Propagation : Seeds
Human Hazards : None
Common Uses : Small tree; edible fruit
Major Problems : Mites; scales; rust
Additional Notes : Sweet-tasting yellow fruit. Many selected cultivars.

Typical Height : 25 Ft.
Drought Tolerance : Medium
Nutritional Requirements : Medium
Light Requirements : High
Leaf Type : Simple
Texture : Medium
Flower Characteristics : Insignificant

Environmental Problems : None

Pouteria sapota *(Photograph p. 167)*

Family : Sapotaceae   Zone : 10B-11

Common Name(s) : Mammee Sapote
Origin : Mexico and Central America
Growth Rate : Fast
Salt Tolerance : Medium
Soil Requirements : Acid
Plant Type : Evergreen tree
Foliage Color : Green
Flowering Season : Fall; winter
Flower Color : White
Propagation : Seeds
Human Hazards : None
Common Uses : Edible fruit; shade tree
Major Problems : Scales; rust
Additional Notes : Usually grown primarily for its edible fruits.

Typical Height : 60 Ft.
Drought Tolerance : Medium
Nutritional Requirements : Medium
Light Requirements : High
Leaf Type : Simple
Texture : Coarse
Flower Characteristics : Insignificant

Environmental Problems : Messy

Pritchardia spp. *(Photograph p. 206)*

Family : Palmae   Zone : 11

Common Name(s) : Pritchardia Palm
Origin : Pacific Islands
Growth Rate : Slow
Salt Tolerance : High
Soil Requirements : Wide
Plant Type : Palm
Foliage Color : Green
Flowering Season : Summer
Flower Color : White
Propagation : Seeds
Human Hazards : None
Common Uses : Palm; tree
Major Problems : Lethal yellowing (highly susceptible); scales
Additional Notes : Most species cold sensitive.

Typical Height : 25 Ft.
Drought Tolerance : High
Nutritional Requirements : Medium
Light Requirements : Medium; high
Leaf Type : Simple; palmately lobed
Texture : Very coarse
Flower Characteristics : Insignificant

Environmental Problems : None

Prunus angustifolia

Common Name(s) : Chickasaw Plum
Origin : Southeastern United States
Growth Rate : Medium
Salt Tolerance : Low
Soil Requirements : Wide
Plant Type : Deciduous shrub
Foliage Color : Green
Flowering Season : Spring
Flower Color : White
Propagation : Seeds; cuttings
Human Hazards : Spiny; poisonous
Common Uses : Edible fruit; shrub
Major Problems : Tent caterpillars
Additional Notes : Root suckers can be a problem on this plant; seeds and leaves poisonous.

Family : Rosaceae   **Zone** : 6-9

Typical Height : 15 Ft.
Drought Tolerance : High
Nutritional Requirements : Medium
Light Requirements : High
Leaf Type : Simple
Texture : Medium
Flower Characteristics : Showy; fragrant

Environmental Problems : Invasive

Prunus caroliniana *(Photograph p. 167)*

Common Name(s) : Cherry Laurel
Origin : Southeastern United States
Growth Rate : Medium
Salt Tolerance : Low
Soil Requirements : Acid
Plant Type : Evergreen tree
Foliage Color : Green; variegated
Flowering Season : Spring
Flower Color : White
Propagation : Seeds; cuttings
Human Hazards : Poisonous
Common Uses : Small tree; hedges
Major Problems : Mites; leaf spot; stem canker; fireblight
Additional Notes : Foliage is poisonous to livestock.
Cultivars
'VARIEGATA' has variegated foliage; 'COMPACTA' is more compact and is often used in hedges.

Family : Rosaceae   **Zone** : 8-9

Typical Height : 25 Ft.
Drought Tolerance : Medium
Nutritional Requirements : Medium
Light Requirements : Medium; high
Leaf Type : Simple
Texture : Medium
Flower Characteristics : Insignificant; fragrant

Environmental Problems : None

Prunus cerasifera

Common Name(s) : Purpleleaf Plum; Myrobalan Plum
Origin : Western Asia
Growth Rate : Fast
Salt Tolerance : Low
Soil Requirements : Wide
Plant Type : Deciduous shrub
Foliage Color : Purple
Flowering Season : Spring
Flower Color : White
Propagation : Cuttings; grafting
Human Hazards : Poisonous
Common Uses : Shrub
Major Problems : Scales; borers; aphids; leafspots
Additional Notes : Rather short-lived; poisonous leaves and seeds.
Cultivars
'ATROPURPUREA' has large leaves, pink flowers, & upright form; 'HOLLYWOOD' has green new leaves that turn purple; 'THUNDERCLOUD' retains purple color longer in season; 'NEWPORTII' has purple-red foliage and single pink flowers; 'KRAUTER VESUVIUS' has very dark and persistent red foliage and a small, rounded form.

Family : Rosaceae   **Zone** : 3-9

Typical Height : 20 Ft.
Drought Tolerance : Medium
Nutritional Requirements : Medium
Light Requirements : High
Leaf Type : Simple
Texture : Medium
Flower Characteristics : Showy; fragrant

Environmental Problems : None

Prunus myrtifolia

Common Name(s) : West Indian Cherry
Origin : South Florida and West Indies
Growth Rate : Medium
Salt Tolerance : Low
Soil Requirements : Wide
Plant Type : Evergreen tree
Foliage Color : Green
Flowering Season : Spring
Flower Color : White
Propagation : Seeds
Human Hazards : Poisonous
Common Uses : Small tree; shade tree
Major Problems : None
Additional Notes : A tropical substitute for P. caroliniana . Poisonous seeds and leaves.

Family : Rosaceae   **Zone** : 10B-11

Typical Height : 25 Ft.
Drought Tolerance : Medium
Nutritional Requirements : Medium
Light Requirements : High
Leaf Type : Simple
Texture : Medium
Flower Characteristics : Insignificant

Environmental Problems : None

Prunus persica

Common Name(s) : Peach
Origin : China
Growth Rate : Medium
Salt Tolerance : Low
Soil Requirements : Wide
Plant Type : Deciduous tree
Foliage Color : Green
Flowering Season : Spring
Flower Color : Pink
Propagation : Grafting; seeds
Human Hazards : Poisonous
Common Uses : Edible fruit; small flowering tree
Major Problems : Root rot; borers; scales
Additional Notes : Use only cultivars selected for Florida use; poisonous leaves and seeds.
Cultivars
Popular cultivars in Florida include: Floridaprince, Floridagold, and Floridaking.

Family : Rosaceae   **Zone** : 5-9

Typical Height : 12 Ft.
Drought Tolerance : Low
Nutritional Requirements : Medium
Light Requirements : High
Leaf Type : Simple
Texture : Medium
Flower Characteristics : Showy

Environmental Problems : None

Prunus umbellata

Common Name(s) : Flatwoods Plum
Origin : Florida
Growth Rate : Fast
Salt Tolerance : Low
Soil Requirements : Wide
Plant Type : Deciduous tree
Foliage Color : Green
Flowering Season : Spring
Flower Color : White
Propagation : Seeds; cuttings
Human Hazards : Poisonous
Common Uses : Edible fruit; small flowering tree; flowering shrub
Major Problems : Tent caterpillars
Additional Notes : Early spring color; fruit quality variable.

Family : Rosaceae   **Zone** : 9-10A

Typical Height : 15 Ft.
Drought Tolerance : Medium
Nutritional Requirements : Medium
Light Requirements : Medium
Leaf Type : Simple
Texture : Medium
Flower Characteristics : Showy

Environmental Problems : None

Pseuderanthemum atropurpureum

Common Name(s) : Purple False Eranthemum; Cafe Con Leche
Origin : Polynesia
Growth Rate : Fast
Salt Tolerance : Medium
Soil Requirements : Wide
Plant Type : Evergreen shrub
Foliage Color : Purple
Flowering Season : Spring; summer; fall
Flower Color : White-purple
Propagation : Cuttings
Human Hazards : None
Common Uses : Specimen plant; flowering shrub
Major Problems : Nematodes; mites; thrips; scales
Additional Notes : Prune hard to maintain shape.

Family : Acanthaceae   **Zone** : 10A-11

Typical Height : 5 Ft.
Drought Tolerance : Low
Nutritional Requirements : Medium
Light Requirements : Medium; low
Leaf Type : Simple
Texture : Medium
Flower Characteristics : Showy

Environmental Problems : None

Pseuderanthemum reticulatum *(Photo. p. 185)*

Common Name(s) : Reticulated Pseuderanthemum
Origin : Polynesia
Growth Rate : Fast
Salt Tolerance : Low
Soil Requirements : Wide
Plant Type : Evergreen shrub
Foliage Color : Green & yellow
Flowering Season : Spring
Flower Color : Purple & white
Propagation : Cuttings
Human Hazards : None
Common Uses : Specimen plant; flowering shrub
Major Problems : Nematodes; mites; thrips; scales
Additional Notes : Young foliage has yellow veins.

Family : Acanthaceae   **Zone** : 10B-11

Typical Height : 3 Ft.
Drought Tolerance : Low
Nutritional Requirements : Medium
Light Requirements : Medium; low
Leaf Type : Simple
Texture : Medium
Flower Characteristics : Showy

Environmental Problems : None

Pseudobombax ellipticum *(Photograph p. 168)*
Common Name(s) : Shavingbrush Tree
Origin : Tropical America and West Indies
Growth Rate : Fast
Salt Tolerance : Medium
Soil Requirements : Wide
Plant Type : Deciduous tree
Foliage Color : Green
Flowering Season : Winter; spring
Flower Color : Red
Propagation : Air layers; large cuttings
Human Hazards : None
Common Uses : Flowering tree
Major Problems : None
Additional Notes : Damaged by hard frosts. Very attractive when in flower.

Family : Bombacaceae   Zone : 10B-11

Typical Height : 25 Ft.
Drought Tolerance : Medium
Nutritional Requirements : Medium
Light Requirements : High
Leaf Type : Palmately compound
Texture : Medium
Flower Characteristics : Showy

Environmental Problems : None

Pseudophoenix sargentii *(Photograph p. 207)*
Common Name(s) : Buccaneer Palm; Cherry Palm
Origin : Caribbean Region
Growth Rate : Slow
Salt Tolerance : High
Soil Requirements : Wide
Plant Type : Palm
Foliage Color : Green
Flowering Season : Summer
Flower Color : Yellow
Propagation : Seeds
Human Hazards : None
Common Uses : Small tree; palm
Major Problems : None
Additional Notes : A very slow growing small native palm.

Family : Palmae   Zone : 10B-11

Typical Height : 10 Ft.
Drought Tolerance : High
Nutritional Requirements : Medium
Light Requirements : Medium; high
Leaf Type : Pinnately compound
Texture : Medium
Flower Characteristics : Insignificant

Environmental Problems : None

Pseudosasa japonica
Common Name(s) : Arrow Bamboo; Metake Bamboo
Origin : Japan
Growth Rate : Fast
Salt Tolerance : Medium
Soil Requirements : Wide
Plant Type : Evergreen shrub
Foliage Color : Green
Flowering Season : n/a
Flower Color : n/a
Propagation : Division
Human Hazards : None
Common Uses : Shrub
Major Problems : None
Additional Notes : A small hardy running bamboo.

Family : Gramineae   Zone : 8-10A

Typical Height : 15 Ft.
Drought Tolerance : Medium
Nutritional Requirements : Medium
Light Requirements : Medium; high
Leaf Type : Simple; linear
Texture : Medium
Flower Characteristics : n/a

Environmental Problems : Invasive

Psidium guajava *(Photograph p. 168)*
Common Name(s) : Guava
Origin : Mexico; Central America
Growth Rate : Medium
Salt Tolerance : Low
Soil Requirements : Wide
Plant Type : Evergreen tree
Foliage Color : Green
Flowering Season : Spring
Flower Color : White
Propagation : Seeds; air layers
Human Hazards : None
Common Uses : Tree; edible fruit
Major Problems : Fruitflies; scales; leafspots
Additional Notes : Fruit can be messy.

Family : Myrtaceae   Zone : 10A-11

Typical Height : 25 Ft.
Drought Tolerance : High
Nutritional Requirements : Medium
Light Requirements : High
Leaf Type : Simple
Texture : Medium
Flower Characteristics : Showy

Environmental Problems : Weedy; messy

Psidium littorale *(Photograph p. 168)*

Common Name(s) : Cattley Guava; Strawberry Guava
Origin : Brazil
Growth Rate : Medium
Salt Tolerance : Low
Soil Requirements : Wide
Plant Type : Evergreen tree
Foliage Color : Green
Flowering Season : Spring
Flower Color : White
Propagation : Seeds; air layers
Human Hazards : None
Common Uses : Edible fruit; small tree
Major Problems : Fruitflies
Additional Notes : Messy edible fruit. Interesting bark texture.
Cultivars
Var. littorale has yellow fruits; var. longipes has purple-red fruits.

Family : Myrtaceae   **Zone** : 10A-11

Typical Height : 20 Ft.
Drought Tolerance : High
Nutritional Requirements : Medium
Light Requirements : Medium; high
Leaf Type : Simple
Texture : Medium
Flower Characteristics : Insignificant; fragrant

Environmental Problems : Messy

Psilotum nudum

Common Name(s) : Whisk Fern
Origin : Southeastern United States & Tropics
Growth Rate : Medium
Salt Tolerance : Low
Soil Requirements : Wide
Plant Type : Herbaceous perennial
Foliage Color : Green
Flowering Season : n/a
Flower Color : n/a
Propagation : Division; spores
Human Hazards : None
Common Uses : Beds; specimen plant; groundcover
Major Problems : None
Additional Notes : Primitive fern-like plant; can be grown as epiphyte.

Family : Psilotaceae   **Zone** : 8-11

Typical Height : 1.5 Ft.
Drought Tolerance : Medium
Nutritional Requirements : Medium
Light Requirements : Medium
Leaf Type : None
Texture : Fine
Flower Characteristics : n/a

Environmental Problems : Weedy

Psychotria nervosa

Common Name(s) : Wild Coffee
Origin : South Florida and West Indies
Growth Rate : Fast
Salt Tolerance : Medium
Soil Requirements : Wide
Plant Type : Evergreen shrub
Foliage Color : Green
Flowering Season : Spring; summer
Flower Color : White
Propagation : Seeds
Human Hazards : None
Common Uses : Shrub
Major Problems : None
Additional Notes : Red berries attract wildlife. Medium texture understory plant.
Cultivars
 P. ligustrifolia is similar, but lacks strong venation.

Family : Rubiaceae   **Zone** : 10B-11

Typical Height : 5 Ft.
Drought Tolerance : Medium
Nutritional Requirements : Low
Light Requirements : Medium; low
Leaf Type : Simple
Texture : Medium
Flower Characteristics : Insignificant

Environmental Problems : None

Ptelea trifoliata

Common Name(s) : Hoptree
Origin : Eastern North America
Growth Rate : Slow
Salt Tolerance : Low
Soil Requirements : Wide
Plant Type : Deciduous tree or shrub
Foliage Color : Green
Flowering Season : Spring
Flower Color : Green
Propagation : Seeds
Human Hazards : None
Common Uses : Small tree; shrub
Major Problems : Leafspots
Additional Notes : Flowers foul smelling; shrubby; can be used as informal hedge.

Family : Rutaceae   **Zone** : 4-9

Typical Height : 20 Ft.
Drought Tolerance : Medium
Nutritional Requirements : Medium
Light Requirements : Medium
Leaf Type : Trifoliate
Texture : Medium
Flower Characteristics : Insignificant

Environmental Problems : None

Ptychosperma elegans *(Photograph p. 207)*

Common Name(s) : Solitaire Palm
Origin : Australia
Growth Rate : Medium
Salt Tolerance : Low
Soil Requirements : Wide
Plant Type : Palm
Foliage Color : Green
Flowering Season : Summer
Flower Color : White
Propagation : Seeds
Human Hazards : None
Common Uses : Tree; palm
Major Problems : None
Additional Notes : A slender, lethal yellowing-resistant palm.

Family : Palmae   **Zone** : 10B-11

Typical Height : 20 Ft.
Drought Tolerance : High
Nutritional Requirements : Medium
Light Requirements : Medium; high
Leaf Type : Pinnately compound
Texture : Medium
Flower Characteristics : Insignificant

Environmental Problems : None

Ptychosperma macarthurii

Common Name(s) : Macarthur Palm
Origin : New Guinea
Growth Rate : Medium
Salt Tolerance : Low
Soil Requirements : Wide
Plant Type : Palm
Foliage Color : Green
Flowering Season : Summer; fall
Flower Color : White
Propagation : Seeds
Human Hazards : None
Common Uses : Multi-trunked tree; palm
Major Problems : Sooty mold
Additional Notes : A slender, multiple trunked palm. Lethal yellowing resistant.

Family : Palmae   **Zone** : 10B-11

Typical Height : 25 Ft.
Drought Tolerance : High
Nutritional Requirements : Medium
Light Requirements : Medium; high
Leaf Type : Pinnately compound
Texture : Medium
Flower Characteristics : Insignificant

Environmental Problems : None

Punica granatum

Common Name(s) : Pomegranate
Origin : Southern Asia
Growth Rate : Medium
Salt Tolerance : Low
Soil Requirements : Wide
Plant Type : Deciduous tree
Foliage Color : Green
Flowering Season : Spring; summer
Flower Color : Orange; red; white
Propagation : Cuttings; air layers
Human Hazards : None
Common Uses : Flowering tree; edible fruit; tree
Major Problems : Root rots
Additional Notes : Not well-adapted for Florida.
Cultivars
'NANA' is a dwarf variety; 'FLORE PLENO' is a double red flowered variety; 'ALBA PLENA' has double white flowers.

Family : Punicaceae   **Zone** : 8-10B

Typical Height : 15 Ft.
Drought Tolerance : High
Nutritional Requirements : Medium
Light Requirements : High
Leaf Type : Simple
Texture : Medium
Flower Characteristics : Showy

Environmental Problems : None

Pyracantha coccinea *(Photograph p. 185)*

Common Name(s) : Red Firethorn
Origin : Southern Europe and Western Asia
Growth Rate : Medium
Salt Tolerance : Medium
Soil Requirements : Wide
Plant Type : Evergreen shrub
Foliage Color : Green
Flowering Season : Spring; summer
Flower Color : White
Propagation : Cuttings
Human Hazards : Spiny
Common Uses : Shrub; hedge; topiary
Major Problems : Fireblight; whiteflies; aphids; mites; sooty mold
Additional Notes : Bright red attractive fruit; many cultivars.
Cultivars
'LALANDEI' is a hardy, red-fruited variety.

Family : Rosaceae   **Zone** : 7-10A

Typical Height : 10 Ft.
Drought Tolerance : Medium
Nutritional Requirements : Medium
Light Requirements : High
Leaf Type : Simple
Texture : Fine
Flower Characteristics : Showy

Environmental Problems : None

Pyracantha koidzumii

Common Name(s) : Dwarf Firethorn
Origin : Japan
Growth Rate : Medium
Salt Tolerance : Medium
Soil Requirements : Wide
Plant Type : Evergreen shrub
Foliage Color : Green; variegated
Flowering Season : Spring; summer
Flower Color : White
Propagation : Cuttings
Human Hazards : Spiny
Common Uses : Shrub; hedge; espalier
Major Problems : Whiteflies; aphids; mites
Additional Notes : Bright red attractive fruit; good for espalier; least hardy of firethorns
Cultivars
'VICTORY' has very dark red berries; 'LOW DENSE' is a compact variety.

Family : Rosaceae   **Zone** : 8-10A

Typical Height : 4 Ft.
Drought Tolerance : Medium
Nutritional Requirements : Medium
Light Requirements : High
Leaf Type : Simple
Texture : Fine
Flower Characteristics : Showy

Environmental Problems : None

Pyrostegia venusta *(Photograph p. 212)*

Common Name(s) : Flame Vine
Origin : Brazil and Paraguay
Growth Rate : Fast
Salt Tolerance : Low
Soil Requirements : Wide
Plant Type : Evergreen vine
Foliage Color : Green
Flowering Season : Winter; spring
Flower Color : Orange
Propagation : Cuttings
Human Hazards : None
Common Uses : Flowering vine
Major Problems : None
Additional Notes : Spectacular flowers in late winter. Prune severely after flowering.

Family : Bignoniaceae   **Zone** : 10B-11

Typical Height : Not applicable
Drought Tolerance : High
Nutritional Requirements : Medium
Light Requirements : Medium; high
Leaf Type : Pinnately compound
Texture : Medium
Flower Characteristics : Showy

Environmental Problems : None

Pyrus calleryana

Common Name(s) : Callery Pear
Origin : China
Growth Rate : Medium
Salt Tolerance : Low
Soil Requirements : Wide
Plant Type : Deciduous tree
Foliage Color : Green
Flowering Season : Spring
Flower Color : White
Propagation : Grafting
Human Hazards : None
Common Uses : Small tree
Major Problems : Fireblight (slightly susceptible)
Additional Notes : Red fall color.
Cultivars
'BRADFORD' is a popular variety with bright red fall color; 'ARISTOCRAT' has a more horizontal branching habit and good purple-red fall color.

Family : Rosaceae   **Zone** : 4-9

Typical Height : 25 Ft.
Drought Tolerance : Medium
Nutritional Requirements : Medium
Light Requirements : High
Leaf Type : Simple
Texture : Medium
Flower Characteristics : Showy

Environmental Problems : None

Quercus alba

Common Name(s) : White Oak
Origin : Eastern United States
Growth Rate : Slow
Salt Tolerance : High
Soil Requirements : Acid
Plant Type : Deciduous tree
Foliage Color : Green
Flowering Season : Spring
Flower Color : Brown
Propagation : Seeds
Human Hazards : None
Common Uses : Shade tree
Major Problems : Root rots; galls; lacebugs
Additional Notes : Has brown to red fall color.

Family : Fagaceae   **Zone** : 4-9

Typical Height : 70 Ft.
Drought Tolerance : High
Nutritional Requirements : Medium
Light Requirements : High
Leaf Type : Simple; pinnately lobed
Texture : Medium
Flower Characteristics : Insignificant

Environmental Problems : None

Quercus austrina

Common Name(s) : Bluff Oak
Origin : Southeastern United States
Growth Rate : Medium
Salt Tolerance : Low
Soil Requirements : Wide
Plant Type : Deciduous tree
Foliage Color : Green
Flowering Season : Spring
Flower Color : Green
Propagation : Seeds
Human Hazards : None
Common Uses : Shade tree
Major Problems : None
Additional Notes : A little-used native oak with attractive bark

Family : Fagaceae   Zone : 7-9

Typical Height : 30 Ft.
Drought Tolerance : Medium
Nutritional Requirements : Medium
Light Requirements : High
Leaf Type : Simple; pinnately lobed
Texture : Medium
Flower Characteristics : Insignificant

Environmental Problems : None

Quercus chapmanii

Common Name(s) : Chapman Oak
Origin : Southeastern United States
Growth Rate : Slow
Salt Tolerance : High
Soil Requirements : Wide
Plant Type : Deciduous tree
Foliage Color : Green
Flowering Season : Spring
Flower Color : Green
Propagation : Seeds
Human Hazards : None
Common Uses : Small tree
Major Problems : None
Additional Notes : A good native oak for dry sandy sites.

Family : Fagaceae   Zone : 8-10A

Typical Height : 35 Ft.
Drought Tolerance : High
Nutritional Requirements : Low
Light Requirements : High
Leaf Type : Simple
Texture : Medium
Flower Characteristics : Insignificant

Environmental Problems : None

Quercus falcata

Common Name(s) : Southern Red Oak
Origin : Southeastern United States
Growth Rate : Medium
Salt Tolerance : High
Soil Requirements : Wide
Plant Type : Deciduous tree
Foliage Color : Green
Flowering Season : Spring
Flower Color : Yellow
Propagation : Seeds
Human Hazards : None
Common Uses : Shade tree
Major Problems : Root rots
Additional Notes : Dull orange fall color.

Family : Fagaceae   Zone : 7-9

Typical Height : 70 Ft.
Drought Tolerance : High
Nutritional Requirements : Medium
Light Requirements : High
Leaf Type : Simple; pinnately lobed
Texture : Medium
Flower Characteristics : Insignificant

Environmental Problems : None

Quercus incana

Common Name(s) : Bluejack Oak; Turkey Oak
Origin : Southeastern United States
Growth Rate : Slow
Salt Tolerance : Low
Soil Requirements : Wide
Plant Type : Deciduous tree
Foliage Color : Green
Flowering Season : Spring
Flower Color : Green
Propagation : Seeds
Human Hazards : None
Common Uses : Small tree
Major Problems : None
Additional Notes : Best for central and north Florida.

Family : Fagaceae   Zone : 8-10A

Typical Height : 25 Ft.
Drought Tolerance : High
Nutritional Requirements : Low
Light Requirements : High
Leaf Type : Simple
Texture : Medium
Flower Characteristics : Insignificant

Environmental Problems : None

Quercus laevis *(Photograph p. 168)*

Common Name(s) : Turkey Oak
Origin : Southeastern United States
Growth Rate : Slow
Salt Tolerance : Low
Soil Requirements : Wide
Plant Type : Deciduous tree
Foliage Color : Green
Flowering Season : Spring
Flower Color : Green
Propagation : Seeds
Human Hazards : None
Common Uses : Shade tree
Major Problems : Root rots

Family : Fagaceae   Zone : 8-9

Typical Height : 45 Ft.
Drought Tolerance : High
Nutritional Requirements : Low
Light Requirements : High
Leaf Type : Simple
Texture : Medium
Flower Characteristics : Insignificant

Environmental Problems : None

Additional Notes : Excellent for dry, sandy sites; red fall color; short-lived.

Quercus laurifolia

Common Name(s) : Laurel Oak
Origin : Southeastern United States
Growth Rate : Fast
Salt Tolerance : Low
Soil Requirements : Wide
Plant Type : Evergreen tree
Foliage Color : Green
Flowering Season : Spring
Flower Color : Green
Propagation : Seeds
Human Hazards : None
Common Uses : Shade tree
Major Problems : Root rots

Family : Fagaceae   Zone : 8-10B

Typical Height : 60 Ft.
Drought Tolerance : High
Nutritional Requirements : Low
Light Requirements : High
Leaf Type : Simple
Texture : Medium
Flower Characteristics : Insignificant

Environmental Problems : None

Additional Notes : A fast growing, but comparatively short-lived oak tree.

Quercus myrtifolia

Common Name(s) : Myrtle Oak
Origin : Southeastern United States
Growth Rate : Slow
Salt Tolerance : High
Soil Requirements : Wide
Plant Type : Evergreen tree
Foliage Color : Green
Flowering Season : Spring
Flower Color : Green
Propagation : Seeds
Human Hazards : None
Common Uses : Small tree
Major Problems : None

Family : Fagaceae   Zone : 8-10A

Typical Height : 20 Ft.
Drought Tolerance : High
Nutritional Requirements : Low
Light Requirements : High
Leaf Type : Simple
Texture : Medium
Flower Characteristics : Insignificant

Environmental Problems : None

Additional Notes : A small native oak good for dry, sandy sites.

Quercus nigra

Common Name(s) : Water Oak
Origin : Southeastern United States
Growth Rate : Fast
Salt Tolerance : Medium
Soil Requirements : Wide
Plant Type : Evergreen tree
Foliage Color : Green
Flowering Season : Spring
Flower Color : Green
Propagation : Seeds
Human Hazards : None
Common Uses : Shade tree
Major Problems : Borers

Family : Fagaceae   Zone : 6-9

Typical Height : 80 Ft.
Drought Tolerance : Medium
Nutritional Requirements : Low
Light Requirements : High
Leaf Type : Simple
Texture : Medium
Flower Characteristics : Insignificant

Environmental Problems : None

Additional Notes : Prefers moist, sandy sites; rather short-lived.

Quercus palustris

Common Name(s) : Pin Oak
Origin : Eastern United States
Growth Rate : Medium
Salt Tolerance : Low
Soil Requirements : Acid
Plant Type : Deciduous tree
Foliage Color : Green
Flowering Season : Spring
Flower Color : Green
Propagation : Seeds; grafting
Human Hazards : None
Common Uses : Shade tree
Major Problems : Fe deficiency; pin oak sawfly
Additional Notes : Has a pyramidal shape.

Family : Fagaceae   Zone : 4-9

Typical Height : 60 Ft.
Drought Tolerance : High
Nutritional Requirements : High
Light Requirements : High
Leaf Type : Simple; pinnately lobed
Texture : Medium
Flower Characteristics : Insignificant

Environmental Problems : None

Quercus phellos

Common Name(s) : Willow Oak
Origin : Eastern United States
Growth Rate : Medium
Salt Tolerance : Low
Soil Requirements : Acid
Plant Type : Deciduous tree
Foliage Color : Green
Flowering Season : Spring
Flower Color : Brown
Propagation : Seeds
Human Hazards : None
Common Uses : Shade tree
Major Problems : None
Additional Notes : Has yellow to red fall color.

Family : Fagaceae   Zone : 6-9

Typical Height : 60 Ft.
Drought Tolerance : High
Nutritional Requirements : Medium
Light Requirements : High
Leaf Type : Simple; linear
Texture : Medium
Flower Characteristics : Insignificant

Environmental Problems : None

Quercus shumardii

Common Name(s) : Shumard Red Oak
Origin : Southeastern United States
Growth Rate : Medium
Salt Tolerance : Low
Soil Requirements : Wide
Plant Type : Deciduous tree
Foliage Color : Green
Flowering Season : Spring
Flower Color : Green
Propagation : Seeds;cuttings
Human Hazards : None
Common Uses : Shade tree
Major Problems : Mites; root rots
Additional Notes : Excellent red fall color.

Family : Fagaceae   Zone : 5-10A

Typical Height : 80 Ft.
Drought Tolerance : High
Nutritional Requirements : Low
Light Requirements : High
Leaf Type : Simple; pinnately lobed
Texture : Medium
Flower Characteristics : Insignificant

Environmental Problems : None

Quercus velutina

Common Name(s) : Black Oak
Origin : Eastern United States
Growth Rate : Medium
Salt Tolerance : Low
Soil Requirements : Wide
Plant Type : Deciduous tree
Foliage Color : Green
Flowering Season : Spring
Flower Color : Green
Propagation : Seeds
Human Hazards : None
Common Uses : Shade tree
Major Problems : None

Family : Fagaceae   Zone : 4-9

Typical Height : 80 Ft.
Drought Tolerance : High
Nutritional Requirements : Medium
Light Requirements : High
Leaf Type : Simple; pinnately lobed
Texture : Coarse
Flower Characteristics : Insignificant

Environmental Problems : None

Additional Notes : Has red fall color; difficult to transplant when large due to tap root.

Quercus virginiana *(Photograph p. 168)*

Common Name(s) : Live Oak
Origin : Southeastern United States
Growth Rate : Medium
Salt Tolerance : High
Soil Requirements : Wide
Plant Type : Evergreen tree
Foliage Color : Green
Flowering Season : Spring
Flower Color : Green
Propagation : Seeds; grafting
Human Hazards : None
Common Uses : Shade tree
Major Problems : Galls; root rot; lacebugs
Additional Notes : A wind resistant, long-lived oak.
Cultivars
Var. geminata is smaller and has cupped leaves.

Family : Fagaceae   **Zone** : 7-10B

Typical Height : 50 Ft.
Drought Tolerance : High
Nutritional Requirements : Low
Light Requirements : High
Leaf Type : Simple
Texture : Medium
Flower Characteristics : Insignificant

Environmental Problems : None

Quisqualis indica

Common Name(s) : Rangoon Creeper
Origin : Southern Asia and East Indies
Growth Rate : Fast
Salt Tolerance : Low
Soil Requirements : Wide
Plant Type : Evergreen vine
Foliage Color : Green
Flowering Season : Summer; fall
Flower Color : White; red; pink
Propagation : Cuttings; suckers
Human Hazards : Poisonous; spiny
Common Uses : Flowering vine
Major Problems : Scales
Additional Notes : Spiny vine that requires regular pruning to keep in bounds.

Family : Combretaceae   **Zone** : 10B-11

Typical Height : Not applicable
Drought Tolerance : High
Nutritional Requirements : Low
Light Requirements : Medium; high
Leaf Type : Simple
Texture : Medium
Flower Characteristics : Showy; fragrant

Environmental Problems : Invasive

Radermachera sinica

Common Name(s) : China Doll
Origin : China
Growth Rate : Fast
Salt Tolerance : Low
Soil Requirements : Acid
Plant Type : Evergreen tree
Foliage Color : Green
Flowering Season : Summer
Flower Color : Yellow
Propagation : Seeds; cuttings
Human Hazards : None
Common Uses : Foliage plant; small tree
Major Problems : Mites; aphids; scale; nematodes
Additional Notes : Often used as a foliage plant, but requires growth retardants.

Family : Bignoniaceae   **Zone** : 10B-11

Typical Height : 15 Ft.
Drought Tolerance : Low
Nutritional Requirements : High
Light Requirements : Medium
Leaf Type : Bipinnately compound
Texture : Medium
Flower Characteristics : Showy

Environmental Problems : None

Randia aculeata

Common Name(s) : White Indigoberry
Origin : Caribbean Region
Growth Rate : Slow
Salt Tolerance : High
Soil Requirements : Wide
Plant Type : Evergreen shrub or tree
Foliage Color : Green
Flowering Season : Year-round
Flower Color : White
Propagation : Seeds
Human Hazards : Spiny
Common Uses : Shrub; small tree
Major Problems : Witch's broom
Additional Notes : This Florida native has spines and white berries on female plants.

Family : Rubiaceae   **Zone** : 10A-11

Typical Height : 8 Ft.
Drought Tolerance : High
Nutritional Requirements : Low
Light Requirements : High
Leaf Type : Simple
Texture : Medium
Flower Characteristics : Insignificant; fragrant

Environmental Problems : None

Ranunculus spp.

Common Name(s) : Buttercup
Origin : Worldwide
Growth Rate : Medium
Salt Tolerance : Low
Soil Requirements : Acid
Plant Type : Herbaceous perennial
Foliage Color : Green
Flowering Season : Spring
Flower Color : Yellow; red; orange; white; pink
Propagation : Division; seeds
Human Hazards : Irritant; poisonous
Common Uses : Beds; cut flowers
Major Problems : Tuber rot

Family : Ranunculaceae   **Zone** : 7-9

Typical Height : .8 Ft.
Drought Tolerance : Low
Nutritional Requirements : High
Light Requirements : High
Leaf Type : Simple
Texture : Fine
Flower Characteristics : Showy

Environmental Problems : None

Additional Notes : Difficult to grow; soak tubers overnight before planting; short-lived.

Raphiolepis indica

Common Name(s) : Indian Hawthorn
Origin : Southern China
Growth Rate : Slow
Salt Tolerance : Medium
Soil Requirements : Wide
Plant Type : Evergreen shrub
Foliage Color : Green
Flowering Season : Spring
Flower Color : Pink
Propagation : Seeds; cuttings
Human Hazards : None
Common Uses : Flowering shrub; hedge
Major Problems : Fireblight; leafspot

Family : Rosaceae   **Zone** : 8-11

Typical Height : 4 Ft.
Drought Tolerance : Medium
Nutritional Requirements : Medium
Light Requirements : Medium
Leaf Type : Simple
Texture : Medium
Flower Characteristics : Showy

Environmental Problems : None

Additional Notes : Best in part shade.
Cultivars
'ALBA' has white flowers; 'MAJESTIC BEAUTY' has pink flowers and is resistant to black leafspot;
'ROSEA' has darker pink flowers.

Raphiolepis umbellata

Common Name(s) : Yedda Hawthorn
Origin : Japan
Growth Rate : Slow
Salt Tolerance : Medium
Soil Requirements : Wide
Plant Type : Evergreen shrub
Foliage Color : Green
Flowering Season : Spring
Flower Color : White
Propagation : Seeds; cuttings
Human Hazards : None
Common Uses : Flowering shrub; hedge
Major Problems : Fireblight; leafspot

Family : Rosaceae   **Zone** : 8-10B

Typical Height : 4 Ft.
Drought Tolerance : Medium
Nutritional Requirements : Medium
Light Requirements : Medium
Leaf Type : Simple
Texture : Medium
Flower Characteristics : Showy; fragrant

Environmental Problems : None

Ravenala madagascariensis *(Photograph p. 169)*

Common Name(s) : Traveler's Tree
Origin : Madagascar
Growth Rate : Medium
Salt Tolerance : Low
Soil Requirements : Wide
Plant Type : Evergreen tree
Foliage Color : Green
Flowering Season : Spring; summer; fall
Flower Color : White
Propagation : Seeds; suckers
Human Hazards : None
Common Uses : Tree
Major Problems : Cercospora leafspot

Family : Strelitziaceae   **Zone** : 10A-11

Typical Height : 25 Ft.
Drought Tolerance : Medium
Nutritional Requirements : Medium
Light Requirements : Medium; high
Leaf Type : Simple
Texture : Very coarse
Flower Characteristics : Showy

Environmental Problems : None

Additional Notes : Suckers from the base. Damaged by hard freezes. Leaves in one plane.

Ravenea rivularis *(Photograph p. 207)*

Common Name(s) : Majesty Palm
Origin : Madagascar
Growth Rate : Fast
Salt Tolerance : Medium
Soil Requirements : Wide
Plant Type : Palm
Foliage Color : Green
Flowering Season : Spring
Flower Color : White
Propagation : Seeds
Human Hazards : None
Common Uses : Foliage plant; tree; palm
Major Problems : None
Additional Notes : A fast-growing palm that somewhat resembles a coconut palm.

Family : Palmae   **Zone** : 10A-11

Typical Height : 50 Ft.
Drought Tolerance : High
Nutritional Requirements : Medium
Light Requirements : Medium; high
Leaf Type : Pinnately compound
Texture : Medium
Flower Characteristics : Insignificant

Environmental Problems : None

Reynosia septentrionalis

Common Name(s) : Darling Plum
Origin : South Florida and Bahamas
Growth Rate : Medium
Salt Tolerance : High
Soil Requirements : Wide
Plant Type : Evergreen tree
Foliage Color : Green
Flowering Season : Spring; summer
Flower Color : Green-yellow
Propagation : Seeds
Human Hazards : None
Common Uses : Small tree; edible fruit
Major Problems : None
Additional Notes : Small black fruits are edible.

Family : Rhamnaceae   **Zone** : 10B-11

Typical Height : 25 Ft.
Drought Tolerance : High
Nutritional Requirements : Low
Light Requirements : High
Leaf Type : Simple
Texture : Medium
Flower Characteristics : Insignificant

Environmental Problems : None

Rhabdadenia biflora

Common Name(s) : Rubber Vine
Origin : Tropical America
Growth Rate : Medium
Salt Tolerance : High
Soil Requirements : Wide
Plant Type : Evergreen vine
Foliage Color : Green
Flowering Season : Year-round
Flower Color : White
Propagation : Cuttings
Human Hazards : Irritant
Common Uses : Flowering vine
Major Problems : None
Additional Notes : A showy-flowered, native vine useful near the coast.

Family : Apocynaceae   **Zone** : 10B-11

Typical Height : Not applicable
Drought Tolerance : Medium
Nutritional Requirements : Medium
Light Requirements : Medium; high
Leaf Type : Simple
Texture : Medium
Flower Characteristics : Showy

Environmental Problems : None

Rhapidophyllum hystrix *(Photograph p. 207)*

Common Name(s) : Needle Palm
Origin : Southeastern United States
Growth Rate : Slow
Salt Tolerance : Medium
Soil Requirements : Wide
Plant Type : Palm
Foliage Color : Green
Flowering Season : Spring
Flower Color : Yellow
Propagation : Seeds; suckers
Human Hazards : Spiny
Common Uses : Foliage plant; shrub; palm
Major Problems : None
Additional Notes : This attractive native species has long needle-like spines on the trunk.

Family : Palmae   **Zone** : 8-10B

Typical Height : 5 Ft.
Drought Tolerance : High
Nutritional Requirements : Medium
Light Requirements : Medium
Leaf Type : Simple; palmately lobed
Texture : Coarse
Flower Characteristics : Insignificant

Environmental Problems : None

Rhapis excelsa *(Photograph p. 207)*

Common Name(s) : Lady Palm
Origin : China and Japan
Growth Rate : Medium
Salt Tolerance : Medium
Soil Requirements : Wide
Plant Type : Palm
Foliage Color : Green
Flowering Season : Summer
Flower Color : White
Propagation : Seeds; division
Human Hazards : None
Common Uses : Shrub; hedge; foliage plant; palm
Major Problems : Fe deficiency; scales; mealybugs
Additional Notes : Leaves of this clumping palm yellow in full sun. Excellent indoor palm.
Cultivars
'VARIEGATA' is variegated.

Family : Palmae   Zone : 10A-11

Typical Height : 7 Ft.
Drought Tolerance : Medium
Nutritional Requirements : Medium
Light Requirements : Medium; low
Leaf Type : Simple; palmately lobed
Texture : Coarse
Flower Characteristics : Insignificant

Environmental Problems : None

Rhapis humilis *(Photograph p. 207)*

Common Name(s) : Slender Lady Palm
Origin : Southern China
Growth Rate : Slow
Salt Tolerance : Medium
Soil Requirements : Wide
Plant Type : Palm
Foliage Color : Green
Flowering Season : Summer
Flower Color : White
Propagation : Seeds; division
Human Hazards : None
Common Uses : Shrub; hedge; foliage plant; palm
Major Problems : Fe deficiency; scales; mealybugs
Additional Notes : Similar to R. excelsa , but with more slender stems and more leaflets.

Family : Palmae   Zone : 10A-11

Typical Height : 7 Ft.
Drought Tolerance : Medium
Nutritional Requirements : Medium
Light Requirements : Medium; low
Leaf Type : Simple; palmately lobed
Texture : Medium
Flower Characteristics : Insignificant

Environmental Problems : None

Rhapis subtilis

Common Name(s) : Thai Dwarf Lady Palm
Origin : Thailand
Growth Rate : Medium
Salt Tolerance : n/a
Soil Requirements : Wide
Plant Type : Palm
Foliage Color : Green
Flowering Season : n/a
Flower Color : n/a
Propagation : Seeds
Human Hazards : None
Common Uses : Foliage plant; palm
Major Problems : Fe deficiency; mealybugs; scales
Additional Notes : This small Rhapis is subject to iron deficiency in containers.

Family : Palmae   Zone : 10B-11

Typical Height : 3 Ft.
Drought Tolerance : Medium
Nutritional Requirements : Medium
Light Requirements : Low; medium
Leaf Type : Simple; palmately lobed
Texture : Medium
Flower Characteristics : Insignificant

Environmental Problems : None

Rheedia aristata

Common Name(s) : n/a
Origin : Cuba
Growth Rate : Medium
Salt Tolerance : n/a
Soil Requirements : Wide
Plant Type : Evergreen tree or shrub
Foliage Color : Green
Flowering Season : n/a
Flower Color : White
Propagation : Seeds
Human Hazards : Spiny
Common Uses : Shrub; small tree
Major Problems : None
Additional Notes : Has thick spine-tipped leaves

Family : Guttiferae   Zone : 10B-11

Typical Height : 25 Ft.
Drought Tolerance : Low
Nutritional Requirements : Medium
Light Requirements : Medium; high
Leaf Type : Simple
Texture : Medium
Flower Characteristics : Insignificant

Environmental Problems : None

Rhexia spp.

Common Name(s) : Meadow Beauty
Origin : Eastern United States
Growth Rate : Medium
Salt Tolerance : Low
Soil Requirements : Acid
Plant Type : Herbaceous perennial
Foliage Color : Green
Flowering Season : Summer; fall
Flower Color : Pink
Propagation : Seeds; division
Human Hazards : None
Common Uses : Beds; borders; rock gardens
Major Problems : None
Additional Notes : Moist soil; native wildflowers that should be planted more widely.

Family : Melastomataceae   **Zone** : 6-10B

Typical Height : 2 Ft.
Drought Tolerance : Low
Nutritional Requirements : Medium
Light Requirements : High
Leaf Type : Simple
Texture : Fine
Flower Characteristics : Showy

Environmental Problems : None

Rhizophora mangle

Common Name(s) : Red Mangrove
Origin : Tropical America
Growth Rate : Medium
Salt Tolerance : High
Soil Requirements : Wide
Plant Type : Evergreen tree
Foliage Color : Green
Flowering Season : Year-round
Flower Color : Yellow
Propagation : Seeds
Human Hazards : None
Common Uses : Tree
Major Problems : None
Additional Notes : A native stilt-rooted tree or shrub growing in salt or brackish water.

Family : Rhizophoraceae   **Zone** : 10B-11

Typical Height : 40 Ft.
Drought Tolerance : Medium
Nutritional Requirements : Low
Light Requirements : High
Leaf Type : Simple
Texture : Medium
Flower Characteristics : Insignificant

Environmental Problems : None

Rhododendron (azalea) hybrids *(Photo. p. 185)*

Common Name(s) : Azalea
Origin : Hybrid
Growth Rate : Medium
Salt Tolerance : Low
Soil Requirements : Acid
Plant Type : Evergreen shrub
Foliage Color : Green
Flowering Season : Spring
Flower Color : White; pink; red; purple
Propagation : Cuttings
Human Hazards : None
Common Uses : Flowering shrub
Major Problems : Root rots; mites; Fe deficiency; thrips; bacterial blight
Additional Notes : Many cultivars having different flower colors are available.
Cultivars
'SWEET FORGIVENESS' is a lavender-flowering cultivar that blooms well in south Florida and grows on alkaline soils.

Family : Ericaceae   **Zone** : 8-10A

Typical Height : 5 Ft.
Drought Tolerance : Low
Nutritional Requirements : High
Light Requirements : Medium; high
Leaf Type : Simple
Texture : Medium
Flower Characteristics : Showy

Environmental Problems : None

Rhododendron austrinum *(Photograph p. 185)*

Common Name(s) : Florida Flame Azalea
Origin : Southeastern United States
Growth Rate : Medium
Salt Tolerance : Low
Soil Requirements : Acid
Plant Type : Deciduous shrub
Foliage Color : Green
Flowering Season : Spring
Flower Color : Yellow-orange
Propagation : Seeds; cuttings
Human Hazards : None
Common Uses : Flowering shrub
Major Problems : Root rot; Fe deficiency
Additional Notes : Brilliant spring flower show; excellent massed under pines.

Family : Ericaceae   **Zone** : 7-9B

Typical Height : 6 Ft.
Drought Tolerance : Low
Nutritional Requirements : High
Light Requirements : Medium
Leaf Type : Simple
Texture : Medium
Flower Characteristics : Showy; fragrant

Environmental Problems : None

Rhododendron canescens *(Photograph p. 186)* Family : Ericaceae Zone : 7-10A

Common Name(s) : Pink Pinxter Azalea; Florida Honeysuckle

Origin : Southeastern United States	Typical Height : 10 Ft.
Growth Rate : Medium	Drought Tolerance : Low
Salt Tolerance : Low	Nutritional Requirements : High
Soil Requirements : Acid	Light Requirements : Medium
Plant Type : Deciduous shrub	Leaf Type : Simple
Foliage Color : Green	Texture : Medium
Flowering Season : Spring	Flower Characteristics : Showy; fragrant
Flower Color : Pink-white	
Propagation : Seeds; cuttings	
Human Hazards : None	Environmental Problems : None

Common Uses : Flowering shrub

Major Problems : Root rot; Fe deficiency

Additional Notes : Best massed in woodland or park-like situations.

Rhododendron chapmannii Family : Ericaceae Zone : 8-9

Common Name(s) : Chapman's Rhododendron

Origin : Florida	Typical Height : 5 Ft.
Growth Rate : Slow	Drought Tolerance : Low
Salt Tolerance : Low	Nutritional Requirements : Medium
Soil Requirements : Acid	Light Requirements : Medium; low
Plant Type : Evergreen shrub	Leaf Type : Simple
Foliage Color : Green	Texture : Medium
Flowering Season : Spring	Flower Characteristics : Showy
Flower Color : Pink	
Propagation : Seeds	
Human Hazards : None	Environmental Problems : None

Common Uses : Flowering shrub

Major Problems : Root rot; Fe deficiency

Additional Notes : The only native evergreen rhododendron in Florida; rare & endangered.

Rhodoleia championii *(Photograph p. 186)* Family : Hamamelidaceae Zone : 8-10A

Common Name(s) : Rhodoleia

Origin : China	Typical Height : 15 Ft.
Growth Rate : Medium	Drought Tolerance : Low
Salt Tolerance : Low	Nutritional Requirements : Medium
Soil Requirements : Acid	Light Requirements : Medium
Plant Type : Evergreen tree	Leaf Type : Simple
Foliage Color : Green	Texture : Medium
Flowering Season : Spring	Flower Characteristics : Showy
Flower Color : Red	
Propagation : Seeds	
Human Hazards : None	Environmental Problems : None

Common Uses : Small flowering tree

Major Problems : None

Additional Notes : A beautiful, small spring-flowering tree for part shade.

Rhoeo spathacea *(Photograph p. 216)* Family : Commelinaceae Zone : 10A-11

Common Name(s) : Oyster Plant

Origin : Caribbean Region	Typical Height : 1.5 Ft.
Growth Rate : Fast	Drought Tolerance : High
Salt Tolerance : Medium	Nutritional Requirements : Low
Soil Requirements : Wide	Light Requirements : High; medium
Plant Type : Herbaceous perennial	Leaf Type : Simple; linear
Foliage Color : Green; purple & green	Texture : Coarse
Flowering Season : Year-round	Flower Characteristics : Insignificant
Flower Color : White	
Propagation : Division	
Human Hazards : Irritant	Environmental Problems : None

Common Uses : Groundcover; foliage plant

Major Problems : None

Additional Notes : The non-flowering dwarf variety is best for ground covers.

Cultivars

'CONCOLOR' has solid green leaves; 'VARIEGATA' has leaves striped above with yellow; 'DWARF' is a non-flowering, spreading, and compact variety.

Rhus copallina

Common Name(s) : Winged Sumac; Shining Sumac
Origin : Eastern United States
Growth Rate : Fast
Salt Tolerance : Low
Soil Requirements : Wide
Plant Type : Deciduous shrub
Foliage Color : Green
Flowering Season : Summer
Flower Color : Green
Propagation : Seeds; root cuttings
Human Hazards : None
Common Uses : Shrub
Major Problems : None
Additional Notes : Suckers profusely; fruit attracts wildlife; red fall color.

Family : Anacardiaceae   **Zone** : 4-10B

Typical Height : 10 Ft.
Drought Tolerance : High
Nutritional Requirements : Low
Light Requirements : High
Leaf Type : Pinnately compound
Texture : Medium
Flower Characteristics : Insignificant

Environmental Problems : Invasive

Rosa hybrids

Common Name(s) : Rose
Origin : Hybrid
Growth Rate : Fast
Salt Tolerance : Low
Soil Requirements : Wide
Plant Type : Deciduous shrub
Foliage Color : Green
Flowering Season : Year-round
Flower Color : White; pink; red; yellow
Propagation : Grafting; budding; cuttings
Human Hazards : Spiny
Common Uses : Flowering shrub; cut flowers; flowering pot plant
Major Problems : Blackspot; rust; aphids; mites
Additional Notes : Many hybrids and cultivars exist.

Family : Rosaceae   **Zone** : 4-10B

Typical Height : 4 Ft.
Drought Tolerance : Medium
Nutritional Requirements : High
Light Requirements : High
Leaf Type : Pinnately compound
Texture : Medium
Flower Characteristics : Showy; fragrant

Environmental Problems : None

Roystonea elata

Common Name(s) : Florida Royal Palm
Origin : South Florida
Growth Rate : Medium
Salt Tolerance : Medium
Soil Requirements : Wide
Plant Type : Palm
Foliage Color : Green
Flowering Season : Spring
Flower Color : Yellow
Propagation : Seeds
Human Hazards : None
Common Uses : Tree; palm
Major Problems : K deficiency; royal palm bug; helminthosporium-complex leafspots
Additional Notes : Trunk diameter more uniform than the Cuban royal palm.

Family : Palmae   **Zone** : 10A-11

Typical Height : 80 Ft.
Drought Tolerance : Medium
Nutritional Requirements : Medium
Light Requirements : High
Leaf Type : Pinnately compound
Texture : Medium
Flower Characteristics : Insignificant

Environmental Problems : None

Roystonea regia *(Photograph p. 208)*

Common Name(s) : Cuban Royal Palm
Origin : Cuba
Growth Rate : Medium
Salt Tolerance : Medium
Soil Requirements : Wide
Plant Type : Palm
Foliage Color : Green
Flowering Season : Spring
Flower Color : Yellow
Propagation : Seeds
Human Hazards : None
Common Uses : Tree; palm
Major Problems : K deficiency; royal palm bug; helminthosporium-complex leafspots
Additional Notes : Too large for most single family homes.

Family : Palmae   **Zone** : 10A-11

Typical Height : 80 Ft.
Drought Tolerance : High
Nutritional Requirements : Medium
Light Requirements : High
Leaf Type : Pinnately compound
Texture : Medium
Flower Characteristics : Insignificant

Environmental Problems : None

Ruellia brittoniana

Common Name(s) : Mexican Bluebell
Origin : Mexico
Growth Rate : Medium
Salt Tolerance : Low
Soil Requirements : Wide
Plant Type : Evergreen shrub
Foliage Color : Green
Flowering Season : Spring; summer; fall
Flower Color : Blue-lavender
Propagation : Seeds; cuttings
Human Hazards : None
Common Uses : Flowering shrub
Major Problems : None
Additional Notes : Useful bedding plant for damp, shady locations.

Family : Acanthaceae   Zone : 10B-11

Typical Height : 2.5 Ft.
Drought Tolerance : Medium
Nutritional Requirements : Medium
Light Requirements : Medium
Leaf Type : Simple
Texture : Medium
Flower Characteristics : Showy

Environmental Problems : Weedy

Ruellia makoyana

Common Name(s) : Monkey Plant
Origin : Brazil
Growth Rate : Medium
Salt Tolerance : Low
Soil Requirements : Wide
Plant Type : Herbaceous perennial
Foliage Color : Green & purple
Flowering Season : Spring; summer; fall
Flower Color : Purple
Propagation : Seeds; cuttings
Human Hazards : None
Common Uses : Groundcover; borders; specimen plant; hanging baskets; foliage plant
Major Problems : Mealybugs
Additional Notes : Attractive foliage with small flowers.

Family : Acanthaceae   Zone : 10B-11

Typical Height : 1 Ft.
Drought Tolerance : Low
Nutritional Requirements : Medium
Light Requirements : Medium
Leaf Type : Simple
Texture : Medium
Flower Characteristics : Showy

Environmental Problems : Weedy

Rumohra adiantiformis *(Photograph p. 216)*

Common Name(s) : Leatherleaf Fern
Origin : Tropical Southern Hemishpere
Growth Rate : Medium
Salt Tolerance : Medium
Soil Requirements : Wide
Plant Type : Herbaceous perennial
Foliage Color : Green
Flowering Season : n/a
Flower Color : n/a
Propagation : Spores; division
Human Hazards : None
Common Uses : Groundcover; foliage plant; cut foliage
Major Problems : Mealybugs; leafhoppers; leaf miners
Additional Notes : Dark green leathery leaves used for cut foliage.

Family : Davalliaceae   Zone : 10A-11

Typical Height : 2 Ft.
Drought Tolerance : Medium
Nutritional Requirements : Medium
Light Requirements : Low; medium
Leaf Type : Bipinnately compound
Texture : Medium
Flower Characteristics : n/a

Environmental Problems : None

Russelia equisetiformis *(Photograph p. 186)*

Common Name(s) : Firecracker Plant
Origin : Mexico and Central America
Growth Rate : Medium
Salt Tolerance : High
Soil Requirements : Wide
Plant Type : Evergreen shrub
Foliage Color : Green
Flowering Season : Year-round
Flower Color : Red
Propagation : Cuttings
Human Hazards : None
Common Uses : Flowering shrub; flowering groundcover; hedge
Major Problems : Nematodes
Additional Notes : Long tubular flowers, wispy green leafless branches.

Family : Scrophulariaceae   Zone : 10B-11

Typical Height : 4 Ft.
Drought Tolerance : High
Nutritional Requirements : Medium
Light Requirements : High
Leaf Type : None
Texture : Fine
Flower Characteristics : Showy

Environmental Problems : None

Sabal causiarum

Common Name(s) : Hat Palm
Origin : Puerto Rico
Growth Rate : Slow
Salt Tolerance : Medium
Soil Requirements : Wide
Plant Type : Palm
Foliage Color : Green
Flowering Season : Summer
Flower Color : Yellow
Propagation : Seeds
Human Hazards : None
Common Uses : Palm
Major Problems : None
Additional Notes : A sabal palm noted for its thick trunk.

Family : Palmae   Zone : 9-11

Typical Height : 50 Ft.
Drought Tolerance : High
Nutritional Requirements : Low
Light Requirements : High
Leaf Type : Simple; palmately lobed
Texture : Very coarse
Flower Characteristics : Insignificant

Environmental Problems : None

Sabal etonia

Common Name(s) : Scrub Palmetto
Origin : Florida
Growth Rate : Slow
Salt Tolerance : Medium
Soil Requirements : Wide
Plant Type : Palm
Foliage Color : Green
Flowering Season : Spring
Flower Color : White
Propagation : Seeds
Human Hazards : None
Common Uses : Shrub; palm
Major Problems : None
Additional Notes : A slow growing native palm. Difficult to transplant.

Family : Palmae   Zone : 9-11

Typical Height : 3 Ft.
Drought Tolerance : High
Nutritional Requirements : Low
Light Requirements : Medium; high
Leaf Type : Simple; palmately lobed
Texture : Very coarse
Flower Characteristics : Insignificant

Environmental Problems : None

Sabal minor

Common Name(s) : Dwarf Palmetto
Origin : Southeastern United States
Growth Rate : Slow
Salt Tolerance : Medium
Soil Requirements : Wide
Plant Type : Palm
Foliage Color : Green
Flowering Season : Summer
Flower Color : White
Propagation : Seeds
Human Hazards : None
Common Uses : Shrub; palm
Major Problems : None
Additional Notes : Native palm that is difficult to transplant.

Family : Palmae   Zone : 7-10B

Typical Height : 6 Ft.
Drought Tolerance : High
Nutritional Requirements : Low
Light Requirements : High
Leaf Type : Simple; palmately lobed
Texture : Very coarse
Flower Characteristics : Insignificant

Environmental Problems : None

Sabal palmetto *(Photograph p. 208)*

Common Name(s) : Cabbage Palmetto; Sabal Palm
Origin : Southeastern United States
Growth Rate : Slow
Salt Tolerance : High
Soil Requirements : Wide
Plant Type : Palm
Foliage Color : Green
Flowering Season : Spring; summer
Flower Color : White
Propagation : Seeds
Human Hazards : None
Common Uses : Tree; palm
Major Problems : Palmetto weevils
Additional Notes : Young palms without trunks cannot be transplanted.

Family : Palmae   Zone : 8-11

Typical Height : 40 Ft.
Drought Tolerance : High
Nutritional Requirements : Low
Light Requirements : High
Leaf Type : Simple; palmately lobed
Texture : Very coarse
Flower Characteristics : Insignificant

Environmental Problems : None

Sabatia spp. *(Photograph p. 200)*

Common Name(s) : Marsh Pinks
Origin : Southeastern United States
Growth Rate : Medium
Salt Tolerance : Low
Soil Requirements : Moist
Plant Type : Herbaceous perennial
Foliage Color : Green
Flowering Season : Spring; summer; fall
Flower Color : Pink; white
Propagation : Seeds
Human Hazards : None
Common Uses : Specimen plant
Major Problems : None
Additional Notes : Attractive wetland wildflowers; <u>S. grandiflora</u> is least hardy.

Family : Gentianaceae   **Zone** : 6-11

Typical Height : 1 Ft.
Drought Tolerance : Low
Nutritional Requirements : Medium
Light Requirements : High
Leaf Type : Simple
Texture : Medium
Flower Characteristics : Showy

Environmental Problems : None

Sagittaria lancifolia

Common Name(s) : Arrowhead
Origin : Western Hemisphere
Growth Rate : Medium
Salt Tolerance : Low
Soil Requirements : Wide
Plant Type : Herbaceous perennial
Foliage Color : Green
Flowering Season : Summer
Flower Color : White
Propagation : Division; seeds
Human Hazards : None
Common Uses : Aquatic
Major Problems : None
Additional Notes : Emergent aquatic grown for tropical foliage in small ponds.

Family : Alismataceae   **Zone** : 8-10B

Typical Height : 3 Ft.
Drought Tolerance : Low
Nutritional Requirements : Medium
Light Requirements : High
Leaf Type : Simple
Texture : Coarse
Flower Characteristics : Showy

Environmental Problems : None

Salix babylonica

Common Name(s) : Weeping Willow
Origin : China
Growth Rate : Fast
Salt Tolerance : Low
Soil Requirements : Wide
Plant Type : Deciduous tree
Foliage Color : Green
Flowering Season : Spring
Flower Color : Yellow
Propagation : Cuttings
Human Hazards : None
Common Uses : Shade tree
Major Problems : Dieback; root rot
Additional Notes : Weak-wooded. Weeping habit

Family : Salicaceae   **Zone** : 5-9

Typical Height : 25 Ft.
Drought Tolerance : Low
Nutritional Requirements : Medium
Light Requirements : High
Leaf Type : Simple
Texture : Fine
Flower Characteristics : Insignificant

Environmental Problems : Weak

Salix caroliniana

Common Name(s) : Coastal Plain Willow
Origin : Southeastern United States
Growth Rate : Fast
Salt Tolerance : Low
Soil Requirements : Wide
Plant Type : Deciduous tree or shrub
Foliage Color : Green
Flowering Season : Spring
Flower Color : Green
Propagation : Cuttings
Human Hazards : None
Common Uses : Small tree; shrub
Major Problems : None
Additional Notes : Grows in wet areas around lakes and ponds.

Family : Salicaceae   **Zone** : 6-10B

Typical Height : 25 Ft.
Drought Tolerance : Low
Nutritional Requirements : Low
Light Requirements : High
Leaf Type : Simple
Texture : Fine
Flower Characteristics : Insignificant

Environmental Problems : None

Salvia argentea

Common Name(s) : Silver Sage
Origin : Southeastern Europe
Growth Rate : Medium
Salt Tolerance : Medium
Soil Requirements : Wide
Plant Type : Herbaceous perennial
Foliage Color : Silver
Flowering Season : Summer
Flower Color : White
Propagation : Seeds; cuttings
Human Hazards : None
Common Uses : Specimen plant
Major Problems : None
Additional Notes : This plant has rather large densely hairy leaves.

Family : Labiatae   **Zone** : 8-10A

Typical Height : 3 Ft.
Drought Tolerance : High
Nutritional Requirements : Medium
Light Requirements : High
Leaf Type : Simple
Texture : Coarse
Flower Characteristics : Showy

Environmental Problems : None

Salvia coccinea

Common Name(s) : Texas Sage
Origin : Southeastern United States
Growth Rate : Medium
Salt Tolerance : Medium
Soil Requirements : Wide
Plant Type : Herbaceous perennial
Foliage Color : Green
Flowering Season : Summer
Flower Color : Red
Propagation : Seeds; cuttings
Human Hazards : None
Common Uses : Beds; specimen plant
Major Problems : None
Additional Notes : This plant has spikes of red and purple flowers.

Family : Labiatae   **Zone** : 7-11

Typical Height : 2 Ft.
Drought Tolerance : High
Nutritional Requirements : Medium
Light Requirements : High
Leaf Type : Simple
Texture : Medium
Flower Characteristics : Showy

Environmental Problems : None

Salvia farinacea *(Photograph p. 199)*

Common Name(s) : Mealycup Sage; Blue Sage
Origin : Texas and New Mexico
Growth Rate : Medium
Salt Tolerance : High
Soil Requirements : Wide
Plant Type : Herbaceous perennial
Foliage Color : Green
Flowering Season : Summer
Flower Color : Blue
Propagation : Seeds; cuttings
Human Hazards : None
Common Uses : Beds; specimen plant
Major Problems : None
Additional Notes : This plant has spikes of small blue flowers. Many cultivars exist.

Family : Labiatae   **Zone** : 8-10B

Typical Height : 2 Ft.
Drought Tolerance : High
Nutritional Requirements : Medium
Light Requirements : High
Leaf Type : Simple
Texture : Medium
Flower Characteristics : Showy

Environmental Problems : None

Samanea saman *(Photograph p. 168)*

Common Name(s) : Rain Tree; Saman
Origin : Topical America
Growth Rate : Fast
Salt Tolerance : n/a
Soil Requirements : Wide
Plant Type : Evergreen tree
Foliage Color : Green
Flowering Season : n/a
Flower Color : Pink
Propagation : Seeds
Human Hazards : None
Common Uses : Shade tree; flowering tree
Major Problems : None
Additional Notes : A broad spreading tree with pink powderpuff flowers.

Family : Leguminosae   **Zone** : 10B-11

Typical Height : 80 Ft.
Drought Tolerance : High
Nutritional Requirements : Low
Light Requirements : High
Leaf Type : Bipinnately compound
Texture : Fine
Flower Characteristics : Showy

Environmental Problems : None

Sanchezia speciosa

Common Name(s) : Sanchezia
Origin : Ecuador
Growth Rate : Fast
Salt Tolerance : Medium
Soil Requirements : Wide
Plant Type : Evergreen shrub
Foliage Color : Variegated
Flowering Season : Spring; summer; fall
Flower Color : Yellow
Propagation : Cuttings
Human Hazards : None
Common Uses : Foliage plant; shrub
Major Problems : Mealybugs; mites; nematodes
Additional Notes : Green leaves patterned with yellow stripes.

Family : Acanthaceae   **Zone** : 11

Typical Height : 6 Ft.
Drought Tolerance : Low
Nutritional Requirements : Medium
Light Requirements : Medium; high
Leaf Type : Simple
Texture : Coarse
Flower Characteristics : Showy

Environmental Problems : None

Sansevieria cylindrica

Common Name(s) : Spear Sansevieria
Origin : Africa
Growth Rate : Slow
Salt Tolerance : High
Soil Requirements : Wide
Plant Type : Herbaceous perennial
Foliage Color : Green
Flowering Season : Summer
Flower Color : White
Propagation : Division; cuttings
Human Hazards : None
Common Uses : Rock gardens; specimen plant; foliage plant
Major Problems : None
Additional Notes : Has tough nearly cylindrical rolled leaves.

Family : Agavaceae   **Zone** : 10B-11

Typical Height : 3 Ft.
Drought Tolerance : High
Nutritional Requirements : Low
Light Requirements : Medium; high
Leaf Type : Simple; linear
Texture : Coarse
Flower Characteristics : Insignificant

Environmental Problems : Invasive

Sansevieria trifasciata

Common Name(s) : Snake Plant
Origin : South Africa
Growth Rate : Slow
Salt Tolerance : High
Soil Requirements : Wide
Plant Type : Herbaceous perennial
Foliage Color : Green & gray-green
Flowering Season : Summer
Flower Color : White
Propagation : Division; cuttings
Human Hazards : None
Common Uses : Rock gardens; groundcover; foliage plant
Major Problems : None
Additional Notes : These tough plants are invasive and difficult to kill. Many cultivars.
Cultivars
'LAURENTII' has yellow bands along the leaf margins; 'HAHNII' is a dwarf cultivar with a compact rosette form; 'FUTURA' is similar to 'LAURENTII', but is more compact and has a narrower yellow leaf band.

Family : Agavaceae   **Zone** : 10B-11

Typical Height : 2 Ft.
Drought Tolerance : High
Nutritional Requirements : Low
Light Requirements : Medium; high
Leaf Type : Simple; linear
Texture : Coarse
Flower Characteristics : Insignificant; fragrant

Environmental Problems : Invasive

Sansevieria zeylanica

Common Name(s) : Ceylon Bowstring Hemp
Origin : Sri Lanka
Growth Rate : Slow
Salt Tolerance : High
Soil Requirements : Wide
Plant Type : Herbaceous perennial
Foliage Color : Green & gray-green
Flowering Season : Summer
Flower Color : White
Propagation : Division; cuttings
Human Hazards : None
Common Uses : Rock gardens; foliage plant
Major Problems : None
Additional Notes : Similar to S. trifasciata .

Family : Agavaceae   **Zone** : 10B-11

Typical Height : 2.5 Ft.
Drought Tolerance : High
Nutritional Requirements : Low
Light Requirements : Medium; high
Leaf Type : Simple; linear
Texture : Coarse
Flower Characteristics : Insignificant; fragrant

Environmental Problems : Invasive

Santalum ellipticum

Common Name(s) : Sandalwood
Origin : Hawaii
Growth Rate : Medium
Salt Tolerance : Low
Soil Requirements : Wide
Plant Type : Evergreen tree or shrub
Foliage Color : Green
Flowering Season : n/a
Flower Color : Pink; red
Propagation : Seeds
Human Hazards : None
Common Uses : Small flowering tree
Major Problems : None
Additional Notes : Fragrant wood is used in furniture. Plant is semiparasitic.

Family : Santalaceae   **Zone** : 10B-11

Typical Height : 20 Ft.
Drought Tolerance : High
Nutritional Requirements : Low
Light Requirements : High
Leaf Type : Simple
Texture : Medium
Flower Characteristics : Showy

Environmental Problems : None

Sapindus saponaria

Common Name(s) : Soapberry
Origin : Tropical America
Growth Rate : Medium
Salt Tolerance : High
Soil Requirements : Wide
Plant Type : Evergreen tree
Foliage Color : Green
Flowering Season : Winter; spring
Flower Color : White
Propagation : Seeds
Human Hazards : Poisonous
Common Uses : Tree
Major Problems : None
Additional Notes : Fruit contains a soap-like material used in some tropical countries.

Family : Sapindaceae   **Zone** : 10A-11

Typical Height : 40 Ft.
Drought Tolerance : High
Nutritional Requirements : Low
Light Requirements : High
Leaf Type : Pinnately compound
Texture : Medium
Flower Characteristics : Insignificant

Environmental Problems : None

Sapium sebiferum

Common Name(s) : Chinese Tallowtree
Origin : China, Japan
Growth Rate : Fast
Salt Tolerance : Low
Soil Requirements : Wide
Plant Type : Deciduous tree
Foliage Color : Green
Flowering Season : Spring
Flower Color : Yellow
Propagation : Seeds
Human Hazards : None
Common Uses : Small tree
Major Problems : None
Additional Notes : Messy fruit; transplants poorly; can naturalize; good fall color.

Family : Euphorbiaceae   **Zone** : 4-10B

Typical Height : 20 Ft.
Drought Tolerance : Medium
Nutritional Requirements : Medium
Light Requirements : Medium
Leaf Type : Simple
Texture : Medium
Flower Characteristics : Insignificant

Environmental Problems : Messy; weedy

Savia bahamensis

Common Name(s) : Maidenbush
Origin : South Florida
Growth Rate : Slow
Salt Tolerance : High
Soil Requirements : Wide
Plant Type : Evergreen shrub
Foliage Color : Green
Flowering Season : Spring
Flower Color : Green
Propagation : Seeds
Human Hazards : None
Common Uses : Hedge; shrub
Major Problems : None
Additional Notes : This Florida native is good for coastal landscapes.

Family : Euphorbiaceae   **Zone** : 10B-11

Typical Height : 9 Ft.
Drought Tolerance : High
Nutritional Requirements : Low
Light Requirements : High
Leaf Type : Simple
Texture : Medium
Flower Characteristics : Insignificant

Environmental Problems : None

Scadoxus multiflorus *(Photograph p. 200)*
Common Name(s) : Blood Lily
Origin : Tropical Africa
Growth Rate : Medium
Salt Tolerance : Low
Soil Requirements : Acid
Plant Type : Herbaceous perennial
Foliage Color : Green
Flowering Season : Summer
Flower Color : Red
Propagation : Division
Human Hazards : Poisonous
Common Uses : Specimen plant; beds
Major Problems : Fungal leaf spot
Additional Notes : Must dry off in winter; partial shade best; many related species.

Family : Amaryllidaceae   Zone : 9-10B

Typical Height : 1.5 Ft.
Drought Tolerance : Low
Nutritional Requirements : Medium
Light Requirements : Low
Leaf Type : Simple
Texture : Coarse
Flower Characteristics : Showy

Environmental Problems : None

Scaevola plumieri
Common Name(s) : Inkberry
Origin : South Florida
Growth Rate : Slow
Salt Tolerance : High
Soil Requirements : Wide
Plant Type : Evergreen shrub
Foliage Color : Green
Flowering Season : Summer
Flower Color : White
Propagation : Seeds; cuttings
Human Hazards : None
Common Uses : Shrub; groundcover
Major Problems : None
Additional Notes : Sprawling shrub is excellent for beach plantings.

Family : Goodeniaceae   Zone : 10A-11

Typical Height : 4 Ft.
Drought Tolerance : High
Nutritional Requirements : Low
Light Requirements : High
Leaf Type : Simple
Texture : Medium
Flower Characteristics : Insignificant

Environmental Problems : None

Scaevola taccada *(Photograph p. 186)*
Common Name(s) : Beach Naupaka
Origin : n/a
Growth Rate : Medium
Salt Tolerance : High
Soil Requirements : Wide
Plant Type : Evergreen shrub
Foliage Color : Green
Flowering Season : Summer
Flower Color : White
Propagation : Seeds; cuttings
Human Hazards : None
Common Uses : Shrub; hedge
Major Problems : Spider mites
Additional Notes : Useful to stabilize sand dunes.

Family : Goodeniaceae   Zone : 10B-11

Typical Height : 5 Ft.
Drought Tolerance : High
Nutritional Requirements : Low
Light Requirements : High
Leaf Type : Simple
Texture : Coarse
Flower Characteristics : Insignificant

Environmental Problems : None

Schaefferia frutescens
Common Name(s) : Florida Boxwood
Origin : Tropical America
Growth Rate : Slow
Salt Tolerance : Medium
Soil Requirements : Alkaline
Plant Type : Evergreen shrub or tree
Foliage Color : Green
Flowering Season : Spring
Flower Color : Green
Propagation : Seeds
Human Hazards : None
Common Uses : Shrub; small tree
Major Problems : None
Additional Notes : Useful as a large, informal hedge.

Family : Celastraceae   Zone : 10B-11

Typical Height : 25 Ft.
Drought Tolerance : High
Nutritional Requirements : Medium
Light Requirements : Medium
Leaf Type : Simple
Texture : Medium
Flower Characteristics : Insignificant

Environmental Problems : None

Schefflera arboricola *(Photograph p. 186)*

Common Name(s) : Dwarf Schefflera
Origin : Taiwan
Growth Rate : Fast
Salt Tolerance : Medium
Soil Requirements : Wide
Plant Type : Evergreen shrub
Foliage Color : Green; variegated
Flowering Season : Summer
Flower Color : White
Propagation : Seeds; cuttings
Human Hazards : None
Common Uses : Shrub; hedge; foliage plant; groundcover
Major Problems : Aphids; scales; mealybugs
Additional Notes : Can be sheared to any size.
Cultivars
'GOLD CAPPELA', 'JACQUELINE', 'TRINETTE', and 'WORTHII' have yellow and green foliage; 'COVETTE' has broad green leaflets.

Family : Araliaceae   **Zone** : 10A-11

Typical Height : 10 Ft.
Drought Tolerance : High
Nutritional Requirements : Medium
Light Requirements : Low; medium; high
Leaf Type : Palmately compound
Texture : Medium
Flower Characteristics : Insignificant

Environmental Problems : None

Schlumbergera spp.

Common Name(s) : Holiday Cactus
Origin : Brazil
Growth Rate : Medium
Salt Tolerance : Low
Soil Requirements : Wide
Plant Type : Succulent epiphyte
Foliage Color : Green
Flowering Season : Fall; winter
Flower Color : Lavender; orange; pink; purple; red; white
Propagation : Cuttings
Human Hazards : None
Common Uses : Specimen plant; flowering pot plant; epiphyte
Major Problems : Root rot
Additional Notes : Epiphytes variously called Thanksgiving & Christmas cactus. Many hybrids.

Family : Cactaceae   **Zone** : 10B-11

Typical Height : 1 Ft.
Drought Tolerance : High
Nutritional Requirements : Low
Light Requirements : Medium
Leaf Type : None
Texture : Medium
Flower Characteristics : Showy

Environmental Problems : None

Scutellaria costaricana

Common Name(s) : Costa Rican Skullcap
Origin : Costa Rica
Growth Rate : Medium
Salt Tolerance : Low
Soil Requirements : Acid
Plant Type : Herbaceous perennial
Foliage Color : Green
Flowering Season : Spring; summer
Flower Color : Red; yellow
Propagation : Cuttings
Human Hazards : None
Common Uses : Borders; specimen plant
Major Problems : None
Additional Notes : Brilliant flower display; frost tender.

Family : Labiatae   **Zone** : 10B-11

Typical Height : 2 Ft.
Drought Tolerance : Low
Nutritional Requirements : High
Light Requirements : Medium
Leaf Type : Simple
Texture : Medium
Flower Characteristics : Showy

Environmental Problems : None

Sedum spectabile

Common Name(s) : Showy Stonecrop
Origin : China and Korea
Growth Rate : Medium
Salt Tolerance : Medium
Soil Requirements : Wide
Plant Type : Succulent perennial
Foliage Color : Green
Flowering Season : Fall
Flower Color : Pink; red; white
Propagation : Cuttings
Human Hazards : None
Common Uses : Borders; rock gardens; specimen plant
Major Problems : None
Additional Notes : A tuberous plant that is nearly indestructible. Non-invasive.

Family : Crassulaceae   **Zone** : 8-10B

Typical Height : 1.5 Ft.
Drought Tolerance : High
Nutritional Requirements : Low
Light Requirements : Medium; high
Leaf Type : Simple
Texture : Fine
Flower Characteristics : Showy

Environmental Problems : None

Selaginella spp. *(Photograph p. 216)*

Common Name(s) : Spikemoss
Origin : Worldwide
Growth Rate : Medium
Salt Tolerance : Low
Soil Requirements : Acid
Plant Type : Herbaceous perennial
Foliage Color : Green; blue-green
Flowering Season : n/a
Flower Color : n/a
Propagation : Division; cuttings
Human Hazards : None
Common Uses : Groundcover
Major Problems : None
Additional Notes : Fern relatives with lacy foliage; some tropical, other species hardy.

Family : Selaginellaceae   Zone : 8-11

Typical Height : 1 Ft.
Drought Tolerance : Low
Nutritional Requirements : Medium
Light Requirements : Medium; low
Leaf Type : Simple; lobed
Texture : Fine
Flower Characteristics : n/a

Environmental Problems : None

Senecio confusus *(Photograph p. 212)*

Common Name(s) : Mexican Flame Vine
Origin : Mexico
Growth Rate : Fast
Salt Tolerance : Low
Soil Requirements : Wide
Plant Type : Evergreen vine
Foliage Color : Green
Flowering Season : Spring; summer; fall
Flower Color : Orange
Propagation : Cuttings; seeds; air layers
Human Hazards : Irritant
Common Uses : Flowering vine
Major Problems : Nematodes; mites; scales; caterpillars
Additional Notes : Frost may kill plants back to the ground.

Family : Compositae   Zone : 10A-11

Typical Height : Not applicable
Drought Tolerance : Medium
Nutritional Requirements : Medium
Light Requirements : High
Leaf Type : Simple
Texture : Medium
Flower Characteristics : Showy

Environmental Problems : None

Serenoa repens *(Photograph p. 208)*

Common Name(s) : Saw Palmetto
Origin : Southeastern United States
Growth Rate : Slow
Salt Tolerance : High
Soil Requirements : Wide
Plant Type : Palm
Foliage Color : Green; blue-green
Flowering Season : Summer
Flower Color : White
Propagation : Seeds
Human Hazards : None
Common Uses : Shrub; groundcover; palm
Major Problems : None
Additional Notes : Tough native plant. Difficult to transplant. Blue form most desirable.

Family : Palmae   Zone : 8-11

Typical Height : 8 Ft.
Drought Tolerance : High
Nutritional Requirements : Low
Light Requirements : Medium; high
Leaf Type : Simple; palmately lobed
Texture : Very coarse
Flower Characteristics : Insignificant; fragrant

Environmental Problems : None

Serissa foetida

Common Name(s) : Serissa
Origin : Southeast Asia
Growth Rate : Medium
Salt Tolerance : Low
Soil Requirements : Wide
Plant Type : Evergreen shrub
Foliage Color : Green; variegated
Flowering Season : Summer
Flower Color : White
Propagation : Cuttings
Human Hazards : None
Common Uses : Flowering shrub; hedge
Major Problems : Nematodes; mites; scales
Additional Notes : Can be pruned to any size.

Family : Rubiaceae   Zone : 10B-11

Typical Height : 3 Ft.
Drought Tolerance : Medium
Nutritional Requirements : Medium
Light Requirements : High
Leaf Type : Simple
Texture : Fine
Flower Characteristics : Showy

Environmental Problems : None

Sesbania punicea

Common Name(s) : Daubentonia; False Poinciana; Purple Rattlebox
Origin : South America
Growth Rate : Fast
Salt Tolerance : Medium
Soil Requirements : Wide
Plant Type : Evergreen shrub
Foliage Color : Green
Flowering Season : Summer
Flower Color : Red-purple
Propagation : Seeds
Human Hazards : Poisonous
Common Uses : Flowering shrub
Major Problems : None
Additional Notes : This plant is fast-growing, but short-lived.

Family : Leguminosae   **Zone** : 9-11

Typical Height : 6 Ft.
Drought Tolerance : High
Nutritional Requirements : Low
Light Requirements : Medium
Leaf Type : Pinnately compound
Texture : Medium
Flower Characteristics : Showy

Environmental Problems : Weedy

Sesbania tripetii

Common Name(s) : Red Wisteria
Origin : Northern Argentina and Brazil
Growth Rate : Fast
Salt Tolerance : Medium
Soil Requirements : Wide
Plant Type : Evergreen shrub
Foliage Color : Green
Flowering Season : Summer
Flower Color : Red
Propagation : Seeds
Human Hazards : Poisonous
Common Uses : Flowering shrub
Major Problems : None
Additional Notes : Has drooping red flower clusters.

Family : Leguminosae   **Zone** : 9-10B

Typical Height : 6 Ft.
Drought Tolerance : High
Nutritional Requirements : Medium
Light Requirements : Medium
Leaf Type : Pinnately compound
Texture : Medium
Flower Characteristics : Showy

Environmental Problems : None

Sesuvium portulacastrum

Common Name(s) : Sea Purslane
Origin : Southeastern United States
Growth Rate : Medium
Salt Tolerance : High
Soil Requirements : Wide
Plant Type : Herbaceous perennial
Foliage Color : Green
Flowering Season : Year-round
Flower Color : Pink
Propagation : Cuttings
Human Hazards : None
Common Uses : Seasides; flowering groundcover
Major Problems : None
Additional Notes : A common native seastrand plant.

Family : Portulaceae   **Zone** : 9-10B

Typical Height : 1.3 Ft.
Drought Tolerance : High
Nutritional Requirements : Low
Light Requirements : High
Leaf Type : Simple
Texture : Medium
Flower Characteristics : Showy

Environmental Problems : None

Setcreasea pallida *(Photograph p. 216)*

Common Name(s) : Purple-heart; Purple Queen
Origin : Mexico
Growth Rate : Fast
Salt Tolerance : Medium
Soil Requirements : Wide
Plant Type : Herbaceous perennial
Foliage Color : Purple
Flowering Season : Year-round
Flower Color : Pink
Propagation : Cuttings
Human Hazards : Irritant
Common Uses : Groundcover; foliage plant
Major Problems : None
Additional Notes : Sprawling, open growth. Will tolerate poor sites.

Family : Commelinaceae   **Zone** : 9-11

Typical Height : 1 Ft.
Drought Tolerance : High
Nutritional Requirements : Low
Light Requirements : Medium; high
Leaf Type : Simple
Texture : Medium
Flower Characteristics : Insignificant

Environmental Problems : None

Severinia buxifolia *(Photograph p. 186)*

Common Name(s) : Boxthorn
Origin : Taiwan and Southern China
Growth Rate : Medium
Salt Tolerance : Medium
Soil Requirements : Wide
Plant Type : Evergreen shrub
Foliage Color : Green
Flowering Season : Spring
Flower Color : White
Propagation : Seeds; cuttings
Human Hazards : Spiny
Common Uses : Shrub; hedge
Major Problems : Scales; whiteflies; sooty mold
Additional Notes : A spiny shrub resembling boxwood. Withstands shearing.

Family : Rutaceae   **Zone** : 9-10B

Typical Height : 6 Ft.
Drought Tolerance : High
Nutritional Requirements : Medium
Light Requirements : High
Leaf Type : Simple
Texture : Fine
Flower Characteristics : Insignificant

Environmental Problems : None

Shibataea kumasaca

Common Name(s) : Bamboo
Origin : Japan
Growth Rate : Medium
Salt Tolerance : n/a
Soil Requirements : Acid
Plant Type : Evergreen shrub
Foliage Color : Green
Flowering Season : n/a
Flower Color : n/a
Propagation : Division
Human Hazards : None
Common Uses : Shrub
Major Problems : None
Additional Notes : A small running bamboo with broad leaves.
Cultivars
'VARIEGATA' has yellow variegation in the leaves.

Family : Gramineae   **Zone** : 8-10A

Typical Height : 5 Ft.
Drought Tolerance : High
Nutritional Requirements : Medium
Light Requirements : Medium; high
Leaf Type : Simple
Texture : Medium
Flower Characteristics : Insignificant

Environmental Problems : Invasive

Simarouba glauca *(Photograph p. 169)*

Common Name(s) : Paradise Tree
Origin : South Florida and West Indies
Growth Rate : Slow
Salt Tolerance : High
Soil Requirements : Wide
Plant Type : Evergreen tree
Foliage Color : Green
Flowering Season : Spring
Flower Color : Yellow
Propagation : Seeds
Human Hazards : None
Common Uses : Shade tree
Major Problems : None
Additional Notes : Does well in exposed locations. New foliage is red.

Family : Simaroubaceae   **Zone** : 10B-11

Typical Height : 40 Ft.
Drought Tolerance : High
Nutritional Requirements : Medium
Light Requirements : High
Leaf Type : Pinnately compound
Texture : Medium
Flower Characteristics : Insignificant

Environmental Problems : None

Sisyrinchium spp.

Common Name(s) : Blue-eyed Grass
Origin : Western Hemisphere
Growth Rate : Medium
Salt Tolerance : Low
Soil Requirements : Acid
Plant Type : Herbaceous perennial
Foliage Color : Green
Flowering Season : Spring
Flower Color : Blue; white
Propagation : Seeds; division
Human Hazards : None
Common Uses : Beds; flowering groundcover
Major Problems : None
Additional Notes : Dainty iris relatives; different species adapted to different habitats.

Family : Iridaceae   **Zone** : 8-10B

Typical Height : 1 Ft.
Drought Tolerance : Low
Nutritional Requirements : Medium
Light Requirements : High; medium
Leaf Type : Simple; linear
Texture : Fine
Flower Characteristics : Showy

Environmental Problems : None

Solandra guttata

Common Name(s) : Goldcup; Chalice Vine
Origin : Mexico
Growth Rate : Medium
Salt Tolerance : Low
Soil Requirements : Wide
Plant Type : Evergreen shrub or vine
Foliage Color : Green
Flowering Season : Summer; fall
Flower Color : White; yellow
Propagation : Cuttings
Human Hazards : Poisonous
Common Uses : Flowering vine; flowering shrub
Major Problems : Nematodes; mites; scales
Additional Notes : Heavy vine requires strong support; flowers poisonous; other species exist.

Family : Solanaceae   **Zone** : 10A-11

Typical Height : Not applicable
Drought Tolerance : Medium
Nutritional Requirements : Medium
Light Requirements : Medium; high
Leaf Type : Simple
Texture : Coarse
Flower Characteristics : Showy; fragrant

Environmental Problems : None

Solanum spp.

Common Name(s) : Marriage Vines
Origin : Tropical America
Growth Rate : Fast
Salt Tolerance : Low
Soil Requirements : Wide
Plant Type : Evergreen vine
Foliage Color : Green
Flowering Season : Summer; fall
Flower Color : Blue; lavender
Propagation : Seeds; cuttings
Human Hazards : Poisonous
Common Uses : Flowering vine
Major Problems : Nematodes; mites; scales
Additional Notes : S. seaforthianum has smooth stems; S. wendlandii has spiny stems.

Family : Solanaceae   **Zone** : 10B-11

Typical Height : Not applicable
Drought Tolerance : Medium
Nutritional Requirements : Medium
Light Requirements : Medium
Leaf Type : Pinnately compound
Texture : Medium
Flower Characteristics : Showy

Environmental Problems : None

Solidago spp.

Common Name(s) : Goldenrods
Origin : North America
Growth Rate : Medium
Salt Tolerance : Low
Soil Requirements : Wide
Plant Type : Herbaceous perennial
Foliage Color : Green
Flowering Season : Summer; fall
Flower Color : Yellow; white
Propagation : Seeds; division
Human Hazards : None
Common Uses : Borders; specimen plant
Major Problems : None
Additional Notes : Many species & hybrids available, some native.

Family : Compositae   **Zone** : 3-10B

Typical Height : 2.5 Ft.
Drought Tolerance : High
Nutritional Requirements : Low
Light Requirements : High
Leaf Type : Simple
Texture : Medium
Flower Characteristics : Showy

Environmental Problems : Weedy

Sophora tomentosa

Common Name(s) : Necklace Pod
Origin : Southeastern United States & Caribbean
Growth Rate : Medium
Salt Tolerance : High
Soil Requirements : Wide
Plant Type : Evergreen shrub
Foliage Color : Green
Flowering Season : Year-round
Flower Color : Yellow
Propagation : Seeds; cuttings
Human Hazards : None
Common Uses : Flowering shrub
Major Problems : Caterpillars
Additional Notes : This Florida native has bright pea-like seeds that self sow.

Family : Leguminosae   **Zone** : 10A-11

Typical Height : 8 Ft.
Drought Tolerance : High
Nutritional Requirements : Low
Light Requirements : High
Leaf Type : Pinnately compound
Texture : Medium
Flower Characteristics : Showy

Environmental Problems : None

Sparaxis spp.

Common Name(s) : Wandflower; Harlequin Flower
Origin : South Africa
Growth Rate : Medium
Salt Tolerance : Low
Soil Requirements : Wide
Plant Type : Herbaceous perennial
Foliage Color : Green
Flowering Season : Summer
Flower Color : White; pink; yellow; purple
Propagation : Division
Human Hazards : None
Common Uses : Specimen plant; beds; cut flower
Major Problems : None
Additional Notes : Short-lived in Florida; can be treated like an annual.

Family : Iridaceae   **Zone** : 8-10B

Typical Height : 1.5 Ft.
Drought Tolerance : Low
Nutritional Requirements : Medium
Light Requirements : High
Leaf Type : Simple; linear
Texture : Medium
Flower Characteristics : Showy

Environmental Problems : None

Sparmannia africana

Common Name(s) : African Hemp; Flowering Linden
Origin : South Africa
Growth Rate : Fast
Salt Tolerance : Low
Soil Requirements : Wide
Plant Type : Evergreen shrub
Foliage Color : Green
Flowering Season : Spring; summer
Flower Color : Purple
Propagation : Cuttings
Human Hazards : None
Common Uses : Flowering shrub
Major Problems : None
Additional Notes : May die back to roots in central Florida.

Family : Tiliaceae   **Zone** : 10B-11

Typical Height : 15 Ft.
Drought Tolerance : Medium
Nutritional Requirements : High
Light Requirements : High
Leaf Type : Simple
Texture : Medium
Flower Characteristics : Showy

Environmental Problems : None

Spathiphyllum spp. *(Photograph p. 200)*

Common Name(s) : Peace Lily
Origin : New World Tropics
Growth Rate : Medium
Salt Tolerance : Low
Soil Requirements : Wide
Plant Type : Herbaceous perennial
Foliage Color : Green
Flowering Season : Spring
Flower Color : White
Propagation : Seeds; division; tissue culture
Human Hazards : None
Common Uses : Beds; foliage plant; flowering perennial
Major Problems : Mites; scales; mealybugs
Additional Notes : Many species and hybrids of varying sizes exist.
Cultivars

Family : Araceae   **Zone** : 10B-11

Typical Height : 2 Ft.
Drought Tolerance : Low
Nutritional Requirements : Medium
Light Requirements : Low; medium
Leaf Type : Simple
Texture : Coarse
Flower Characteristics : Showy

Environmental Problems : None

'CLEVELANDII' is a smaller variety with rather narrow leaves; 'MAUNA LOA' refers to large cultivars with broad leaves; 'LONDONII' is medium-sized and has thick, broad leaves; 'WALLISII' is a small variety with narrow leaves; 'TASSON' and 'PETITE' are dwarf cultivars.

Spathodea campanulata *(Photograph p. 169)*

Common Name(s) : African Tulip Tree
Origin : Tropical Africa
Growth Rate : Fast
Salt Tolerance : Medium
Soil Requirements : Wide
Plant Type : Evergreen tree
Foliage Color : Green
Flowering Season : Winter; spring
Flower Color : Orange; yellow
Propagation : Seeds; cuttings
Human Hazards : None
Common Uses : Flowering tree
Major Problems : None
Additional Notes : Requires little maintenance but is a messy tree. Brittle wood.

Family : Bignoniaceae   **Zone** : 10B-11

Typical Height : 60 Ft.
Drought Tolerance : High
Nutritional Requirements : Medium
Light Requirements : High
Leaf Type : Pinnately compound
Texture : Coarse
Flower Characteristics : Showy

Environmental Problems : Messy

Sphaeropteris cooperi *(Photograph p. 169)*

Common Name(s) : Australian Tree Fern
Origin : Australia
Growth Rate : Slow
Salt Tolerance : Low
Soil Requirements : Wide
Plant Type : Evergreen tree (fern)
Foliage Color : Green
Flowering Season : n/a
Flower Color : n/a
Propagation : Spores
Human Hazards : None
Common Uses : Small tree; foliage plant
Major Problems : Mites; mealybugs
Additional Notes : Will tolerate full sun if given enough water.

Family : Cyatheaceae   **Zone** : 10B-11

Typical Height : 20 Ft.
Drought Tolerance : Low
Nutritional Requirements : Medium
Light Requirements : Medium; high
Leaf Type : Bipinnately compound
Texture : Fine
Flower Characteristics : n/a

Environmental Problems : None

Spiraea cantonensis

Common Name(s) : Reeve's Spirea
Origin : China
Growth Rate : Medium
Salt Tolerance : Low
Soil Requirements : Wide
Plant Type : Deciduous shrub
Foliage Color : Green
Flowering Season : Spring
Flower Color : White
Propagation : Seeds; cuttings
Human Hazards : None
Common Uses : Flowering shrub
Major Problems : None
Additional Notes : Has arching stems covered in spring with white flowers.

Family : Rosaceae   **Zone** : 7-9

Typical Height : 5 Ft.
Drought Tolerance : Medium
Nutritional Requirements : Medium
Light Requirements : High
Leaf Type : Simple
Texture : Medium
Flower Characteristics : Showy

Environmental Problems : None

Sprekelia formosissima *(Photograph p. 200)*

Common Name(s) : Aztec Lily
Origin : Mexico
Growth Rate : Medium
Salt Tolerance : Low
Soil Requirements : Wide
Plant Type : Herbaceous perennial
Foliage Color : Green
Flowering Season : Spring; summer
Flower Color : Red
Propagation : Division; seeds
Human Hazards : None
Common Uses : Beds
Major Problems : Bulb rots
Additional Notes : Keep dry in winter; may repeat bloom if alternately wet and dry in summer.

Family : Amaryllidaceae   **Zone** : 8-10B

Typical Height : 1.5 Ft.
Drought Tolerance : Medium
Nutritional Requirements : Medium
Light Requirements : High
Leaf Type : Simple; linear
Texture : Medium
Flower Characteristics : Showy

Environmental Problems : None

Stapelia spp.

Common Name(s) : Carrion Flower
Origin : Tropical and South Africa
Growth Rate : Medium
Salt Tolerance : Medium
Soil Requirements : Wide
Plant Type : Succulent perennial
Foliage Color : Green
Flowering Season : Summer
Flower Color : Purple & yellow
Propagation : Seeds; cuttings
Human Hazards : None
Common Uses : Rock gardens; specimen plant
Major Problems : Stem rots; scales; mealybugs
Additional Notes : Creeping succulent with angular stems. Foul-smelling flowers.

Family : Asclepiadaceae   **Zone** : 10B-11

Typical Height : 1 Ft.
Drought Tolerance : High
Nutritional Requirements : Low
Light Requirements : Medium; high
Leaf Type : None
Texture : Medium
Flower Characteristics : Showy

Environmental Problems : None

Stenocarpus sinuatus *(Photograph p. 169)*
Common Name(s) : Firewheel Tree
Origin : Australia
Growth Rate : Medium
Salt Tolerance : Low
Soil Requirements : Wide
Plant Type : Evergreen tree
Foliage Color : Green
Flowering Season : Spring; summer
Flower Color : Red
Propagation : Seeds
Human Hazards : None
Common Uses : Flowering tree
Major Problems : None
Additional Notes : Juvenile leaves are lobed; columnar growth habit.

Family : Proteaceae   Zone : 10A-11

Typical Height : 40 Ft.
Drought Tolerance : Medium
Nutritional Requirements : Medium
Light Requirements : High
Leaf Type : Simple; pinnately lobed
Texture : Coarse
Flower Characteristics : Showy

Environmental Problems : None

Stephanotis floribunda *(Photograph p. 212)*
Common Name(s) : Madagascar Jasmine
Origin : Madagascar
Growth Rate : Medium
Salt Tolerance : Medium
Soil Requirements : Wide
Plant Type : Evergreen vine
Foliage Color : Green
Flowering Season : Summer
Flower Color : White
Propagation : Seeds; cuttings
Human Hazards : None
Common Uses : Flowering vine
Major Problems : Nematodes
Additional Notes : Popular flowers for wedding bouquets.

Family : Asclepiadaceae   Zone : 10B-11

Typical Height : Not applicable
Drought Tolerance : High
Nutritional Requirements : Medium
Light Requirements : High; medium
Leaf Type : Simple
Texture : Medium
Flower Characteristics : Showy; fragrant

Environmental Problems : None

Sterculia foetida
Common Name(s) : Indian Almond; Bangar Nut
Origin : Old World Tropics
Growth Rate : Fast
Salt Tolerance : Low
Soil Requirements : Wide
Plant Type : Deciduous tree
Foliage Color : Green
Flowering Season : Winter; spring
Flower Color : Red & yellow
Propagation : Seeds
Human Hazards : None
Common Uses : Flowering tree
Major Problems : None
Additional Notes : Flowers have a foul stench.

Family : Sterculiaceae   Zone : 10B-11

Typical Height : 75 Ft.
Drought Tolerance : Medium
Nutritional Requirements : Medium
Light Requirements : High
Leaf Type : Palmately compound
Texture : Coarse
Flower Characteristics : Showy

Environmental Problems : None

Sternbergia lutea
Common Name(s) : Autumn Crocus
Origin : Southern Europe and Asia Minor
Growth Rate : Medium
Salt Tolerance : Low
Soil Requirements : Acid; well-drained
Plant Type : Herbaceous perennial
Foliage Color : Green
Flowering Season : Fall
Flower Color : Yellow
Propagation : Division
Human Hazards : None
Common Uses : Beds; borders
Major Problems : None
Additional Notes : Increases readily where successful.

Family : Amaryllidaceae   Zone : 6-9

Typical Height : .5 Ft.
Drought Tolerance : Medium
Nutritional Requirements : Medium
Light Requirements : High
Leaf Type : Simple; linear
Texture : Fine
Flower Characteristics : Showy

Environmental Problems : None

Stigmaphyllon littorale

Common Name(s) : Brazilian Golden Vine
Origin : Brazil to Argentina
Growth Rate : Medium
Salt Tolerance : Medium
Soil Requirements : Wide
Plant Type : Evergreen vine
Foliage Color : Green
Flowering Season : Spring; summer; fall
Flower Color : Yellow
Propagation : Cuttings
Human Hazards : None
Common Uses : Flowering vine
Major Problems : None
Additional Notes : Tuberous rooted, requires little care after establishment.

Family : Malpighiaceae   **Zone** : 10A-11

Typical Height : Not applicable
Drought Tolerance : Medium
Nutritional Requirements : Medium
Light Requirements : Medium; high
Leaf Type : Simple
Texture : Medium
Flower Characteristics : Showy

Environmental Problems : None

Stokesia laevis

Common Name(s) : Stoke's Aster
Origin : Southern United States
Growth Rate : Medium
Salt Tolerance : Low
Soil Requirements : Wide
Plant Type : Herbaceous perennial
Foliage Color : Green
Flowering Season : Summer
Flower Color : Blue; lavender; pink; purple; white; yellow
Propagation : Division; seeds
Human Hazards : None
Common Uses : Borders; cut flowers; specimen plant
Major Problems : None
Additional Notes : Many color selections have been made of this Florida native plant.

Family : Compositae   **Zone** : 5-10B

Typical Height : 1.5 Ft.
Drought Tolerance : Medium
Nutritional Requirements : Medium
Light Requirements : High
Leaf Type : Simple
Texture : Medium
Flower Characteristics : Showy

Environmental Problems : None

Strelitzia nicolai *(Photograph p. 187)*

Common Name(s) : White Bird of Paradise
Origin : Africa
Growth Rate : Slow
Salt Tolerance : Medium
Soil Requirements : Wide
Plant Type : Evergreen tree
Foliage Color : Green
Flowering Season : Summer; fall
Flower Color : White
Propagation : Seeds; suckers
Human Hazards : None
Common Uses : Multi-trunked tree; large shrub
Major Problems : Scales
Additional Notes : Multiple trunked tree, leaves can be messy.

Family : Strelitziaceae   **Zone** : 9B-11

Typical Height : 20 Ft.
Drought Tolerance : High
Nutritional Requirements : Medium
Light Requirements : Medium; high
Leaf Type : Simple
Texture : Coarse
Flower Characteristics : Showy

Environmental Problems : Messy

Strelitzia reginae *(Photograph p. 200)*

Common Name(s) : Bird of Paradise
Origin : South Africa
Growth Rate : Medium
Salt Tolerance : Low
Soil Requirements : Wide
Plant Type : Herbaceous perennial
Foliage Color : Green
Flowering Season : Summer; fall
Flower Color : Orange & blue
Propagation : Division; seeds
Human Hazards : None
Common Uses : Flowering perennial; cut flowers
Major Problems : Scales
Additional Notes : Slow growing clumping plant with excellent cut flowers.

Family : Strelitziaceae   **Zone** : 10A-11

Typical Height : 3 Ft.
Drought Tolerance : High
Nutritional Requirements : Medium
Light Requirements : Medium; high
Leaf Type : Simple
Texture : Coarse
Flower Characteristics : Showy

Environmental Problems : None

Strobilanthes dyeranus *(Photograph p. 200)*

Common Name(s) : Persian Shield
Origin : Burma
Growth Rate : Medium
Salt Tolerance : Low
Soil Requirements : Wide
Plant Type : Shrub
Foliage Color : Purple & variegated
Flowering Season : Summer; fall
Flower Color : Lavender
Propagation : Cuttings
Human Hazards : None
Common Uses : Shrub; foliage plant
Major Problems : Nematodes
Additional Notes : Beautiful metallic purple leaves.

Family : Acanthaceae   **Zone** : 10B-11

Typical Height : 3 Ft.
Drought Tolerance : Low
Nutritional Requirements : Medium
Light Requirements : Medium
Leaf Type : Simple
Texture : Medium
Flower Characteristics : Showy

Environmental Problems : None

Styrax grandifolius *(Photograph p. 169)*

Common Name(s) : Snowbell
Origin : Southeastern United States
Growth Rate : Medium
Salt Tolerance : Low
Soil Requirements : Acid
Plant Type : Deciduous shrub or tree
Foliage Color : Green
Flowering Season : Spring
Flower Color : White
Propagation : Seeds; air layering
Human Hazards : None
Common Uses : Small flowering tree; flowering shrub
Major Problems : None
Additional Notes : Shade tolerant; can be trained as a tree.

Family : Styracaceae   **Zone** : 6-9

Typical Height : 12 Ft.
Drought Tolerance : Low
Nutritional Requirements : High
Light Requirements : Medium
Leaf Type : Simple
Texture : Medium
Flower Characteristics : Showy; fragrant

Environmental Problems : None

Suriana maritima

Common Name(s) : Bay Cedar
Origin : Tropical America
Growth Rate : Slow
Salt Tolerance : High
Soil Requirements : Wide
Plant Type : Evergreen shrub
Foliage Color : Green
Flowering Season : Year-round
Flower Color : Yellow
Propagation : Seeds
Human Hazards : None
Common Uses : Shrub
Major Problems : None
Additional Notes : This Florida native is well adapted to coastal landscapes.

Family : Surianaceae   **Zone** : 10B-11

Typical Height : 10 Ft.
Drought Tolerance : High
Nutritional Requirements : Low
Light Requirements : High
Leaf Type : Simple
Texture : Fine
Flower Characteristics : Insignificant

Environmental Problems : None

Swietenia mahagoni *(Photograph p. 170)*

Common Name(s) : Mahogany
Origin : Caribbean Region
Growth Rate : Fast
Salt Tolerance : High
Soil Requirements : Wide
Plant Type : Evergreen tree
Foliage Color : Green
Flowering Season : Spring
Flower Color : Green-yellow
Propagation : Seeds
Human Hazards : None
Common Uses : Shade tree
Major Problems : Webworms; borers
Additional Notes : Tolerates high winds.

Family : Meliaceae   **Zone** : 10B-11

Typical Height : 60 Ft.
Drought Tolerance : High
Nutritional Requirements : Low
Light Requirements : High
Leaf Type : Pinnately compound
Texture : Medium
Flower Characteristics : Insignificant

Environmental Problems : None

Syagrus amara

Common Name(s) : Overtop Palm
Origin : Lesser Antilles
Growth Rate : Medium
Salt Tolerance : High
Soil Requirements : Wide
Plant Type : Palm
Foliage Color : Green
Flowering Season : Spring
Flower Color : Yellow-white
Propagation : Seeds
Human Hazards : None
Common Uses : Tree; palm
Major Problems : Mn deficiency

Family : Palmae   **Zone** : 10B-11

Typical Height : 60 Ft.
Drought Tolerance : High
Nutritional Requirements : Medium
Light Requirements : High
Leaf Type : Pinnately compound
Texture : Medium
Flower Characteristics : Insignificant

Environmental Problems : None

Additional Notes : This self-cleaning palm is similar in appearance to queen palm.

Syagrus romanzoffiana *(Photograph p. 208)*

Common Name(s) : Queen Palm; Cocos Plumosa
Origin : Southern Brazil to Argentina
Growth Rate : Medium
Salt Tolerance : Medium
Soil Requirements : Acid
Plant Type : Palm
Foliage Color : Green
Flowering Season : Year-round
Flower Color : White
Propagation : Seeds
Human Hazards : None
Common Uses : Tree; palm
Major Problems : Very susceptible to potassium and manganese deficiencies.

Family : Palmae   **Zone** : 10A-11

Typical Height : 40 Ft.
Drought Tolerance : High
Nutritional Requirements : High
Light Requirements : Medium; high
Leaf Type : Pinnately compound
Texture : Medium
Flower Characteristics : Insignificant

Environmental Problems : Messy

Additional Notes : Fruit is messy.

Syagrus schizophylla

Common Name(s) : Arikury Palm
Origin : Brazil
Growth Rate : Slow
Salt Tolerance : Medium
Soil Requirements : Wide
Plant Type : Palm
Foliage Color : Green
Flowering Season : Summer
Flower Color : White
Propagation : Seeds
Human Hazards : Spiny
Common Uses : Small tree; palm
Major Problems : Lethal yellowing (slightly susceptible)

Family : Palmae   **Zone** : 10A-11

Typical Height : 15 Ft.
Drought Tolerance : High
Nutritional Requirements : Medium
Light Requirements : Medium; high
Leaf Type : Palmately compound
Texture : Medium
Flower Characteristics : Insignificant

Environmental Problems : None

Additional Notes : A small palm with interesting persistant leaf bases.

Symplocos tinctoria

Common Name(s) : Sweetleaf
Origin : Southeastern United States
Growth Rate : Medium
Salt Tolerance : Low
Soil Requirements : Acid
Plant Type : Evergreen tree or shrub
Foliage Color : Green
Flowering Season : Spring
Flower Color : Yellow
Propagation : Seeds; cuttings; air layering
Human Hazards : None
Common Uses : Small tree; shrub
Major Problems : None

Family : Symplocaceae   **Zone** : 6-10A

Typical Height : 20 Ft.
Drought Tolerance : Low
Nutritional Requirements : High
Light Requirements : Medium
Leaf Type : Simple
Texture : Medium
Flower Characteristics : Insignificant

Environmental Problems : None

Additional Notes : A shade-tolerant native for moist sites; sweet-tasting leaves.

Synadenium grantii

Common Name(s) : African Milkbush
Origin : Central East Africa
Growth Rate : Medium
Salt Tolerance : High
Soil Requirements : Wide
Plant Type : Evergreen shrub
Foliage Color : Green; red
Flowering Season : Spring; summer; fall
Flower Color : Red
Propagation : Cuttings
Human Hazards : Irritant
Common Uses : Flowering shrub
Major Problems : None
Additional Notes : Milky sap is irritating.
Cultivars
'RUBRA' has red leaves.

Family : Euphorbiaceae   **Zone** : 10B-11

Typical Height : 7 Ft.
Drought Tolerance : High
Nutritional Requirements : Low
Light Requirements : High
Leaf Type : Simple
Texture : Medium
Flower Characteristics : Showy

Environmental Problems : None

Syngonium podophyllum

Common Name(s) : Syngonium
Origin : Mexico to Panama
Growth Rate : Fast
Salt Tolerance : Low
Soil Requirements : Wide
Plant Type : Evergreen vine
Foliage Color : Green; variegated
Flowering Season : Summer
Flower Color : Green
Propagation : Cuttings
Human Hazards : None
Common Uses : Vine; groundcover
Major Problems : Mites; scales; fungal and bacterial leafspots and rots
Additional Notes : Numerous cultivars, mature leaves deeply lobed.
Cultivars
'EMERALD GEM' has bright green foliage; 'WHITE BUTTERFLY' has whitish foliage; 'MAYA RED' has brown-pink new leaves; 'PINK ALLUSION' is compact with a fine pink midvein; 'LEMON LIME', 'ROBUSTA', and 'MAXIMA BUTTERFLY' are compact free-branching forms of 'WHITE BUTTERFLY'; 'BOB ALLUSION' has round leaves with a red midvein.

Family : Araceae   **Zone** : 10B-11

Typical Height : Not applicable
Drought Tolerance : Medium
Nutritional Requirements : Medium
Light Requirements : Medium; low
Leaf Type : Simple
Texture : Coarse
Flower Characteristics : Insignificant

Environmental Problems : Invasive

Synsepalum dulcificum

Common Name(s) : Miracle Fruit
Origin : West Africa
Growth Rate : Slow
Salt Tolerance : Low
Soil Requirements : Acid
Plant Type : Evergreen shrub
Foliage Color : Green
Flowering Season : Spring; summer; fall
Flower Color : White
Propagation : Seeds
Human Hazards : None
Common Uses : Shrub; edible fruit
Major Problems : Fe deficiency
Additional Notes : Attractive red edible fruit makes sour food taste sweet.

Family : Sapotaceae   **Zone** : 10B-11

Typical Height : 6 Ft.
Drought Tolerance : Low
Nutritional Requirements : Medium
Light Requirements : Medium; high
Leaf Type : Simple
Texture : Medium
Flower Characteristics : Insignificant

Environmental Problems : None

Syzygium cumini

Common Name(s) : Jambolan Plum; Java Plum
Origin : Southeast Asia
Growth Rate : Fast
Salt Tolerance : Low
Soil Requirements : Wide
Plant Type : Evergreen tree
Foliage Color : Green
Flowering Season : Spring
Flower Color : White
Propagation : Seeds
Human Hazards : None
Common Uses : Shade tree
Major Problems : None
Additional Notes : A very large tree with extremely messy fruit.

Family : Myrtaceae   **Zone** : 10B-11

Typical Height : 75 Ft.
Drought Tolerance : High
Nutritional Requirements : Low
Light Requirements : High
Leaf Type : Simple
Texture : Coarse
Flower Characteristics : Insignificant

Environmental Problems : Messy

Syzygium jambos *(Photograph p. 170)*

Common Name(s) : Rose Apple
Origin : East Indies
Growth Rate : Fast
Salt Tolerance : Low
Soil Requirements : Wide
Plant Type : Evergreen tree
Foliage Color : Green
Flowering Season : Spring
Flower Color : White
Propagation : Seeds
Human Hazards : None
Common Uses : Small flowering tree; edible fruit
Major Problems : None
Additional Notes : Fruit tastes like a rose blossom smells. New growth red.

Family : Myrtaceae   **Zone** : 10B-11

Typical Height : 25 Ft.
Drought Tolerance : High
Nutritional Requirements : Medium
Light Requirements : High
Leaf Type : Simple
Texture : Medium
Flower Characteristics : Showy

Environmental Problems : None

Syzygium paniculatum

Common Name(s) : Brush Cherry
Origin : Australia
Growth Rate : Medium
Salt Tolerance : Medium
Soil Requirements : Wide
Plant Type : Evergreen shrub or tree
Foliage Color : Green
Flowering Season : Spring; summer; fall
Flower Color : White
Propagation : Seeds
Human Hazards : None
Common Uses : Flowering shrub; small flowering tree; edible fruit
Major Problems : Scales; mites
Additional Notes : Edible reddish purple fruits.
Cultivars
'COMPACTA' is a more compact form; 'VARIEGATA' has variegated foliage.

Family : Myrtaceae   **Zone** : 10B-11

Typical Height : 12 Ft.
Drought Tolerance : Medium
Nutritional Requirements : Low
Light Requirements : High
Leaf Type : Simple
Texture : Medium
Flower Characteristics : Showy

Environmental Problems : None

Tabebuia caraiba *(Photograph p. 170)*

Common Name(s) : Silver Trumpet Tree
Origin : Paraguay
Growth Rate : Medium
Salt Tolerance : Medium
Soil Requirements : Wide
Plant Type : Semi-deciduous tree
Foliage Color : Silver-green
Flowering Season : Spring
Flower Color : Yellow
Propagation : Seeds; grafting
Human Hazards : None
Common Uses : Flowering tree
Major Problems : None
Additional Notes : Asymmetrical growth habit. Corky bark. Spectacular flowers.

Family : Bignonicaeae   **Zone** : 10A-11

Typical Height : 25 Ft.
Drought Tolerance : High
Nutritional Requirements : Medium
Light Requirements : High
Leaf Type : Palmately compound
Texture : Medium
Flower Characteristics : Showy

Environmental Problems : None

Tabebuia chrysantha

Common Name(s) : Yellow Trumpet Tree
Origin : Mexico to Venezuela
Growth Rate : Medium
Salt Tolerance : Medium
Soil Requirements : Wide
Plant Type : Deciduous tree
Foliage Color : Green
Flowering Season : Spring
Flower Color : Yellow
Propagation : Seeds
Human Hazards : None
Common Uses : Flowering tree
Major Problems : None
Additional Notes : Has spectacular yellow flowers on a leafless tree.

Family : Bignonicaeae   **Zone** : 10A-11

Typical Height : 25 Ft.
Drought Tolerance : High
Nutritional Requirements : Medium
Light Requirements : High
Leaf Type : Palmately compound
Texture : Medium
Flower Characteristics : Showy

Environmental Problems : None

Tabebuia chrysotricha *(Photograph p. 170)*

Common Name(s) : Golden Tabebuia
Origin : South America
Growth Rate : Medium
Salt Tolerance : Medium
Soil Requirements : Wide
Plant Type : Deciduous tree
Foliage Color : Green
Flowering Season : Spring
Flower Color : Yellow
Propagation : Seeds
Human Hazards : None
Common Uses : Flowering tree
Major Problems : None
Additional Notes : Has an open growth habit. Flowers on bare branches.

Family : Bignoniaceae   **Zone** : 10A-11

Typical Height : 40 Ft.
Drought Tolerance : High
Nutritional Requirements : Medium
Light Requirements : High
Leaf Type : Palmately compound
Texture : Medium
Flower Characteristics : Showy

Environmental Problems : None

Tabebuia heterophylla *(Photograph p. 170)*

Common Name(s) : Pink Trumpet Tree
Origin : West Indies
Growth Rate : Medium
Salt Tolerance : Medium
Soil Requirements : Wide
Plant Type : Evergreen tree
Foliage Color : Green
Flowering Season : Spring; summer
Flower Color : Pink; white
Propagation : Seeds
Human Hazards : None
Common Uses : Flowering tree
Major Problems : None
Additional Notes : Flowers sporadically throughout the warm season.

Family : Bignoniaceae   **Zone** : 10A-11

Typical Height : 25 Ft.
Drought Tolerance : High
Nutritional Requirements : Medium
Light Requirements : High
Leaf Type : Palmately compound
Texture : Medium
Flower Characteristics : Showy

Environmental Problems : None

Tabebuia impetiginosa *(Photograph p. 171)*

Common Name(s) : Purple Tabebuia
Origin : Brazil
Growth Rate : Slow
Salt Tolerance : Medium
Soil Requirements : Wide
Plant Type : Deciduous tree
Foliage Color : Green
Flowering Season : Spring
Flower Color : Purple
Propagation : Seeds
Human Hazards : None
Common Uses : Flowering tree
Major Problems : None
Additional Notes : Open growth habit.

Family : Bignoniaceae   **Zone** : 10A-11

Typical Height : 15 Ft.
Drought Tolerance : High
Nutritional Requirements : Medium
Light Requirements : High
Leaf Type : Palmately compound
Texture : Medium
Flower Characteristics : Showy

Environmental Problems : None

Tabebuia pentaphylla

Common Name(s) : Pink Tabebuia
Origin : Central America
Growth Rate : Medium
Salt Tolerance : Medium
Soil Requirements : Wide
Plant Type : Evergreen tree
Foliage Color : Green
Flowering Season : Spring
Flower Color : Pink; white
Propagation : Seeds
Human Hazards : None
Common Uses : Small flowering tree
Major Problems : None
Additional Notes : An uncommon, but excellent Tabebuia for south Florida.

Family : Bignoniaceae   **Zone** : 10B-11

Typical Height : 30 Ft.
Drought Tolerance : High
Nutritional Requirements : Medium
Light Requirements : High
Leaf Type : Palmately compound
Texture : Medium
Flower Characteristics : Showy

Environmental Problems : None

Tabebuia rosea

Common Name(s) : Pink Poui; Rosy Trumpet Tree
Origin : Mexico to Venezuela and Ecuador
Growth Rate : Medium
Salt Tolerance : Medium
Soil Requirements : Wide
Plant Type : Evergreen tree
Foliage Color : Green
Flowering Season : Winter
Flower Color : Pink
Propagation : Seeds
Human Hazards : None
Common Uses : Flowering tree
Major Problems : None
Additional Notes : A very showy pink flowering tree.

Family : Bignoniaceae   **Zone** : 10B-11

Typical Height : 40 Ft.
Drought Tolerance : High
Nutritional Requirements : Medium
Light Requirements : High
Leaf Type : Palmately compound
Texture : Medium
Flower Characteristics : Showy

Environmental Problems : None

Tabebuia umbellata

Common Name(s) : Tabebuia
Origin : Brazil
Growth Rate : Slow
Salt Tolerance : Medium
Soil Requirements : Wide
Plant Type : Deciduous tree
Foliage Color : Green
Flowering Season : Spring
Flower Color : Yellow
Propagation : Seeds
Human Hazards : None
Common Uses : Flowering tree
Major Problems : None
Additional Notes : Open growth habit.

Family : Bignoniaceae   **Zone** : 10A-11

Typical Height : 15 Ft.
Drought Tolerance : High
Nutritional Requirements : Medium
Light Requirements : High
Leaf Type : Palmately compound
Texture : Medium
Flower Characteristics : Showy; fragrant

Environmental Problems : None

Tabernaemontana divaricata

Common Name(s) : Crape Jasmine
Origin : India
Growth Rate : Medium
Salt Tolerance : Medium
Soil Requirements : Wide
Plant Type : Evergreen shrub
Foliage Color : Green
Flowering Season : Spring; summer; fall
Flower Color : White
Propagation : Seeds; cuttings
Human Hazards : None
Common Uses : Flowering shrub; hedge
Major Problems : Scales; mites; sooty mold; nematodes
Additional Notes : Single and double flowered cultivars exist.

Family : Apocynaceae   **Zone** : 10B-11

Typical Height : 7 Ft.
Drought Tolerance : Low
Nutritional Requirements : Medium
Light Requirements : Medium; high
Leaf Type : Simple
Texture : Medium
Flower Characteristics : Showy; fragrant

Environmental Problems : None

Tacca spp.

Common Name(s) : Bat Flower
Origin : Tropics
Growth Rate : Medium
Salt Tolerance : Low
Soil Requirements : Acid
Plant Type : Herbaceous perennial
Foliage Color : Green
Flowering Season : Year-round
Flower Color : Brown
Propagation : Division; seeds
Human Hazards : None
Common Uses : Beds; specimen plant
Major Problems : None
Additional Notes : Unusual flower; may be bedded out in light shade.

Family : Taccaceae   **Zone** : 10B-11

Typical Height : 1.5 Ft.
Drought Tolerance : Low
Nutritional Requirements : Medium
Light Requirements : Medium
Leaf Type : Simple
Texture : Coarse
Flower Characteristics : Showy

Environmental Problems : None

Tamarindus indica *(Photograph p. 170)*

Common Name(s) : Tamarind
Origin : East Indies
Growth Rate : Medium
Salt Tolerance : Medium
Soil Requirements : Wide
Plant Type : Evergreen tree
Foliage Color : Green
Flowering Season : Spring; summer
Flower Color : Yellow-orange
Propagation : Seeds; air layers; cuttings
Human Hazards : None
Common Uses : Shade tree; edible fruit
Major Problems : None
Additional Notes : Extremely wind resistant. Edible pulp of seed pods used in steak sauces.

Family : Leguminosae   Zone : 10B-11

Typical Height : 50 Ft.
Drought Tolerance : High
Nutritional Requirements : Medium
Light Requirements : High
Leaf Type : Pinnately compound
Texture : Fine
Flower Characteristics : Insignificant

Environmental Problems : None

Taxodium ascendens

Common Name(s) : Pond Cypress
Origin : Southeastern United States
Growth Rate : Medium
Salt Tolerance : Medium
Soil Requirements : Wide
Plant Type : Deciduous tree
Foliage Color : Green
Flowering Season : Spring
Flower Color : n/a
Propagation : Seeds
Human Hazards : None
Common Uses : Shade tree
Major Problems : None
Additional Notes : Pyramidal growth habit when young. Scale-like foliage instead of needles.

Family : Taxodiaceae   Zone : 7-10B

Typical Height : 70 Ft.
Drought Tolerance : High
Nutritional Requirements : Low
Light Requirements : High
Leaf Type : Scale-like
Texture : Fine
Flower Characteristics : Cone

Environmental Problems : None

Taxodium distichum *(Photograph p. 171)*

Common Name(s) : Bald Cypress
Origin : Southeastern United States
Growth Rate : Medium
Salt Tolerance : Medium
Soil Requirements : Wide
Plant Type : Deciduous tree
Foliage Color : Green
Flowering Season : Spring
Flower Color : n/a
Propagation : Seeds
Human Hazards : None
Common Uses : Shade tree
Major Problems : None
Additional Notes : Pyramidal growth habit when young.

Family : Taxodiaceae   Zone : 4-10B

Typical Height : 70 Ft.
Drought Tolerance : High
Nutritional Requirements : Low
Light Requirements : High
Leaf Type : Needles
Texture : Fine
Flower Characteristics : Cone

Environmental Problems : None

Taxus floridana

Common Name(s) : Florida Yew
Origin : Florida
Growth Rate : Slow
Salt Tolerance : Low
Soil Requirements : Acid
Plant Type : Evergreen shrub or tree
Foliage Color : Green
Flowering Season : Spring
Flower Color : n/a
Propagation : Seeds; cuttings
Human Hazards : Poisonous
Common Uses : Shrub; small tree
Major Problems : Scales; root rot
Additional Notes : Near extinction in wild; attractive red fruit in fall.

Family : Taxaceae   Zone : 8-9

Typical Height : 15 Ft.
Drought Tolerance : Medium
Nutritional Requirements : High
Light Requirements : Medium
Leaf Type : Needle
Texture : Fine
Flower Characteristics : Insignificant

Environmental Problems : None

Tecoma stans *(Photograph p. 171)*

Common Name(s) : Yellow Elder
Origin : Caribbean Region
Growth Rate : Fast
Salt Tolerance : Medium
Soil Requirements : Wide
Plant Type : Evergreen tree or shrub
Foliage Color : Green
Flowering Season : Year-round
Flower Color : Yellow
Propagation : Seeds
Human Hazards : None
Common Uses : Small flowering tree; flowering shrub
Major Problems : None
Additional Notes : Can be trained into a tree.

Family : Bignoniaceae   **Zone** : 10B-11

Typical Height : 15 Ft.
Drought Tolerance : High
Nutritional Requirements : Medium
Light Requirements : High
Leaf Type : Pinnately compound
Texture : Medium
Flower Characteristics : Showy

Environmental Problems : None

Tecomanthe venusta *(Photograph p. 212)*

Common Name(s) : Tecomanthe
Origin : New Guinea
Growth Rate : Medium
Salt Tolerance : Low
Soil Requirements : Wide
Plant Type : Evergreen vine
Foliage Color : Green
Flowering Season : Spring; summer
Flower Color : Red
Propagation : Seeds; cuttings
Human Hazards : None
Common Uses : Flowering vine
Major Problems : None
Additional Notes : Flowers produced on old wood.

Family : Bignoniaceae   **Zone** : 11

Typical Height : 10 Ft.
Drought Tolerance : Low
Nutritional Requirements : Medium
Light Requirements : Medium; high
Leaf Type : Pinnately compound
Texture : Medium
Flower Characteristics : Showy

Environmental Problems : None

Tecomaria capensis

Common Name(s) : Cape Honeysuckle
Origin : South Africa
Growth Rate : Fast
Salt Tolerance : Medium
Soil Requirements : Wide
Plant Type : Evergreen shrub or vine
Foliage Color : Green
Flowering Season : Summer; fall
Flower Color : Orange; red; yellow
Propagation : Cuttings
Human Hazards : None
Common Uses : Flowering shrub; flowering vine
Major Problems : Scales; mites; nematodes; root rots
Additional Notes : Needs frequent pruning to retain shrub form.

Family : Bignoniaceae   **Zone** : 10B-11

Typical Height : 6 Ft.
Drought Tolerance : Medium
Nutritional Requirements : Medium
Light Requirements : High
Leaf Type : Pinnately compound
Texture : Medium
Flower Characteristics : Showy

Environmental Problems : None

Tectona grandis

Common Name(s) : Teak
Origin : India to Malay Peninsula
Growth Rate : Medium
Salt Tolerance : Low
Soil Requirements : Wide
Plant Type : Evergreen tree
Foliage Color : Green
Flowering Season : Summer
Flower Color : White
Propagation : Seeds; root suckers
Human Hazards : None
Common Uses : Timber; shade tree
Major Problems : None
Additional Notes : A large tree grown primarily for its beautiful rot-resistant wood.

Family : Verbenaceae   **Zone** : 10B-11

Typical Height : 120 Ft.
Drought Tolerance : Medium
Nutritional Requirements : Medium
Light Requirements : High
Leaf Type : Simple
Texture : Coarse
Flower Characteristics : Showy

Environmental Problems : None

Terminalia catappa *(Photograph p. 171)*

Common Name(s) : Tropical Almond
Origin : Madagascar and East Indies
Growth Rate : Medium
Salt Tolerance : High
Soil Requirements : Wide
Plant Type : Deciduous tree
Foliage Color : Green
Flowering Season : Spring
Flower Color : Green
Propagation : Seeds
Human Hazards : None
Common Uses : Shade tree
Major Problems : Thrips
Additional Notes : Excellent red fall color prior to leaf drop. Brittle wood.

Family : Combretaceae   **Zone** : 10B-11

Typical Height : 30 Ft.
Drought Tolerance : High
Nutritional Requirements : Low
Light Requirements : High
Leaf Type : Simple
Texture : Coarse
Flower Characteristics : Insignificant

Environmental Problems : None

Terminalia muelleri

Common Name(s) : Mueller's Terminalia
Origin : Australia
Growth Rate : Medium
Salt Tolerance : Medium
Soil Requirements : Wide
Plant Type : Evergreen tree
Foliage Color : Green
Flowering Season : Spring
Flower Color : White
Propagation : Seeds
Human Hazards : None
Common Uses : Small tree
Major Problems : None

Family : Combretaceae   **Zone** : 10B-11

Typical Height : 20 Ft.
Drought Tolerance : Medium
Nutritional Requirements : Medium
Light Requirements : High
Leaf Type : Simple
Texture : Medium
Flower Characteristics : Insignificant

Environmental Problems : Messy

Ternstroemia gymnanthera

Common Name(s) : Cleyera
Origin : India to Japan
Growth Rate : Medium
Salt Tolerance : Low
Soil Requirements : Wide
Plant Type : Evergreen tree or shrub
Foliage Color : Green
Flowering Season : Spring
Flower Color : Yellow
Propagation : Cuttings
Human Hazards : None
Common Uses : Small tree; shrub; hedge
Major Problems : Scales
Additional Notes : Excellent hedge or screen for shady areas.

Family : Theaceae   **Zone** : 10A-11

Typical Height : 15 Ft.
Drought Tolerance : Medium
Nutritional Requirements : High
Light Requirements : Low
Leaf Type : Simple
Texture : Medium
Flower Characteristics : Insignificant

Environmental Problems : None

Tetrapanax papyriferus

Common Name(s) : Rice-paper Plant
Origin : Taiwan and Southern China
Growth Rate : Medium
Salt Tolerance : Low
Soil Requirements : Wide
Plant Type : Evergreen shrub
Foliage Color : Green
Flowering Season : Spring; summer; fall
Flower Color : White
Propagation : Seeds
Human Hazards : Irritant
Common Uses : Flowering shrub
Major Problems : Mealybugs
Additional Notes : Bold foliage texture; spreads by rhizomes.

Family : Araliaceae   **Zone** : 10A-11

Typical Height : 8 Ft.
Drought Tolerance : Medium
Nutritional Requirements : Medium
Light Requirements : Medium; high
Leaf Type : Palmately compound
Texture : Coarse
Flower Characteristics : Showy

Environmental Problems : Invasive

Tetrazygia bicolor *(Photograph p. 187)*

Common Name(s) : Florida Tetrazygia
Origin : South Florida and West Indies
Growth Rate : Medium
Salt Tolerance : Medium
Soil Requirements : Wide
Plant Type : Evergreen shrub
Foliage Color : Green
Flowering Season : Spring; summer
Flower Color : White
Propagation : Seeds
Human Hazards : None
Common Uses : Flowering shrub; hedge
Major Problems : None
Additional Notes : Attractive foliage. Can be difficult in cultivation.

Family : Melastomataceae   **Zone** : 10B-11

Typical Height : 10 Ft.
Drought Tolerance : High
Nutritional Requirements : Low
Light Requirements : High; medium
Leaf Type : Simple
Texture : Medium
Flower Characteristics : Showy

Environmental Problems : None

Thalia geniculata

Common Name(s) : Thalia
Origin : Tropical America
Growth Rate : Fast
Salt Tolerance : Low
Soil Requirements : Acid
Plant Type : Herbaceous perennial
Foliage Color : Green
Flowering Season : Spring; summer
Flower Color : Purple
Propagation : Division
Human Hazards : None
Common Uses : Aquatic
Major Problems : None
Additional Notes : A nice tall accent for the water or bog garden.

Family : Marantaceae   **Zone** : 10A-11

Typical Height : 6 Ft.
Drought Tolerance : Low
Nutritional Requirements : Medium
Light Requirements : Medium
Leaf Type : Simple
Texture : Coarse
Flower Characteristics : Insignificant

Environmental Problems : None

Thelypteris palustris

Common Name(s) : Marsh Fern
Origin : Temperate Northern Hemisphere
Growth Rate : Medium
Salt Tolerance : Low
Soil Requirements : Wide
Plant Type : Herbaceous perennial
Foliage Color : Green
Flowering Season : n/a
Flower Color : n/a
Propagation : Spores; division
Human Hazards : None
Common Uses : Beds; specimen plant; foliage plant
Major Problems : None
Additional Notes : Very tolerant of wet sites.

Family : Thelypteridaceae   **Zone** : 3-10A

Typical Height : 2.5 Ft.
Drought Tolerance : Low
Nutritional Requirements : Medium
Light Requirements : Low; medium
Leaf Type : Pinnately compound
Texture : Medium
Flower Characteristics : n/a

Environmental Problems : None

Thermopsis caroliniana

Common Name(s) : Carolina Thermopsis; Carolina Lupine
Origin : North Carolina to Georgia
Growth Rate : Medium
Salt Tolerance : Low
Soil Requirements : Wide
Plant Type : Herbaceous perennial
Foliage Color : Green
Flowering Season : Summer
Flower Color : Yellow
Propagation : Seeds; division
Human Hazards : None
Common Uses : Borders; cut flowers; specimen plant
Major Problems : None
Additional Notes : A legume native to Georgia & N. Carolina. Flowers in 2 years from seed.

Family : Leguminosae   **Zone** : 8-10A

Typical Height : 3 Ft.
Drought Tolerance : Medium
Nutritional Requirements : Low
Light Requirements : High
Leaf Type : Pinnately compound
Texture : Medium
Flower Characteristics : Showy

Environmental Problems : None

Thespesia populnea

Common Name(s) : Seaside Mahoe
Origin : Old World Tropics
Growth Rate : Fast
Salt Tolerance : High
Soil Requirements : Wide
Plant Type : Evergreen tree
Foliage Color : Green
Flowering Season : Year-round
Flower Color : Yellow-red
Propagation : Seeds; cuttings; air layers
Human Hazards : None
Common Uses : Flowering tree
Major Problems : None
Additional Notes : Flowers open yellow and turn maroon by nightfall.

Family : Malvaceae   **Zone** : 10B-11

Typical Height : 40 Ft.
Drought Tolerance : High
Nutritional Requirements : Medium
Light Requirements : High
Leaf Type : Simple
Texture : Coarse
Flower Characteristics : Showy

Environmental Problems : Weedy

Thevetia peruviana *(Photograph p. 187)*

Common Name(s) : Yellow Oleander
Origin : Tropical America
Growth Rate : Medium
Salt Tolerance : High
Soil Requirements : Wide
Plant Type : Evergreen shrub or tree
Foliage Color : Green
Flowering Season : Spring; summer; fall
Flower Color : Yellow; orange
Propagation : Seeds; cuttings
Human Hazards : Poisonous
Common Uses : Flowering shrub; small flowering tree
Major Problems : Caterpillars
Additional Notes : Yellow angular fruit very poisonous.

Family : Apocynaceae   **Zone** : 10B-11

Typical Height : 12 Ft.
Drought Tolerance : Medium
Nutritional Requirements : Medium
Light Requirements : High
Leaf Type : Simple; linear
Texture : Medium
Flower Characteristics : Showy; fragrant

Environmental Problems : None

Thrinax morrisii *(Photograph p. 208)*

Common Name(s) : Key Thatch Palm
Origin : Florida Keys
Growth Rate : Slow
Salt Tolerance : High
Soil Requirements : Wide
Plant Type : Palm
Foliage Color : Green & silver
Flowering Season : Spring
Flower Color : White
Propagation : Seeds
Human Hazards : None
Common Uses : Small tree; palm
Major Problems : None
Additional Notes : A small slow growing native palm.

Family : Palmae   **Zone** : 10B-11

Typical Height : 20 Ft.
Drought Tolerance : High
Nutritional Requirements : Low
Light Requirements : Medium; high
Leaf Type : Simple; palmately lobed
Texture : Very coarse
Flower Characteristics : Insignificant

Environmental Problems : None

Thrinax parviflora

Common Name(s) : Thatch Palm
Origin : Jamaica
Growth Rate : Slow
Salt Tolerance : High
Soil Requirements : Wide
Plant Type : Palm
Foliage Color : Green
Flowering Season : Spring; summer; fall
Flower Color : White
Propagation : Seeds
Human Hazards : None
Common Uses : Small tree; palm
Major Problems : None
Additional Notes : A slow growing palm. Rarely cultivated.

Family : Palmae   **Zone** : 10B-11

Typical Height : 20 Ft.
Drought Tolerance : High
Nutritional Requirements : Low
Light Requirements : High
Leaf Type : Simple; palmately lobed
Texture : Very coarse
Flower Characteristics : Insignificant

Environmental Problems : None

Thrinax radiata

Common Name(s) : Florida Thatch Palm
Origin : South Florida and West Indies
Growth Rate : Slow
Salt Tolerance : High
Soil Requirements : Wide
Plant Type : Palm
Foliage Color : Green
Flowering Season : Spring
Flower Color : White
Propagation : Seeds
Human Hazards : None
Common Uses : Small tree; palm
Major Problems : None
Additional Notes : An excellent slow growing native palm.

Family : Palmae   **Zone** : 10B-11

Typical Height : 20 Ft.
Drought Tolerance : High
Nutritional Requirements : Low
Light Requirements : Medium; high
Leaf Type : Simple; palmately lobed
Texture : Very coarse
Flower Characteristics : Insignificant

Environmental Problems : None

Thunbergia alata *(Photograph p. 212)*

Common Name(s) : Black-eyed Susan Vine
Origin : Tropical Africa
Growth Rate : Fast
Salt Tolerance : Low
Soil Requirements : Wide
Plant Type : Evergreen vine
Foliage Color : Green
Flowering Season : Summer; fall
Flower Color : Yellow-orange; white
Propagation : Seeds; cuttings
Human Hazards : None
Common Uses : Flowering vine; hanging basket
Major Problems : Spider mites
Additional Notes : Can be grown as an annual in colder climates.

Family : Acanthaceae   **Zone** : 10B-11

Typical Height : Not applicable
Drought Tolerance : Low
Nutritional Requirements : Medium
Light Requirements : Medium; high
Leaf Type : Simple
Texture : Medium
Flower Characteristics : Showy

Environmental Problems : None

Thunbergia erecta

Common Name(s) : Bush Clock Vine; King's Mantle
Origin : Tropical Africa
Growth Rate : Medium
Salt Tolerance : Medium
Soil Requirements : Wide
Plant Type : Evergreen shrub
Foliage Color : Green
Flowering Season : Year-round
Flower Color : Purple; white
Propagation : Cuttings
Human Hazards : None
Common Uses : Flowering shrub; hedge
Major Problems : None
Additional Notes : Prune frequently to maintain good form.

Family : Acanthaceae   **Zone** : 10B-11

Typical Height : 5 Ft.
Drought Tolerance : Low
Nutritional Requirements : Medium
Light Requirements : Medium; high
Leaf Type : Simple
Texture : Fine
Flower Characteristics : Showy

Environmental Problems : None

Thunbergia fragrans

Common Name(s) : Sweet Clock Vine
Origin : India and Sri Lanka
Growth Rate : Fast
Salt Tolerance : Low
Soil Requirements : Wide
Plant Type : Evergreen vine
Foliage Color : Green
Flowering Season : Summer; fall
Flower Color : White
Propagation : Seeds; cuttings
Human Hazards : None
Common Uses : Flowering vine
Major Problems : None
Additional Notes : Can become weedy, self seeds.

Family : Acanthaceae   **Zone** : 10A-11

Typical Height : Not applicable
Drought Tolerance : Medium
Nutritional Requirements : Medium
Light Requirements : High
Leaf Type : Simple
Texture : Medium
Flower Characteristics : Showy

Environmental Problems : Weedy

Thunbergia grandiflora *(Photograph p. 212)*

Common Name(s) : Bengal Clock Vine; Sky Vine
Origin : India
Growth Rate : Fast
Salt Tolerance : Low
Soil Requirements : Wide
Plant Type : Evergreen vine
Foliage Color : Green
Flowering Season : Summer; fall
Flower Color : White; blue
Propagation : Cuttings
Human Hazards : None
Common Uses : Flowering vine
Major Problems : Fe deficiency
Additional Notes : A very rampant vine.

Family : Acanthaceae   Zone : 10B-11

Typical Height : Not applicable
Drought Tolerance : Medium
Nutritional Requirements : Medium
Light Requirements : Medium
Leaf Type : Simple
Texture : Coarse
Flower Characteristics : Showy

Environmental Problems : Invasive

Tibouchina clavata

Common Name(s) : Tibouchina
Origin : Brazil
Growth Rate : Fast
Salt Tolerance : Low
Soil Requirements : Wide
Plant Type : Evergreen shrub
Foliage Color : Silver-green
Flowering Season : Spring; summer; fall
Flower Color : Purple
Propagation : Cuttings
Human Hazards : None
Common Uses : Flowering shrub
Major Problems : None
Additional Notes : Has very hairy leaves. Straggly growth requires frequent pruning.

Family : Melastomataceae   Zone : 10B-11

Typical Height : 6 Ft.
Drought Tolerance : Low
Nutritional Requirements : Medium
Light Requirements : High
Leaf Type : Simple
Texture : Medium
Flower Characteristics : Showy

Environmental Problems : None

Tibouchina granulosa *(Photograph p. 187)*

Common Name(s) : Purple Glory Tree
Origin : Brazil
Growth Rate : Medium
Salt Tolerance : Low
Soil Requirements : Acid
Plant Type : Evergreen tree or shrub
Foliage Color : Green
Flowering Season : Spring; summer; fall
Flower Color : Purple
Propagation : Cuttings; air layers
Human Hazards : None
Common Uses : Small flowering tree; flowering shrub
Major Problems : Mites; root rot; nematodes
Additional Notes : Has winged young stems.

Family : Melastomataceae   Zone : 10B-11

Typical Height : 20 Ft.
Drought Tolerance : Low
Nutritional Requirements : Medium
Light Requirements : Medium; high
Leaf Type : Simple
Texture : Medium
Flower Characteristics : Showy

Environmental Problems : None

Tibouchina urvilleana

Common Name(s) : Glorybush
Origin : Southern Brazil
Growth Rate : Medium
Salt Tolerance : Low
Soil Requirements : Acid
Plant Type : Evergreen shrub
Foliage Color : Green
Flowering Season : Spring; summer; fall
Flower Color : Purple
Propagation : Cuttings; air layers
Human Hazards : None
Common Uses : Flowering shrub
Major Problems : Mites; root rot; nematodes
Additional Notes : Grows best in central Florida.

Family : Melastomataceae   Zone : 9B-10B

Typical Height : 10 Ft.
Drought Tolerance : Low
Nutritional Requirements : Medium
Light Requirements : Medium; high
Leaf Type : Simple
Texture : Medium
Flower Characteristics : Showy

Environmental Problems : None

Tilia floridana

Common Name(s) : Florida Basswood
Origin : Florida
Growth Rate : Fast
Salt Tolerance : Low
Soil Requirements : Acid
Plant Type : Deciduous tree
Foliage Color : Green
Flowering Season : Spring; summer
Flower Color : Yellow
Propagation : Seeds; cuttings
Human Hazards : None
Common Uses : Shade tree
Major Problems : Chewing insects
Additional Notes : Sprouts vigorously from base; good nectar source for bees.

Family : Tiliaceae   **Zone** : 8-10B

Typical Height : 45 Ft.
Drought Tolerance : Low
Nutritional Requirements : High
Light Requirements : Medium
Leaf Type : Simple
Texture : Medium
Flower Characteristics : Insignificant

Environmental Problems : None

Tillandsia spp. *(Photograph p. 201)*

Common Name(s) : Air Plant
Origin : Mexico and Central America
Growth Rate : Slow
Salt Tolerance : n/a
Soil Requirements : Well-drained
Plant Type : Perennial epiphyte
Foliage Color : Green; silver-green
Flowering Season : Winter; spring
Flower Color : Purple; red; red and yellow
Propagation : Seeds; division
Human Hazards : None
Common Uses : Epiphyte
Major Problems : None
Additional Notes : Many species are cultivated.

Family : Bromeliaceae   **Zone** : 10A-11

Typical Height : 1 Ft.
Drought Tolerance : High
Nutritional Requirements : Low
Light Requirements : Medium; high
Leaf Type : Simple; linear
Texture : Medium
Flower Characteristics : Showy

Environmental Problems : None

Tipuana tipu

Common Name(s) : Pride-of-Bolivia; Rosewood
Origin : Southern Brazil and Bolivia
Growth Rate : Fast
Salt Tolerance : Low
Soil Requirements : Wide
Plant Type : Evergreen tree
Foliage Color : Green
Flowering Season : Spring; summer
Flower Color : Yellow
Propagation : Seeds
Human Hazards : None
Common Uses : Flowering tree
Major Problems : None
Additional Notes : Wood is used as a source of rosewood.

Family : Leguminosae   **Zone** : 10B-11

Typical Height : 40 Ft.
Drought Tolerance : Medium
Nutritional Requirements : Medium
Light Requirements : High
Leaf Type : Pinnately compound
Texture : Fine
Flower Characteristics : Showy

Environmental Problems : None

Torreya taxifolia

Common Name(s) : Stinking Cedar; Florida Nutmeg
Origin : Florida
Growth Rate : Slow
Salt Tolerance : Low
Soil Requirements : Acid
Plant Type : Evergreen tree
Foliage Color : Green
Flowering Season : Spring
Flower Color : n/a
Propagation : Seeds; cuttings
Human Hazards : None
Common Uses : Small tree
Major Problems : Scales; root rot; stem blight
Additional Notes : Rare and endangered native conifer.

Family : Taxaceae   **Zone** : 8-9

Typical Height : 20 Ft.
Drought Tolerance : Low
Nutritional Requirements : High
Light Requirements : Medium
Leaf Type : Needle
Texture : Medium
Flower Characteristics : Insignificant

Environmental Problems : None

Trachelospermum asiaticum

Common Name(s) : Small Leaf Confederate Jasmine
Origin : Japan and Korea
Growth Rate : Medium
Salt Tolerance : Medium
Soil Requirements : Wide
Plant Type : Evergreen vine
Foliage Color : Green
Flowering Season : Summer
Flower Color : Yellow
Propagation : Cuttings
Human Hazards : None
Common Uses : Flowering vine; flowering groundcover
Major Problems : Scales; whiteflies; sooty mold
Additional Notes : Forms a thick mat which eliminates weeds.
Cultivars

Family : Apocynaceae   **Zone** : 8-10B

Typical Height : .8 Ft.
Drought Tolerance : Medium
Nutritional Requirements : Medium
Light Requirements : High; medium
Leaf Type : Simple
Texture : Medium
Flower Characteristics : Showy; fragrant

Environmental Problems : None

'VARIEGATUM' has variegated foliage; 'BRONZE BEAUTY' has bronze new foliage; 'RED TOP' has reddish new growth; 'MINI MOUND' and 'MIMIMA' are extremely compact.

Trachelospermum jasminoides

Common Name(s) : Confederate Jasmine
Origin : China
Growth Rate : Medium
Salt Tolerance : Medium
Soil Requirements : Wide
Plant Type : Evergreen vine
Foliage Color : Green; variegated
Flowering Season : Spring
Flower Color : White
Propagation : Cuttings
Human Hazards : None
Common Uses : Flowering groundcover; flowering vine
Major Problems : Scales; sooty mold
Cultivars

Family : Apocynaceae   **Zone** : 8-10B

Typical Height : Not applicable
Drought Tolerance : Medium
Nutritional Requirements : Medium
Light Requirements : Medium; high
Leaf Type : Simple
Texture : Medium
Flower Characteristics : Showy; fragrant

Environmental Problems : None

'VARIEGATUM' has variegated foliage and is said to be hardier; 'MANDAIANUM' is a low dense shrub and has yellow flowers.

Trachycarpus fortunei *(Photograph p. 208)*

Common Name(s) : Windmill Palm
Origin : China
Growth Rate : Slow
Salt Tolerance : Medium
Soil Requirements : Wide
Plant Type : Palm
Foliage Color : Green
Flowering Season : Spring
Flower Color : White
Propagation : Seeds
Human Hazards : None
Common Uses : Small tree; palm
Major Problems : Lethal yellowing (moderately susceptible)
Additional Notes : A very cold hardy palm.

Family : Palmae   **Zone** : 8B-10B

Typical Height : 25 Ft.
Drought Tolerance : High
Nutritional Requirements : Medium
Light Requirements : Medium; high
Leaf Type : Simple; palmately lobed
Texture : Very coarse
Flower Characteristics : Insignificant

Environmental Problems : None

Tradescantia ohiensis

Common Name(s) : Spiderwort
Origin : Eastern United States
Growth Rate : Fast
Salt Tolerance : Low
Soil Requirements : Wide
Plant Type : Herbaceous perennial
Foliage Color : Green
Flowering Season : Spring; summer
Flower Color : Blue
Propagation : Cuttings
Human Hazards : None
Common Uses : Groundcover
Major Problems : None
Additional Notes : Cut stems to ground in mid-summer to re-flower in fall.

Family : Commelinaceae   **Zone** : 3-10B

Typical Height : 1.5 Ft.
Drought Tolerance : Low
Nutritional Requirements : Medium
Light Requirements : Medium
Leaf Type : Simple
Texture : Medium
Flower Characteristics : Showy

Environmental Problems : None

Tradescantia virginiana

Common Name(s) : Spiderwort
Origin : Eastern United States
Growth Rate : Fast
Salt Tolerance : Low
Soil Requirements : Wide
Plant Type : Herbaceous perennial
Foliage Color : Green
Flowering Season : Spring; summer
Flower Color : Blue; white; pink; red
Propagation : Cuttings
Human Hazards : None
Common Uses : Beds; borders
Major Problems : None
Additional Notes : Cut stems to ground in mid-summer to re-flower in fall.
Cultivars
Many cultivars exist.

Family : Commelinaceae   Zone : 6-10A

Typical Height : 1.5 Ft.
Drought Tolerance : Low
Nutritional Requirements : Medium
Light Requirements : Medium
Leaf Type : Simple
Texture : Medium
Flower Characteristics : Showy

Environmental Problems : None

Trevesia palmata

Common Name(s) : Snowflake Tree; Tropical Snowflake
Origin : Northern India to Southwestern China
Growth Rate : Medium
Salt Tolerance : Low
Soil Requirements : Wide
Plant Type : Evergreen shrub or tree
Foliage Color : Green
Flowering Season : Summer
Flower Color : White
Propagation : Cuttings
Human Hazards : None
Common Uses : Shrub; small tree
Major Problems : Mealybugs; scales; sooty mold
Additional Notes : New leaves resemble large snowflakes.

Family : Araliaceae   Zone : 10B-11

Typical Height : 15 Ft.
Drought Tolerance : Medium
Nutritional Requirements : Medium
Light Requirements : Medium; high
Leaf Type : Simple; palmately lobed
Texture : Coarse
Flower Characteristics : Insignificant

Environmental Problems : None

Tricyrtis spp.

Common Name(s) : Toad Lily
Origin : Himalayas to Japan and Taiwan
Growth Rate : Medium
Salt Tolerance : Low
Soil Requirements : Acid
Plant Type : Herbaceous perennial
Foliage Color : Green
Flowering Season : Spring; summer
Flower Color : White; brown; yellow
Propagation : Seeds; division
Human Hazards : None
Common Uses : Borders; rock gardens
Major Problems : None
Additional Notes : Hybrid forms available; should be more widely tried in north Florida.

Family : Liliaceae   Zone : 7-9

Typical Height : 2.5 Ft.
Drought Tolerance : Low
Nutritional Requirements : Medium
Light Requirements : Medium
Leaf Type : Simple
Texture : Medium
Flower Characteristics : Showy

Environmental Problems : None

Trimezia martinicensis

Common Name(s) : Trimezia
Origin : Tropical America
Growth Rate : Medium
Salt Tolerance : Low
Soil Requirements : Wide
Plant Type : Herbaceous perennial
Foliage Color : Green
Flowering Season : Spring; summer
Flower Color : Yellow
Propagation : Division
Human Hazards : None
Common Uses : Beds; flowering perennial
Major Problems : None
Additional Notes : A tropical iris relative.

Family : Iridaceae   Zone : 11

Typical Height : 1 Ft.
Drought Tolerance : Medium
Nutritional Requirements : Medium
Light Requirements : Medium
Leaf Type : Simple; linear
Texture : Medium
Flower Characteristics : Showy

Environmental Problems : None

Triphasia trifolia *(Photograph p. 187)*

Common Name(s) : Limeberry	**Family** : Rutaceae **Zone** : 9-10B
Origin : Southern Asia and East Indies	**Typical Height** : 7 Ft.
Growth Rate : Slow	**Drought Tolerance** : High
Salt Tolerance : Medium	**Nutritional Requirements** : Medium
Soil Requirements : Wide	**Light Requirements** : High
Plant Type : Evergreen shrub or tree	**Leaf Type** : Trifoliate
Foliage Color : Green	**Texture** : Fine
Flowering Season : Spring; summer; fall	**Flower Characteristics** : Insignificant; fragrant

Flower Color : White
Propagation : Seeds; cuttings
Human Hazards : None   **Environmental Problems** : None
Common Uses : Shrub; hedge; edible fruit; small tree
Major Problems : Nematodes; scales; whiteflies; sooty mold
Additional Notes : Thorny branches. Can be trained as a small tree.

Triplaris americana

Common Name(s) : Long John; Palo Santo Tree	**Family** : Polygonaceae **Zone** : 10B-11
Origin : South America	**Typical Height** : 25 Ft.
Growth Rate : Medium	**Drought Tolerance** : Medium
Salt Tolerance : Low	**Nutritional Requirements** : Medium
Soil Requirements : Wide	**Light Requirements** : High
Plant Type : Evergreen tree	**Leaf Type** : Simple
Foliage Color : Green	**Texture** : Coarse
Flowering Season : Winter; spring	**Flower Characteristics** : Showy

Flower Color : Red
Propagation : Seeds
Human Hazards : None   **Environmental Problems** : None
Common Uses : Small flowering tree
Major Problems : None
Additional Notes : Red female flowers in panicles.

Tripsacum dactyloides

Common Name(s) : Fakahatchee Grass; Eastern Gama Grass	**Family** : Gramineae **Zone** : 8-11
Origin : Southeastern USA to South America	**Typical Height** : 2 Ft.
Growth Rate : Medium	**Drought Tolerance** : High
Salt Tolerance : Medium	**Nutritional Requirements** : Low
Soil Requirements : Wide	**Light Requirements** : High
Plant Type : Herbaceous perennial	**Leaf Type** : Simple; linear
Foliage Color : Green	**Texture** : Fine
Flowering Season : Fall	**Flower Characteristics** : Insignificant

Flower Color : Gold
Propagation : Seeds; division
Human Hazards : None   **Environmental Problems** : None
Common Uses : Groundcover
Major Problems : None
Additional Notes : Has broader leaves than T. floridana .

Tripsacum floridana

Common Name(s) : Florida Tripsacum; Florida Gama Grass	**Family** : Gramineae **Zone** : 8-11
Origin : South Florida	**Typical Height** : 1 Ft.
Growth Rate : Medium	**Drought Tolerance** : High
Salt Tolerance : Medium	**Nutritional Requirements** : Low
Soil Requirements : Wide	**Light Requirements** : High
Plant Type : Herbaceous perennial	**Leaf Type** : Simple; linear
Foliage Color : Green	**Texture** : Fine
Flowering Season : Fall	**Flower Characteristics** : Insignificant

Flower Color : Gold
Propagation : Seeds; division
Human Hazards : None   **Environmental Problems** : None
Common Uses : Groundcover
Major Problems : None
Additional Notes : Has narrower leaves than T. dactyloides .

Trithrinax acanthocoma *(Photograph p. 209)*

Common Name(s) : Spiny Fiber Palm
Origin : Southern Brazil
Growth Rate : Medium
Salt Tolerance : Medium
Soil Requirements : Well-drained
Plant Type : Palm
Foliage Color : Green
Flowering Season : Summer
Flower Color : Yellow
Propagation : Seeds
Human Hazards : Spiny
Common Uses : Palm
Major Problems : Phytophthora bud rot

Family : Palmae   **Zone** : 9-11

Typical Height : 15 Ft.
Drought Tolerance : High
Nutritional Requirements : Low
Light Requirements : High
Leaf Type : Simple; palmately lobed
Texture : Very coarse
Flower Characteristics : Insignificant

Environmental Problems : None

Additional Notes : Very tolerant of poor soils; persistent leafbases are spiny and fibrous.

Tritonia crocata

Common Name(s) : Tritonia
Origin : South Africa
Growth Rate : Medium
Salt Tolerance : Low
Soil Requirements : Wide
Plant Type : Herbaceous perennial
Foliage Color : Green
Flowering Season : Summer
Flower Color : Red; orange
Propagation : Division; seeds
Human Hazards : None
Common Uses : Beds; borders; cut flowers
Major Problems : None

Family : Iridaceae   **Zone** : 7-10B

Typical Height : 1.5 Ft.
Drought Tolerance : Medium
Nutritional Requirements : Medium
Light Requirements : Medium
Leaf Type : Simple; linear
Texture : Coarse
Flower Characteristics : Showy

Environmental Problems : None

Additional Notes : Several cultivars exist. Does well for several years without division.

Tulbaghia violacea

Common Name(s) : Society Garlic
Origin : South Africa
Growth Rate : Medium
Salt Tolerance : Medium
Soil Requirements : Wide
Plant Type : Herbaceous perennial
Foliage Color : Green
Flowering Season : Spring; summer; fall
Flower Color : Purple
Propagation : Division
Human Hazards : None
Common Uses : Flowering groundcover
Major Problems : None

Family : Amaryllidaceae   **Zone** : 10A-11

Typical Height : 1.8 Ft.
Drought Tolerance : Medium
Nutritional Requirements : Medium
Light Requirements : Medium; high
Leaf Type : Simple; linear
Texture : Fine
Flower Characteristics : Showy

Environmental Problems : None

Additional Notes : Does not flower well in shade. Plants garlic scented.

Tupidanthus calyptratus

Common Name(s) : Tupidanthus; Mallet Flower
Origin : Cambodia
Growth Rate : Medium
Salt Tolerance : n/a
Soil Requirements : Wide
Plant Type : Evergreen shrub
Foliage Color : Green
Flowering Season : n/a
Flower Color : Green
Propagation : Seeds; cuttings
Human Hazards : None
Common Uses : Foliage plant; shrub
Major Problems : Scales

Family : Araliaceae   **Zone** : 10B-11

Typical Height : 10 Ft.
Drought Tolerance : Medium
Nutritional Requirements : Medium
Light Requirements : Medium; high
Leaf Type : Palmately compound
Texture : Coarse
Flower Characteristics : Insignificant

Environmental Problems : None

Additional Notes : Very similar in appearance to Brassaia actinophylla . Has thicker leaves.

Turnera ulmifolia *(Photograph p. 188)*
Common Name(s) : Yellow Alder
Origin : Caribbean Region
Growth Rate : Fast
Salt Tolerance : High
Soil Requirements : Wide
Plant Type : Evergreen shrub
Foliage Color : Green
Flowering Season : Year-round
Flower Color : Yellow
Propagation : Cuttings
Human Hazards : None
Common Uses : Flowering shrub; flowering groundcover
Major Problems : Whiteflies; aphids; mealybugs
Additional Notes : Straggly when unpruned.

Family : Turneraceae   Zone : 10B-11

Typical Height : 3 Ft.
Drought Tolerance : Medium
Nutritional Requirements : Low
Light Requirements : Medium; high
Leaf Type : Simple
Texture : Medium
Flower Characteristics : Showy

Environmental Problems : None

Ulmus alata *(Photograph p. 171)*
Common Name(s) : Winged Elm
Origin : Southeastern United States
Growth Rate : Medium
Salt Tolerance : Low
Soil Requirements : Wide
Plant Type : Deciduous tree
Foliage Color : Green
Flowering Season : Spring
Flower Color : Green
Propagation : Seeds
Human Hazards : None
Common Uses : Shade tree
Major Problems : None
Additional Notes : Interesting corky winged bark.

Family : Ulmaceae   Zone : 5-9

Typical Height : 25 Ft.
Drought Tolerance : High
Nutritional Requirements : Medium
Light Requirements : High
Leaf Type : Simple
Texture : Medium
Flower Characteristics : Insignificant

Environmental Problems : None

Ulmus americana
Common Name(s) : American Elm
Origin : North America
Growth Rate : Fast
Salt Tolerance : Low
Soil Requirements : Wide
Plant Type : Deciduous tree
Foliage Color : Green
Flowering Season : Spring
Flower Color : Green
Propagation : Seeds; cuttings
Human Hazards : None
Common Uses : Shade tree
Major Problems : Dutch elm disease; phloem necrosis
Additional Notes : Beautiful vase shape.
Cultivars
'AMERICANA', 'IOWA STATE', 'DELAWARE II', and 'LIBERTAS' are reported to be resistant to Dutch elm disease.

Family : Ulmaceae   Zone : 2-9

Typical Height : 85 Ft.
Drought Tolerance : Medium
Nutritional Requirements : Medium
Light Requirements : High
Leaf Type : Simple
Texture : Medium
Flower Characteristics : Insignificant

Environmental Problems : None

Ulmus crassifolia
Common Name(s) : Cedar Elm
Origin : Southern United States
Growth Rate : Medium
Salt Tolerance : Low
Soil Requirements : Wide
Plant Type : Deciduous tree
Foliage Color : Green
Flowering Season : Spring
Flower Color : Green
Propagation : Seeds; cuttings
Human Hazards : None
Common Uses : Shade tree
Major Problems : None
Additional Notes : Often has corky wings on new twigs.

Family : Ulmaceae   Zone : 7-9

Typical Height : 40 Ft.
Drought Tolerance : High
Nutritional Requirements : Medium
Light Requirements : High
Leaf Type : Simple
Texture : Medium
Flower Characteristics : Insignificant

Environmental Problems : None

Ulmus parvifolia *(Photograph p. 171)*

Common Name(s) : Chinese Elm
Origin : China and Japan
Growth Rate : Medium
Salt Tolerance : Low
Soil Requirements : Wide
Plant Type : Evergreen tree
Foliage Color : Green
Flowering Season : Spring
Flower Color : Green
Propagation : Seeds; cuttings
Human Hazards : None
Common Uses : Shade tree
Major Problems : Borers; chewing insects
Additional Notes : Has a weeping growth habit; blotchy exfoliating bark is attractive.
Cultivars
'DRAKE' has sweeping upright branches; 'PENDENS' has a weeping habit.

Family : Ulmaceae   Zone : 6-10B

Typical Height : 40 Ft.
Drought Tolerance : High
Nutritional Requirements : Medium
Light Requirements : High
Leaf Type : Simple
Texture : Fine
Flower Characteristics : Insignificant

Environmental Problems : None

Ulmus pumila

Common Name(s) : Dwarf Elm
Origin : Siberia, China
Growth Rate : Fast
Salt Tolerance : Medium
Soil Requirements : Wide
Plant Type : Deciduous tree
Foliage Color : Green
Flowering Season : Spring
Flower Color : Green
Propagation : Seeds
Human Hazards : None
Common Uses : Shade tree
Major Problems : Mites
Additional Notes : Short-lived.
Cultivars
'PENDULA' has a weeping habit.

Family : Ulmaceae   Zone : 3-9

Typical Height : 20 Ft.
Drought Tolerance : Medium
Nutritional Requirements : Low
Light Requirements : High
Leaf Type : Simple
Texture : Fine
Flower Characteristics : Insignificant

Environmental Problems : None

Uniola paniculata *(Photograph p. 201)*

Common Name(s) : Sea Oats
Origin : Southeastern United States
Growth Rate : Medium
Salt Tolerance : High
Soil Requirements : Wide
Plant Type : Herbaceous perennial
Foliage Color : Green
Flowering Season : Spring; summer
Flower Color : White
Propagation : Seeds; division
Human Hazards : None
Common Uses : Seasides
Major Problems : None
Additional Notes : A native endangered grass for beach plantings.

Family : Gramineae   Zone : 8-11

Typical Height : 4 Ft.
Drought Tolerance : High
Nutritional Requirements : Low
Light Requirements : High
Leaf Type : Simple; linear
Texture : Fine
Flower Characteristics : Insignificant

Environmental Problems : None

Urechites lutea

Common Name(s) : Wild Allamanda
Origin : South Florida and West Indies
Growth Rate : Medium
Salt Tolerance : Medium
Soil Requirements : Wide
Plant Type : Evergreen vine
Foliage Color : Green
Flowering Season : Year-round
Flower Color : Yellow
Propagation : Cuttings
Human Hazards : Poisonous
Common Uses : Flowering vine
Major Problems : None
Additional Notes : A showy native vine for coastal situations.

Family : Apocynaceae   Zone : 10B-11

Typical Height : Not applicable
Drought Tolerance : High
Nutritional Requirements : Medium
Light Requirements : Medium; high
Leaf Type : Simple
Texture : Medium
Flower Characteristics : Showy

Environmental Problems : None

Vaccinium myrsinites

Common Name(s) : Shiny Blueberry
Origin : Southeastern United States
Growth Rate : Slow
Salt Tolerance : Low
Soil Requirements : Acid
Plant Type : Evergreen shrub
Foliage Color : Green
Flowering Season : Spring
Flower Color : White; pink
Propagation : Division; cuttings
Human Hazards : None
Common Uses : Shrub
Major Problems : None
Additional Notes : This Florida native prefers acid soil. Spreads by runners.

Family : Ericaceae   Zone : 7-10B

Typical Height : 2 Ft.
Drought Tolerance : High
Nutritional Requirements : Low
Light Requirements : Medium; high
Leaf Type : Simple
Texture : Fine
Flower Characteristics : Insignificant

Environmental Problems : None

Valeriana officinalis

Common Name(s) : Common Valerian
Origin : Northern Hemisphere
Growth Rate : Medium
Salt Tolerance : Low
Soil Requirements : Wide
Plant Type : Herbaceous perennial
Foliage Color : Green
Flowering Season : Summer
Flower Color : Pink-white
Propagation : Seeds; division
Human Hazards : None
Common Uses : Cut flowers; specimen plant
Major Problems : None
Additional Notes : Attractive fern-like foliage. Flowers in one year from seed.

Family : Valerianaceae   Zone : 3-10B

Typical Height : 3 Ft.
Drought Tolerance : Medium
Nutritional Requirements : Medium
Light Requirements : Medium; high
Leaf Type : Pinnately compound
Texture : Medium
Flower Characteristics : Showy; fragrant

Environmental Problems : None

Vanilla planifolia

Common Name(s) : Vanilla Orchid
Origin : Tropical America
Growth Rate : Slow
Salt Tolerance : Low
Soil Requirements : Wide
Plant Type : Evergreen vine
Foliage Color : Green
Flowering Season : Summer; fall
Flower Color : Yellow & orange
Propagation : Cuttings
Human Hazards : None
Common Uses : Edible; vine
Major Problems : None
Additional Notes : Vanilla extract obtained from fruit pods. Hand pollination required.

Family : Orchidaceae   Zone : 10B-11

Typical Height : Not applicable
Drought Tolerance : Medium
Nutritional Requirements : Medium
Light Requirements : Medium
Leaf Type : Simple
Texture : Medium
Flower Characteristics : Insignificant; fragrant

Environmental Problems : None

Veitchia joannis (Photograph p. 209)

Common Name(s) : Joannis Palm
Origin : Fiji Islands
Growth Rate : Fast
Salt Tolerance : Medium
Soil Requirements : Wide
Plant Type : Palm
Foliage Color : Green
Flowering Season : Summer
Flower Color : White
Propagation : Seeds
Human Hazards : None
Common Uses : Tree; palm
Major Problems : None
Additional Notes : A tall palm resistant to lethal yellowing.

Family : Palmae   Zone : 10B-11

Typical Height : 60 Ft.
Drought Tolerance : High
Nutritional Requirements : Medium
Light Requirements : Medium; high
Leaf Type : Pinnately compound
Texture : Coarse
Flower Characteristics : Insignificant

Environmental Problems : None

Veitchia mcdanielsii *(Photograph p. 209)*

Common Name(s) : Sunshine Palm
Origin : New Caledonia
Growth Rate : Fast
Salt Tolerance : Medium
Soil Requirements : Wide
Plant Type : Palm
Foliage Color : Green
Flowering Season : Summer
Flower Color : White
Propagation : Seeds
Human Hazards : None
Common Uses : Tree; palm
Major Problems : None
Additional Notes : A tall palm resistant to lethal yellowing.

Family : Palmae   **Zone** : 10B-11

Typical Height : 60 Ft.
Drought Tolerance : High
Nutritional Requirements : Medium
Light Requirements : Medium; high
Leaf Type : Pinnately compound
Texture : Coarse
Flower Characteristics : Insignificant

Environmental Problems : None

Veitchia merrillii *(Photograph p. 209)*

Common Name(s) : Manila Palm; Adonidia Palm; Christmas Palm
Origin : Philippines
Growth Rate : Medium
Salt Tolerance : Medium
Soil Requirements : Wide
Plant Type : Palm
Foliage Color : Green
Flowering Season : Summer
Flower Color : White
Propagation : Seeds
Human Hazards : None
Common Uses : Small tree; palm
Major Problems : Lethal yellowing (highly susceptible)
Additional Notes : Attractive fruit around Christmas time.

Family : Palmae   **Zone** : 10B-11

Typical Height : 15 Ft.
Drought Tolerance : High
Nutritional Requirements : Medium
Light Requirements : Medium; high
Leaf Type : Pinnately compound
Texture : Coarse
Flower Characteristics : Insignificant

Environmental Problems : None

Veitchia montgomeryana

Common Name(s) : Montgomery Palm
Origin : New Hebrides Islands
Growth Rate : Fast
Salt Tolerance : Medium
Soil Requirements : Wide
Plant Type : Palm
Foliage Color : Green
Flowering Season : Summer
Flower Color : White
Propagation : Seeds
Human Hazards : None
Common Uses : Tree; palm
Major Problems : Lethal yellowing (slightly susceptible)
Additional Notes : Makes nice vertical accent.

Family : Palmae   **Zone** : 10B-11

Typical Height : 35 Ft.
Drought Tolerance : High
Nutritional Requirements : Medium
Light Requirements : Medium; high
Leaf Type : Pinnately compound
Texture : Coarse
Flower Characteristics : Insignificant

Environmental Problems : None

Veitchia winin

Common Name(s) : Winin Palm
Origin : New Hebrides Islands
Growth Rate : Fast
Salt Tolerance : Medium
Soil Requirements : Wide
Plant Type : Palm
Foliage Color : Green
Flowering Season : Summer
Flower Color : White
Propagation : Seeds
Human Hazards : None
Common Uses : Tree; palm
Major Problems : None
Additional Notes : A tall palm resistant to lethal yellowing.

Family : Palmae   **Zone** : 10B-11

Typical Height : 50 Ft.
Drought Tolerance : High
Nutritional Requirements : Medium
Light Requirements : Medium; high
Leaf Type : Pinnately compound
Texture : Coarse
Flower Characteristics : Insignificant

Environmental Problems : None

Verbascum spp.

Common Name(s) : Mullein
Origin : Mediterranean Region
Growth Rate : Medium
Salt Tolerance : Medium
Soil Requirements : Wide
Plant Type : Biennial
Foliage Color : Green
Flowering Season : Summer; fall
Flower Color : Lavender; orange; pink; red; white; yellow
Propagation : Root cuttings; seeds
Human Hazards : None
Common Uses : Borders; specimen plant
Major Problems : None
Additional Notes : Rosette foliage the first year, flowers the second. Some species weedy.

Family : Scrophulariaceae   **Zone** : 4-10A

Typical Height : 3.5 Ft.
Drought Tolerance : High
Nutritional Requirements : Low
Light Requirements : High
Leaf Type : Simple
Texture : Coarse
Flower Characteristics : Showy

Environmental Problems : None

Viburnum obovatum

Common Name(s) : Black Haw
Origin : Southeastern United States
Growth Rate : Medium
Salt Tolerance : Low
Soil Requirements : Wide
Plant Type : Evergreen shrub
Foliage Color : Green
Flowering Season : Spring
Flower Color : White
Propagation : Cuttings; seeds
Human Hazards : None
Common Uses : Flowering shrub
Major Problems : None
Additional Notes : Excellent for informal hedges.

Family : Caprifoliaceae   **Zone** : 7-10B

Typical Height : 6 Ft.
Drought Tolerance : High
Nutritional Requirements : Low
Light Requirements : Medium; high
Leaf Type : Simple
Texture : Fine
Flower Characteristics : Showy

Environmental Problems : None

Viburnum odoratissimum

Common Name(s) : Sweet Viburnum
Origin : India to Japan
Growth Rate : Medium
Salt Tolerance : Low
Soil Requirements : Wide
Plant Type : Evergreen shrub
Foliage Color : Green
Flowering Season : Spring
Flower Color : White
Propagation : Seeds; cuttings
Human Hazards : None
Common Uses : Shrub; hedge
Major Problems : Aphids; scales; thrips; mites; sooty mold; stem canker
Additional Notes : Requires regular pruning to maintain shape and size.
Cultivars
Var. awabuki has large glossy leaves.

Family : Caprifoliaceae   **Zone** : 8-10B

Typical Height : 8 Ft.
Drought Tolerance : Medium
Nutritional Requirements : Medium
Light Requirements : Medium; high
Leaf Type : Simple
Texture : Medium
Flower Characteristics : Insignificant; fragrant

Environmental Problems : None

Viburnum rufidulum

Common Name(s) : Rusty Blackhaw
Origin : Southeastern United States
Growth Rate : Medium
Salt Tolerance : Low
Soil Requirements : Wide
Plant Type : Deciduous tree
Foliage Color : Green
Flowering Season : Fall
Flower Color : White
Propagation : Cuttings; seeds
Human Hazards : None
Common Uses : Small flowering tree
Major Problems : None
Additional Notes : Largely pest-free; attractive fruit.

Family : Caprifoliaceae   **Zone** : 6-9

Typical Height : 20 Ft.
Drought Tolerance : Medium
Nutritional Requirements : Medium
Light Requirements : Medium; high
Leaf Type : Simple
Texture : Medium
Flower Characteristics : Showy

Environmental Problems : None

Viburnum suspensum

Common Name(s) : Sandankwa Viburnum
Origin : Ryukyu Islands
Growth Rate : Medium
Salt Tolerance : Low
Soil Requirements : Wide
Plant Type : Evergreen shrub
Foliage Color : Green
Flowering Season : Summer
Flower Color : Pink-white
Propagation : Seeds; cuttings
Human Hazards : None
Common Uses : Shrub; hedge
Major Problems : Scales; whiteflies; nematodes
Additional Notes : Easily maintained at any size.

Family : Caprifoliaceae   **Zone** : 8-10B

Typical Height : 6 Ft.
Drought Tolerance : Low
Nutritional Requirements : Medium
Light Requirements : Medium; high
Leaf Type : Simple
Texture : Medium
Flower Characteristics : Insignificant

Environmental Problems : None

Viburnum tinus *(Photograph p. 187)*

Common Name(s) : Laurestinus
Origin : Mediterranean Region
Growth Rate : Medium
Salt Tolerance : Low
Soil Requirements : Wide
Plant Type : Evergreen shrub
Foliage Color : Green
Flowering Season : Winter
Flower Color : Pink; white
Propagation : Seeds; cuttings
Human Hazards : None
Common Uses : Flowering shrub; hedge
Major Problems : Aphids; thrips; nematodes; root rots
Additional Notes : Attractive fruit; excellent hedge or screen.
Cultivars
'COMPACTUM' is a more compact variety; 'STRICTUM' has an upright form; 'VARIEGATUM' has variegated foliage.

Family : Caprifoliaceae   **Zone** : 7-9

Typical Height : 7 Ft.
Drought Tolerance : Medium
Nutritional Requirements : Medium
Light Requirements : Medium; high
Leaf Type : Simple
Texture : Medium
Flower Characteristics : Showy; fragrant

Environmental Problems : None

Vinca major

Common Name(s) : Greater Periwinkle
Origin : Europe
Growth Rate : Fast
Salt Tolerance : Low
Soil Requirements : Wide
Plant Type : Evergreen perennial
Foliage Color : Green
Flowering Season : Spring
Flower Color : Lavender
Propagation : Division; cuttings
Human Hazards : Poisonous
Common Uses : Beds; groundcover
Major Problems : None
Additional Notes : An attractive groundcover, but all plant parts are poisonous.

Family : Apocynaceae   **Zone** : 8-10A

Typical Height : 1 Ft.
Drought Tolerance : Medium
Nutritional Requirements : Medium
Light Requirements : Medium; high
Leaf Type : Simple
Texture : Medium
Flower Characteristics : Showy

Environmental Problems : None

Viola floridana

Common Name(s) : Florida Violet
Origin : Eastern Florida
Growth Rate : Medium
Salt Tolerance : Low
Soil Requirements : Acid
Plant Type : Herbaceous perennial
Foliage Color : Green
Flowering Season : Spring
Flower Color : Blue; white
Propagation : Seeds; division
Human Hazards : None
Common Uses : Beds; groundcover
Major Problems : None
Additional Notes : A pretty native violet useful in woodland settings; other species native.

Family : Violaceae   **Zone** : 8-10B

Typical Height : .5 Ft.
Drought Tolerance : Low
Nutritional Requirements : Medium
Light Requirements : Medium
Leaf Type : Simple
Texture : Medium
Flower Characteristics : Showy

Environmental Problems : None

Vitex agnus-castus *(Photograph p. 188)*
Common Name(s) : Chaste Tree
Origin : Southern Europe
Growth Rate : Medium
Salt Tolerance : Medium
Soil Requirements : Wide
Plant Type : Deciduous shrub
Foliage Color : Green
Flowering Season : Summer
Flower Color : Blue
Propagation : Cuttings
Human Hazards : None
Common Uses : Flowering shrub
Major Problems : Scales; nematodes; mushroom root rot
Additional Notes : Ungainly unless pruned.

Family : Verbenaceae   Zone : 7-10B

Typical Height : 12 Ft.
Drought Tolerance : Medium
Nutritional Requirements : Medium
Light Requirements : High
Leaf Type : Palmately compound
Texture : Medium
Flower Characteristics : Showy; fragrant

Environmental Problems : None

Vitex trifolia *(Photograph p. 188)*
Common Name(s) : Vitex
Origin : Asia to Australia
Growth Rate : Medium
Salt Tolerance : Medium
Soil Requirements : Wide
Plant Type : Deciduous shrub
Foliage Color : Green; variegated
Flowering Season : Summer
Flower Color : Blue
Propagation : Seeds; cuttings
Human Hazards : None
Common Uses : Flowering shrub
Major Problems : Scales; mushroom root rot
Additional Notes : Cultivar 'VARIEGATA' is most commonly planted.
Cultivars
'VARIEGATA' has variegated foliage; var. simplicifolia is prostrate with simple leaves.

Family : Verbenaceae   Zone : 9-10B

Typical Height : 10 Ft.
Drought Tolerance : Medium
Nutritional Requirements : Medium
Light Requirements : High
Leaf Type : Simple or trifoliate
Texture : Medium
Flower Characteristics : Showy

Environmental Problems : None

Vriesia splendens
Common Name(s) : Flaming Sword
Origin : French Guiana
Growth Rate : Slow
Salt Tolerance : Low
Soil Requirements : Well-drained
Plant Type : Perennial epiphyte
Foliage Color : Green & brown
Flowering Season : Spring; summer; fall
Flower Color : Red & yellow
Propagation : Division; seeds
Human Hazards : None
Common Uses : Epiphyte; foliage plant; specimen plant
Major Problems : Scales
Additional Notes : This bromeliad has green & brown banded foliage and a spike of red bracts.

Family : Bromeliaceae   Zone : 10B-11

Typical Height : 3 Ft.
Drought Tolerance : High
Nutritional Requirements : Low
Light Requirements : Medium
Leaf Type : Simple; linear
Texture : Coarse
Flower Characteristics : Showy

Environmental Problems : None

Washingtonia filifera *(Photograph p. 209)*
Common Name(s) : Desert Fan Palm
Origin : California
Growth Rate : Medium
Salt Tolerance : Medium
Soil Requirements : Wide
Plant Type : Palm
Foliage Color : Green
Flowering Season : Spring
Flower Color : White
Propagation : Seeds
Human Hazards : Spiny
Common Uses : Tree; palm
Major Problems : Phytophthora bud rot; weevils; scales
Additional Notes : Often hybridizes with W. robusta . Trunk diameter is much larger.

Family : Palmae   Zone : 8-11

Typical Height : 50 Ft.
Drought Tolerance : High
Nutritional Requirements : Medium
Light Requirements : High
Leaf Type : Simple; palmately lobed
Texture : Very coarse
Flower Characteristics : Insignificant

Environmental Problems : None

Washingtonia robusta *(Photograph p. 209)*

Common Name(s) : Washington Palm
Origin : Mexico
Growth Rate : Fast
Salt Tolerance : Medium
Soil Requirements : Wide
Plant Type : Palm
Foliage Color : Green
Flowering Season : Spring
Flower Color : White
Propagation : Seeds
Human Hazards : Spiny
Common Uses : Tree; palm
Major Problems : Phytophthora bud rot; weevils; scales
Additional Notes : A tall slender palm often retaining the old leaves.

Family : Palmae   **Zone** : 8-11

Typical Height : 100 Ft.
Drought Tolerance : High
Nutritional Requirements : Medium
Light Requirements : High
Leaf Type : Simple; palmately lobed
Texture : Very coarse
Flower Characteristics : Insignificant

Environmental Problems : None

Watsonia spp.

Common Name(s) : Watsonia
Origin : South Africa and Madagascar
Growth Rate : Medium
Salt Tolerance : Low
Soil Requirements : Wide
Plant Type : Herbaceous perennial
Foliage Color : Green
Flowering Season : Spring; summer
Flower Color : Red; white; orange; pink
Propagation : Division; seeds
Human Hazards : None
Common Uses : Beds; borders; cut flowers
Major Problems : Stem rots (on corms)
Additional Notes : May be left undisturbed for several years.

Family : Iridaceae   **Zone** : 8-10B

Typical Height : 3 Ft.
Drought Tolerance : Low
Nutritional Requirements : Medium
Light Requirements : Medium
Leaf Type : Simple; linear
Texture : Medium
Flower Characteristics : Showy

Environmental Problems : None

Wedelia trilobata

Common Name(s) : Wedelia
Origin : West Indies
Growth Rate : Fast
Salt Tolerance : High
Soil Requirements : Wide
Plant Type : Herbaceous perennial
Foliage Color : Green
Flowering Season : Year-round
Flower Color : Yellow
Propagation : Cuttings
Human Hazards : None
Common Uses : Flowering groundcover; seasides;
Major Problems : Mites; chewing insects
Additional Notes : Good all around ground cover, but can be invasive.

Family : Compositae   **Zone** : 10A-11

Typical Height : .8 Ft.
Drought Tolerance : Medium
Nutritional Requirements : Low
Light Requirements : High
Leaf Type : Simple
Texture : Medium
Flower Characteristics : Showy

Environmental Problems : Invasive

Westringia rosmariniformis

Common Name(s) : Victorian Rosemary
Origin : Southeastern Australia
Growth Rate : Medium
Salt Tolerance : Medium
Soil Requirements : Wide
Plant Type : Evergreen shrub
Foliage Color : Green
Flowering Season : Spring; summer
Flower Color : White
Propagation : Seeds; cuttings
Human Hazards : None
Common Uses : Flowering shrub; hedge
Major Problems : None
Additional Notes : Good hedge plant for warm temperate areas.

Family : Labiatae   **Zone** : 9-10A

Typical Height : 5 Ft.
Drought Tolerance : High
Nutritional Requirements : Medium
Light Requirements : High
Leaf Type : Simple
Texture : Medium
Flower Characteristics : Showy

Environmental Problems : None

Wisteria sinensis

Common Name(s) : Chinese Wisteria
Origin : China
Growth Rate : Fast
Salt Tolerance : Low
Soil Requirements : Wide
Plant Type : Deciduous vine
Foliage Color : Green
Flowering Season : Spring
Flower Color : Blue-purple
Propagation : Seeds; cuttings
Human Hazards : Poisonous
Common Uses : Flowering vine
Major Problems : Thrips; mites

Family : Leguminosae   Zone : 5-9

Typical Height : Not applicable
Drought Tolerance : Medium
Nutritional Requirements : Medium
Light Requirements : High
Leaf Type : Pinnately compound
Texture : Medium
Flower Characteristics : Showy

Environmental Problems : Weedy

Additional Notes : Has attractive pendulous clusters of bluish flowers. Seeds are poisonous.

Wodyetia bifurcata *(Photograph p. 209)*

Common Name(s) : Foxtail Palm
Origin : Northern Australia
Growth Rate : Fast
Salt Tolerance : Medium
Soil Requirements : Wide
Plant Type : Palm
Foliage Color : Green
Flowering Season : n/a
Flower Color : White
Propagation : Seeds
Human Hazards : None
Common Uses : Palm; small tree
Major Problems : None

Family : Palmae   Zone : 10A-11

Typical Height : 30 Ft.
Drought Tolerance : High
Nutritional Requirements : Medium
Light Requirements : High
Leaf Type : Pinnately compound
Texture : Medium
Flower Characteristics : Insignificant

Environmental Problems : None

Additional Notes : Leaves resemble a foxtail; very well adapted to Florida.

Xanthosoma lindenii *(Photograph p. 201)*

Common Name(s) : Indian Kale; Spoon Flower
Origin : Colombia
Growth Rate : Medium
Salt Tolerance : Medium
Soil Requirements : Wide
Plant Type : Herbaceous perennial
Foliage Color : Variegated
Flowering Season : Summer; fall
Flower Color : White
Propagation : Division; cuttings
Human Hazards : None
Common Uses : Specimen plant; foliage plant
Major Problems : Root rots

Family : Araceae   Zone : 10B-11

Typical Height : 5 Ft.
Drought Tolerance : Medium
Nutritional Requirements : Medium
Light Requirements : Medium; high
Leaf Type : Simple
Texture : Coarse
Flower Characteristics : Insignificant

Environmental Problems : None

Additional Notes : Has attractive arrow-shaped foliage.

Xanthosoma sagittifolium

Common Name(s) : Yautia
Origin : West Indies
Growth Rate : Fast
Salt Tolerance : Low
Soil Requirements : Wide
Plant Type : Herbaceous perennial
Foliage Color : Green
Flowering Season : Summer
Flower Color : Green
Propagation : Division
Human Hazards : Irritant
Common Uses : Edible; shrub
Major Problems : Root rots

Family : Araceae   Zone : 10B-11

Typical Height : 6 Ft.
Drought Tolerance : Medium
Nutritional Requirements : Medium
Light Requirements : Medium; high
Leaf Type : Simple
Texture : Very coarse
Flower Characteristics : Insignificant

Environmental Problems : None

Additional Notes : Grown primarily for its edible tubers.

Ximenia americana

Common Name(s) : Tallowwood Plum
Origin : South Florida and West Indies
Growth Rate : Medium
Salt Tolerance : High
Soil Requirements : Wide
Plant Type : Evergreen tree or shrub
Foliage Color : Green
Flowering Season : Year-round
Flower Color : Yellow
Propagation : Seeds
Human Hazards : Spiny
Common Uses : Edible fruit; small tree; shrub
Major Problems : None
Additional Notes : Spiny stems; edible yellow fruits.

Family : Olacaceae   **Zone** : 10B-11

Typical Height : 25 Ft.
Drought Tolerance : High
Nutritional Requirements : Low
Light Requirements : High
Leaf Type : Simple
Texture : Medium
Flower Characteristics : Insignificant; fragrant

Environmental Problems : None

Xylosma congestum

Common Name(s) : Xylosma
Origin : China
Growth Rate : Medium
Salt Tolerance : Low
Soil Requirements : Wide
Plant Type : Evergreen shrub
Foliage Color : Green
Flowering Season : Fall
Flower Color : Green
Propagation : Seeds
Human Hazards : Spiny
Common Uses : Shrub; hedge
Major Problems : None
Additional Notes : Thorny stems; pest-free.

Family : Flacourtiaceae   **Zone** : 8-10B

Typical Height : 15 Ft.
Drought Tolerance : Medium
Nutritional Requirements : Medium
Light Requirements : Medium
Leaf Type : Simple
Texture : Medium
Flower Characteristics : Insignificant

Environmental Problems : None

Yucca aloifolia *(Photograph p. 188)*

Common Name(s) : Spanish Bayonet
Origin : Southeastern United States, Mexico
Growth Rate : Medium
Salt Tolerance : High
Soil Requirements : Wide
Plant Type : Evergreen shrub
Foliage Color : Green
Flowering Season : Spring
Flower Color : White
Propagation : Suckers; cuttings
Human Hazards : Spiny
Common Uses : Flowering shrub
Major Problems : Yucca moth caterpillars
Additional Notes : Excellent seaside plant. Dangerous dagger-like leaves.

Family : Agavaceae   **Zone** : 8-10B

Typical Height : 14 Ft.
Drought Tolerance : High
Nutritional Requirements : Low
Light Requirements : High
Leaf Type : Simple; linear
Texture : Coarse
Flower Characteristics : Showy

Environmental Problems : None

Yucca elephantipes

Common Name(s) : Spineless Yucca
Origin : Mexico and Central America
Growth Rate : Medium
Salt Tolerance : Medium
Soil Requirements : Wide
Plant Type : Evergreen tree
Foliage Color : Green
Flowering Season : Summer; fall
Flower Color : White
Propagation : Seeds; cuttings
Human Hazards : None
Common Uses : Flowering tree; foliage plant
Major Problems : Yucca moth caterpillars
Additional Notes : One of the few yuccas without dangerous spiny leaf tips.
Cultivars
'VARIEGATA' has variegated foliage.

Family : Agavaceae   **Zone** : 10B-11

Typical Height : 25 Ft.
Drought Tolerance : High
Nutritional Requirements : Low
Light Requirements : High
Leaf Type : Simple; linear
Texture : Coarse
Flower Characteristics : Showy

Environmental Problems : None

Yucca filamentosa

Common Name(s) : Adam's Needle
Origin : Southeastern United States
Growth Rate : Medium
Salt Tolerance : High
Soil Requirements : Wide
Plant Type : Evergreen shrub
Foliage Color : Green
Flowering Season : Spring
Flower Color : White
Propagation : Seeds; suckers; cuttings
Human Hazards : Spiny
Common Uses : Flowering shrub
Major Problems : None

Family : Agavaceae   **Zone** : 7-10B

Typical Height : 3 Ft.
Drought Tolerance : High
Nutritional Requirements : Low
Light Requirements : High
Leaf Type : Simple; linear
Texture : Coarse
Flower Characteristics : Showy

Environmental Problems : None

Additional Notes : Leaves have filamentous threads on margins and a spine at the tip.
Cultivars
'VARIEGATA' has yellow-white margined leaves.

Yucca gloriosa

Common Name(s) : Spanish Dagger
Origin : Southern Usa, Mexico, and West Indies
Growth Rate : Slow
Salt Tolerance : High
Soil Requirements : Wide
Plant Type : Evergreen shrub
Foliage Color : Green
Flowering Season : Summer
Flower Color : White
Propagation : Seeds; division; cuttings
Human Hazards : Spiny
Common Uses : Flowering shrub
Major Problems : Yucca moth caterpillars
Additional Notes : Sharp-tipped leaves are dangerous.

Family : Agavaceae   **Zone** : 9-11

Typical Height : 10 Ft.
Drought Tolerance : High
Nutritional Requirements : Low
Light Requirements : High
Leaf Type : Simple; linear
Texture : Coarse
Flower Characteristics : Showy

Environmental Problems : None

Yucca rostrata

Common Name(s) : Yucca
Origin : Texas and Northern Mexico
Growth Rate : Medium
Salt Tolerance : High
Soil Requirements : Wide
Plant Type : Evergreen shrub or tree
Foliage Color : Green
Flowering Season : Spring
Flower Color : White
Propagation : Seeds; cuttings
Human Hazards : Spiny
Common Uses : Flowering shrub; small flowering tree
Major Problems : Yucca moth caterpillars
Additional Notes : A tree-like species.

Family : Agavaceae   **Zone** : 9-10B

Typical Height : 12 Ft.
Drought Tolerance : High
Nutritional Requirements : Low
Light Requirements : High
Leaf Type : Simple; linear
Texture : Coarse
Flower Characteristics : Showy

Environmental Problems : None

Yucca smalliana

Common Name(s) : Bear Grass; Adam's Needle
Origin : Southeastern United States
Growth Rate : Medium
Salt Tolerance : High
Soil Requirements : Wide
Plant Type : Evergreen shrub
Foliage Color : Green
Flowering Season : Spring
Flower Color : White
Propagation : Suckers; cuttings; seeds
Human Hazards : Spiny
Common Uses : Flowering shrub
Major Problems : None
Additional Notes : Very similar to Y. filamentosa .

Family : Agavaceae   **Zone** : 7-10B

Typical Height : 3 Ft.
Drought Tolerance : High
Nutritional Requirements : Low
Light Requirements : High
Leaf Type : Simple; linear
Texture : Coarse
Flower Characteristics : Showy

Environmental Problems : None

Zamia domingensis

Common Name(s) : Dominican Coontie
Origin : Hispaniola
Growth Rate : Medium
Salt Tolerance : Medium
Soil Requirements : Wide
Plant Type : Evergreen shrub; cycad
Foliage Color : Green
Flowering Season : n/a
Flower Color : n/a
Propagation : Seeds; division
Human Hazards : Poisonous
Common Uses : Specimen plant; ground cover
Major Problems : Mealybugs; scales
Additional Notes : Similar to Z. pumila , but larger.

Family : Zamiaceae   **Zone** : 9B-11

Typical Height : 2 Ft.
Drought Tolerance : High
Nutritional Requirements : Medium
Light Requirements : Medium; high
Leaf Type : Pinnately compound
Texture : Medium
Flower Characteristics : Cone

Environmental Problems : None

Zamia fischeri

Common Name(s) : Fischer Zamia
Origin : Mexico
Growth Rate : Slow
Salt Tolerance : Low
Soil Requirements : Wide
Plant Type : Evergreen shrub (cycad)
Foliage Color : Green
Flowering Season : n/a
Flower Color : n/a
Propagation : Seeds
Human Hazards : Poisonous
Common Uses : Shrub; specimen plant; groundcover
Major Problems : Scales
Additional Notes : A fern-like cycad with small, toothed leaflets.

Family : Zamiaceae   **Zone** : 10B-11

Typical Height : 3 Ft.
Drought Tolerance : Medium
Nutritional Requirements : Medium
Light Requirements : Medium; high
Leaf Type : Pinnately compound
Texture : Medium
Flower Characteristics : n/a

Environmental Problems : None

Zamia furfuracea *(Photograph p. 188)*

Common Name(s) : Cardboard Palm
Origin : Mexico
Growth Rate : Slow
Salt Tolerance : High
Soil Requirements : Wide
Plant Type : Evergreen shrub; cycad
Foliage Color : Green
Flowering Season : Summer
Flower Color : n/a
Propagation : Seeds
Human Hazards : Poisonous
Common Uses : Shrub; hedge; groundcover
Major Problems : Scales; mealybugs
Additional Notes : Has a typical cycad rosette form with stiff broad leaflets.

Family : Zamiaceae   **Zone** : 9B-11

Typical Height : 3 Ft.
Drought Tolerance : High
Nutritional Requirements : Low
Light Requirements : High
Leaf Type : Pinnately compound
Texture : Coarse; medium
Flower Characteristics : Cone

Environmental Problems : None

Zamia pumila *(Photograph p. 188)*

Common Name(s) : Coontie
Origin : Florida
Growth Rate : Slow
Salt Tolerance : High
Soil Requirements : Wide
Plant Type : Evergreen shrub; cycad
Foliage Color : Green
Flowering Season : n/a
Flower Color : n/a
Propagation : Seeds; division
Human Hazards : Poisonous
Common Uses : Groundcover; seasides;
Major Problems : Atala caterpillars (an endangered species); scales
Additional Notes : Roots of this small native cycad were once used as a source of starch.

Family : Zamiaceae   **Zone** : 8B-11

Typical Height : 2 Ft.
Drought Tolerance : High
Nutritional Requirements : Low
Light Requirements : Medium; high
Leaf Type : Pinnately compound
Texture : Medium
Flower Characteristics : Cone

Environmental Problems : None

Zamia skinneri

Family : Zamiaceae   **Zone** : 10B-11

Common Name(s) : Skinner Cycad
Origin : Central America
Growth Rate : Slow
Salt Tolerance : Low
Soil Requirements : Wide
Plant Type : Evergreen shrub; cycad
Foliage Color : Green
Flowering Season : Summer
Flower Color : n/a
Propagation : Seeds
Human Hazards : Poisonous
Common Uses : Shrub; groundcover
Major Problems : Scales
Additional Notes : Good cycad for shade.

Typical Height : 3 Ft.
Drought Tolerance : Medium
Nutritional Requirements : Low
Light Requirements : Medium
Leaf Type : Pinnately compound
Texture : Coarse; medium
Flower Characteristics : Cone

Environmental Problems : None

Zantedeschia spp. *(Photograph p. 201)*

Family : Araceae   **Zone** : 8-10B

Common Name(s) : Calla Lily
Origin : South Africa
Growth Rate : Medium
Salt Tolerance : Low
Soil Requirements : Acid
Plant Type : Herbaceous perennial
Foliage Color : Green
Flowering Season : Spring; summer
Flower Color : White; pink; yellow; orange
Propagation : Division; seeds
Human Hazards : Irritant
Common Uses : Beds; borders; cut flowers
Major Problems : Bacterial rots
Additional Notes : Does poorly in southern Florida; keep moist during growth.

Typical Height : 2 Ft.
Drought Tolerance : Low
Nutritional Requirements : Medium
Light Requirements : Medium
Leaf Type : Simple
Texture : Coarse
Flower Characteristics : Showy; fragrant

Environmental Problems : None

Zanthoxylum clava-herculis

Family : Rutaceae   **Zone** : 8-10B

Common Name(s) : Southern Prickly-ash; Hercules' Club; Toothache Tree
Origin : Southeastern United States
Growth Rate : Medium
Salt Tolerance : Medium
Soil Requirements : Wide
Plant Type : Deciduous shrub or tree
Foliage Color : Green
Flowering Season : Spring
Flower Color : White
Propagation : Seeds; root cuttings; suckers
Human Hazards : Spiny
Common Uses : Small tree; shrub
Major Problems : None
Additional Notes : Folk remedy for toothaches.

Typical Height : 30 Ft.
Drought Tolerance : High
Nutritional Requirements : Medium
Light Requirements : Medium
Leaf Type : Pinnately compound
Texture : Medium
Flower Characteristics : Insignificant

Environmental Problems : None

Zanthoxylum fagara

Family : Rutaceae   **Zone** : 10B-11

Common Name(s) : Wild Lime
Origin : Tropical America
Growth Rate : Medium
Salt Tolerance : High
Soil Requirements : Wide
Plant Type : Evergreen shrub or tree
Foliage Color : Green
Flowering Season : Year-round
Flower Color : Yellow
Propagation : Seeds; root cuttings
Human Hazards : Spiny
Common Uses : Small tree; shrub
Major Problems : None
Additional Notes : Has recurved prickles. Foliage has lime aroma when bruised.

Typical Height : 25 Ft.
Drought Tolerance : High
Nutritional Requirements : Low
Light Requirements : High
Leaf Type : Pinnately compound
Texture : Fine
Flower Characteristics : Insignificant

Environmental Problems : None

Zebrina pendula

Common Name(s) : Wandering Jew
Origin : Mexico
Growth Rate : Fast
Salt Tolerance : Low
Soil Requirements : Wide
Plant Type : Herbaceous perennial
Foliage Color : Purple & green
Flowering Season : Year-round
Flower Color : Pink
Propagation : Cuttings
Human Hazards : None
Common Uses : Groundcover; foliage plant; hanging basket
Major Problems : None
Additional Notes : Adds color beneath trees. Does not tolerate foot traffic.

Family : Commelinaceae   **Zone** : 10B-11

Typical Height : .8 Ft.
Drought Tolerance : Medium
Nutritional Requirements : Low
Light Requirements : Medium; low
Leaf Type : Simple
Texture : Medium
Flower Characteristics : Insignificant

Environmental Problems : Invasive

Zelkova serrata

Common Name(s) : Japanese Zelkova
Origin : Japan and Korea
Growth Rate : Fast
Salt Tolerance : Low
Soil Requirements : Wide
Plant Type : Deciduous tree
Foliage Color : Green
Flowering Season : Spring
Flower Color : Green
Propagation : Seeds; cuttings
Human Hazards : None
Common Uses : Shade tree
Major Problems : None
Additional Notes : Has a graceful vase shape.

Family : Ulmaceae   **Zone** : 5-9

Typical Height : 60 Ft.
Drought Tolerance : High
Nutritional Requirements : Medium
Light Requirements : High
Leaf Type : Simple
Texture : Medium
Flower Characteristics : Insignificant

Environmental Problems : None

Zephyranthes atamasco

Common Name(s) : Atamasco Lily
Origin : Southeastern United States
Growth Rate : Slow
Salt Tolerance : Low
Soil Requirements : Acid
Plant Type : Herbaceous perennial
Foliage Color : Green
Flowering Season : Spring
Flower Color : White
Propagation : Division
Human Hazards : None
Common Uses : Beds; borders
Major Problems : None
Additional Notes : Prefers shade and rich, moist soil.

Family : Amaryllidaceae   **Zone** : 7-10A

Typical Height : .5 Ft.
Drought Tolerance : Low
Nutritional Requirements : Medium
Light Requirements : Medium
Leaf Type : Simple; linear
Texture : Fine
Flower Characteristics : Showy

Environmental Problems : None

Zephyranthes spp. and hybrids *(Photo. p. 216)*

Common Name(s) : Zephyr Lilies; Rain Lilies
Origin : Tropical America
Growth Rate : Fast
Salt Tolerance : Medium
Soil Requirements : Wide
Plant Type : Herbaceous perennial
Foliage Color : Green; gray
Flowering Season : Spring; summer; fall
Flower Color : White; pink; yellow; red; orange
Propagation : Seed; division
Human Hazards : Poisonous
Common Uses : Beds; flowering groundcover
Major Problems : None
Additional Notes : Flower after rain storm; species vary by season of bloom.
Cultivars
   Z. rosea has pink flowers and is evergreen; Z. candida has white flowers; Z. citrina is yellow-flowered.

Family : Amaryllidaceae   **Zone** : 8-11

Typical Height : .5 Ft.
Drought Tolerance : High
Nutritional Requirements : Medium
Light Requirements : High; medium
Leaf Type : Simple; linear
Texture : Fine
Flower Characteristics : Showy

Environmental Problems : None

Zephyranthes treatiae *(Photograph p. 201)*

Common Name(s) : Zephyr Lily
Origin : Southeastern United States
Growth Rate : Slow
Salt Tolerance : Low
Soil Requirements : Acid
Plant Type : Herbaceous perennial
Foliage Color : Green
Flowering Season : Spring
Flower Color : White; pink
Propagation : Division
Human Hazards : None
Common Uses : Beds; borders
Major Problems : None

Family : Amaryllidaceae   Zone : 8-10B

Typical Height : .5 Ft.
Drought Tolerance : Low
Nutritional Requirements : Medium
Light Requirements : High
Leaf Type : Simple; linear
Texture : Fine
Flower Characteristics : Showy

Environmental Problems : None

Additional Notes : Can naturalize in lawn; increases quickly; Z. simpsonii similar.

Zingiber spectabile *(Photograph p. 201)*

Common Name(s) : Blushing Ginger
Origin : Malaya
Growth Rate : Fast
Salt Tolerance : Low
Soil Requirements : Wide
Plant Type : Herbaceous perennial
Foliage Color : Green
Flowering Season : Spring
Flower Color : Yellow & pink
Propagation : Division
Human Hazards : None
Common Uses : Cut flowers; specimen plant
Major Problems : None

Family : Zingiberaceae   Zone : 10B-11

Typical Height : 5 Ft.
Drought Tolerance : Medium
Nutritional Requirements : Medium
Light Requirements : Medium; high
Leaf Type : Simple
Texture : Coarse
Flower Characteristics : Showy

Environmental Problems : None

Additional Notes : Deciduous foliage. Spectacular blushing flowers on separate stalks.

Zingiber zerumbet

Common Name(s) : Pine Cone Ginger
Origin : India and Malay Peninsula
Growth Rate : Fast
Salt Tolerance : Medium
Soil Requirements : Wide
Plant Type : Herbaceous perennial
Foliage Color : Green; variegated
Flowering Season : Summer
Flower Color : Red
Propagation : Division
Human Hazards : None
Common Uses : Specimen plant
Major Problems : None

Family : Zingiberaceae   Zone : 9-11

Typical Height : 3.5 Ft.
Drought Tolerance : Medium
Nutritional Requirements : Medium
Light Requirements : Medium; high
Leaf Type : Simple
Texture : Coarse
Flower Characteristics : Showy

Environmental Problems : None

Additional Notes : Deciduous foliage. Pine cone like flowers produced on separate stalks.
Cultivars
'VARIEGATA' has white leaf margins.

Zizyphus mauritiana

Common Name(s) : Indian Jujube Tree
Origin : India
Growth Rate : Medium
Salt Tolerance : Low
Soil Requirements : Wide
Plant Type : Evergreen tree
Foliage Color : Green
Flowering Season : Summer
Flower Color : White
Propagation : Seeds; root cuttings; grafting
Human Hazards : Spiny
Common Uses : Edible fruit; small tree
Major Problems : Rust

Family : Rhamnaceae   Zone : 10B-11

Typical Height : 35 Ft.
Drought Tolerance : Medium
Nutritional Requirements : Medium
Light Requirements : High
Leaf Type : Simple
Texture : Medium
Flower Characteristics : Insignificant; fragrant

Environmental Problems : None

Additional Notes : Edible fruit. Thorny weeping branches.

Zombia antillarum

Common Name(s) : Zombie Palm
Origin : Hispaniola
Growth Rate : Slow
Salt Tolerance : High
Soil Requirements : Wide
Plant Type : Palm
Foliage Color : Green
Flowering Season : Summer
Flower Color : White
Propagation : Seed
Human Hazards : Spiny
Common Uses : Specimen plant; shrub
Major Problems : None
Additional Notes : Clustering palm with attractive but spiny stems.

Family : Palmae   **Zone** : 10B-11

Typical Height : 12 Ft.
Drought Tolerance : High
Nutritional Requirements : Low
Light Requirements : High
Leaf Type :
Texture : Coarse
Flower Characteristics : Inconspicuous

Environmental Problems : None

*Common Names
and Synonyms*

Index of common names and synonyms

COMMON NAME / <u>Synonym</u> : <u>Scientific Name</u> , information page, **photograph page**

ABELIA : <u>Abelia</u> X <u>grandiflora</u> , 1

ABYSSINIAN GLADIOLUS : <u>Acidanthera</u> <u>bicolor</u> , 5

<u>Acer</u> <u>floridanum</u> : <u>A.</u> <u>barbatum</u> , 3

ACHIMENES : <u>Achimenes</u> spp., 5, **189**

<u>Achras</u> <u>sapota</u> : <u>Manilkara</u> <u>zapota</u> , 254, **164**

<u>Actinophloeus</u> <u>macarthurii</u> : <u>Ptychosperma</u> <u>macarthurii</u> , 306

ADAM'S NEEDLE : <u>Yucca</u> <u>filamentosa</u>, <u>Y.</u> <u>smalliana</u> , 362

<u>Adenium</u> <u>multiflorum</u> : <u>A.</u> <u>obesum</u> , 7, **172**

<u>Adonidia</u> <u>merrillii</u> : <u>Veitchia</u> <u>merrillii</u> , 355, **209**

ADONIDIA PALM : <u>Veitchia</u> <u>merrillii</u> , 355, **209**

AFRICAN DAISY : <u>Gamolepis</u> <u>chrysanthemoides</u> , 133

AFRICAN HEMP : <u>Sparmannia</u> <u>africana</u> , 330

AFRICAN IRIS : <u>Dietes</u> <u>vegeta</u> , 103, **213**

AFRICAN MAHOGANY : <u>Khaya</u> <u>nyasica</u> , 235

AFRICAN MILKBUSH : <u>Synadenium</u> <u>grantii</u> , 336

AFRICAN MILK TREE : <u>Euphorbia</u> <u>trigona</u> , 123, **178**

AFRICAN OIL PALM : <u>Elaeis</u> <u>guineensis</u> , 111, **204**

AFRICAN TULIP TREE : <u>Spathodea</u> <u>campanulata</u> , 330, **169**

AIR PLANT : <u>Tillandsia</u> spp., 347, **201**

AKEE : <u>Blighia</u> <u>sapida</u> , 39, **154**

ALEXANDRA PALM : <u>Archontophoenix</u> <u>alexandrae</u> , 24, **202**

ALGERIAN IVY : <u>Hedera</u> <u>canariensis</u> , 143, **214**

ALLIGATOR APPLE : <u>Annona</u> <u>glabra</u> , 20

ALLIGATOR LILY : <u>Hymenocallis</u> <u>palmeri</u> , 218

ALLIGATOR PEAR : <u>Persea</u> <u>americana</u> , 280

ALLSPICE : <u>Pimenta</u> <u>dioica</u> , 289

<u>Aloe</u> <u>vera</u> : <u>A.</u> <u>barbadensis</u> , 16, **189**

<u>Alpinia</u> <u>speciosa</u> : <u>A.</u> <u>zerumbet</u> , 17, **190**

<u>Alsophila</u> <u>cooperi</u> : <u>Sphaeropteris</u> <u>cooperi</u> , 331, **169**

ALUMINUM PLANT : <u>Pilea</u> <u>cadierei</u> , 288

AMARYLLIS : <u>Hippeastrum</u> X <u>hybridum</u> , 150, **198**

AMAZON ELEPHANT'S EAR : <u>Alocasia</u> X <u>amazonica</u> , 15, **190**

AMAZON LILY : <u>Eucharis</u> <u>amazonica</u> , 116, **195**

AMAZONIAN ZEBRA PLANT : <u>Aechmea</u> <u>chantinii</u> , 7

AMERICAN ELM : <u>Ulmus</u> <u>americana</u> , 352

AMERICAN HOLLY : <u>Ilex</u> <u>opaca</u> , 221

AMERICAN HOPHORNBEAM : <u>Ostrya</u> <u>virginiana</u> , 272, **165**

AMERICAN HORNBEAM : <u>Carpinus</u> <u>caroliniana</u> , 58

AMERICAN PAPYRUS : <u>Cyperus</u> <u>haspan</u> , 97

AMETHYST SEA HOLLY : <u>Eryngium</u> <u>amethystinum</u> , 114

<u>Amomum</u> <u>cardamonum</u> : <u>Elettaria</u> <u>cardamonum</u> , 111

ANGEL'S TRUMPET : <u>Brugmansia</u> <u>versicolor</u>, <u>B.</u> X <u>candida</u> , 42, **174**

ANISE TREE : <u>Illicium</u> <u>anisatum</u> , 222, **162**

ANNATTO : <u>Bixa</u> <u>orellana</u> , 38, **153**

ANTHONY'S RICK-RACK : <u>Cryptocereus</u> <u>anthonyanus</u> , 93

APPLE BLOSSOM SHOWER : <u>Cassia</u> <u>javanica</u> , 61, **156**

ARABIAN JASMINE : <u>Jasminum</u> <u>sambac</u> , 229

<u>Aralia</u> <u>elegantissima</u> : <u>Dizygotheca</u> <u>elegantissima</u> , 105

<u>Araucaria</u> <u>excelsa</u> : <u>A.</u> <u>heterophylla</u> , 24, **153**

ARECA PALM : <u>Chrysalidocarpus</u> <u>lutescens</u> , 72, **203**

<u>Arecastrum</u> <u>romanzoffianum</u> : <u>Syagrus</u> <u>romanzoffiana</u> , 335, **208**

ARGENTINE TRUMPET VINE : <u>Clystostoma</u> <u>callistegioides</u> , 79

ARIKURY PALM : <u>Syagrus</u> <u>schizophylla</u> , 335

<u>Arikuryroba</u> <u>schizophylla</u> : <u>Syagrus</u> <u>schizophylla</u> , 335

ARROW ARUM : <u>Peltandra</u> <u>virginica</u> , 277

ARROW BAMBOO : <u>Pseudosasa</u> <u>japonica</u> , 304

ARROWHEAD : <u>Sagittaria</u> <u>lancifolia</u> , 320

ARROWROOT : <u>Maranta</u> <u>arundinacea</u> , 255

ARTILLERY PLANT : <u>Pilea</u> <u>microphylla</u> , 288, **215**

ASH-LEAVED MAPLE : <u>Acer</u> <u>negundo</u> , 3

ASIAN BUTTERFLY BUSH : <u>Buddleia</u> <u>asiatica</u> , 44

ASPARAGUS FERN : <u>Asparagus</u> <u>setaceus</u>, <u>A.</u> <u>densiflorus</u> , 28

<u>Asparagus</u> <u>meyerii</u> : <u>A.</u> <u>densiflorus</u> 'Myers' , 27, **213**

<u>Asparagus</u> <u>plumosus</u> : <u>A.</u> <u>setaceus</u> , 28

<u>Asparagus</u> <u>sprengeri</u> : <u>A.</u> <u>densiflorus</u> 'Sprengeri' , 27, **213**

ASSAI PALM : <u>Euterpe</u> <u>edulis</u> , 123

ATAMASCO LILY : <u>Zephyranthes</u> <u>atamasco</u> , 365

ATLAS CEDAR : <u>Cedrus</u> <u>atlantica</u> , 63, **156**

ATTENUATE HOLLY : <u>Ilex</u> X <u>attenuata</u> , 220

AUSTRALIAN FAN PALM : <u>Livistona</u> <u>australis</u> , 245

AUSTRALIAN TREE FERN : <u>Sphaeropteris</u> <u>cooperi</u> , 331, **169**

AUTOGRAPH TREE : <u>Clusia</u> <u>rosea</u> , 79, **157**

AUTUMN CROCUS : <u>Sternbergia</u> <u>lutea</u> , 332

AVOCADO : <u>Persea</u> <u>americana</u> , 280

AZALEA : <u>Rhododendron (Azalea)</u> hybrids, 315, **185**

AZORES JASMINE : <u>Jasminum</u> <u>fluminense</u> , 227

AZTEC LILY : <u>Sprekelia</u> <u>formosissima</u> , 331, **200**

BABOON FLOWER : <u>Babiana</u> spp., 30

BABY RUBBER PLANT : <u>Peperomia</u> <u>obtusifolia</u> , 279

BABY SUN ROSE : <u>Aptenia</u> <u>cordifolia</u> , 24

BAILEY COPERNICIA PALM : <u>Copernicia</u> <u>baileyana</u> , 84

BALD CYPRESS : <u>Taxodium</u> <u>distichum</u> , 340, **171**

BALFOUR ARALIA : <u>Polyscias</u> <u>pinnata</u> , 299, **185**

BALLOON FLOWER : <u>Platycodon</u> <u>grandiflorus</u> , 294

BAMBOO PALM : <u>Chamaedorea</u> <u>erumpens</u>, <u>C.</u> <u>seifrizii</u> , 68

<u>Bambusa</u> <u>falcata</u> : <u>Chimonobambusa</u> <u>falcata</u> , 70

BANANA PLANT : <u>Nymphioides</u> spp., 268

BANANA SHRUB : <u>Michelia</u> <u>figo</u> , 257, **182**

BANDANA OF THE EVERGLADES : <u>Canna</u> <u>flaccida</u> , 56

BANGAR NUT : <u>Sterculia</u> <u>foetida</u> , 332

BANYAN TREE : <u>Ficus</u> <u>benghalensis</u> , 126, **160**

BAOBAB : <u>Adansonia</u> <u>digitata</u> , 6

BARBADOS ALOE : <u>Aloe</u> <u>barbadensis</u> , 16, **189**

BARBADOS CHERRY : <u>Malpighia</u> <u>glabra</u> , 252, **182**

BARBADOS GOOSEBERRY : <u>Pereskia</u> <u>aculeata</u> , 280

BASKET FLOWER : <u>Hymenocallis</u> <u>narcissifolia</u> , 218, **197**

BAT FLOWER : <u>Tacca</u> spp., 339

<u>Bauhinia</u> <u>alba</u> : <u>B.</u> <u>variegata</u> 'Candida' , 34, **154**

<u>Bauhinia</u> <u>galpinii</u> : <u>B.</u> <u>punctata</u> , 33, **173**

BAY CEDAR : <u>Suriana</u> <u>maritima</u> , 334

BAY-LEAVED CAPER TREE : <u>Capparis</u> <u>flexuosa</u> , 56

BEACH NAUPAKA : <u>Scaevola</u> <u>taccada</u> , 324, **186**

BEACH SUNFLOWER : <u>Helianthus</u> <u>debilis</u> , 145, **214**

BEAR GRASS : <u>Yucca</u> <u>smalliana</u> , 362

BEAUTYBERRY : <u>Callicarpa</u> <u>americana</u> , 51

BEE BALM : <u>Monarda</u> <u>didyma</u> , 258

BELLA CALATHEA : <u>Calathea</u> <u>bella</u> , 49

BELLFLOWERS : <u>Campanula</u> spp., 54

<u>Beloperone</u> <u>guttata</u> : <u>Justicia</u> <u>brandegeana</u> , 232

BENGAL CLOCK VINE : <u>Thunbergia</u> <u>grandiflora</u> , 346, **212**

BENJAMIN FIG : <u>Ficus</u> <u>benjamina</u> , 126

BIRD OF PARADISE SHRUB : <u>Caesalpinia gilliesii</u> , 47

BIRD OF PARADISE : <u>Strelitzia reginae</u> , 333, **200**

BIRDS-EYE BUSH : <u>Ochna serrulata</u> , 268

BIRDSNEST ANTHURIUM : <u>Anthurium hookeri</u>, <u>A. salviniae</u>, <u>A. guayanum</u> , 22

BIRDSNEST FERN : <u>Asplenium nidus</u> , 28, **191**

BIRDSNEST PHILODENDRON : <u>Philodendron wendlandii</u> , 283

BISCHOFIA : <u>Bischofia javanica</u> , 38

BISHOPWOOD : <u>Bischofia javanica</u> , 38

BISMARCK PALM : <u>Bismarckia nobilis</u> , 38, **202**

BLACK BAMBOO : <u>Phyllostachys nigra</u> , 287

BLACK CALABASH : <u>Amphitecna latifolia</u> , 19

BLACK IRONWOOD : <u>Krugiodendron ferreum</u> , 236, **163**

BLACK MANGROVE : <u>Avicennia germinans</u> , 30

BLACK OAK : <u>Quercus velutina</u> , 310

BLACK OLIVE : <u>Bucida buceras</u> , 44

BLACK SAPOTE : <u>Diospyros dignya</u> , 104

BLACK TUPELO : <u>Nyssa sylvatica</u> , 268

BLACK-EYED SUSAN VINE : <u>Thunbergia alata</u> , 345, **212**

BLACKBEAD : <u>Pithecellobium guadelupense</u> , 293

BLACKBERRY LILY : <u>Belamcanda chinensis</u> , 36

BLANKET FLOWER : <u>Gaillardia pulchella</u> , 132, **214**

BLEEDING HEART : <u>Clerodendrum thomsoniae</u> , 78

BLETIA : <u>Bletilla striata</u> , 39

BLOLLY : <u>Guapira discolor</u> , 139

BLOOD LEAF : <u>Iresine</u> spp., 224

BLOOD LILY : <u>Scatoxus multiflorus</u> , 324, **200**

BLUE DAZE : <u>Evolvulus glomeratus</u> , 124, **213**

BLUE FESCUE : <u>Festuca ovina</u> var. <u>glauca</u> , 125

BLUE FLAG : <u>Iris hexagona</u> var. <u>savannarum</u>, <u>I. virginica</u> , 225

BLUE GINGER : <u>Dichorisandra thyrsiflora</u> , 101, **194**

BLUE LATAN PALM : <u>Latania loddigesii</u> , 239

BLUE PHLOX : <u>Phlox divaricata</u> , 283, **199**

BLUE SAGE : <u>Eranthemum pulchellum</u>, <u>Salvia farinacea</u> , 113

BLUE SCREWPINE : <u>Pandanus baptistii</u> , 273

BLUE-EYED GRASS : <u>Sisrynchium</u> spp., 328

BLUEBELL BARLERIA : <u>Barleria cristata</u> , 32

BLUEJACK OAK : <u>Quercus incana</u> , 308

BLUFF OAK : <u>Quercus austrina</u> , 308

BLUSHING BROMELIAD : <u>Neoregelia</u> <u>carolinae</u> , 265, **199**

BLUSHING GINGER : <u>Zingiber</u> <u>spectabile</u> , 366, **201**

BO TREE : <u>Ficus</u> <u>religiosa</u> , 128

BOLIVIAN SUNSET : <u>Gloxinia</u> <u>sylvatica</u> , 137, **214**

BORDER GRASS : <u>Ophiopogon</u> <u>japonicus</u> , 270

BOSTON FERN : <u>Nephrolepis</u> <u>exaltata</u> , 266, **215**

BOTTLE PALM : <u>Hyophorbe</u> <u>lagenicaulis</u> , 218, **204**

BOTTLE PONYTAIL : <u>Beaucarnea</u> <u>gracilis</u> , 34

BOUGAINVILLEA : <u>Bougainvillea</u> <u>spectabilis</u>, <u>B.</u> <u>glabra</u> , 40, **173**

BOUNDARY TREE : <u>Newbouldia</u> <u>laevis</u> , 266

BOWER PLANT : <u>Pandorea</u> <u>jasminoides</u> , 274

BOX ELDER : <u>Acer</u> <u>negundo</u> , 3

BOX HONEYSUCKLE : <u>Lonicera</u> <u>nitida</u> , 247

BOX-LEAF EUGENIA : <u>Eugenia</u> <u>foetida</u> , 118

BOXTHORN : <u>Severinia</u> <u>buxifolia</u> , 328, **186**

BRAZIL BEAUTYLEAF : <u>Calophyllum</u> <u>brasiliense</u> , 53

BRAZILIAN GOLDEN VINE : <u>Stigmaphyllon</u> <u>littorale</u> , 333

BRIDALVEIL TREE : <u>Caesalpinia</u> <u>granadillo</u> , 48, **154**

BRONZE LOQUAT : <u>Eriobotrya</u> <u>deflexa</u> , 113

BRUSH CHERRY : <u>Syzygium</u> <u>paniculatum</u> , 337

BUCCANEER PALM : <u>Pseudophoenix</u> <u>sargentii</u> , 304, **207**

BUDDHA BAMBOO : <u>Bambusa</u> <u>ventricosa</u> , 31

BUDDHA'S BELLY BAMBOO : <u>Bambusa</u> <u>ventricosa</u> , 31

BUDDHIST BAUHINIA : <u>Bauhinia</u> <u>variegata</u> , 34, **154**

BUGLEWEED : <u>Ajuga</u> <u>reptans</u> , 11

BULLOCK'S HEART : <u>Annona</u> <u>reticulata</u> , 21

BULNESIA : <u>Bulnesia</u> <u>arborea</u> , 45, **154**

<u>Bumelia</u> <u>salicifolia</u> : <u>Dipholis</u> <u>salicifolia</u> , 104

BUNYA-BUNYA TREE : <u>Araucaria</u> <u>bidwillii</u> , 24

BURBIDGEA : <u>Burbidgea</u> <u>schizocheila</u> , 46, **192**

BURSTING HEART : <u>Euonymus</u> <u>americana</u> , 118

BUSH ALLAMANDA : <u>Allamanda</u> <u>neriifolia</u> , 13

BUSH CASSIA : <u>Cassia</u> <u>surattensis</u> , 62

BUSH CLOCK VINE : <u>Thunbergia</u> <u>erecta</u> , 345

BUTTERCUP : <u>Ranunculus</u> spp., 312

BUTTERCUP TREE : <u>Cochlospermum</u> <u>vitifolium</u> , 82

BUTTERFLY BUSH : <u>Buddleia</u> <u>officinalis</u> , 45

BUTTERFLY FLOWER : <u>Bauhinia</u> <u>monandra</u> , 33

BUTTERFLY GINGER : <u>Hedychium</u> <u>coronarium</u> , 144

BUTTERFLY IRIS : <u>Dietes</u> <u>vegeta</u> , 103, **213**

BUTTERFLY WEED : <u>Asclepias</u> <u>tuberosa</u> , 27

BUTTONBUSH : <u>Cephalanthus</u> <u>occidentalis</u> , 65

BUTTONWOOD : <u>Conocarpus</u> <u>erectus</u> , 84, **158**

<u>Byrsonima</u> <u>cuneatas</u> : <u>B.</u> <u>lucida</u> , 47

CABADA PALM : <u>Chrysalidocarpus</u> <u>cabadae</u> , 72

CABBAGE ANGELIN : <u>Andira</u> <u>inermis</u> , 20

CABBAGE PALMETTO : <u>Sabal</u> <u>palmetto</u> , 319, **208**

CABBAGE TREE : <u>Cordyline</u> <u>australis</u> , 85

CADAGA : <u>Eucalyptus</u> <u>torelliana</u> , 116

CAFE CON LECHE : <u>Pseuderanthemum</u> <u>atropurpureum</u> , 303

CAIMITO : <u>Chrysophyllum</u> <u>cainito</u> , 73

CALABASH : <u>Crescentia</u> <u>cujete</u> , 90

CALADIUM : <u>Caladium</u> X <u>hortulanum</u> , 48, **192**

CALAMONDIN ORANGE : X <u>citrofortunella</u> <u>mitis</u> , 74

CALATHEA : <u>Calathea</u> <u>picturata</u>, <u>C.</u> <u>louisae</u>, <u>C.</u> <u>roseopicta</u>, <u>C.</u> <u>warscewiczii</u>, <u>C.</u> <u>bachemiana</u> , 49

CALICO FLOWER : <u>Aristolochia</u> <u>elegans</u> , 27

CALLA LILY : <u>Zantedeschia</u> spp., 364, **201**

CALLERY PEAR : <u>Pyrus</u> <u>calleryana</u> , 307

<u>Calophyllum</u> <u>antillanum</u> : <u>C.</u> <u>brasiliense</u> , 53

CAMPHOR TREE : <u>Cinnamomum</u> <u>camphora</u> , 73, **157**

CANARY ISLAND DATE PALM : <u>Phoenix</u> <u>canariensis</u> , 284, **206**

CANDELABRA ALOE : <u>Aloe</u> <u>arborescens</u> , 16

CANDELABRA PLANT : <u>Aloe</u> <u>arborescens</u> , 16

CANDLE BUSH : <u>Cassia</u> <u>alata</u> , 60, **175**

CANDLENUT : <u>Aleurites</u> <u>moluccana</u> , 12

<u>Canella</u> <u>albaluccana</u> : <u>C.</u> <u>winterana</u> , 55

CANISTEL : <u>Pouteria</u> <u>campechiana</u> , 301

CAPE COWSLIP : <u>Lachenalia</u> spp., 237

CAPE FIGWORT : <u>Phygelius</u> <u>capensis</u> , 286

CAPE FUCHSIA : <u>Phygelius</u> <u>capensis</u> , 286

CAPE HONEYSUCKLE : <u>Tecomaria</u> <u>capensis</u> , 341

CAPE JASMINE : <u>Gardenia</u> <u>jasminoides</u> , 133

CAPULIN : <u>Muntingia</u> <u>calabura</u> , 260

CARAMBOLA : <u>Averrhoa</u> <u>carambola</u> , 29

CARDAMON : <u>Elettaria</u> <u>cardamomum</u> , 111

CARDAMON GINGER : <u>Elettaria</u> <u>cardamomum</u> , 111

CARDBOARD PALM : <u>Zamia</u> <u>furfuracea</u> , 363, **188**

CARDINAL FLOWER : <u>Lobelia</u> <u>cardinalis</u> , 246

CARDINAL SPEAR : <u>Erythrina</u> <u>herbacea</u> , 114

CARIBBEAN AGAVE : <u>Agave</u> <u>angustifolia</u> , 9

CARIBBEAN HELICONIA : <u>Heliconia</u> <u>caribaea</u> , 146, **196**

CARICATURE PLANT : <u>Graptophyllum</u> <u>pictum</u> , 138, **179**

CAROLINA ALLSPICE : <u>Calycanthus</u> <u>floridus</u> , 53

CAROLINA LUPINE : <u>Thermopsis</u> <u>caroliniana</u> , 343

CAROLINA YELLOW JASMINE : <u>Gelsemium</u> <u>sempervirens</u> , 135

CARPENTARIA PALM : <u>Carpentaria</u> <u>acuminata</u> , 57, **202**

CARPET BUGLEWEED : <u>Ajuga</u> <u>reptans</u> , 11

CARRION FLOWER : <u>Stapelia</u> spp., 331

CARROTWOOD : <u>Cupaniopsis</u> <u>anacardiopsis</u> , 94

CASSANDRA : <u>Chamaedaphne</u> <u>calyculata</u> , 67

CAST IRON PLANT : <u>Aspidistra</u> <u>elatior</u> , 28

CASTOR BEAN BEGONIA : <u>Begonia</u> X <u>ricinifolius</u> , 36

CAT PALM : <u>Chamaedorea</u> <u>cataractarum</u> , 67, **203**

CAT'S CLAW : <u>Pithecellobium</u> <u>unguis-cati</u> , 293

CATALPA : <u>Catalpa</u> <u>bignonioides</u> , 62

CATESBY LILY : <u>Lilium</u> <u>catesbei</u> , 242

CATHEDRAL CACTUS : <u>Euphorbia</u> <u>trigona</u> , 123, **178**

CATTLEY GUAVA : <u>Psidium</u> <u>littorale</u> , 305, **168**

CATTLEYA ORCHID : <u>Cattleya</u> spp., 63, **193**

CECROPIA : <u>Cecropia</u> <u>palmata</u> , 63, **156**

CEDAR ELM : <u>Ulmus</u> <u>crassifolia</u> , 352

CENTURY PLANT : <u>Agave</u> <u>americana</u> , 9, **172**

CERIMAN : <u>Monstera</u> <u>deliciosa</u> , 259

CEYLON BOWSTRING HEMP : <u>Sansevieria</u> <u>zeylanica</u> , 322

CEYLON GOOSEBERRY : <u>Dovyalis</u> <u>hebecarpa</u> , 106

<u>Chalcas</u> <u>exotica</u> : <u>Murraya</u> <u>paniculata</u> , 260

CHALICE VINE : <u>Solandra</u> <u>guttata</u> , 329

CHAMAL : <u>Dioon</u> <u>edule</u> , 103

CHAPMAN'S OAK : <u>Quercus</u> <u>chapmanii</u> , 308

CHASTE TREE : <u>Vitex</u> <u>agnus-castus</u> , 358, **188**

CHENILLE PLANT : <u>Acalypha</u> <u>hispida</u> , 3, **172**

CHEROKEE BEAN : <u>Erythrina</u> <u>herbacea</u> , 114

CHERRY LAUREL : <u>Prunus</u> <u>caroliniana</u> , 302, **167**

CHERRY OF THE RIO GRANDE : <u>Eugenia</u> <u>aggregata</u> , 116

CHERRY PALM : <u>Pseudophoenix</u> <u>sargentii</u> , 304, **207**

CHICKASAW PLUM : <u>Prunus</u> <u>angustifolia</u> , 302

CHICKEN GIZZARD ARALIA : <u>Polyscias</u> <u>crispata</u> , 298

CHINA DOLL : <u>Radermachera</u> <u>sinica</u> , 311

CHINA WOOD-OIL TREE : <u>Aleurites</u> <u>fordii</u> , 12

CHINABERRY : <u>Melia</u> <u>azedarach</u> , 256

CHINESE ANISE : <u>Illicium</u> <u>anisatum</u> , 222, **162**

CHINESE ELM : <u>Ulmus</u> <u>parvifolia</u> , 353, **171**

CHINESE EVERGREEN : <u>Aglaonema</u> <u>modestum</u> , 11

CHINESE FAN PALM : <u>Livistona</u> <u>chinensis</u> , 245, **205**

CHINESE FRINGE TREE : <u>Chionanthus</u> <u>retusus</u> , 70

CHINESE HAT PLANT : <u>Holmskioldia</u> <u>sanguinea</u> , 150

CHINESE HIBISCUS : <u>Hibiscus</u> <u>rosa-sinensis</u> , 149, **179**

CHINESE HOLLY : <u>Ilex</u> <u>cornuta</u> , 220, **180**

CHINESE IXORA : <u>Ixora</u> <u>chinensis</u> , 225

CHINESE JUNIPER : <u>Juniperus</u> <u>chinensis</u> , 231, **162**

CHINESE PARASOL TREE : <u>Firmiana</u> <u>simplex</u> , 130

CHINESE PHOTINIA : <u>Photinia</u> <u>serrulata</u> , 286

CHINESE PISTACHE : <u>Pistacia</u> <u>chinensis</u> , 292

CHINESE PRIVET : <u>Ligustrum</u> <u>sinense</u> , 242

CHINESE REDBUD : <u>Cercis</u> <u>chinensis</u> , 66

CHINESE TALLOWTREE : <u>Sapium</u> <u>sebiferum</u> , 323

CHINESE TARO : <u>Alocasia</u> <u>cucullata</u> , 14, **190**

CHINESE WISTERIA : <u>Wisteria</u> <u>sinensis</u> , 360

CHOLLA CACTUS : <u>Opuntia</u> spp., 270, **183**

CHRISTMAS BERRY : <u>Lycium</u> <u>carolinianum</u> , 248

CHRISTMAS PALM : <u>Veitchia</u> <u>merrillii</u> , 355, **209**

<u>Chrysanthemum</u> X <u>morifolium</u> : <u>Dendranthema</u> X <u>grandiflorum</u> , 100

CIGAR PLANT : <u>Cuphea</u> <u>ignea</u> , 94, **176**

CINNAMON FERN : <u>Osmunda</u> <u>regalis</u> , 272

<u>Citrus</u> <u>mitislis</u> : X <u>citrofortunella</u> <u>mitis</u> , 74

CLEYERA : <u>Cleyera</u> <u>japonica</u>, <u>Ternstroemia</u> <u>gymnanthera</u> , 79

CLIFF DATE : <u>Phoenix</u> <u>rupicola</u> , 285

CLIMBING HYDRANGEA : <u>Decumaria</u> <u>barbara</u> , 99

CLUSTERING FISHTAIL PALM : <u>Caryota</u> <u>mitis</u> , 59

COASTAL PLAIN WILLOW : <u>Salix</u> <u>caroliniana</u> , 320

COCKSPUR CORAL TREE : <u>Erythrina</u> <u>crista-gallii</u> , 114

COCONUT PALM : <u>Cocos</u> <u>nucifera</u> , 82, **203**

COCOPLUM : <u>Chrysobalanus</u> <u>icaco</u> , 72, **175**

<u>Cocos</u> <u>australiscaco</u> : <u>Butia</u> <u>capitata</u> , 46, **202**

<u>Cocos</u> <u>plumosaa</u> : <u>Syagrus</u> <u>romanzoffiana</u> , 335, **208**

COFFEE COLUBRINA : <u>Colubrina</u> <u>arborescens</u> , 83

COIN VINE : <u>Dalbergia</u> <u>ecastophyllum</u> , 99

COLEUS : <u>Coleus</u> X <u>hybridus</u> , 82

<u>Collinia</u> <u>eleganss</u> : <u>Chamaedorea</u> <u>elegans</u> , 68

COLVILLE'S GLORY : <u>Colvillea</u> <u>racemosa</u> , 83

COMMON BAMBOO : <u>Bambusa</u> <u>vulgaris</u> , 32, **173**

COMMON CAMELLIA : <u>Camellia</u> <u>japonica</u> , 54, **175**

COMMON LANTANA : <u>Lantana</u> <u>camara</u> , 238, **215**

COMMON MULBERRY : <u>Morus</u> <u>alba</u> , 259

COMMON VALERIAN : <u>Valeriana</u> <u>officinalis</u> , 354

CONFEDERATE JASMINE : <u>Trachelospermum</u> <u>jasminoides</u> , 348

COONTIE : <u>Zamia</u> <u>pumila</u> , 363, **188**

COPPERLEAF : <u>Acalypha</u> <u>wilkesiana</u> , 3, **172**

COPPERPOD : <u>Peltophorum</u> <u>pterocarpum</u>, <u>P.</u> <u>dubium</u> , 277

CORAL ARDISIA : <u>Ardisia</u> <u>crenata</u> , 25, **173**

CORAL BEAN : <u>Erythrina</u> <u>herbacea</u> , 114

CORAL BERRY VASE : <u>Aechmea</u> <u>fulgens</u> , 8

CORAL HONEYSUCKLE : <u>Lonicera</u> <u>sempervirens</u> , 247

CORAL PLANT : <u>Jatropha</u> <u>multifida</u> , 230

CORAL TREE : <u>Erythrina</u> <u>variegata</u> <u>orientalis</u> , 115, **159**

CORAL VINE : <u>Antigonon</u> <u>leptopus</u> , 23, **210**

CORALBERRY : <u>Ardisia</u> <u>crenata</u> , 25, **173**

COSTA RICAN PALM : <u>Chamadeorea</u> <u>costaricana</u> , 68

COSTA RICAN SKULLCAP : <u>Scutellaria</u> <u>costaricana</u> , 325

<u>Costus</u> <u>sanguineusricana</u> : <u>C.</u> <u>pulverolentus</u> , 88

COTTON CANDY TREE : <u>Muntingia</u> <u>calabura</u> , 260

COTTON-LEAVED JATROPHA : <u>Jatropha</u> <u>gossypifolia</u> , 229

COUNCIL TREE : <u>Ficus</u> <u>altissima</u> , 125

CRABWOOD : <u>Gymnanthes</u> <u>lucida</u> , 140

CRAPE MYRTLE : <u>Lagerstroemia</u> <u>indica</u> , 237, **163**

CREEPING FIG : <u>Ficus</u> <u>pumila</u> , 128, **211**

CREEPING JUNIPER : <u>Juniperus</u> <u>horizontalis</u> , 232, **214**

CREEPING LILYTURF : <u>Liriope</u> <u>spicata</u> , 244

CREPE GINGER : <u>Costus</u> <u>speciosus</u> , 88, **193**

CROSS VINE : <u>Bignonia</u> <u>capreolata</u> , 37

CROSSANDRA : <u>Crossandra</u> <u>infundibuliformis</u> , 92, **194**

CROTON : <u>Codiaeum</u> <u>variegatum</u> <u>pictum</u> , 82, **175**

CROWN-OF-THORNS : <u>Euphorbia</u> <u>milii</u> , 121

CUBAN PETTICOAT PALM : <u>Copernicia</u> <u>macroglossa</u> , 85

CUBAN PINE : <u>Pinus</u> <u>caribaea</u> , 290

CUBAN ROYAL PALM : <u>Roystonea</u> <u>regia</u> , 317, **208**

CUP-LEAVED ARALIA : <u>Polyscias</u> <u>scutellaria</u> , 300

CURTAIN PLANT : <u>Kalanchoe</u> <u>pinnata</u> , 234

CUT-LEAVED FAN PALM : <u>Livistona</u> <u>decipiens</u> , 245, **205**

CUTLEAF MORNING GLORY : <u>Merremia</u> <u>dissecta</u> , 257

<u>Cyrtostachys</u> <u>lakka</u> : <u>C.</u> <u>renda</u> , 98, **204**

DAHOON HOLLY : <u>Ilex</u> <u>cassine</u> , 220

DANCING LADY ORCHID : <u>Oncidium</u> spp., 269

DARLING PLUM : <u>Reynosia</u> <u>septentrionalis</u> , 313

DATE PALM : <u>Phoenix</u> <u>dactylifera</u> , 284, **206**

DAUBENTONIA : <u>Sesbania</u> <u>punicea</u> , 327

DAWN REDWOOD : <u>Metasequoia</u> <u>glyptostroboides</u> , 257

DAY LILY : <u>Hemerocallis</u> spp., 148, **197**

DENDROBIUM ORCHID : <u>Dendrobium</u> spp., 100

DEODAR CEDAR : <u>Cedrus</u> <u>deodara</u> , 64

DESERT FAN PALM : <u>Washingtonia</u> <u>filifera</u> , 358, **209**

DESERT PRIVET : <u>Peperomia</u> <u>magnoliifolia</u> , 279, **215**

DESERT ROSE : <u>Adenium</u> <u>obesum</u>, <u>Echeveria</u> <u>rosea</u> , 7, **172**

DEVIL'S POTATO : <u>Echites</u> <u>umbellata</u> , 110

<u>Dictyosperma</u> <u>aureum</u> : <u>D.</u> <u>album</u> var. <u>aureum</u> , 101, **204**

<u>Dictyosperma</u> <u>rubra</u> : <u>D.</u> <u>album</u> var. <u>rubra</u> , 101, **204**

<u>Dipladenia</u> <u>sanderi</u> : <u>Mandevilla</u> <u>sanderi</u> , 253

DOMINICAN COONTIE : <u>Zamia</u> <u>domingensis</u> , 363

DOWNY JASMINE : <u>Jasminum</u> <u>multiflorum</u> , 228

<u>Dracaena</u> <u>godseffiana</u> : <u>D.</u> <u>surculosa</u> , 107

DRAGON TREE : <u>Dracaena</u> <u>draco</u> , 106, **159**

DWARF CENTURY PLANT : <u>Agave</u> <u>desmettiana</u> , 10

DWARF ELM : <u>Ulmus</u> <u>pumila</u> , 353

DWARF EUPHORBIA : <u>Euphorbia</u> <u>bergeri</u> , 120

DWARF FIRETHORN : <u>Pyracantha</u> <u>koidzumii</u> , 307

DWARF GINGER : <u>Hedychium</u> <u>aureum</u> , 143

DWARF GINGER LILY : <u>Kaempferia</u> <u>roscoeana</u> , 233

DWARF HUCKLEBERRY : <u>Gaylussacia</u> <u>dumosa</u> , 134

DWARF LILYTURF : <u>Ophiopogon</u> <u>japonicus</u> , 270

DWARF MYRTLE : <u>Myrtus</u> <u>communis</u> , 263

DWARF PALMETTO : <u>Sabal</u> <u>minor</u> , 319

DWARF PAPYRUS : <u>Cyperus</u> <u>isocladus</u> , 97

DWARF POINCIANA : <u>Caesalpinia</u> <u>pulcherrima</u> , 48, **174**

DWARF SCHEFFLERA : <u>Schefflera</u> <u>arboricola</u> , 325, **186**

DWARF TREE FERN : <u>Blechnum</u> <u>gibbum</u> , 38

DWARF WAX MYRTLE : <u>Myrica</u> <u>pusilla</u> , 262

DYCKIA : <u>Dyckia</u> <u>brevifolia</u> , 109

EAR TREE : <u>Enterolobium</u> <u>cyclocarpum</u> , 112

EARLEAF ACACIA : <u>Acacia</u> <u>auriculiformis</u> , 1

EARTH STAR : <u>Cryptanthus</u> spp., 92, **194**

EAST INDIAN LOTUS : <u>Nelumbo</u> <u>nucifera</u> , 264

EASTERN GAMA GRASS : <u>Tripsacum</u> <u>dactyloides</u> , 350

EASTERN RED CEDAR : <u>Juniperus</u> <u>virginiana</u> , 232

EDIBLE BANANA : <u>Musa</u> <u>acuminata</u>, <u>M.</u> X <u>paradisiaca</u> , 260

EDIBLE FIG : <u>Ficus</u> <u>carica</u> , 126, **160**

EGGFRUIT : <u>Pouteria</u> <u>campechiana</u> , 301

ELEPHANT APPLE : <u>Dillenia</u> <u>indica</u> , 103

ELEPHANT BUSH : <u>Portulacaria</u> <u>afra</u> , 301

ELEPHANT EAR : <u>Alocasia</u> <u>odora</u>, <u>A.</u> <u>plumbea</u> , 15

ELKHORN FERN : <u>Polypodium</u> <u>grandiceps</u> , 297

<u>Enallagma</u> <u>latifolia</u> : <u>Amphitecna</u> <u>latifolia</u> , 19

ENGLISH IVY : <u>Hedera</u> <u>helix</u> , 143

EPIDENDRUM ORCHIDS : <u>Epidendrum</u> spp., 112

<u>Epidendrum</u> <u>radicans</u> : <u>E.</u> <u>ibaguense</u> , 112, **195**

ERECT BOTTLEBRUSH : <u>Callistemon</u> <u>rigidus</u> , 52, **155**

ERECT SWORD FERN : <u>Nephrolepis</u> <u>cordifolia</u> , 266

<u>Erythrina</u> <u>indica</u> <u>picta</u> : <u>E.</u> <u>variegata</u> var. <u>orientalis</u> , 115, **159**

<u>Eucharis</u> <u>grandiflora</u> : <u>E.</u> <u>amazonica</u> , 116, **195**

<u>Eugenia</u> <u>myrtifolia</u> : <u>Syzygium</u> <u>paniculatum</u> , 337

<u>Euphorbia</u> <u>bojeri</u> : <u>E.</u> <u>milii</u> , 121

<u>Euphorbia</u> <u>polychroma</u> : <u>E.</u> <u>epithymoides</u> , 120

<u>Euphorbia</u> <u>splendens</u> : <u>E.</u> <u>milii</u> , 121

EUROPEAN FAN PALM : <u>Chamaerops</u> <u>humilis</u> , 69, **203**

EVERGLADES PALM : <u>Acoelorrhaphe</u> <u>wrightii</u> , 5, **202**

EVERGLADES VELVETSEED : <u>Guettarda</u> <u>elliptica</u> , 140

FAKAHATCHEE GRASS : <u>Tripsacum</u> <u>dactyloides</u> , 350

FALL ORCHID TREE : <u>Bauhinia</u> <u>purpurea</u> , 33

FALSE ARALIA : <u>Dizygotheca</u> <u>elegantissima</u> , 105

FALSE DRAGONHEAD : <u>Physostegia</u> <u>virginiana</u> , 288

FALSE HEATHER : <u>Cuphea</u> <u>hyssopifolia</u> , 94, **213**

FALSE INDIGO : <u>Baptisia</u> spp., 32

FALSE POINCIANA : <u>Sesbania</u> <u>punicea</u> , 327

FANCY-LEAVED CALADIUM : <u>Caladium</u> X <u>hortulanum</u> , 48, **192**

FATSIA : <u>Fatsia</u> <u>japonica</u> , 124, **179**

FEIJOA : <u>Feijoa</u> <u>sellowiana</u> , 125, **178**

FENCE POCHOTE : <u>Bombacopsis</u> <u>fendleri</u> , 39

FERNLEAF ARALIA : <u>Polyscias</u> <u>filicifolia</u> , 298, **184**

FEVERTREE : <u>Pinckneya</u> <u>pubens</u> , 289

<u>Ficus</u> <u>brevifolia</u> : <u>F.</u> <u>citrifolia</u> , 127

<u>Ficus</u> <u>laevigata</u> : <u>F.</u> <u>citrifolia</u> , 127

<u>Ficus</u> <u>nitida</u> : <u>F.</u> <u>retusa</u> 'Nitida' , 129, **161**

<u>Ficus</u> <u>pandurata</u> : <u>F.</u> <u>lyrata</u> , 127, **161**

<u>Ficus</u> <u>repens</u> : <u>F.</u> <u>pumila</u> , 128, **211**

FIDDLELEAF FIG : <u>Ficus</u> <u>lyrata</u> , 127, **161**

FIDDLEWOOD : <u>Citharexylum</u> <u>fruticosum</u> , 74

FIERY COSTUS : <u>Costus</u> <u>igneus</u> , 88

FIRECRACKER PLANT : <u>Russelia</u> <u>equisetiformis</u> , 318, **186**

FIREWHEEL TREE : <u>Stenocarpus</u> <u>sinuatus</u> , 332, **169**

FISH POISON TREE : <u>Piscidia</u> <u>piscipula</u> , 292

FISHBONE CACTUS : <u>Euphorbia</u> <u>polycantha</u> , 122

FLAMBOYANT : <u>Delonix</u> <u>regia</u> , 100, **159**

FLAME BOTTLE TREE : <u>Brachychiton</u> <u>acerifolius</u> , 41, **154**

FLAME OF THE FOREST : <u>Butea</u> <u>monosperma</u> , 46, **155**

FLAME OF THE WOODS : <u>Ixora</u> <u>coccinea</u> , 226

FLAME TREE : <u>Delonix</u> <u>regia</u> , 100, **159**

FLAME VINE : <u>Pyrostegia</u> <u>venusta</u> , 307, **212**

FLAMING SWORD : <u>Vriesia</u> <u>splendens</u> , 358

FLAMINGO FLOWER : <u>Anthurium</u> <u>andraeanum</u> , 21, **191**

FLAMINGO PLANT : <u>Justicia</u> <u>carnea</u> , 233, **181**

FLATWOODS PLUM : <u>Prunus</u> <u>umbellata</u> , 303

FLAX LILY : <u>Dianella</u> <u>ensifolia</u> , 101

FLOATING HEARTS : <u>Nymphoides</u> spp., 268

FLORIDA ANISE : <u>Illicium</u> <u>floridanum</u> , 222, **162**

FLORIDA BASSWOOD : <u>Tilia</u> <u>floridana</u> , 347

FLORIDA BOXWOOD : <u>Schaefferia frutescens</u> , 324

FLORIDA BUCKEYE : <u>Aesculus pavia</u> , 8, **172**

FLORIDA FLAME AZALEA : <u>Rhododendron austrinum</u> , 315, **185**

FLORIDA GAMA GRASS : <u>Tripsacum floridana</u> , 350

FLORIDA HONEYSUCKLE : <u>Rhododendron canescens</u> , 316, **186**

FLORIDA LILAC : <u>Lonchocarpus</u> spp., 247

FLORIDA MAPLE : <u>Acer barbatum</u> , 3

FLORIDA MAYTEN : <u>Maytenus phyllanthoides</u> , 255

FLORIDA NUTMEG : <u>Torreya taxifolia</u> , 347

FLORIDA PRIVET : <u>Forestiera segregata</u> , 131

FLORIDA ROYAL PALM : <u>Roystonea elata</u> , 317

FLORIDA TETRAZYGIA : <u>Tetrazygia bicolor</u> , 343, **187**

FLORIDA THATCH PALM : <u>Thrinax parviflora</u> , 344

FLORIDA TRIPSACUM : <u>Tripsacum floridana</u> , 350

FLORIDA VIOLET : <u>Viola floridana</u> , 357

FLORIDA YEW : <u>Taxus floridana</u> , 340

FLORISTS' CHRYSANTHEMUM : <u>Dendranthema</u> X <u>morifolium</u> , 100

FLOSS-SILK TREE : <u>Chorisia speciosa</u> , 71, **157**

FLOWERING DOGWOOD : <u>Cornus florida</u> , 86, **158**

FLOWERING LINDEN : <u>Sparmannia africana</u> , 330

FLOWERING MAPLE : <u>Abutilon pictum</u> , 1

FLOWERING ONIONS : <u>Allium</u> spp., 14

FLOWERING PEPEROMIA : <u>Peperomia fraseri</u> , 278

FORMOSAN GUM : <u>Liquidambar formosana</u> , 243

FORTNIGHT LILY : <u>Dietes vegeta</u> , 103, **213**

FORTUNE OSMANTHUS : <u>Osmanthus fortunei</u> , 271

FOUNTAIN GRASS : <u>Pennisetum setaceum</u> , 277

FOXTAIL PALM : <u>Wodyetia bifurcata</u> , 360, **209**

FRAGRANT CALLISIA : <u>Callisia fragrans</u> , 52, **213**

FRAGRANT DRACAENA : <u>Dracaena fragrans</u> , 106, **177**

FRAGRANT WATERLILY : <u>Nymphaea odorata</u> , 267

FRANGIPANI : <u>Plumeria rubra</u>, <u>P. alba</u> , 295, **167**

FRASER MAGNOLIA : <u>Magnolia fraseri</u> , 250

FRASER PHOTINIA : <u>Photinia</u> X <u>fraseri</u> , 286

FRINGE TREE : <u>Chionanthus virginicus</u> , 71, **157**

FRINGED HIBISCUS : <u>Hibiscus schizopetalus</u> , 149, **179**

GAILLARDIA : <u>Gaillardia pulchella</u> , 132, **214**

GALLBERRY : <u>Ilex glabra</u> , 221

GANGES PRIMROSE : <u>Asystasis gangetica</u> , 29

GARBERIA : <u>Garberia fruticosa</u> , 133

GARDEN CANNA : <u>Canna</u> X <u>generalis</u> , 56, **192**

<u>Gardenia radicans</u> : <u>Gardenia jasminoides</u> 'Radicans' , 133

GARLIC VINE : <u>Cydista aequinoctialis</u> , 96, **210**

GAZANIA : <u>Gazania</u> spp., 134

GEBANG PALM : <u>Corypha elata</u> , 88, **204**

GEIGER TREE : <u>Cordia sebestena</u> , 85, **158**

GERBERA DAISY : <u>Gerbera jamesonii</u> , 135

GIANT ALOCASIA : <u>Alocasia macrorrhiza</u> , 14

GIANT CALADIUM : <u>Alocasia cuprea</u> , 14

GIANT DRACAENA : <u>Cordyline australis</u> , 85

GIANT FISHTAIL PALM : <u>Caryota rumphiana</u> , 59

GIANT SPIDER LILY : <u>Crinum</u> X <u>amabile</u> , 91, **193**

GIANT THORNY BAMBOO : <u>Bambusa arundinacea</u> , 31

GIANT TIMBER BAMBOO : <u>Phyllostachys bambusioides</u> , 287

GINGERBREAD PALM : <u>Hyphaene</u> spp., 219

GLADIOLUS : <u>Gladiolus</u> spp., 135

GLAUCOUS CASSIA : <u>Cassia surattensis</u> , 62

GLOBBA : <u>Globba atrosanguinea, G. winitti</u> , 136

GLORYBUSH : <u>Tibouchina urvilleana</u> , 346

GLOSSY ABELIA : <u>Abelia</u> X <u>grandiflora</u> , 1

GLOSSY PRIVET : <u>Ligustrum lucidum</u> , 242

GOLD CLUB : <u>Orontium aquaticum</u> , 271

GOLD COAST JASMINE : <u>Jasminum dichotomum</u> , 227

GOLD DUST DRACAENA : <u>Dracaena surculosa</u> , 107

GOLDCUP : <u>Solandra guttata</u> , 329

GOLDEN BAMBOO : <u>Phyllostachys aurea</u> , 287

GOLDEN CANNA : <u>Canna flaccida</u> , 56

GOLDEN CREEPER : <u>Ernodea littoralis</u> , 114

GOLDEN DEWDROP : <u>Duranta repens</u> , 108, **178**

GOLDEN RAIN TREE : <u>Koelreuteria bipinnata, K. elegans</u> , 236, **163**

GOLDEN SHOWER : <u>Cassia fistula</u> , 61, **156**

GOLDEN SHRIMP PLANT : <u>Pachystachys lutea</u> , 273, **183**

GOLDEN SHRUB DAISY : <u>Euryops pectinatus</u> , 123

GOLDEN TABEBUIA : <u>Tabebuia chrysotricha</u> , 338, **170**

GOLDEN TORCH HELICONIA : <u>Heliconia</u> X 'Golden Torch' , 148, **196**

GOLDEN WONDER : <u>Cassia splendida</u> , 62

GOLDENROD : <u>Solidago</u> spp., 329

GOLDFLOWER : <u>Hypericum</u> X <u>moserianum</u> , 219

GOUT PLANT : <u>Jatropha</u> <u>podagrica</u> , 230

GOVERNOR'S PLUM : <u>Flacourtia</u> <u>indica</u> , 130

GRAND LICUALA : <u>Licuala</u> <u>grandis</u> , 241, **205**

GRAPE IVY : <u>Cissus</u> <u>rhombifolia</u> , 74

GRAPEFRUIT : <u>Citrus</u> X <u>paradisi</u> , 76

GRASSY-LEAVED SWEET FLAG : <u>Acorus</u> <u>gramineus</u> , 6

GREATER PERIWINKLE : <u>Vinca</u> <u>major</u> , 357

GREEN ASH : <u>Fraxinus</u> <u>pennsylvanica</u> , 132

GREEN DRAGONS : <u>Arisaema</u> <u>draconitum</u> , 26

GREEN ISLAND FIG : <u>Ficus</u> 'Green Island' , 129

GROUNDSEL : <u>Baccharis</u> <u>halimifolia</u> , 30

GRUGRU PALM : <u>Acrocromia</u> <u>totai</u> , 6

GRUMACHAMA : <u>Eugenia</u> <u>brasiliensis</u> , 117, **159**

GUANABANA : <u>Annona</u> <u>muricata</u> , 20, **153**

GUAVA : <u>Psidium</u> <u>guajava</u> , 304, **168**

GUIANA CHESTNUT : <u>Pachira</u> <u>aquatica</u> , 272

GUIANA PLUM : <u>Drypetes</u> <u>lateriflora</u> , 108

GULF LICARIA : <u>Licaria</u> <u>triandra</u> , 241, **163**

GUM ARABIC TREE : <u>Acacia</u> <u>nilotica</u> , 2

GUMBO LIMBO : <u>Bursera</u> <u>simaruba</u> , 46, **154**

HARDY STATICE : <u>Limonium</u> <u>latifolium</u> , 243

HARLEQUIN FLOWER : <u>Sparaxis</u> spp., 330

HAWTHORNS : <u>Crataegus</u> spp., 89

HEARTLEAF PHILODENDRON : <u>Philodendron</u> <u>scandens</u> var. <u>oxycardium</u> , 282

HEAVENLY BAMBOO : <u>Nandina</u> <u>domestica</u> , 263

HEDGE BAMBOO : <u>Bambusa</u> <u>glaucescens</u> , 31

HEDGE CACTUS : <u>Cereus</u> <u>peruvianus</u> , 66

<u>Heliconia</u> <u>bicolor</u> : <u>H.</u> <u>angusta</u> , 145

<u>Heliconia</u> <u>humilis</u> : <u>H.</u> <u>bihai</u> , 146

HELIOTROPE : <u>Heliotropium</u> spp., 148

HENNA : <u>Lawsonia</u> <u>inermis</u> , 239

HERALD'S TRUMPET : <u>Beaumontia</u> <u>grandiflora</u> , 35

HERCULE'S CLUB : <u>Zanthoxylum</u> <u>clava-herculis</u> , 364

HIBISCUS : <u>Hibiscus</u> <u>rosa-sinensis</u> , 149, **179**

HIDDEN LILY : <u>Curcuma</u> spp., 95

HOLIDAY CACTUS : <u>Schlumbergera</u> spp., 325

HOLIDAY HELICONIA : <u>Heliconia angusta</u> , 145

HOLLY FERN : <u>Cyrtomium falcatum</u> , 98

HOLLY GRAPE : <u>Mahonia fortunei</u> , 251

HOLLY OLIVE : <u>Osmanthus heterophyllus</u> , 271

HOLLY OSMANTHUS : <u>Osmanthus heterophyllus</u> , 271

HONDAPARA : <u>Dillenia indica</u> , 103

HONG KONG ORCHID TREE : <u>Bauhinia blakeana</u> , 32

HOP TREE : <u>Ptelea trifoliata</u> , 305

HORSERADISH TREE : <u>Moringa pterygosperma</u> , 259

HOSPITA COPERNICIA : <u>Copernicia hospita</u> , 84, **203**

HOTTENTOT FIG : <u>Carpobrotus</u> spp., 58

HUCKLEBERRY : <u>Gaylussacia dumosa</u> , 134

HURRICANE LILIES : <u>Lycoris</u> spp., 248

HURRICANE PALM : <u>Dictyosperma album</u> , 101, **204**

HYACINTH BEAN : <u>Dolichos lablab</u> , 105

HYBRID IXORA : <u>Ixora</u> hybrids, 226, 180

HYDRANGEA : <u>Hydrangea macrophylla</u> , 152, **180**

<u>Hymenocallis calathina</u> : <u>H. narcissiflora</u> , 218, **197**

IFAFA LILY : <u>Cyrtanthus mackenii</u> , 98

ILANG ILANG : <u>Cananga odorata</u> , 55, **155**

IMPERIAL PHILODENDRON : <u>Philodendron speciosum</u> , 282

INCA LILY : <u>Alstroemeria pulchella</u> , 18

INDIAN ALMOND : <u>Sterculia foetida</u> , 332

INDIAN HAWTHORN : <u>Raphiolepis indica</u> , 312

INDIAN JUJUBE TREE : <u>Zizphus mauritiana</u> , 366

INDIAN KALE : <u>Xanthosoma lindenii</u> , 360, **201**

INDIAN LAUREL : <u>Ficus retusa</u>, <u>Calophyllum inophyllum</u> , 129, **161**

INDIAN ROSEWOOD : <u>Dalbergia sissoo</u> , 99

INDIAN RUBBER TREE : <u>Ficus elastica</u> , 127

INKBERRY : <u>Scaevola plumieri</u> , 324

IRONWOOD : <u>Eugenia confusa</u> , 117

ISMENE : <u>Hymenocallis narcissiflora</u> , 218, **197**

ITALIAN CYPRESS : <u>Cupressus sempervirens</u> , 94

<u>Ixora macrothyrsairens</u> : <u>I. duffii</u> , 226

JABOTICABA : <u>Myrciaria cauliflora</u> , 262, **165**

JABURAN LILYTURF : <u>Ophiopogon jaburan</u> , 270

JACARANDA : <u>J. mimosifolia</u> , 226, **162**

<u>Jacaranda acutifolia</u> : <u>Jacaranda mimosifolia</u> , 226, **162**

JACK IN THE PULPIT : <u>Arisaema</u> <u>triphylla</u> , 26

<u>Jacobinia</u> <u>carnea</u> : <u>Justicia</u> <u>carnea</u> , 233, **181**

JACOB'S COAT : <u>Acalypha</u> <u>wilkesiana</u> , 3, **172**

JACQUEMONTIA : <u>Jacquemontia</u> spp., 227

JADE PLANT : <u>Crassula</u> <u>argentea</u> , 89, **176**

JAMAICAN CAPER : <u>Capparis</u> <u>cynophallophora</u> , 56

JAMAICAN DOGWOOD : <u>Piscidia</u> <u>piscipula</u> , 292

JAMAICAN RAIN TREE : <u>Brya</u> <u>ebenus</u> , 44

JAMBOLAN PLUM : <u>Syzygium</u> <u>cumini</u> , 336

JAPANESE ARDISIA : <u>Ardisia</u> <u>japonica</u> , 25

JAPANESE AUCUBA : <u>Aucuba</u> <u>japonica</u> , 29

JAPANESE BARBERRY : <u>Berberis</u> <u>thunbergii</u> , 36, **173**

JAPANESE BLACK PINE : <u>Pinus</u> <u>thunbergiana</u> , 291

JAPANESE BOXWOOD : <u>Buxus</u> <u>microphylla</u> var. <u>japonica</u> , 47

JAPANESE CEDAR : <u>Cryptomeria</u> <u>japonica</u> , 93

JAPANESE CLEMATIS : <u>Clematis</u> <u>dioscoreifolia</u> , 77

JAPANESE DOGWOOD : <u>Cornus</u> <u>kousa</u> , 86

JAPANESE ENONYMUS : <u>Euonymus</u> <u>japonica</u> , 119

JAPANESE GARDEN JUNIPER : <u>Juniperus</u> <u>chinensis</u> var. <u>procumbens</u> , 231

JAPANESE HOLLY : <u>Ilex</u> <u>crenata</u> , 220

JAPANESE HONEYSUCKLE : <u>Lonicera</u> <u>japonica</u> , 247

JAPANESE IRIS : <u>Iris</u> <u>kaempferi</u> , 224

JAPANESE MAPLE : <u>Acer</u> <u>palmatum</u> , 4, **172**

JAPANESE PERSIMMON : <u>Diospyros</u> <u>kaki</u> , 104

JAPANESE PHOTINIA : <u>Photinia</u> <u>glabra</u> , 285

JAPANESE PITTOSPORUM : <u>Pittosporum</u> <u>tobira</u> , 293, **184**

JAPANESE PLUM YEW : <u>Cephalotaxus</u> <u>harringtonia</u> , 65

JAPANESE PRIVET : <u>Ligustrum</u> <u>japonicum</u> , 241

JAPANESE SHIELD FERN : <u>Dryopteris</u> <u>erythrosora</u> , 108

JAPANESE WOOD FERN : <u>Dryopteris</u> <u>erythrosora</u> , 108

JAPANESE ZELKOVA : <u>Zelkova</u> <u>serrata</u> , 365

<u>Jasminum</u> <u>pubescens</u> : <u>J.</u> <u>multiflorum</u> , 228

<u>Jasminum</u> <u>simplicifolium</u> : <u>J.</u> <u>volubile</u> , 229

JAVA GLORYBOWER : <u>Clerodendrum</u> <u>speciosissimum</u> , 78

JAVA PLUM : <u>Syzygium</u> <u>cumini</u> , 336

JELLY PALM : <u>Butia</u> <u>capitata</u> , 46, **202**

JERUSALEM THORN : <u>Parkinsonia</u> <u>aculeata</u> , 274, **165**

JOANNIS PALM : <u>Veitchia</u> <u>joannis</u> , 354, **209**

JOEWOOD : Jacquinia keyensis , 227

JUPITER'S BEARD : Centranthus ruber , 65

KAFFIR LILY : Clivia miniata , 79, **193**

KAFFIR PLUM : Harpephyllum caffrum , 142

KAHILI LILY : Hedychium gardnerianum , 144

KAKI : Diospyros kaki , 104

KALANCHOE : Kalanchoe blossfeldiana , 234

KAPOK TREE : Ceiba pentandra , 64, **156**

KASSOD TREE : Cassia siamea , 62

KENTIA PALM : Howea forsterana , 151, **204**

KEY LIME : Citrus aurantiifolia , 74

KEY THATCH PALM : Thrinax morrisii , 344, **208**

KING ALEXANDER PALM : Archontophoenix alexandrae , 24, **202**

KING SAGO : Cycas revoluta , 96, **176**

KING'S MANTLE : Thunbergia erecta , 345

Koelreuteria formosana : K. elegans , 236, **163**

KOPSIA : Ochrosia parviflora , 269

KOREAN BOXWOOD : Buxus microphylla var. koreana , 47

KOUSA DOGWOOD : Cornus kousa , 86

KRUG HOLLY : Ilex krugiana , 221

KUMQUAT : Fortunella japonica , 131

LACY LADY ARALIA : Evodia suaveolens var. ridleyi , 124

LADY JANE ANTHURIUM : Anthurium 'Lady Jane' , 21, **191**

LADY OF THE NIGHT : Brassavola spp., 43

LADY PALM : Rhapis excelsa , 314, **207**

LANCE DRACAENA : Dracaena thalioides , 108

LANCEWOOD : Nectandra coriacea , 264, **165**

LAUREL OAK : Quercus laurifolia , 309

LAURELWOOD : Calophyllum inophyllum , 53, **155**

LAURESTINUS : Viburnum tinus , 357, **187**

LAVENDER FLOWERING BANANA : Musa ornata , 261, **198**

LAVENDER STAR FLOWER : Grewia caffra , 138

LAZY DAISY : Aphanostephus skirrhobasis , 23

LEADWOOD : Krugiodendron ferreum , 236, **163**

LEATHER FERN : Acrostichum daneifolium , 6

LEATHERLEAF : Chamaedaphne calyculata , 67

LEATHERLEAF MAHONIA : Mahonia bealei , 251, **181**

LEATHERLEAF FERN : Rumohra adiantiformis , 318, **216**

LEBBEK TREE : <u>Albizia</u> <u>lebbeck</u> , 12

LEMON : <u>Citrus</u> <u>limon</u> , 75

LEMON BOTTLEBRUSH : <u>Callistemon</u> <u>citrinus</u> , 52

LEMON VINE : <u>Pereskia</u> <u>aculeata</u> , 280

LEMONGRASS : <u>Cymbopogon</u> <u>citratus</u> , 96

LEOPARD LILY : <u>Lachenalia</u> spp., 237

LESSER BOUGAINVILLEA : <u>Bougainvillea</u> <u>glabra</u> , 40, **173**

<u>Leucophyllum</u> <u>texanum</u> : <u>L.</u> <u>frutescens</u> , 240, **181**

LIATRUS : <u>Liatrus</u> spp., 240

LIFE PLANT : <u>Kalanchoe</u> <u>gastonis-bonnieri</u> , 234

LIGNUM-VITAE : <u>Guaiacum</u> <u>sanctum,</u> <u>G.</u> <u>officinale</u> , 139

LILY OF THE NILE : <u>Agapanthus</u> <u>africanus</u> , 9, **189**

LILYTURF : <u>Liriope</u> <u>muscari</u> , 244

LIME : <u>Citrus</u> <u>latifolia</u> , 75

LIMEBERRY : <u>Triphasia</u> <u>trifolia</u> , 350, **187**

LINGARO : <u>Elaeagnus</u> <u>philippensis</u> , 110

LITCHI : <u>Litchi</u> <u>chinensis</u> , 245

LITTLELEAF BOX : <u>Buxus</u> <u>microphylla</u> var. <u>japonica</u> , 47

LIVE OAK : <u>Quercus</u> <u>virginiana</u> , 311, **168**

LIVE-FOREVER : <u>Kalanchoe</u> <u>pinnata</u> , 234

LOBLOLLY BAY : <u>Gordonia</u> <u>lasianthus</u> , 137, **161**

LOBLOLLY PINE : <u>Pinus</u> <u>taeda</u> , 291

LOBSTER CLAW : <u>Heliconia</u> <u>rostrata,</u> <u>H.</u> <u>bihai</u> , 147, **196**

LOCUSTBERRY : <u>Byrsonima</u> <u>lucida</u> , 47

LOFTY FIG : <u>Ficus</u> <u>altissima</u> , 125

LONG JOHN : <u>Triplaris</u> <u>americana</u> , 350

LONG-LEAVED BLOLLY : <u>Guapira</u> <u>longifolia</u> , 139

LONGAN : <u>Euphoria</u> <u>longan</u> , 123, **160**

LONGLEAF PINE : <u>Pinus</u> <u>palustris</u> , 291

LOQUAT : <u>Eriobotrya</u> <u>japonica</u> , 113, **159**

LOROPETALUM : <u>Loropetalum</u> <u>chinense</u> , 248

LOUISIANA IRIS : <u>Iris</u> 'Louisiana hybrids, 224

LUSTERLEAF HOLLY : <u>Ilex</u> <u>latifolia</u> , 221

LYCHEE : <u>Litchi</u> <u>chinensis</u> , 245

<u>Lysiloma</u> <u>bahamense</u> : <u>L.</u> <u>latisiliqua</u> , 249

MACADAMIA NUT : <u>Macadamia</u> <u>integrifolia</u> , 249

MACARTHUR PALM : <u>Ptychosperma</u> <u>macarthurii</u> , 306

MADAGASCAR JASMINE : <u>Stephanotis</u> <u>floribunda</u> , 332, **212**

MADAGASCAR OLIVE : <u>Noronhia</u> <u>emarginata</u> , 267, **183**

MADAGASCAR PALM : <u>Pachypodium</u> <u>lamerei</u> , 273

MADAGASCAR RUBBER VINE : <u>Cryptostegia</u> <u>madagascariensis</u> , 93, **210**

MAHOE : <u>Hibiscus</u> <u>tiliaceus</u> , 150, **162**

MAHOGANY : <u>Swietenia</u> <u>mahagoni</u> , 334, **170**

MAIDENBUSH : <u>Savia</u> <u>bahamensis</u> , 323

MAIDENHAIR FERNS : <u>Adiantum</u> spp., 7, **189**

MAIDENHAIR TREE : <u>Ginkgo</u> <u>biloba</u> , 135

MAJESTY PALM : <u>Ravenea</u> <u>rivularis</u> , 313, **207**

MALABAR CHESTNUT : <u>Pachira</u> <u>aquatica</u> , 272

MALABAR GLORY LILY : <u>Gloriosa</u> <u>superba</u> , 137

MALE BAMBOO : <u>Dendrocalamus</u> <u>strictus</u> , 100

MALLET FLOWER : <u>Tupidanthus</u> <u>calyptratus</u> , 351

MAMMEE APPLE : <u>Mammea</u> <u>americana</u> , 253

MAMMEE SAPOTE : <u>Pouteria</u> <u>sapota</u> , 301, **167**

MANDARIN ORANGE : <u>Citrus</u> <u>reticulata</u> , 75

MANDEVILLA : <u>Mandevilla</u> <u>sanderi</u> , 253

MANGO : <u>Mangifera</u> <u>indica</u> , 253, **164**

MANILA PALM : <u>Veitchia</u> <u>merrillii</u> , 355, **209**

MANILA TAMARIND : <u>Pithecellobium</u> <u>dulce</u> , 292

MARINE IVY : <u>Cissus</u> <u>incisa</u> , 73

MARLBERRY : <u>Ardisia</u> <u>escallonioides</u> , 25

MARRIAGE VINE : <u>Solanum</u> spp., 329

MARSH ELDER : <u>Iva</u> <u>frutescens</u> , 225

MARSH FERN : <u>Thelypteris</u> <u>palustris</u> , 343

<u>Mascarena</u> <u>lagenicaulis</u> : <u>Hyophorbe</u> <u>lagenicaulis</u> , 218, **204**

<u>Mascarena</u> <u>verschafeltii</u> : <u>Hyophorbe</u> <u>verschafeltii</u> , 218

MASTIC : <u>Mastichodendron</u> <u>foetidissimum</u> , 255

MASTWOOD : <u>Calophyllum</u> <u>inophyllum</u> , 53, **155**

MAUEY DEL CUMBRE : <u>Agave</u> <u>atrovirens</u> , 9

MAYA PALM : <u>Gaussia</u> <u>maya</u> , 134

MAYTENUS : <u>Maytenus</u> <u>undatus</u> , 256

MEADOW BEAUTY : <u>Rhexia</u> spp., 315

MEALYCUP SAGE : <u>Salvia</u> <u>farinacea</u> , 321, **199**

MEDINELLA : <u>Medinella</u> <u>magnifica</u> , 256, **182**

MEDITERRANEAN ALOE : <u>Aloe</u> <u>barbadensis</u> , 16, **189**

MEMORIA-CORSII DUMBCANE : <u>Dieffenbachia</u> X <u>memoria-corsii</u> , 102

MENTOR BARBERRY : <u>Berberis</u> X <u>mentorensis</u> , 37

METAKE BAMBOO : <u>Pseudosasa japonica</u> , 304

MEXICAN BLUEBELL : <u>Ruellia brittoniana</u> , 318

MEXICAN CAESALPINIA : <u>Caesalpinia mexicana</u> , 48

MEXICAN CALABASH : <u>Crescentia alata</u> , 89

MEXICAN FLAME VINE : <u>Senecio confusus</u> , 326, **212**

MEXICAN HEATHER : <u>Cuphea hyssopifolia</u> , 94, **213**

MEXICAN VASE : <u>Aechmea mexicana</u> , 8

MICKEY MOUSE PLANT : <u>Ochna serrulata</u> , 268

MICROSPADIX PALM : <u>Chamaedorea microspadix</u> , 69

MILK AND WINE LILY : <u>Crinum latifolium</u> var. <u>zeylanicum</u> , 91, **194**

MILKSTRIPED EUPHORBIA : <u>Euphorbia lactea</u> , 121

MILLETTIA : <u>Millettia ovalifolia</u> , 258, **164**

MIMOSA : <u>Albizia julibrissin</u> , 12, **153**

MIMUSOPS : <u>Manilkara roxburghiana</u> , 254

<u>Mimusops kaki</u> : <u>Manilkara kauki</u> , 254

<u>Mimusops roxburghiana</u> : <u>Manilkara roxburghiana</u> , 254

MING ARALIA : <u>Polyscias fruticosa</u> , 299, **184**

MINIATURE FISHTAIL PALM : <u>Chamaedorea metallica</u> , 68

MIRACLE FRUIT : <u>Synsepalum dulcificum</u> , 336

MIRAGUAMA PALM : <u>Coccothrinax miraguama</u> , 81

MISTFLOWER : <u>Eupatorium coelestinum</u> , 119

MOHINTLI : <u>Justicia spicigera</u> , 233

MONDO GRASS : <u>Ophiopogon japonicus</u> , 270

MONKEY GRASS : <u>Ophiopogon japonicus</u> , 270

MONKEY PLANT : <u>Ruellia makoyana</u> , 318

MONTEBRETIA : <u>Crocosmia</u> X <u>crocosmiiflora</u> , 92

MONTGOMERY PALM : <u>Veitchia montgomeryana</u> , 355

MOORE'S MACROZAMIA : <u>Macrozamia moorei</u> , 249

<u>Moraea bicolor</u> : <u>Dietes bicolor</u> , 102

<u>Moraea vegeta</u> : <u>Dietes vegeta</u> , 103, **213**

MORNING GLORY : <u>Ipomoea stolonifera</u>, <u>I.</u> <u>fistulosa</u>, <u>I.</u> spp., 223

MOSS ROSE : <u>Portulaca grandiflora</u> , 300, **216**

MOTH ORCHID : <u>Phalaenopsis</u> spp., 281

MOTHER IN LAW'S TONGUE : <u>Albizia lebbeck</u> , 12

MOUNTAIN LAUREL : <u>Kalmia latifolia</u> , 235, **181**

MUELLER'S TERMINALIA : <u>Terminalia muelleri</u> , 342

MULLEIN : <u>Verbascum</u> spp., 356

MYROBALAN PLUM : <u>Prunus cerasifera</u> , 302

MYRTLE OAK : <u>Quercus</u> <u>myrtifolia</u> , 309

MYRTLE OF THE RIVER : <u>Calyptranthes</u> <u>zuzygium</u> , 54

NAGAMI KUMQUAT : <u>Fortunella</u> <u>margarita</u> , 131

NAGI PODOCARPUS : <u>Podocarpus</u> <u>nagi</u> , 296, **167**

NANDINA : <u>Nandina</u> <u>domestica</u> , 263

NATAL PLUM : <u>Carissa</u> <u>macrocarpa</u> , 57, **175**

<u>Neanthe</u> <u>bella</u> : <u>Chamaedorea</u> <u>elegans</u> , 68

NECKLACE POD : <u>Sophora</u> <u>tomentosa</u> , 329

NEEDLE PALM : <u>Rhapidophyllum</u> <u>hystrix</u> , 313, **207**

NEEM TREE : <u>Azadirachta</u> <u>indica</u> , 30

NERVE PLANT : <u>Fittonia</u> <u>verschafeltii</u> , 130, **213**

NEW ZEALAND FLAX : <u>Phormium</u> <u>tenax</u> , 285

<u>Nicolaia</u> <u>elatior</u> : <u>Etlingera</u> <u>elatior</u> , 115, **195**

NIGHT-BLOOMING CEREUS : <u>Hylocereus</u> <u>undatus</u> , 217, **211**

NIGHT-BLOOMING JESSAMINE : <u>Cestrum</u> <u>nocturnum</u> , 67

NORFOLK ISLAND PINE : <u>Araucaria</u> <u>heterophylla</u> , 24, **153**

NOTA FIG : <u>Ficus</u> <u>nota</u> , 128

NOVEMBER SHOWER TREE : <u>Cassia</u> <u>multijuga</u> , 61

NUN'S ORCHID : <u>Phaius</u> <u>tankervilliae</u> , 281, **199**

NYASALAND MAHOGANY : <u>Khaya</u> <u>nyasica</u> , 235

OAKLEAF ARALIA : <u>Polyscias</u> <u>obtusa</u> , 299, **185**

OAKLEAF HYDRANGEA : <u>Hydrangea</u> <u>quercifolia</u> , 152

OBEDIENCE PLANT : <u>Maranta</u> <u>arundinacea</u> , 255

OBEDIENT PLANT : <u>Physostegia</u> <u>virginiana</u> , 288

OCHROSIA : <u>Ochrosia</u> <u>elliptica</u> , 269, **165**

OCTOPUS TREE : <u>Brassaia</u> <u>actinophylla</u> , 41, **174**

OLD MAN PALM : <u>Coccothrinax</u> <u>crinita</u> , 81, **203**

OLDHAM BAMBOO : <u>Bambusa</u> <u>oldhamii</u> , 31

OLEANDER : <u>Nerium</u> <u>oleander</u> , 266, **182**

OLEASTER : <u>Elaeagnus</u> <u>latifolia</u> , 110

<u>Opsiandra</u> <u>maya</u> : <u>Gaussia</u> <u>maya</u> , 134

ORANGE JASMINE : <u>Murraya</u> <u>paniculata</u> , 260

ORANGE JESSAMINE : <u>Murraya</u> <u>paniculata</u> , 260

ORANGE STAR : <u>Guzmania</u> <u>lingulata</u> var. <u>minor</u> , 140

ORCHID CACTUS : <u>Epiphyllum</u> spp., 112

ORCHID TREE : <u>Bauhinia</u> <u>variegata</u> , 34, **154**

ORIENTAL ARBORVITAE : <u>Platycladus</u> <u>orientalis</u> , 294, **184**

ORIENTAL SWEETGUM : <u>Liquidambar</u> <u>orientalis</u> , 243

OTAHEITE GOOSEBERRY : <u>Phyllanthus</u> <u>acidus</u> , 286, **166**

OVAL KUMQUAT : <u>Fortunella</u> <u>margarita</u> , 131

OVERTOP PALM : <u>Syagrus</u> <u>amara</u> , 335

OXEYE DAISY : <u>Chrysanthemum</u> <u>leucanthemum</u> , 72

OYSTER PLANT : <u>Rhoeo</u> <u>spathacea</u> , 316, **216**

PAGODA FLOWER : <u>Clerodendrum</u> <u>paniculatum</u> , 77, **176**

PAINTED DROP-TONGUE : <u>Aglaonema</u> <u>crispum</u> , 11

PAINTED FINGERNAIL : <u>Neoregelia</u> <u>spectabilis</u> , 265

PALAY RUBBER VINE : <u>Cryptostegia</u> <u>grandiflora</u> , 93

PALE LID FLOWER : <u>Calyptranthes</u> <u>pallens</u> , 53, **174**

PALM GRASS : <u>Curculigo</u> <u>capitulata</u> , 95

PALO SANTO TREE : <u>Triplaris</u> <u>americana</u> , 350

PALO VERDE : <u>Parkinsonia</u> <u>aculeata</u> , 274, **165**

PAMPAS GRASS : <u>Cortaderia</u> <u>selloana</u> , 87, **193**

PANAMA HAT PLANT : <u>Carludovica</u> <u>palmata</u> , 57

PANDA PLANT : <u>Kalanchoe</u> <u>tomentosa</u> , 234

PAPAYA : <u>Carica</u> <u>papaya</u> , 57, **156**

PAPER FLOWER : <u>Bougainvillea</u> <u>glabra</u> , 40, **173**

PAPER MULBERRY : <u>Broussonetia</u> <u>papyrifera</u> , 42

PAPYRUS : <u>Cyperus</u> <u>papyrus</u> , 97, **195**

PARADISE TREE : <u>Simarouba</u> <u>glauca</u> , 328, **169**

PARAKEET FLOWER : <u>Heliconia</u> <u>psittacorum</u> , 147, **196**

PARLOR PALM : <u>Chamaedorea</u> <u>elegans</u> , 68

<u>Parmentiera</u> <u>alata</u> : <u>Crescentia</u> <u>alata</u> , 89

PARROT FLOWER : <u>Heliconia</u> <u>latispatha</u>, <u>Alstroemeria</u> <u>pulchella</u> , 18

PASCUITA : <u>Euphorbia</u> <u>leucocephala</u> , 121

PASSION FRUIT : <u>Passiflora</u> <u>edulis</u> , 276

PAUROTIS PALM : <u>Acoelorrhaphe</u> <u>wrightii</u> , 5, **202**

<u>Paurotis</u> <u>wrightii</u> : <u>Acoelorrhaphe</u> <u>wrightii</u> , 5, **202**

PEACE LILY : <u>Spathiphyllum</u> spp., 330, **200**

PEACH : <u>Prunus</u> <u>persica</u> , 303

PEACOCK LILY : <u>Kaempferia</u> <u>roscoeana</u> , 233

PEACOCK ORCHID : <u>Acidanthera</u> <u>bicolor</u> , 5

PEACOCK PLANT : <u>Calathea</u> <u>makoyana</u> , 50, **192**

PECAN : <u>Carya</u> <u>illinoinensis</u> , 59

PELICAN FLOWER : <u>Aristolochia</u> <u>grandiflora</u> , 27, **210**

<u>Peltophorum</u> <u>inerme</u> : <u>P.</u> <u>pterocarpum</u> , 277, **165**

PENCIL TREE : <u>Euphorbia</u> <u>tirucalli</u> , 122

PURPLE HEART : Setcreasea pallida , 327, **216**

PURPLE PASSION VINE : Gynura aurantiaca , 141

PURPLE QUEEN : Setcreasea pallida , 327, **216**

PURPLE RATTLEBOX : Sesbania punicea , 327

PURPLE TABEBUIA : Tabebuia impetiginosa , 338, **171**

PURPLELEAF PLUM : Prunus cerasifera , 302

PURSLANE : Portulaca grandiflora , 300, **216**

PUSSY EARS : Kalanchoe tomentosa , 234

PYGMY DATE PALM : Phoenix roebelenii , 284, **206**

Pyrus angustifolia : Malus angustifolia , 252

QUEEN PALM : Syagrus romanzoffiana , 335, **208**

QUEEN SAGO : Cycas circinalis , 95, **176**

QUEEN'S CRAPE MYRTLE : Lagerstroemia speciosa , 237, **163**

QUEEN'S WREATH : Petrea volubilis , 281, **211**

RABBIT'S FOOT FERN : Davallia fejeensis , 99

RADIATOR PLANT : Peperomia maculosa , 279

RADICALIS PALM : Chamaedorea radicalis , 69

RAILROAD VINE : Ipomoea pes-caprae , 223

RAIN LILIES : Habranthus spp., 141, **214**

RAIN TREE : Samanea saman , 321, **168**

RANGOON CREEPER : Quisqualis indica , 311

RAPANEA : Myrsine guianensis , 263

RATTLESNAKE PLANT : Calathea lancifolia , 49, **192**

RED BAUHINIA : Bauhinia punctata , 33, **173**

RED BAY : Persea borbonia , 280

RED BUCKEYE : Aesculus pavia , 8, **172**

RED FIRETHORN : Pyracantha coccinea , 306, **185**

RED FLOWERING BANANA : Musa coccinea , 260, **198**

RED GINGER : Alpinia purpurata , 17, **190**

RED IXORA : Ixora coccinea , 226

RED LATAN PALM : Latania lontaroides , 239, **205**

RED MANGROVE : Rhizophora mangle , 315

RED MAPLE : Acer rubrum , 4, **153**

RED MULBERRY : Morus rubra , 259

RED OSIER DOGWOOD : Cornus sericea , 87

RED PASSION FLOWER : Passiflora coccinea , 275, **211**

RED POWDERPUFF : Calliandra haematocephala , 51, **175**

RED SILK-COTTON TREE : Bombax ceiba , 40

RED SPURGE : <u>Euphorbia</u> <u>cotinifolia</u> , 120, **178**

RED STOPPER : <u>Eugenia</u> <u>confusa</u>, <u>E.</u> <u>rhombea</u> , 117

RED VALERIAN : <u>Centranthus</u> <u>ruber</u> , 65

RED WISTERIA : <u>Sesbania</u> <u>tripetii</u> , 327

RED-EDGED DRACAENA : <u>Dracaena</u> <u>marginata</u> , 107

RED-HOT POKER PLANT : <u>Kniphofia</u> spp., 236

REDBIRD FLOWER : <u>Pedilanthus</u> <u>tithymaloides</u> , 276, **183**

REDBUD : <u>Cercis</u> <u>canadensis</u> , 66, **157**

REDLEAF PHOTINIA : <u>Photinia</u> X <u>fraseri</u>, <u>P.</u> <u>glabra</u> , 286

REED PALM : <u>Chamaedorea</u> <u>seifrizii</u> , 69

REED-STEM EPIDENDRUM : <u>Epidendrum</u> <u>ibaguense</u> , 112, **195**

REEVE'S SPIREA : <u>Spiraea</u> <u>cantonensis</u> , 331

REFLEXED DRACAENA : <u>Dracaena</u> <u>reflexa</u> , 107, **177**

RETICULATED PSEUDERANTHEMUM : <u>Pseuderanthemum</u> <u>reticulatum</u> , 303, **185**

REX BEGONIA : <u>Begonia</u> X <u>rex-cultorum</u> , 35, **191**

RHODOLEIA : <u>Rhodoleia</u> <u>championii</u> , 316

<u>Rhoeo</u> <u>discolorpionii</u> : <u>R.</u> <u>spathacea</u> , 316, **216**

<u>Rhyticocos</u> <u>amara</u> : <u>Syagrus</u> <u>amara</u> , 335

RIBBONBUSH : <u>Homalocladium</u> <u>platycladum</u> , 151

RICE-PAPER PLANT : <u>Tetrapanax</u> <u>papyriferus</u> , 342

RIVER BIRCH : <u>Betula</u> <u>nigra</u> , 37

ROSE : <u>Rosa</u> hybrids, 317

ROSE APPLE : <u>Syzygium</u> <u>jambos</u> , 337, **170**

ROSE MALLOW : <u>Hibiscus</u> <u>moscheutos</u> , 149

ROSE OF SHARON : <u>Hibiscus</u> <u>syriacus</u> , 150

ROSELEAF ARALIA : <u>Polyscias</u> <u>guilfoylei</u> , 299

ROSEMARY : <u>Ceratiola</u> <u>ericoides</u> , 65

ROSEWOOD : <u>Tipuana</u> <u>tipu</u> , 347

ROSY TRUMPET TREE : <u>Tabebuia</u> <u>rosea</u> , 339

ROTHSCHILD GLORIOSA LILY : <u>Gloriosa</u> <u>rothschildiana</u> , 136, **211**

ROUGH VELVETSEED : <u>Guettarda</u> <u>scabra</u> , 140

ROUND CARDAMON : <u>Amomum</u> <u>compactum</u> , 18

ROUND HOLLY : <u>Ilex</u> <u>rotunda</u> , 222, **180**

ROUNDLEAF LIVISTONA : <u>Livistona</u> <u>rotundifolia</u> , 246, **205**

ROYAL FERN : <u>Osmunda</u> <u>regalis</u> , 272

ROYAL POINCIANA : <u>Delonix</u> <u>regia</u> , 100, **159**

RUBBER VINE : <u>Rhabdadenia</u> <u>biflora</u>, <u>Echites</u> <u>umbellata</u> , 110

RUSSIAN OLIVE : <u>Elaeagnus</u> <u>angustifolia</u> , 110

RUSTY BLACKHAW : <u>Viburnum rufidulum</u> , 356

RUSTY FIG : <u>Ficus rubiginosa</u> , 129, **160**

RUSTY LYONIA : <u>Lyonia ferruginea</u> , 248

RUSTY PITTOSPORUM : <u>Pittosporum ferrugineum</u> , 293

SABAL PALM : <u>Sabal palmetto</u> , 319, **208**

SABICU : <u>Lysiloma sabicu</u> , 249

SACRED FIG : <u>Ficus religiosa</u> , 128

SACRED LOTUS : <u>Nelumbo nucifera</u> , 264

SAGISI PALM : <u>Heterospathe elata</u> , 148

SALTBUSH : <u>Baccharis halimifolia</u> , 30

SAMAN : <u>Samanea saman</u> , 321, **168**

SANCHEZIA : <u>Sanchezia speciosa</u> , 322

SAND PINE : <u>Pinus clausa</u> , 290

SANDALWOOD : <u>Santalum ellipticum</u> , 323

SANDANKWA VIBURNUM : <u>Viburnum suspensum</u> , 357

SANDBOX TREE : <u>Hura crepitans</u> , 152

SANDER SCREWPINE : <u>Pandanus sanderi</u> , 273, **183**

SANDER'S ELEPHANT EAR : <u>Alocasia sanderana</u> , 15

SANDHILL LAUREL : <u>Kalmia hirsuta</u> , 235

SANTA MARIA : <u>Calophyllum brasiliense</u> , 53

SAPODILLA : <u>Manilkara zapota</u> , 254, **164**

SARGENT JUNIPER : <u>Juniperus chinensis</u> var. <u>sargentii</u> , 231

SASANQUA CAMELLIA : <u>Camellia sasanqua</u> , 54

SATIN LEAF : <u>Chrysophyllum oliviforme</u> , 73, **157**

SATSUMA ORANGE : <u>Citrus reticulata</u> , 75

SAUCER MAGNOLIA : <u>Magnolia</u> X <u>soulangiana</u> , 251

SAUSAGE TREE : <u>Kigelia pinnata</u> , 235, **163**

SAW FERN : <u>Blechnum serrulatum</u> , 39

SAW PALMETTO : <u>Serenoa repens</u> , 326, **208**

SAWGRASS : <u>Cladium jamaicensis</u> , 77

<u>Scaevola frutescens</u> : <u>S. taccada</u> , 324, **186**

SCARBOROUGH LILY : <u>Cyrtanthus purpuratus</u> , 98

SCARLET FREESIA : <u>Lapeirousia laxa</u> , 238

SCARLET GINGER LILY : <u>Hedychium coccineum</u> , 143, **195**

SCARLET LEADWORT : <u>Plumbago indica</u> , 295

SCARLET PLUME : <u>Euphorbia fulgens</u> , 121

SCARLET SPIRAL FLAG : <u>Costus spiralis</u> , 89

SCHEFFLERA : <u>Brassaia actinophylla</u> , 41, **174**

SCREWPINE : <u>Pandanus</u> <u>utilis</u> , 274, **166**

SCRUB BOTTLE TREE : <u>Brachychiton</u> <u>discolor</u> , 41

SCRUB HICKORY : <u>Carya</u> <u>floridana</u> , 58

SCRUB PALMETTO : <u>Sabal</u> <u>etonia</u> , 319

SCRUB PINE : <u>Pinus</u> <u>virginiana</u> , 291

SEA GRAPE : <u>Coccoloba</u> <u>uvifera</u> , 80, **158**

SEA HIBISCUS : <u>Hibiscus</u> <u>tiliaceus</u> , 150, **162**

SEA LAVENDER : <u>Mallotonia</u> <u>gnaphalodes</u> , 251, **182**

SEA OATS : <u>Uniola</u> <u>paniculata</u> , 353, **201**

SEA PURSLANE : <u>Sesuvium</u> <u>portulacastrum</u> , 327

SEACOAST BEACH ELDER : <u>Iva</u> <u>imbricata</u> , 225

<u>Seaforthia</u> <u>elegans</u> : <u>Ptychosperma</u> <u>elegans</u> , 306, **207**

SEALING WAX PALM : <u>Cyrtostachys</u> <u>renda</u> , 98, **204**

SEASHORE PALM : <u>Allagoptera</u> <u>arenaria</u> , 13

SEASIDE MAHOE : <u>Thespesia</u> <u>populnea</u> , 344

SENEGAL DATE : <u>Phoenix</u> <u>reclinata</u> , 284, **206**

SENTRY PALM : <u>Howea</u> <u>forsterana</u> , 151, **204**

SERISSA : <u>Serissa</u> <u>foetida</u> , 326

SERVICEBERRY : <u>Amelanchier</u> <u>arborea</u> , 18

SEVEN-YEAR APPLE : <u>Casasia</u> <u>clusiifolia</u> , 60

SHADBUSH : <u>Amelanchier</u> <u>arborea</u> , 18

SHAVINGBRUSH TREE : <u>Pseudobombax</u> <u>ellipticum</u> , 304, **168**

SHELL GINGER : <u>Alpinia</u> <u>zerumbet</u> , 17, **190**

SHELLFLOWER : <u>Alpinia</u> <u>zerumbet</u> , 17, **190**

SHINING JASMINE : <u>Jasminum</u> <u>nitidum</u> , 228, **180**

SHINING SUMAC : <u>Rhus</u> <u>copallina</u> , 317

SHINY BLUEBERRY : <u>Vaccinium</u> <u>myrsinites</u> , 354

SHORE JUNIPER : <u>Juniperus</u> <u>conferta</u> , 231

SHORTLEAF FIG : <u>Ficus</u> <u>citrifolia</u> , 127

SHOWER OF GOLD : <u>Galphimia</u> <u>glauca</u> , 132, **179**

SHOWY COMBRETUM : <u>Combretum</u> <u>grandiflorum</u> , 83

SHRIMP PLANT : <u>Justicia</u> <u>brandegeana</u> , 232

SHUMARD RED OAK : <u>Quercus</u> <u>shumardii</u> , 310

SICKLE BAMBOO : <u>Chimonobambusa</u> <u>falcata</u> , 70

SICKLETHORN VINE : <u>Asparagus</u> <u>falcatus</u> , 28

SILK OAK : <u>Grevillea</u> <u>robusta</u> , 138, **161**

SILK-COTTON TREE : <u>Ceiba</u> <u>pentandra</u> , 64, **156**

SILK-FLOSS TREE : <u>Chorisia</u> <u>speciosa</u> , 71, **157**

SILVER DOLLAR TREE : <u>Eucalyptus</u> <u>cinerea</u> , 115

SILVER LEAF DAISY : <u>Euryops</u> <u>pectinatus</u> , 123

SILVER MAPLE : <u>Acer</u> <u>saccharinum</u> , 4

SILVER PALM : <u>Coccothrinax</u> <u>argentata</u> , 80

SILVER SAGE : <u>Salvia</u> <u>argentea</u> , 321

SILVER SEA OXEYE : <u>Borrichia</u> <u>arborescens</u> , 40

SILVER TRUMPET TREE : <u>Tabebuia</u> <u>caraiba</u> , 337, **170**

SILVER VASE : <u>Aechmea</u> <u>fasciata</u> , 8, **189**

SILVERBELL : <u>Halesia</u> <u>carolina</u> , 141, **161**

SILVERTHORN : <u>Elaeagnus</u> <u>pungens</u> , 111

SINGAPORE HOLLY : <u>Malpighia</u> <u>coccigera</u> , 252

SISSOO : <u>Dalbergia</u> <u>sissoo</u> , 99

SKINNER CYCAD : <u>Zamia</u> <u>skinneri</u> , 364

SKY VINE : <u>Thunbergia</u> <u>grandiflora</u> , 346, **212**

SLASH PINE : <u>Pinus</u> <u>elliottii</u> , 290, **166**

SLENDER BUCKTHORN : <u>Bumelia</u> <u>reclinata</u> , 45

SLENDER LADY PALM : <u>Rhapis</u> <u>humilis</u> , 314, **207**

SMALL LEAF CONFEDERATE JASMINE : <u>Trachelospermum</u> <u>asiaticum</u> , 348

SNAIL SEED : <u>Cocculus</u> <u>laurifolius</u> , 81

SNAKE LILY : <u>Amorphophallus</u> spp., 18

SNAKEBEARD : <u>Ophiopogon</u> <u>jaburan</u> , 270

SNAKEWOOD : <u>Cecropia</u> <u>palmata</u> , 63, **156**

SNEEZEWEED : <u>Helenium</u> <u>autumnale</u> , 145

SNOW IN SUMMER : <u>Melaleuca</u> <u>decora</u> , 256

SNOWBELL : <u>Styrax</u> <u>grandifolius</u> , 334, **169**

SNOWBERRY : <u>Chiococca</u> <u>alba</u> , 70

SNOWBUSH : <u>Breynia</u> <u>disticha</u> , 42, **174**

SNOWFLAKE : <u>Leucojum</u> spp., 240

SNOWFLAKE TREE : <u>Trevesia</u> <u>palmata</u> , 349

SOAP ALOE : <u>Aloe</u> <u>saponaria</u> , 16

SOAPBERRY : <u>Sapindus</u> <u>saponaria</u> , 323

SOCIETY GARLIC : <u>Tulbaghia</u> <u>violacea</u> , 351

SOFT RUSH : <u>Juncus</u> <u>effusus</u> , 230

SOLITAIRE PALM : <u>Ptychosperma</u> <u>elegans</u> , 306, **207**

SOUR ORANGE : <u>Citrus</u> <u>aurantium</u> , 75

SOURSOP : <u>Annona</u> <u>muricata</u> , 20, **153**

SOURWOOD : <u>Oxydendrum</u> <u>arboreum</u> , 272

SOUTHERN BLUE FLAG : <u>Iris</u> <u>virginica</u> , 225

SOUTHERN CRAB APPLE : <u>Malus</u> <u>angustifolia</u> , 252

SOUTHERN MAGNOLIA : <u>Magnolia</u> <u>grandiflora</u> , 250, **164**

SOUTHERN PRICKLY-ASH : <u>Zanthoxylum</u> <u>clava-herculis</u> , 364

SOUTHERN RED CEDAR : <u>Juniperus</u> <u>silicicola</u> , 232, **162**

SOUTHERN RED OAK : <u>Quercus</u> <u>falcata</u> , 308

SPADE-LEAF PHILODENDRON : <u>Philodendron</u> <u>domesticum</u> , 281

SPANISH BAYONET : <u>Yucca</u> <u>aloifolia</u> , 361, **188**

SPANISH CHERRY : <u>Mimusops</u> <u>elengi</u> , 258

SPANISH DAGGER : <u>Yucca</u> <u>gloriosa</u> , 362

SPANISH LIME : <u>Melicoccus</u> <u>bijugatus</u> , 257

SPANISH STOPPER : <u>Eugenia</u> <u>foetida</u> , 118

SPATTERDOCK : <u>Nuphar</u> <u>luteum</u> , 267

SPEAR SANSEVIERIA : <u>Sansevieria</u> <u>cylindrica</u> , 322

SPICEBERRY : <u>Eugenia</u> <u>rhombea</u> , 118

SPICEWOOD : <u>Calyptranthes</u> <u>pallens</u> , 53, **174**

SPIDER LILY : <u>Hymenocallis</u> <u>latifolia</u>, <u>H.</u> <u>caroliniana</u> , 217

SPIDER PLANT : <u>Chlorophytum</u> <u>comosum</u> , 71

SPIDERWORT : <u>Tradescantia</u> <u>virginiana</u>, <u>T.</u> <u>ohiensis</u> , 348

SPIKEMOSS : <u>Selaginella</u> spp., 326, **216**

SPIKERUSH : <u>Eleocharis</u> <u>cellulosa</u> , 111

SPINDLE PALM : <u>Hyophorbe</u> <u>verschaffeltii</u> , 218

SPINDLE TREE : <u>Euonymus</u> <u>japonica</u> , 119

SPINELESS CENTURY PLANT : <u>Agave</u> <u>attenuata</u> , 10

SPINELESS YUCCA : <u>Yucca</u> <u>elephantipes</u> , 361

SPINY BLACK OLIVE : <u>Bucida</u> <u>spinosa</u> , 44

SPINY DIOON : <u>Dioon</u> <u>spinulosum</u> , 103, **177**

SPINY FIBER PALM : <u>Trithrinax</u> <u>acanthocoma</u> , 351, **209**

SPINY LICUALA : <u>Licuala</u> <u>spinosa</u> , 241, **205**

SPOON FLOWER : <u>Xanthosoma</u> <u>lindenii</u> , 360, **201**

SPOTTED DUMBCANE : <u>Dieffenbachia</u> <u>maculata</u> , 102, **195**

SPREADING EUONYMUS : <u>Euonymus</u> <u>fortunei</u> , 119

SPRUCE PINE : <u>Pinus</u> <u>glabra</u> , 290

SPURGE : <u>Euphorbia</u> <u>epithymoides</u>, <u>E.</u> <u>biglandulosa</u> , 120

ST. JOHN'S WORT : <u>Hypericum</u> X <u>moserianum</u> , 219

ST. THOMAS TREE : <u>Bauhinia</u> <u>tomentosa</u> , 34

STAGHORN FERN : <u>Platycerium</u> <u>bifurcatum</u> , 294, **199**

STAR APPLE : <u>Chrysophyllum</u> <u>cainito</u> , 73

STAR BEGONIA : <u>Begonia</u> <u>heracleifolia</u> , 35

STAR FLOWER : <u>Grewia</u> <u>occidentalis</u> , 138

STAR FRUIT : <u>Averrhoa</u> <u>carambola</u> , 29

STAR GOOSEBERRY : <u>Phyllanthus</u> <u>acidus</u> , 286, **166**

STAR MAGNOLIA : <u>Magnolia</u> <u>stellata</u> , 250

STAR OF BETHLEHEM : <u>Ornithogalum</u> <u>umbellatum</u> , 270

<u>Stenolobium</u> <u>stansllatum</u> : <u>Tecoma</u> <u>stans</u> , 341, **171**

STIFF DOGWOOD : <u>Cornus</u> <u>stricta</u> , 87

STIMPSON'S STOPPER : <u>Myrcianthes</u> <u>fragrans</u> , 262

STINKING CEDAR : <u>Torreya</u> <u>taxifolia</u> , 347

STOKE'S ASTER : <u>Stokesia</u> <u>laevis</u> , 333

STOPLIGHT PILEA : <u>Pilea</u> <u>serpyllifolia</u> , 289, **215**

STRANGLER FIG : <u>Ficus</u> <u>aurea</u> , 126

STRAWBERRY BUSH : <u>Euonymus</u> <u>americana</u> , 118

STRAWBERRY GUAVA : <u>Psidium</u> <u>littorale</u> , 305, **168**

STRICTA HELICONIA : <u>Heliconia</u> <u>stricta</u> , 147, **197**

STRING LILY : <u>Crinum</u> <u>americanum</u> , 90

STRONGBARK : <u>Bourreria</u> <u>suculenta</u> var. <u>revoluta</u> , 41

STUNTWOOD : <u>Acacia</u> <u>nilotica</u> , 2

SUGAR APPLE : <u>Annona</u> <u>squamosa</u> , 21

SUGAR PALM : <u>Arenga</u> <u>pinnata</u> , 26

SUGARBERRY : <u>Celtis</u> <u>laevigata</u> , 64

SUNDROPS : <u>Oenothera</u> spp., 269

SUNSHINE PALM : <u>Veitchia</u> <u>mcdanielsii</u> , 355, **209**

SURINAM CHERRY : <u>Eugenia</u> <u>uniflora</u> , 118, **178**

SWAMP DOGWOOD : <u>Cornus</u> <u>stricta</u> , 87

SWAMP FERN : <u>Blechnum</u> <u>serrulatum</u> , 39

SWAMP LILY : <u>Crinum</u> <u>americanum</u> , 90

SWAMP MAHOGANY : <u>Eucalyptus</u> <u>robusta</u> , 115

SWAMP MALLOW : <u>Hibiscus</u> <u>coccineus</u> , 149

SWEET ACACIA : <u>Acacia</u> <u>farnesiana</u> , 2

SWEET CLOCK VINE : <u>Thunbergia</u> <u>fragrans</u> , 345

SWEET FLAG : <u>Acorus</u> <u>calamus</u> , 5

SWEET ORANGE : <u>Citrus</u> <u>sinensis</u> , 76

SWEET OSMANTHUS : <u>Osmanthus</u> <u>fragrans</u> , 271

SWEET SHRUB : <u>Calycanthus</u> <u>floridus</u> , 53

SWEET VIBURNUM : <u>Viburnum</u> <u>odoratissimum</u> , 356

SWEETBAY : <u>Magnolia</u> <u>virginiana</u> , 250, **164**

SWEETGUM : <u>Liquidambar</u> <u>styraciflua</u> , 244

SWEETLEAF : <u>Symplocos</u> <u>tinctoria</u> , 335

SWEETSOP : <u>Annona</u> <u>squamosa</u> , 21

SWISS CHEESE PLANT : <u>Monstera</u> <u>deliciosa</u> , 259

SWORD FERN : <u>Nephrolepis</u> <u>biserrata</u> , 265

SYCAMORE : <u>Platanus</u> <u>occidentalis</u> , 294

SYNGONIUM : <u>Syngonium</u> <u>podophyllum</u> , 336

<u>Tabebuia</u> <u>argenteallum</u> : <u>T.</u> <u>caraiba</u> , 337, **170**

TALLOWOOD PLUM : <u>Ximenia</u> <u>americana</u> , 361

TAMARIND : <u>Tamarindus</u> <u>indica</u> , 340, **170**

TANGELO : <u>Citrus</u> X <u>tangelo</u> , 76

TANGERINE : <u>Citrus</u> <u>reticulata</u> , 75

TANGOR : <u>Citrus</u> X <u>nobilis</u> , 76

TARFLOWER : <u>Befaria</u> <u>racemosa</u> , 35

TARO : <u>Colocasia</u> <u>esculenta</u>, <u>Alocasia</u> <u>macrorrhiza</u> , 82

TAWNYBERRY : <u>Ilex</u> <u>krugiana</u> , 221

<u>Taxodium</u> <u>distichum</u> var. <u>nutans</u> : <u>Taxodium</u> <u>ascendens</u> , 340

TEAK : <u>Tectona</u> <u>grandis</u> , 341

<u>Tecoma</u> <u>capensis</u> : <u>Tecomaria</u> <u>capensis</u> , 341

TECOMANTHE : <u>Tecomanthe</u> <u>venusta</u> , 341, **212**

TEDDY BEAR PALM : <u>Neodypsis</u> <u>lastelliana</u> , 264

TEXAS SAGE : <u>Leucophyllum</u> <u>frutescens</u>, <u>Salvia</u> <u>coccinea</u> , 240, **181**

TEXAS WILD OLIVE : <u>Cordia</u> <u>boissieri</u> , 85, **158**

THAI DWARF LADY PALM : <u>Rhapis</u> <u>subtilis</u> , 314

THALIA : <u>Thalia</u> <u>geniculata</u> , 343

THATCH PALM : <u>Thrinax</u> <u>radiata</u> , 345

THIN-LEAVED SUNFLOWER : <u>Helianthus</u> <u>decapetalus</u> , 145

THORNLESS HONEY LOCUST : <u>Gleditsia</u> <u>triacanthos</u> var. <u>inermis</u> , 136

THRASK ALOE : <u>Aloe</u> <u>thraskii</u> , 16

THRYALLIS : <u>Galphimia</u> <u>gracillis</u> , 133

<u>Thryallis</u> <u>glaucalis</u> : <u>Galphimia</u> <u>glauca</u> , 132, **179**

<u>Thuja</u> <u>orientalis</u> : <u>Platycladus</u> <u>orientalis</u> , 294, **184**

THUNBERGIA GARDENIA : <u>Gardenia</u> <u>thunbergia</u> , 134

TI PLANT : <u>Cordyline</u> <u>terminalis</u> , 86, **176**

TOAD LILY : <u>Tricyrtis</u> spp., 349

TODDY FISHTAIL PALM : <u>Caryota</u> <u>urens</u> , 60, **202**

TOOG TREE : <u>Bischofia</u> <u>javanica</u> , 38

TOOTHACHE TREE : <u>Zanthoxylum</u> <u>clava-herculis</u> , 364

TORCH GINGER : <u>Etlingera</u> <u>elatior</u> , 115, **195**

WEEPING BOTTLEBRUSH : <u>Callistemon viminalis</u> , 52, **155**

WEEPING FIG : <u>Ficus benjamina</u> , 126

WEEPING PODOCARPUS : <u>Podocarpus gracilior</u> , 296, **166**

WEEPING WILLOW : <u>Salix babylonica</u> , 320

WEST INDIAN CHERRY : <u>Prunus myrtifolia</u> , 302

WEST INDIAN EBONY : <u>Brya ebenus</u> , 44

WEST INDIAN HOLLY : <u>Leea coccinea</u> , 239

WEST INDIAN LAUREL : <u>Ficus perforata</u> , 128

WHISK FERN : <u>Psilotum nudum</u> , 305

WHITE BIRD OF PARADISE : <u>Strelitzia nicolai</u> , 333, **187**

WHITE BUTTONWOOD : <u>Laguncularia racemosa</u> , 237

WHITE FLOSS-SILK TREE : <u>Chorisia insignis</u> , 71

WHITE FRANGIPANI : <u>Plumeria alba</u> , 295, **166**

WHITE INDIGOBERRY : <u>Randia aculeata</u> , 311

WHITE IRONWOOD : <u>Hypelate trifoliata</u> , 219

WHITE LILYTURF : <u>Ophiopogon jaburan</u> , 270

WHITE MANGROVE : <u>Laguncularia racemosa</u> , 237

WHITE MULBERRY : <u>Morus alba</u> , 259

WHITE OAK : <u>Quercus alba</u> , 307

WHITE STOPPER : <u>Eugenia axillaris</u> , 117

WILD ALLAMANDA : <u>Urechites lutea</u> , 353

WILD BIRDSNEST FERN : <u>Asplenium serratum</u> , 29

WILD CENTURY PLANT : <u>Agave neglecta</u> , 10

WILD CINNAMON : <u>Canella winterana</u> , 55

WILD COFFEE : <u>Psychotria nervosa</u> , 305

WILD COTTON : <u>Gossypium hirsutum</u> , 137

WILD DATE PALM : <u>Phoenix sylvestris</u> , 285, **206**

WILD DILLY : <u>Manilkara bahamensis</u> , 254

WILD LIME : <u>Zanthoxylum fagara</u> , 364

WILD OLIVE : <u>Forestiera segregata</u>, <u>Elaeagnus latifolia</u> , 131

WILD SAPODILLA : <u>Manilkara bahamensis</u> , 254

WILD TAMARIND : <u>Lysiloma latisiliqua</u> , 249

WILLOW OAK : <u>Quercus phellos</u> , 310

WINDMILL PALM : <u>Trachycarpus fortunei</u> , 348, **208**

WINGED ELM : <u>Ulmus alata</u> , 352, **171**

WINGED SUMAC : <u>Rhus copallina</u> , 317

WININ PALM : <u>Veitchia winin</u> , 355

WINTERGREEN BARBERRY : <u>Berberis julianae</u> , 36, **173**

WITCH HAZEL : <u>Hamamelis</u> <u>virginiana</u> , 141

WOOLY CONGEA : <u>Congea</u> <u>tomentosa</u> , 83, **210**

WOOLY MORNING GLORY : <u>Argyreia</u> <u>nervosa</u> , 26

XYLOSMA : <u>Xylosma</u> <u>congestum</u> , 361

YARROW : <u>Achillea</u> spp., 4

YAUPON HOLLY : <u>Ilex</u> <u>vomitoria</u> , 222

YAUTIA : <u>Xanthosoma</u> <u>sagittifolium</u> , 360

YEDDA HAWTHORN : <u>Raphiolepis</u> <u>umbellata</u> , 312

YELLOW ALDER : <u>Turnera</u> <u>ulmifolia</u> , 352, **188**

YELLOW ALLAMANDA : <u>Allamanda</u> <u>cathartica</u> , 13

YELLOW BAUHINIA : <u>Bauhinia</u> <u>tomentosa</u> , 34

YELLOW ELDER : <u>Tecoma</u> <u>stans</u> , 341, **171**

YELLOW GINGER : <u>Hedychium</u> <u>flavum</u> , 144

YELLOW JASMINE : <u>Jasminum</u> <u>humile</u> , 228

YELLOW MORAEA : <u>Dietes</u> <u>bicolor</u> , 102

YELLOW OLEANDER : <u>Thevetia</u> <u>peruviana</u> , 344, **187**

YELLOW POINCIANA : <u>Peltophorum</u> <u>pterocarpum</u> , 277, **165**

YELLOW POND LILY : <u>Nuphar</u> <u>luteum</u> , 267

YELLOW RUNNING BAMBOO : <u>Phyllostachys</u> <u>viridis</u> , 288

YELLOW SAGE : <u>Lantana</u> <u>camara</u> , 238, **215**

YELLOW TRUMPET TREE : <u>Tabebuia</u> <u>chrysantha</u> , 337

YELLOW-GROOVE BAMBOO : <u>Phyllostachys</u> <u>aureosulcata</u> , 287

YELLOWTOP : <u>Flaveria</u> <u>linearis</u> , 130

YESTERDAY TODAY AND TOMORROW : <u>Brunfelsia</u> <u>australis</u>, <u>B.</u> <u>pauciflora</u> , 43, **174**

YEW PODOCARPUS : <u>Podocarpus</u> <u>macrophyllus</u> , 296, **167**

YLANG YLANG : <u>Cananga</u> <u>odorata</u> , 55, **155**

ZEBRA CALATHEA : <u>Calathea</u> <u>zebrina</u> , 51, **192**

ZEBRA HAWORTHIA : <u>Haworthia</u> <u>faciata</u> , 142

ZEBRA PLANT : <u>Aphelandra</u> spp., 23

ZEPHYR LILY : <u>Zephyranthes</u> <u>treatiae</u> , 366, **201**

ZIGZAG CACTUS : <u>Cryptocereus</u> <u>anthonyanus</u> , 93

Tolerances and Florida Native Plants

Florida native plants

GROUNDCOVERS

Borrichia arborescens
Canavalia maritima
Chiococca pinetorum
Conradina grandiflora
Crossopetalum ilicifolium
Dyschoriste oblongifolia
Ernodea littoralis
Helianthus debilis
Ilex vomitoria
Ipomoea fistulosa
Ipomoea pes-caprae
Ipomoea stolonifera
Iva imbricata
Kalmia hirsuta
Lantana ovatifolia var. reclinata
Licania michauxii
Lippia nodiflora
Mitchella repens
Peperomia obtusifolia
Serenoa repens
Sesuvium portulacastrum
Tripsacum floridana
Uniola paniculata
Urechites lutea
Viola floridana
Zamia pumila

HERBACEOUS PERENNIALS

Acrostichum daneifolium
Agave neglecta
Aphanostephus skirrhobasis
Arisaema dracontium
Arisaema triphylla
Asclepias tuberosa
Asplenium serratum
Baptisia spp.
Blechnum serrulatum
Canna flaccida
Crinum americanum
Eleocharis cellulosa
Encyclia spp.
Flaveria linearis
Helenium autumnale
Hibiscus coccineus
Hibiscus moscheutos
Hymenocallis caroliniana
Hymenocallis floridana
Hymenocallis latifolia
Hymenocallis palmeri
Iris hexagona
Iris virginica
Lilium catesbaei
Lippia nodiflora
Lobelia cardinalis
Nephrolepis exaltata
Nuphar luteum macrophyllum
Nymphoides spp.
Opuntia spp.
Orontium aquaticum
Osmunda regalis
Peltandra virginica
Peperomia obtusifolia
Phlox divaricata
Pistia stratiotes
Pontederia cordata
Psilotum nudum
Rhexia spp.
Sabatia spp.
Salvia coccinea
Sesuvium portulacastrum
Sisyrinchium spp.

Stokesia laevis
Thalia geniculata
Tillandsia spp.
Tripsacum floridana
Uniola paniculata
Viola floridana
Zephyranthes atamasco
Zephyranthes treatiae

SHRUBS

Acacia farnesiana
Acacia pinetorum
Acoelorrhaphe wrightii
Aesculus pavia
Amphitecna latifolia
Amyris elemifera
Angadenia berterii
Ardisia escallonioides
Asclepias tuberosa
Baccharis halamifolia
Befaria racemosa
Borrichia arborescens
Bourreria succulenta var. revoluta
Bumelia reclinata
Byrsonima lucida
Callicarpa americana
Calycanthus floridus
Calyptranthes pallens
Calyptranthes zuzygium
Capparis cynophallophora
Capparis flexuosa
Casasia clusiifolia
Cassia bahamensis
Cephalanthus occidentalis
Ceratiola ericoides
Chiococca alba
Chrysobalanus icaco
Coccoloba uvifera
Colubrina arborescens
Conocarpus erectus var. sericeus
Cornus drummondii
Cornus sericea
Cornus stricta
Dalbergia ecastophyllum
Dipholis salicifolia
Dodanaea viscosa
Drypetes lateriflora
Duranta repens
Erythrina herbacea
Eugenia foetida
Eugenia rhombea
Euonymus americana
Exostema caribaeum
Forestiera segregata
Garberia fruticosa
Gaylussacia dumosa
Gossypium hirsutum
Guaiacum sanctum
Guettarda elliptica
Guettarda scabra
Hamamelis virginiana
Hamelia patens
Hydrangea quercifolia
Ilex cassine
Ilex glabra
Ilex opaca
Ilex vomitoria
Illicium floridanum
Iva frutescens
Jacquinia keyensis
Juniperus silicicola
Kalmia hirsuta
Kalmia latifolia

Licania michauxii
Lycium carolinianum
Lyonia ferruginia
Mallotonia gnaphalodes
Maytenus phyllanthoides
Mitchella repens
Myrcianthes fragrans
Myrica cerifera
Myrica pusilla
Myrsine guianensis
Pinckneya pubens
Pithecellobium guadelupense
Pithecellobium unguis-cati
Prunus angustifolia
Psychotria nervosa
Randia aculeata
Rhapidophyllum hystrix
Rhododendron austrinum
Rhododendron canescens
Rhododendron chapmannii
Rhus copallina
Sabal etonia
Sabal minor
Salix caroliniana
Savia bahamensis
Scaevola plumieri
Serenoa repens
Sophora tomentosa
Styrax grandifolius
Suriana maritima
Symplocos tinctoria
Taxus floridana
Tecoma stans
Tetrazygia bicolor
Vaccinium myrsinites
Viburnum obovatum
Yucca aloifolia
Yucca filamentosa
Yucca gloriosa
Yucca smalliana
Ximenia americana
Zanthoxylum clava-herculis

TREES

Acacia choriophylla
Acacia farnesiana
Acer barbatum
Acer rubrum
Acer saccharinum
Acoelorrhaphe wrightii
Aesculus pavia
Amphitecna latifolia
Amyris elemifera
Annona glabra
Ardisia escallonioides
Avicennia germinans
Betula nigra
Bourreria succulenta var. revoluta
Bursera simaruba
Byrsonima lucida
Calyptranthes zuzygium
Canella winterana
Capparis flexuosa
Carpinus caroliniana
Carya aquatica
Carya floridana
Carya glabra
Catalpa bignonioides
Celtis laevigata
Cercis canadensis
Chionanthus virginicus
Chamaecyparis thyoides
Chrysophyllum oliviforme

Florida native plants

TREES (Cont.)

Citharexylum fruticosum
Clusia rosea
Coccoloba diversifolia
Coccoloba uvifera
Coccothrinax argentata
Colubrina arborescens
Conocarpus erectus
Cordia sebestena
Cornus florida
Crataegus spp.
Diospyros virginiana
Dipholis salicifolia
Drypetes lateriflora
Eugenia axillaris
Eugenia confusa
Eugenia foetida
Eugenia rhombea
Exostema caribaeum
Ficus aurea
Ficus citrifolia
Fraxinus caroliniana
Gleditsia triacanthos var. inermis
Gordonia lasianthus
Guaiacum sanctum
Guapira discolor
Guapira longifolia
Guettarda elliptica
Guettarda scabra
Gymnanthes lucida
Halesia carolina
Hibiscus tiliaceus
Hypelate trifoliata
Ilex cassine
Ilex krugiana
Ilex opaca
Ilex vomitoria
Jacquinia keyensis
Juniperus silicicola
Juniperus virginiana
Krugiodendron ferreum
Laguncularia racemosa

Licaria triandra
Liquidambar styraciflua
Liriodendron tulipifera
Lyonia ferruginea
Lysiloma latisiliqua
Magnolia fraseri var. pyramidata
Magnolia grandiflora
Magnolia virginiana
Malus angustifolia
Mastichodendron foetisdissimum
Meliccoccus bijugatus
Myrcianthes fragrans
Myrica cerifera
Nectandra coriacea
Nyssa aquatica
Nyssa sylvatica
Ostrya virginiana
Oxydendron arboreum
Persea borbonia
Pinckneya pubens
Pinus clausa
Pinus elliottii
Pinus glabra
Pinus palustris
Pinus taeda
Piscidia piscipula
Pithecellobium guadelupense
Pithecellobium unguis-cati
Platanus occidentalis
Prunus caroliniana
Prunus myrtifolia
Prunus umbellata
Pseudophoenix sargentii
Ptelea trifoliata
Quercus austrina
Quercus chapmanii
Quercus falcata
Quercus incana
Quercus laevis
Quercus laurifolia
Quercus myrtifolia
Quercus nigra
Quercus shumardii

Quercus virginiana
Reynosia septentrionalis
Rhizophora mangle
Roystonea elata
Sabal palmetto
Salix caroliniana
Sapindus saponaria
Schaefferia frutescens
Simarouba glauca
Styrax grandifolius
Swietenia mahogani
Symplocos tinctoria
Taxodium distichum
Taxus floridana
Tecoma stans
Thrinax morrisii
Thrinax parviflora
Thrinax radiata
Tilia floridana
Torreya taxifolia
Ulmus alata
Ulmus americana
Viburnum rufidulum
Ximenia americana
Zanthoxylum clava-herculis
Zanthoxylum fagara

VINES

Ampelopsis arborea
Bignonia capreolata
Campsis radicans
Chiococca alba
Cissus incisa
Decumaria barbara
Echites umbellata
Gelsemium sempervirens
Jacquemontia spp.
Lonicera sempervirens
Merremia dissecta
Parthenocissus quinquefolia
Rhabdadenia biflora
Urechites lutea

Highly salt tolerant plants

GROUNDCOVERS

Aptenia cordifolia
Borrichia arborescens
Canavallia maritima
Carpobrotus spp.
Conradina grandiflora
Ernodea littoralis
Euphorbia milii
Evolvulus glomeratus
Festuca ovina var. glauca
Helianthus debilis
Ipomoea pes-caprae
Juniperus conferta
Lantana montevidensis
Licania michauxii
Lippia nodiflora
Liriope spicata
Portulaca grandiflora
Pittosporum tobira
Russelia equisetiformis
Sansevieria trifasciata
Scaevola plumieri
Serenoa repens
Sesuvium portulacastrum
Turnera ulmifolia
Wedelia trilobata

Zamia furfuracea
Zamia pumila

HERBACEOUS PERENNIALS

Acrostichum daneifolium
Agave americana
Agave angustifolia
Agave atrovirens
Agave desmettiana
Agave neglecta
Aloe arborescens
Aloe barbadensis
Aloe saponaria
Aloe thraskii
Carpobrotus spp.
Catharanthus roseus
Cortaderia selloana
Crinum americanum
Echeveria rosea
Eleocharis cellulosa
Eryngium amethystinum
Evolvulus glomeratus
Festuca ovina var. glauca
Flaveria linearis
Gaillardia pulchella
Hemerocallis spp.

Hymenocallis latifolia
Iva imbricata
Limonium latifolium
Lippia nodiflora
Liriope spicata
Opuntia spp.
Portulaca grandiflora
Phormium tenax
Salvia farinacea
Sansevieria cylindrica
Sansevieria trifasciata
Sansevieria zeylanica
Sesuvium portulacastrum
Uniola paniculata
Wedelia trilobata

SHRUBS

Acacia farnesiana
Ardisia escallonioides
Baccharis halimifolia
Borrichia arborescens
Bumelia reclinata
Capparis cynophallophora
Capparis flexuosa
Carissa macrocarpa
Casasia clusiifolia

Highly salt tolerant plants

SHRUBS (Cont.)

Cassia bahamensis
Ceratiola ericoides
Chrysobalanus icaco
Coccoloba uvifera
Conradina grandiflora
Dalbergia ecastophyllum
Dodanaea viscosa
Elaeagnus angustifolia
Elaeagnus philippensis
Ernodea littoralis
Erythrina herbacea
Eugenia rhombea
Euphorbia acrurensis
Euphorbia fulgens
Euphorbia lactea
Euphorbia polycantha
Euphorbia punicea
Euphorbia tirucalli
Euphorbia trigona
Forestiera segregata
Gossypium hirsutum
Guaiacum officinale
Guaiacum sanctum
Hibiscus tiliaceus
Ilex vomitoria
Iva frutescens
Juniperus conferta
Lantana camara
Lantana montevidensis
Licania michauxii
Lonicera nitida
Lycium carolinianum
Mallotonia gnaphalodes
Maytenus undatus
Myrcianthes fragrans
Myrica pusilla
Myrsine guianensis
Nerium oleander
Ochrosia elliptica
Ochrosia parviflora
Pandanus baptistii
Pandanus sanderi
Pithecellobium guadalupense
Pittosporum tobira
Portulacaria afra
Russelia equisetiformis
Scaevola plumieri
Scaevola taccada
Sophora tomentosa
Suriana maritima
Synadenium grantii
Thevetia peruviana
Turnera ulmifolia
Ximenia americana

Yucca aloifolia
Yucca filamentosa
Yucca gloriosa
Yucca smalliana
Zamia domingensis
Zamia furfuracea
Zamia pumila

TREES

Acacia auriculiformis
Acacia choriophylla
Acacia pinetorum
Amphitecna latifolia
Amyris elemifera
Avicennia germinans
Bucida buceras
Bumelia tenax
Bursera simaruba
Calophyllum brasiliense
Calophyllum inophyllum
Clusia rosea
Coccoloba diversifolia
Colubrina arborescens
Conocarpus erectus
Cordia sebestena
Dracaena draco
Elaeagnus latifolia
Elaeagnus pungens
Eugenia axillaris
Eugenia confusa
Eugenia foetida
Guapira longifolia
Guettarda scabra
Hypelate trifoliata
Ilex krugiana
Jacquinia keyensis
Juniperus silicicola
Laguncularia racemosa
Lysiloma latisiliqua
Lysiloma sabicu
Magnolia grandiflora
Malpighia glabra
Manilkara roxburghiana
Manilkara zapota
Mastichodendron foetidissimum
Melia azedarach
Myrica cerifera
Noronhia emarginata
Pandanus utilis
Pandanus veitchii
Parkinsonia aculeata
Persea borbonia
Pinus clausa
Pinus elliottii
Pinus thunbergiana

Piscidia piscipula
Pithecellobium unguis-cati
Plumeria alba
Plumeria rubra
Quercus alba
Quercus chapmanii
Quercus falcata
Quercus myrtifolia
Quercus virginiana
Randia aculeata
Reynosia septentrionalis
Rhizophora mangle
Sapindus saponaria
Simarouba glauca
Swietenia mahagoni
Terminalia catappa
Thevetia peruviana
Thespesia populnea
Yucca rostrata
Zanthoxylum fagara

VINES

Bougainvillea glabra
Bougainvillea spectabilis
Canavallia maritima
Chiococca alba
Cissus incisa
Cryptostegia grandiflora
Hylocereus undatus
Ipomoea pes-caprae
Pereskia aculeata
Rhabdadenia biflora

PALMS

Allagoptera arenaria
Coccothrinax alta
Coccothrinax argentata
Coccothrinax crinita
Coccothrinax miraguama
Cocos nucifera
Dictyosperma album
Hyophorbe lagenicaulis
Hyophorbe verschaffeltii
Hyphaene spp.
Phoenix dactylifera
Pritchardia spp.
Pseudophoenix sargentii
Sabal palmetto
Serenoa repens
Syagrus amara
Thrinax morrisii
Thrinax parviflora
Thrinax radiata
Zombia antillarum

Moderately salt tolerant plants

GROUNDCOVERS

Aspidistra elatior
Asystasia gangetica
Bauhinia punctata
Callisia fragrans
Cyrtomium falcatum
Epipremnum aureum
Euonymus fortunei
Euphorbia epithymoides
Hedera canariensis
Hedera helix
Ipomoea fistulosa
Ipomoea spp.

Ipomoea stolonifera
Juniperus chinensis
Juniperus chinensis var. procumbens
Juniperus chinensis var. sargentii
Juniperus horizontalis
Kalanchoe blossfeldiana
Lantana ovatifolia var. reclinata
Liriope muscari
Lonicera japonica
Malpighia coccigera
Ophiopogon jaburan
Ophiopogon japonicus
Plumbago auriculata
Rhoeo spathacea

Rumohra adiantiformis
Schefflera arboricola
Setcreasea pallida
Trachelospermum asiaticum
Trachelospermum jasminoides
Tripsacum dactyloides
Tripsacum floridana
Tulbaghia violacea
Zephyranthes spp. and hybrids

HERBACEOUS PERENNIALS

Achillea spp.
Agave attenuata

Moderately salt tolerant plants

HERBACEOUS (Cont.)

Alpinia mutica
Alpinia zerumbet
Ananas comosus
Asparagus densiflorus
Aspidistra elatior
Asystasia gangetica
Belamcanda chinensis
Burbidgea schizocheila
Callisia fragrans
Cereus peruvianus
Chrysanthemum leucanthemum
Cladium jamaicensis
Costus igneus
Costus pulverulentus
Costus speciosus
Costus spiralis
Crassula argentea
Crinum asiaticum
Crinum X amabile
Crinum X augustum
Cryptanthus spp.
Cyperus alternifolius
Cyperus haspan
Cyperus isocladus
Cyperus papyrus
Cyrtomium falcatum
Dianella ensifolia
Dyckia brevifolia
Etlingera elatior
Euphorbia biglandulosa
Euphorbia epithymoides
Gazania spp.
Gynura aurantiaca
Habranthus spp.
Hedychium aureum
Hedychium coccineum
Hedychium coronarium
Hedychium flavum
Hedychium gardnerianum
Hedychium greenei
Heliconia bihai
Heliconia caribaea
Heliconia collinsiana
Heliconia latispatha
Heliconia psittacorum
Heliconia stricta
Heliconia wagnerana
Heliconia X 'Golden Torch'
Heliotropium spp.
Iresine spp.
Juncus effusus
Kalanchoe blossfeldiana
Kalanchoe gastonis-bonnieri
Kalanchoe pinnata
Kalanchoe tomentosa
Kniphofia spp.
Lachenalia spp.
Liriope muscari
Musa zebrina
Ophiopogon jaburan
Ophiopogon japonicus
Ornithogalum umbellatum
Pilea cadierei
Polianthes geminiflora
Rhoeo spathacea
Rumohra adiantiformis
Salvia argentea
Salvia coccinea
Sedum spectabile
Setcreasea pallida
Stapelia spp.
Tripsacum dactyloides

Tripsacum floridana
Tulbaghia violacea
Xanthosoma lindenii
Zephyranthes spp. and hybrids
Zingiber zerumbet

SHRUBS

Acalypha hispida
Acalypha wilkesiana
Adenium obesum
Allamanda neriifolia
Angadenia berterii
Bambusa arundinacea
Bambusa glaucescens
Bambusa vulgaris
Bauhinia punctata
Berberis julianae
Bourreria succulenta var. revoluta
Brassaia actinophylla
Brunfelsia americana
Brunfelsia grandiflora
Brunfelsia pauciflora
Buddleia officinalis
Caesalpinia pulcherrima
Calyptranthes pallens
Calyptranthes zuzygium
Cassia alata
Cassia bicapsularis
Cassia splendida
Cestrum nocturnum
Codiaeum variegatum var. pictum
Cycas circinalis
Cycas revoluta
Dioon edule
Dioon spinulosum
Dizygotheca elegantissima
Drypetes lateriflora
Duranta repens
Eranthemum pulchellum
Eugenia brasiliensis
Eugenia uniflora
Euonymus fortunei
Euryops pectinatus
Exostema caribaeum
Fatsia japonica
Feijoa sellowiana
Ficus 'Green Island'
Forestiera segregata var. pinetorum
Fortunella japonica
Fortunella margarita
Galphimia glauca
Galphimia gracilis
Garberia fruticosa
Grewia occidentalis
Hamelia patens
Hedera helix
Hibiscus rosa-sinensis
Hibiscus schizopetalus
Holmskioldia sanguinea
Homalocladium platycladum
Ilex glabra
Ilex X attenuata
Ixora chinensis
Ixora coccinea
Ixora duffii
Ixora hybrids
Jasminum nitidum
Jatropha gossypifolia
Jatropha integerrima
Jatropha multifida
Jatropha podagrica
Juniperus chinensis var. procumbens
Juniperus chinensis var. sargentii

Juniperus horizontalis
Juniperus virginiana
Lantana ovatifolia var. reclinata
Lawsonia inermis
Leea coccinea
Leucophyllum frutescens
Ligustrum japonicum
Mahonia bealei
Mahonia fortunei
Malpighia coccigera
Manilkara bahamensis
Murraya paniculata
Pachypodium lamerei
Pedilanthus tithymaloides
Philodendron goeldii
Phyllostachys aurea
Phyllostachys aureosulcata
Phyllostachys bambusioides
Phyllostachys viridis
Plumbago auriculata
Plumbago indica
Polyscias crispata
Polyscias filicifolia
Polyscias fruticosa
Polyscias guilfoylei
Polyscias pinnata
Polyscias obtusa
Polyscias scutellaria
Pseuderanthemum atropurpureum
Pseudosasa japonica
Psychotria nervosa
Pyracantha coccinea
Pyracantha koidzumii
Raphiolepis indica
Raphiolepis umbellata
Sanchezia speciosa
Schefflera arboricola
Sesbania punicea
Sesbania tripetii
Severinia buxifolia
Tabernaemontana divaricata
Tecoma stans
Tetrazygia bicolor
Thunbergia erecta
Vitex agnus-castus
Vitex trifolia
Westringia rosmariniformis

TREES

Adansonia digitata
Albizia julibrissin
Albizia lebbeck
Aleurites fordii
Aleurites moluccana
Andira inermis
Annona glabra
Annona muricata
Annona squamosa
Araucaria bidwillii
Araucaria heterophylla
Beaucarnea gracilis
Beaucarnea recurvata
Bischofia javanica
Blighia sapida
Brachychiton acerifolius
Brachychiton discolor
Broussonetia papyrifera
Brya ebenus
Bucida spinosa
Butea monosperma
Byrsonima lucida
Callistemon citrinus
Callistemon rigidus

Moderately salt tolerant plants

TREES (Cont.)

Callistemon viminalis
Canella winterana
Carya floridana
Cassia fistula
Cassia javanica
Cecropia palmata
Ceiba aesculifolia
Ceiba pentandra
Chorisia insignis
Chorisia speciosa
Chrysophyllum cainito
Chrysophyllum oliviforme
Citharexylum fruticosum
Cochlospermum vitifolium
Cordia boissieri
Cordyline australis
Crescentia alata
Crescentia cujete
Cupaniopsis anacardiopsis
Cupressus sempervirens
Dalbergia sissoo
Delonix regia
Dipholis salicifolia
Eriobotrya japonica
Erythrina crista-gallii
Erythrina variegata var. orientalis
Eucalyptus cinerea
Eucalyptus torelliana
Ficus altissima
Ficus aurea
Ficus benghalensis
Ficus benjamina
Ficus carica
Ficus elastica
Ficus lyrata
Ficus nota
Ficus perforata
Ficus religiosa
Ficus retusa
Ficus rubiginosa
Ficus triangularis
Gleditsia triacanthos var. inermis
Grevillea robusta
Guapira discolor
Guettarda elliptica
Gymnanthes lucida
Harpephyllum caffrum
Ilex cassine
Ilex opaca
Juniperus chinensis
Krugiodendron ferreum
Licaria triandra
Mammea americana
Mangifera indica
Manilkara kauki
Maytenus phyllanthoides
Melaleuca decora

Melicoccus bijugatus
Mimusops elengi
Nectandra coriacea
Newbouldia laevis
Pachira aquatica
Parmentiera cereifera
Peltophorum dubium
Peltophorum pterocarpum
Phyllanthus acidus
Pinus caribaea
Pinus virginiana
Pithecellobium dulce
Pittosporum ferrugineum
Plumeria rubra
Podocarpus gracilior
Podocarpus macrophyllus
Podocarpus nagi
Podocarpus neriifolius
Pongamia pinnata
Pouteria campechiana
Pouteria sapota
Pseudobombax ellipticum
Quercus nigra
Schaefferia frutescens
Spathodea campanulata
Strelitzia nicolai
Syzygium paniculatum
Tabebuia caraiba
Tabebuia chrysantha
Tabebuia chrysotricha
Tabebuia heterophylla
Tabebuia impetiginosa
Tabebuia pentaphylla
Tabebuia rosea
Tabebuia umbellata
Tamarindus indica
Taxodium ascendens
Taxodium distichum
Terminalia muelleri
Triphasia trifolia
Ulmus pumila
Yucca elephantipes
Zanthoxylum clava-herculis

VINES

Ampelopsis arborea
Congea tomentosa
Cryptostegia madagascariensis
Epipremnum aureum
Ficus pumila
Hedera canariensis
Ipomoea fistulosa
Ipomoea spp.
Ipomoea stolonifera
Jasminum volubile
Lonicera japonica
Lonicera sempervirens
Mandevilla sanderi

Mandevilla splendens
Merremia dissecta
Passiflora caerulea
Petrea volubilis
Philodendron domesticum
Philodendron scandens var. oxycardium
Stephanotis floribunda
Stigmaphyllon littorale
Tecomaria capensis
Trachelospermum asiaticum
Trachelospermum jasminoides
Urechites lutea

PALMS

Acoelorrhaphe wrightii
Acrocomia totai
Bismarckia nobilis
Butia capitata
Chrysalidocarpus cabadae
Chrysalidocarpus lutescens
Copernicia baileyana
Copernicia hospita
Copernicia macroglossa
Elaeis guineensis
Howea forsterana
Latania loddigesii
Livistona australis
Livistona chinensis
Livistona decipiens
Livistona mariae
Livistona saribus
Phoenix canariensis
Phoenix reclinata
Phoenix rupicola
Phoenix sylvestris
Ravenea rivularis
Rhapidophyllum hystrix
Rhapis excelsa
Rhapis humilis
Roystonea elata
Roystonea regia
Sabal causiarum
Sabal etonia
Sabal minor
Syagrus romanzoffiana
Syagrus schizophylla
Trachycarpus fortunei
Trithrinax acanthocoma
Veitchia joannis
Veitchia mcdanielsii
Veitchia merrilli
Veitchia montgomeryana
Veitchia winin
Washingtonia filifera
Washingtonia robusta
Wodyetia bifurcata

Highly drought tolerant plants

GROUNDCOVERS

Aechmea bracteata
Aechmea chantinii
Aechmea fasciata
Aechmea fulgens
Aechmea mexicana
Aptenia cordifolia
Asystasia gangetica
Bauhinia punctata
Borrichia arborescens

Callisia fragrans
Canavallia maritima
Carpobrotus spp.
Chiococca pinetorum
Conradina grandiflora
Crossopetalum ilicifolium
Epipremnum aureum
Ernodea littoralis
Euphorbia milii
Festuca ovina var. glauca
Helianthus debilis

Ipomoea pes-caprae
Ipomoea stolonifera
Juniperus chinensis
Juniperus chinensis var. procumbens
Juniperus chinensis var. sargentii
Juniperus conferta
Juniperus horizontalis
Kalanchoe blossfeldiana
Lantana camara
Lantana montevidensis
Lantana ovatifolia var. reclinata

Highly drought tolerant plants

GROUNDCOVERS (Cont.)

Licania michauxii
Lippia nodiflora
Liriope muscari
Liriope spicata
Parthenocissus quinquefolia
Portulaca grandiflora
Rhoeo spathacea
Russelia equisetiformis
Sansevieria trifasciata
Scaevola plumieri
Schefflera arboricola
Sesuvium portulacastrum
Setcreasea pallida
Tripsacum dactyloides
Tripsacum floridana
Zamia furfuracea
Zamia pumila
Zephyranthes spp. and hybrids

HERBACEOUS PERENNIALS

Achillea spp.
Aechmea bracteata
Aechmea chantinii
Aechmea fasciata
Aechmea fulgens
Aechmea mexicana
Agave americana
Agave angustifolia
Agave atrovirens
Agave attenuata
Agave desmettiana
Agave neglecta
Aloe arborescens
Aloe barbadensis
Aloe saponaria
Aloe thraskii
Ananas comosus
Aphanostephus skirrhobasis
Asclepias tuberosa
Asparagus densiflorus
Asystasia gangetica
Baptisia spp.
Callisia fragrans
Carpobrotus spp.
Catharanthus roseus
Centranthus ruber
Cereus peruvianus
Chrysanthemum leucanthemum
Cortaderia selloana
Crassula argentea
Cryptanthus spp.
Dyckia brevifolia
Echeveria rosea
Echinacea purpurea
Eryngium amethystinum
Euphorbia biglandulosa
Festuca ovina var. glauca
Gaillardia pulchella
Gazania spp.
Habranthus spp.
Haworthia fasciata
Hemerocallis spp.
Hymenocallis latifolia
Iva imbricata
Kalanchoe blossfeldiana
Kalanchoe gastonis-bonnieri
Kalanchoe pinnata
Kalanchoe tomentosa
Limonium latifolium
Lippia nodiflora
Liriope muscari

Liriope spicata
Oenothera spp.
Opuntia spp.
Phormium tenax
Portulaca grandiflora
Rhoeo spathacea
Salvia argentea
Salvia coccinea
Salvia farinacea
Sansevieria cylindrica
Sansevieria trifasciata
Sansevieria zeylanica
Sedum spectabile
Sesuvium portulacastrum
Setcreasea pallida
Solidago spp.
Stapelia spp.
Strelitzia reginae
Tripsacum dactyloides
Tripsacum floridana
Uniola paniculata
Wedelia trilobata
Zephyranthes spp. and hybrids

SHRUBS

Acacia farnesiana
Acacia pinetorum
Amyris elemifera
Angadenia berterii
Asclepias tuberosa
Asparagus falcatus
Baccharis halimifolia
Bambusa glaucescens
Bauhinia punctata
Bougainvillea glabra
Bougainvillea spectabilis
Bourreria succulenta var. revoluta
Brassaia actinophylla
Brya ebenus
Bucida spinosa
Bumelia reclinata
Bumelia tenax
Byrsonima lucida
Caesalpinia pulcherrima
Calliandra haematocephala
Calliandra surinamensis
Callicarpa americana
Calyptranthes pallens
Capparis cynophallophora
Capparis flexuosa
Carissa macrocarpa
Casasia clusiifolia
Cassia bahamensis
Ceratiola ericoides
Cercis chinensis
Cereus peruvianus
Chamaerops humilis
Chiococca alba
Chrysalidocarpus lutescens
Coccoloba uvifera
Codiaeum variegatum var. pictum
Colubrina arborescens
Conocarpus erectus
Cordyline australis
Crataegus spp.
Cryptostegia grandiflora
Cycas circinalis
Cycas revoluta
Cycas taiwaniana
Dalbergia ecastophyllum
Dendrocalamus strictus
Dioon edule
Dioon spinulosum

Dodanaea viscosa
Dracaena marginata
Dracaena reflexa
Dracaena thalioides
Drypetes lateriflora
Duranta repens
Elaeagnus angustifolia
Elaeagnus latifolia
Elaeagnus philippensis
Elaeagnus pungens
Erythrina herbacea
Eugenia coronata
Eugenia foetida
Eugenia rhombea
Euphorbia acrurensis
Euphorbia milii
Euphorbia polycantha
Euphorbia punicea
Euphorbia tirucalli
Euphorbia trigona
Euryops pectinatus
Exostema caribaeum
Feijoa sellowiana
Forestiera segregata
Forestiera segregata var. pinetorum
Fortunella margarita
Garberia fruticosa
Gardenia thunbergia
Gaylussacia dumosa
Gossypium hirsutum
Guaiacum officinale
Guaiacum sanctum
Guettarda scabra
Hamelia patens
Hibiscus tiliaceus
Ilex vomitoria
Iva frutescens
Jacquinia keyensis
Jatropha gossypifolia
Jatropha integerrima
Jatropha multifida
Jatropha podagrica
Juniperus chinensis
Juniperus chinensis var. sargentii
Juniperus conferta
Juniperus silicicola
Juniperus virginiana
Lagerstroemia indica
Lantana camara
Lantana montevidensis
Leucophyllum frutescens
Ligustrum japonicum
Lonicera nitida
Lycium carolinianum
Lyonia ferruginea
Macrozamia moorei
Mallotonia gnaphalodes
Malpighia glabra
Malvaviscus arboreus
Manilkara bahamensis
Maytenus phyllanthoides
Maytenus undatus
Murraya paniculata
Myrcianthes fragrans
Myrica cerifera
Myrica pusilla
Myrsine guianensis
Myrtus communis
Nerium oleander
Ochrosia elliptica
Ochrosia parviflora
Pandanus baptistii
Pandanus sanderi
Philodendron goeldii

Highly drought tolerant plants

SHRUBS (Cont.)

Phyllostachys aurea
Pithecellobium guadalupense
Pithecellobium unguis-cati
Polyscias crispata
Polyscias filicifolia
Polyscias fruticosa
Polyscias guilfoylei
Polyscias pinnata
Polyscias obtusa
Polyscias scutellaria
Portulacaria afra
Prunus angustifolia
Randia aculeata
Rhapidophyllum hystrix
Rhus copallina
Russelia equisetiformis
Savia bahamensis
Scaevola plumieri
Scaevola taccada
Schaefferia frutescens
Schefflera arboricola
Sesbania punicea
Sesbania tripetii
Severinia buxifolia
Shibataea kumasaca
Sophora tomentosa
Strelitzia nicolai
Suriana maritima
Synadenium grantii
Tecoma stans
Tetrazygia bicolor
Triphasia trifolia
Vaccinium myrsinites
Viburnum obovatum
Westringia rosmariniformis
Ximenia americana
Yucca aloifolia
Yucca filamentosa
Yucca gloriosa
Yucca rostrata
Yucca smalliana
Zamia domingensis
Zamia furfuracea
Zamia pumila
Zanthoxylum clava-herculis
Zanthoxylum fagara

TREES

Acacia auriculiformis
Acacia choriophylla
Acacia farnesiana
Acacia nilotica
Acacia pinetorum
Adansonia digitata
Albizia julibrissin
Albizia lebbeck
Aleurites fordii
Aleurites moluccana
Amphitecna latifolia
Amyris elemifera
Araucaria heterophylla
Azadirachta indica
Bauhinia blakeana
Bauhinia monandra
Bauhinia purpurea
Bauhinia variegata
Beaucarnea gracilis
Beaucarnea recurvata
Blighia sapida
Bourreria succulenta var. revoluta
Brachychiton acerifolius

Brachychiton discolor
Brassaia actinophylla
Broussonetia papyrifera
Brya ebenus
Bucida buceras
Bucida spinosa
Bulnesia arborea
Bumelia tenax
Bursera simaruba
Butea monosperma
Butia capitata
Byrsonima lucida
Canella winterana
Carya floridana
Carya glabra
Carya illinoinensis
Cassia fistula
Ceiba aesculifolia
Ceiba pentandra
Celtis laevigata
Cercis canadensis
Chorisia insignis
Chorisia speciosa
Chrysophyllum oliviforme
Citharexylum fruticosum
Clusia rosea
Coccoloba diversifolia
Coccoloba uvifera
Cochlospermum vitifolium
Colubrina arborescens
Conocarpus erectus
Cordia boissieri
Cordia sebestena
Cordyline australis
Corylus colurna
Crataegus spp.
Crescentia alata
Delonix regia
Dipholis salicifolia
Dracaena draco
Drypetes lateriflora
Elaeagnus angustifolia
Elaeagnus latifolia
Elaeagnus pungens
Eriobotrya japonica
Erythrina crista-gallii
Erythrina variegata var. orientalis
Eucalyptus cinerea
Eucalyptus torelliana
Eugenia axillaris
Eugenia confusa
Eugenia coronata
Eugenia foetida
Eugenia rhombea
Exostema caribaeum
Ficus altissima
Ficus aurea
Ficus benghalensis
Ficus benjamina
Ficus citrifolia
Ficus elastica
Ficus lyrata
Ficus perforata
Ficus religiosa
Ficus retusa
Gleditsia triacanthos var. inermis
Guaiacum officinale
Guaiacum sanctum
Guapira discolor
Guapira longifolia
Guettarda scabra
Gymnanthes lucida
Harpulia arborea
Heterospathe elata

Hibiscus tiliaceus
Hypelate trifoliata
Ilex cassine
Ilex krugiana
Ilex opaca
Ilex vomitoria
Jacaranda mimosifolia
Jacquinia keyensis
Juniperus chinensis
Juniperus silicicola
Juniperus virginiana
Khaya nyasica
Krugiodendron ferreum
Lagerstroemia indica
Lagerstroemia speciosa
Latania loddigesii
Licaria triandra
Ligustrum japonicum
Liquidambar formosana
Liquidambar orientalis
Liquidambar styraciflua
Lyonia ferruginea
Lysiloma latisiliqua
Lysiloma sabicu
Malpighia glabra
Mammea americana
Manilkara bahamensis
Manilkara roxburghiana
Manilkara zapota
Mastichodendron foetidissimum
Maytenus phyllanthoides
Melaleuca decora
Melia azedarach
Melicoccus bijugatus
Millettia ovalifolia
Moringa pterygosperma
Morus alba
Morus rubra
Murraya paniculata
Myrcianthes fragrans
Myrica cerifera
Nectandra coriacea
Noronhia emarginata
Ochrosia elliptica
Ostrya virginiana
Pandanus utilis
Pandanus veitchii
Parkinsonia aculeata
Peltophorum dubium
Peltophorum pterocarpum
Persea americana
Persea borbonia
Phyllanthus acidus
Pimenta dioica
Pinus caribaea
Pinus clausa
Pinus elliottii
Pinus palustris
Pinus taeda
Pinus thunbergiana
Pinus virginiana
Piscidia piscipula
Pistacia chinensis
Pithecellobium guadalupense
Pithecellobium unguis-cati
Pittosporum ferrugineum
Plumeria alba
Plumeria rubra
Pongamia pinnata
Pseudophoenix sargentii
Psidium guajava
Psidium littorale
Punica granatum
Quercus alba

Highly drought tolerant plants

TREES (Cont.)

Quercus chapmanii
Quercus falcata
Quercus incana
Quercus laevis
Quercus laurifolia
Quercus myrtifolia
Quercus palustris
Quercus phellos
Quercus shumardii
Quercus velutina
Quercus virginiana
Randia aculeata
Reynosia septentrionalis
Samanea saman
Santalum ellipticum
Sapindus saponaria
Schaefferia frutescens
Simarouba glauca
Spathodea campanulata
Strelitzia nicolai
Swietenia mahagoni
Syzygium cumini
Syzygium jambos
Tabebuia caraiba
Tabebuia chrysantha
Tabebuia chrysotricha
Tabebuia heterophylla
Tabebuia impetiginosa
Tabebuia pentaphylla
Tabebuia rosea
Tabebuia umbellata
Tamarindus indica
Taxodium ascendens
Taxodium distichum
Tecoma stans
Terminalia catappa
Thespesia populnea
Thrinax morrisii
Thrinax parviflora
Thrinax radiata
Trachycarpus fortunei
Triphasia trifolia
Ulmus alata
Ulmus crassifolia
Ulmus parvifolia
Ximenia americana
Yucca elephantipes
Yucca rostrata
Zanthoxylum clava-herculis
Zanthoxylum fagara

Zelkova serrata

VINES

Antigonon leptopus
Asparagus falcatus
Bougainvillea glabra
Bougainvillea spectabilis
Campsis radicans
Canavallia maritima
Chiococca alba
Cissus incisa
Cryptostegia grandiflora
Cryptostegia madagascariensis
Cydista aequinoctialis
Epipremnum aureum
Ficus pumila
Hoya spp.
Hylocereus undatus
Ipomoea pes-caprae
Ipomoea stolonifera
Jacquemontia spp.
Mandevilla sanderi
Mandevilla splendens
Parthenocissus quinquefolia
Pereskia aculeata
Philodendron domesticum
Philodendron scandens var. oxycardium
Pyrostegia venusta
Quisqualis indica
Stephanotis floribunda
Urechites lutea

PALMS

Acrocomia totai
Allagoptera arenaria
Archontophoenix alexandrae
Archontophoenix cunninghamiana
Bismarckia nobilis
Butia capitata
Chamaerops humilis
Chrysalidocarpus cabadae
Chrysalidocarpus lutescens
Coccothrinax alta
Coccothrinax argentata
Coccothrinax crinita
Coccothrinax miraguama
Cocos nucifera
Copernicia baileyana
Copernicia hospita
Copernicia macroglossa

Corypha elata
Gaussia maya
Heterospathe elata
Hyophorbe lagenicaulis
Hyophorbe verschaffeltii
Hyphaene spp.
Latania loddigesii
Livistona australis
Livistona chinensis
Livistona decipiens
Livistona mariae
Livistona rotundifolia
Livistona saribus
Neodypsis decaryi
Neodypsis lastelliana
Phoenix canariensis
Phoenix dactylifera
Phoenix reclinata
Phoenix roebelenii
Phoenix rupicola
Phoenix sylvestris
Pritchardia spp.
Pseudophoenix sargentii
Ptychosperma elegans
Ptychosperma macarthurii
Ravenea rivularis
Rhapidophyllum hystrix
Roystonea regia
Sabal causiarum
Sabal etonia
Sabal minor
Sabal palmetto
Serenoa repens
Syagrus amara
Syagrus romanzoffiana
Syagrus schizophylla
Thrinax morrisii
Thrinax parviflora
Thrinax radiata
Trachycarpus fortunei
Trithrinax acanthocoma
Veitchia joannis
Veitchia mcdanielsii
Veitchia merrilli
Veitchia montgomeryana
Veitchia winin
Washingtonia filifera
Washingtonia robusta
Wodyetia bifurcata
Zombia antillarum

Moderately drought tolerant plants

GROUNDCOVERS

Ajuga reptans
Allamanda violacea
Ardisia japonica
Aspidistra elatior
Begonia heracleifolia
Buxus microphylla var. japonica
Buxus microphylla var. koreana
Calathea makoyana
Cephalotaxus harringtonia
Chlorophytum comosum
Cyrtomium falcatum
Dyschoriste oblongifolia
Euphorbia epithymoides
Evolvulus glomeratus
Ficus montana
Gelsemium sempervirens

Hedera canariensis
Hedera helix
Hymenocallis floridana
Ipomoea fistulosa
Ipomoea spp.
Jasminum mesnyi
Kaempferia pulchra
Kaempferia roscoeana
Kalmia hirsuta
Lonicera japonica
Malpighia coccigera
Nandina domestica
Ophiopogon jaburan
Ophiopogon japonicus
Pellionia daveauana
Peperomia dahlstedtii
Peperomia fraseri
Peperomia glabella

Peperomia hirta
Peperomia maculosa
Peperomia magnoliifolia
Peperomia obtusifolia
Peperomia scandens
Pilea microphylla
Pilea serpyllifolia
Pittosporum tobira
Plumbago auriculata
Psilotum nudum
Rumohra adiantiformis
Syngonium podophyllum
Trachelospermum asiaticum
Trachelospermum jasminoides
Tulbaghia violacea
Turnera ulmifolia
Vinca major
Wedelia trilobata

Moderately drought tolerant plants

GROUNDCOVERS (Cont.)

Zamia fischeri
Zamia skinneri
Zebrina pendula

HERBACEOUS PERENNIALS

Agapanthus africanus
Ajuga reptans
Allium spp.
Alpinia mutica
Alpinia purpurata
Alpinia sanderae
Alpinia zerumbet
Anthurium clarinervium
Aspidistra elatior
Asplenium serratum
Begonia heracleifolia
Begonia X ricinifolia
Belamcanda chinensis
Bletilla striata
Burbidgea schizocheila
Calathea makoyana
Campanula spp.
Canna X generalis
Chlorophytum comosum
Cladium jamaicensis
Clivia miniata
Costus igneus
Costus pulverulentus
Costus speciosus
Costus spiralis
Crinum americanum
Crinum asiaticum
Crinum bulbispermum
Crinum X amabile
Crinum X augustum
Crinum zeylanicum
Crocosmia X crocosmiiflora
Curcuma roscoeana
Cymbopogon citratus
Cyrtanthus mackenii
Cyrtanthus purpuratus
Cyrtomium falcatum
Dianella ensifolia
Dichorisandra thyrsiflora
Dietes vegeta
Dyschoriste oblongifolia
Elettaria cardamomum
Encyclia spp.
Etlingera elatior
Eucomis spp.
Euphorbia epithymoides
Evolvulus glomeratus
Flaveria linearis
Gerbera jamesonii
Gladiolus spp.
Globba atrosanguinea
Globba winitti
Gynura aurantiaca
Hedychium aureum
Hedychium coccineum
Hedychium coronarium
Hedychium flavum
Hedychium gardnerianum
Hedychium greenei
Helenium autumnale
Helianthus decapetalus
Heliconia angusta
Heliconia bihai
Heliconia caribaea
Heliconia collinsiana
Heliconia latispatha

Heliconia rostrata
Heliconia stricta
Heliconia wagnerana
Heliotropium spp.
Hippeastrum X hybridum
Hosta spp.
Hymenocallis caroliniana
Hymenocallis floridana
Hymenocallis narcissiflora
Hymenocallis palmeri
Iris kaempferi
Kaempferia pulchra
Kaempferia roscoeana
Kniphofia spp.
Lachenalia spp.
Lavandula angustifolia
Liatrus spp.
Lycoris spp.
Monarda didyma
Musa ornata
Nephrolepis exaltata
Ophiopogon jaburan
Ophiopogon japonicus
Ornithogalum umbellatum
Pellionia daveauana
Pennisetum setaceum
Peperomia dahlstedtii
Peperomia fraseri
Peperomia glabella
Peperomia hirta
Peperomia maculosa
Peperomia magnoliifolia
Peperomia obtusifolia
Peperomia scandens
Phaius tankervilliae
Philodendron spp.
Philodendron wendlandii
Phygelius capensis
Physostegia virginiana
Pilea microphylla
Pilea serpyllifolia
Platycodon grandiflorus
Polianthes geminiflora
Polypodium grandiceps
Polypodium scolopendria
Psilotum nudum
Rumohra adiantiformis
Sprekelia formosissima
Sternbergia lutea
Stokesia laevis
Thermopsis caroliniana
Trimezia martinicensis
Tritonia crocata
Tulbaghia violacea
Valeriana officinalis
Vinca major
Xanthosoma lindenii
Xanthosoma sagittifolium
Zebrina pendula
Zingiber spectabile
Zingiber zerumbet

SHRUBS

Abelia X grandiflora
Allamanda neriifolia
Allamanda violacea
Amelanchier arborea
Ardisia escallonioides
Ardisia japonica
Aucuba japonica
Bambusa arundinacea
Bambusa oldhamii
Bambusa ventricosa

Bambusa vulgaris
Bauhinia tomentosa
Befaria racemosa
Berberis julianae
Berberis thunbergii
Berberis X mentorensis
Breynia disticha
Brunfelsia americana
Brunfelsia australis
Brunfelsia grandiflora
Brunfelsia pauciflora
Buddleia officinalis
Buxus microphylla var. japonica
Buxus microphylla var. koreana
Caesalpinia gilliesii
Calycanthus floridus
Cassia alata
Cassia bicapsularis
Cassia multijuga
Cassia splendida
Cassia surattensis
Cephalotaxus harringtonia
Cestrum nocturnum
Chimonobambusa falcata
Chrysobalanus icaco
X citrofortunella mitis
Clerodendrum paniculatum
Clerodendrum speciosissimum
Cocculus laurifolius
Cordyline terminalis
Dizygotheca elegantissima
Dovyalis hebecarpa
Dracaena deremensis
Dracaena fragrans
Dracaena surculosa
Eugenia aggregata
Eugenia uniflora
Euphorbia cotinifolia
Euphorbia leucocephala
Fatsia japonica
Ficus montana
Ficus 'Green Island'
Fortunella japonica
Galphimia glauca
Galphimia gracilis
Gamolepis chrysanthemoides
Grewia caffra
Grewia occidentalis
Hedera helix
Hibiscus schizopetalus
Homalocladium platycladum
Hypericum X moserianum
Ilex cornuta
Ilex glabra
Ilex X attenuata
Illicium floridanum
Ixora chinensis
Ixora coccinea
Ixora duffii
Ixora hybrids
Jasminum humile
Jasminum mesnyi
Jasminum nitidum
Jasminum sambac
Kalmia hirsuta
Lawsonia inermis
Ligustrum sinense
Loropetalum chinense
Mahonia bealei
Mahonia fortunei
Malpighia coccigera
Myrciaria cauliflora
Nandina domestica
Ochna serrulata

SHRUBS (Cont.)

Osmanthus fragrans
Osmanthus heterophyllus
Osmanthus X fortunei
Philodendron selloum
Philodendron speciosum
Philodendron williamsii
Photinia glabra
Photinia serrulata
Photinia X fraseri
Phyllostachys aureosulcata
Phyllostachys bambusioides
Phyllostachys nigra
Phyllostachys viridis
Pittosporum tobira
Platycladus orientalis
Plumbago auriculata
Plumbago indica
Prunus cerasifera
Pseudosasa japonica
Psychotria nervosa
Ptelea trifoliata
Pyracantha coccinea
Pyracantha koidzumii
Raphiolepis indica
Raphiolepis umbellata
Rosa hybrids
Ruellia brittoniana
Serissa foetida
Sparmannia africana
Spiraea cantonensis
Ternstroemia gymnanthera
Tetrapanax papyriferus
Tupidanthus calyptratus
Turnera ulmifolia
Viburnum odoratissimum
Viburnum tinus
Vitex agnus-castus
Vitex trifolia
Xylosma congestum
Zamia skinneri

TREES

Acer barbatum
Acer negundo
Aesculus pavia
Andira inermis
Annona muricata
Annona reticulata
Annona squamosa
Araucaria bidwillii
Averrhoa carambola
Bauhinia forficata
Bischofia javanica
Bixa orellana
Bombacopsis fendleri
Bombax ceiba
Buddleia asiatica
Caesalpinia granadillo
Caesalpinia mexicana
Callistemon citrinus
Callistemon rigidus
Callistemon viminalis
Calophyllum brasiliense
Calophyllum inophyllum
Cananga odorata
Carpinus caroliniana
Cassia fistula
Cassia javanica
Cassia siamea
Cecropia palmata
Cedrus atlantica

Cedrus deodara
Chionanthus virginicus
Chrysophyllum cainito
Cinnamomum camphora
Citrus aurantiifolia
Citrus aurantium
Citrus latifolia
Citrus limon
Citrus reticulata
Citrus sinensis
Citrus X nobilis
Citrus X paradisi
Citrus X tangelo
Colvillea racemosa
Cornus drummondii
Cornus kousa
Crescentia cujete
Cryptomeria japonica
Cupaniopsis anacardiopsis
Cupressus sempervirens
Dalbergia sissoo
Dillenia indica
Diospyros dignya
Diospyros kaki
Diospyros virginiana
Enterolobium cyclocarpum
Eriobotrya deflexa
Eucalyptus robusta
Euonymus japonica
Euphoria longan
Ficus aspera
Ficus carica
Ficus nota
Ficus rubiginosa
Ficus triangularis
Firmiana simplex
Flacourtia indica
Fraxinus pennsylvanica
Ginkgo biloba
Grevillea robusta
Guettarda elliptica
Hamamelis virginiana
Harpephyllum caffrum
Hura crepitans
Ilex rotunda
Illicium anisatum
Kigelia pinnata
Koelreuteria bipinnata
Koelreuteria elegans
Litchi chinensis
Lonchocarpus sp.
Macadamia integrifolia
Magnolia grandiflora
Malus angustifolia
Mangifera indica
Manilkara kauki
Metasequoia glyptostroboides
Mimusops elengi
Muntingia calabura
Newbouldia laevis
Oxydendrum arboreum
Pachira aquatica
Parmentiera cereifera
Pithecellobium dulce
Podocarpus gracilior
Podocarpus macrophyllus
Podocarpus nagi
Podocarpus neriifolius
Pouteria campechiana
Pouteria sapota
Prunus caroliniana
Prunus myrtifolia
Prunus umbellata
Pseudobombax ellipticum

Pyrus calleryana
Quercus austrina
Quercus nigra
Ravenala madagascariensis
Rhizophora mangle
Sapium sebiferum
Stenocarpus sinuatus
Sterculia foetida
Syzygium paniculatum
Taxus floridana
Tectona grandis
Terminalia muelleri
Thevetia peruviana
Tipuana tipu
Trevesia palmata
Triplaris americana
Ulmus americana
Ulmus pumila
Viburnum rufidulum
Zizyphus mauritiana

VINES

Allamanda cathartica
Ampelopsis arborea
Argyreia nervosa
Aristolochia elegans
Aristolochia grandiflora
Beaumontia grandiflora
Cissus rhombifolia
Clematis dioscoreifolia
Clytostoma callistegioides
Combretum grandiflorum
Congea tomentosa
Decumaria barbara
Dolichos lablab
Echites umbellata
Gelsemium sempervirens
Gloriosa rothschildiana
Gloriosa superba
Hedera canariensis
Ipomoea fistulosa
Ipomoea spp.
Jasminum dichotomum
Jasminum fluminense
Jasminum multiflorum
Jasminum officinale
Jasminum volubile
Lonicera japonica
Lonicera sempervirens
Merremia dissecta
Monstera deliciosa
Pandorea jasminoides
Passiflora caerulea
Passiflora coccinea
Passiflora edulis
Passiflora quadrangularis
Petrea volubilis
Podranea ricasoliana
Rhabdadenia biflora
Senecio confusus
Solandra guttata
Solanum spp.
Stigmaphyllon littorale
Syngonium podophyllum
Tecomaria capensis
Thunbergia fragrans
Thunbergia grandiflora
Trachelospermum asiaticum
Trachelospermum jasminoides
Vanilla planifolia
Wisteria sinensis

Moderately drought tolerant plants

PALMS

Acoelorrhaphe wrightii
Arenga pinnata
Caryota mitis
Caryota rumphiana
Caryota urens
Chamaedorea costaricana
Chamaedorea elegans

Chamaedorea erumpens
Chamaedorea metallica
Chamaedorea microspadix
Chamaedorea radicalis
Chamaedorea seifrizii
Cyrtostachys renda
Dictyosperma album
Elaeis guineensis
Euterpe edulis

Howea forsterana
Licuala grandis
Licuala spinosa
Rhapis excelsa
Rhapis humilis
Rhapis subtilis
Roystonea elata

Plants with
Environmental Problems

Plants with environmental problems

Scientific <u>Name</u> - Common Name(s) : **Environmental Problem(s)**

<u>Acacia auriculiformis</u> - Earleaf Acacia : **Messy; Weak**

<u>Acer negundo</u> - Box Elder; Ash-leaved Maple : **Weak**

<u>Albizia julibrissin</u> - Mimosa : **Weedy; Weak**

<u>Albizia lebbeck</u> - Mother In Law's Tongue; Lebbek Tree : **Weak**

<u>Aleurites fordii</u> - Tung Oil Tree; China Wood-oil Tree : **Messy**

<u>Aleurites moluccana</u> - Candlenut : **Weedy**

<u>Alstroemeria pulchella</u> - Inca Lily; Parrot Flower : **Invasive**

<u>Ampelopsis arborea</u> - Pepper Vine : **Weedy**

<u>Amphitecna latifolia</u> - Black Calabash : **Weak**

<u>Antigonon leptopus</u> - Coral Vine : **Weedy**

<u>Averrhoa carambola</u> - Carambola; Star Fruit : **Messy**

<u>Baccharis halimifolia</u> - Groundsel Bush; Salt Bush : **Weedy**

<u>Bambusa arundinacea</u> - Giant Thorny Bamboo : **Invasive**

<u>Bambusa glaucescens</u> - Hedge Bamboo : **Invasive**

<u>Bambusa oldhamii</u> - Oldham Bamboo : **Invasive**

<u>Bambusa vulgaris</u> - Common Bamboo : **Invasive**

<u>Barleria cristata</u> - Bluebell Barleria; Philippine Violet : **Weedy**

<u>Bauhinia blakeana</u> - Hong Kong Orchid Tree : **Weak; Messy**

<u>Bauhinia forficata</u> - Brazilian Orchid Tree : **Messy**

<u>Bauhinia monandra</u> - Butterfly Flower : **Weak; Messy**

<u>Bauhinia purpurea</u> - Fall Orchid Tree : **Weak; Messy**

<u>Bauhinia variegata</u> - Orchid Tree; Buddhist Bauhinia : **Weak; Messy**

<u>Bischofia javanica</u> - Bishopwood; Bischofia; Toog Tree : **Weak; Weedy**

<u>Blighia sapida</u> - Akee; Vegetable Brain : **Messy**

<u>Brassaia actinophylla</u> - Schefflera; Umbrella Tree; Octopus Tree : **Invasive; Messy**

<u>Breynia disticha</u> - Snowbush : **Weedy**

<u>Broussonetia papyrifera</u> - Paper Mulberry : **Weedy**

<u>Bulnesia arborea</u> - Bulnesia : **Weak**

<u>Bursera simaruba</u> - Gumbo Limbo; Tourist Tree : **Weak**

<u>Calophyllum inophyllum</u> - Mastwood; Laurelwood; Indian Laurel : **Messy**

<u>Cananga odorata</u> - Ylang Ylang; Ilang Ilang : **Weak**

<u>Carica papaya</u> - Papaya : **Weedy**

<u>Catalpa bignonioides</u> - Catalpa : **Weak**

<u>Cecropia palmata</u> - Snakewood; Cecropia : **Messy; Weak**

<u>Chimonobambusa falcata</u> - Sickle Bamboo : **Invasive**

Chrysanthemum leucanthemum - Oxeye Daisy : **Weedy**

Cinnamomum camphora - Camphor Tree : **Weedy; Messy**

Citrus aurantiifolia - Key Lime : **Messy**

Citrus aurantium - Sour Orange : **Messy**

Citrus latifolia - Persian Lime; Lime : **Messy**

Citrus limon - Lemon : **Messy**

Citrus reticulata - Tangerine; Mandarin Orange; Satsuma Orange : **Messy**

Citrus sinensis - Sweet Orange : **Messy**

Citrus X nobilis - Tangor : **Messy**

Citrus X paradisi - Grapefruit : **Messy**

Citrus X tangelo - Tangelo : **Messy**

Clerodendrum paniculatum - Pagoda Flower : **Invasive**

Clerodendrum speciosissimum - Java Glorybower : **Invasive**

Cochlospermum vitifolium - Buttercup Tree : **Weak**

Delonix regia - Royal Poinciana; Flame Tree; Flamboyant Tree : **Weak; Messy**

Dianella ensifolia - Flax Lily; Umbrella Dracaena : **Weedy**

Dillenia indica - Hondapara; Elephant Apple : **Messy**

Diospyros dignya - Black Sapote : **Messy**

Dolichos lablab - Hyacinth Bean : **Invasive**

Enterolobium cyclocarpum - Ear Tree : **Invasive**

Eugenia uniflora - Surinam Cherry : **Weedy**

Eupatorium coelestinum - Mistflower : **Invasive**

Ficus altissima - Lofty Fig; Council Tree : **Invasive**

Ficus aurea - Strangler Fig : **Invasive**

Ficus benghalensis - Banyan Tree : **Invasive; Messy**

Ficus benjamina - Weeping Fig; Benjamin Fig : **Invasive**

Ficus elastica - Indian Rubber Tree : **Invasive; Messy**

Ficus lyrata - Fiddleleaf Fig : **Messy**

Ficus pumila - Creeping Fig : **Invasive**

Ficus religiosa - Sacred Fig; Bo Tree : **Invasive**

Ficus retusa - Indian Laurel : **Invasive**

Firmiana simplex - Chinese Parasol Tree : **Weedy; Messy**

Galphimia gracilis - Thryallis : **Weak**

Grevillea robusta - Silk Oak : **Weak**

Heliconia latispatha - Parrot Flower : **Invasive**

Heliconia psittacorum - Parakeet Flower : **Invasive**

Heliconia X 'Golden Torch' - Golden Torch Heliconia : **Invasive**

Hibiscus tiliaceus - Mahoe; Sea Hibiscus : **Invasive; Weak**

Ipomoea spp. - Morning-glory : **Invasive**

Jasminum dichotomum - Gold Coast Jasmine : **Weedy**

Jasminum fluminense - Azores Jasmine : **Weedy**

Jatropha gossypifolia - Cotton-leaved Jatropha : **Weedy**

Justicia brandegeana - Shrimp Plant : **Weedy**

Kalanchoe pinnata - Live-forever; Curtain Plant : **Weedy**

Koelreuteria elegans - Golden Shower Tree : **Weedy**

Lantana camara - Yellow Sage; Common Lantana : **Weedy**

Leea coccinea - West Indian Holly : **Irritant**

Lippia nodiflora - Matchweed : **Weedy**

Lonicera japonica - Japanese Honeysuckle : **Invasive**

Lycium carolinianum - Christmas Berry : **Invasive**

Malus angustifolia - Southern Crab Apple : **Invasive**

Mangifera indica - Mango : **Messy**

Melia azedarach - Chinaberry : **Weak; Weedy**

Merremia dissecta - Cutleaf Morning Glory : **Weedy**

Morus alba - White Mulberry; Common Mulberry : **Messy**

Morus rubra - Red Mulberry : **Messy**

Muntingia calabura - Capulin; Cotton Candy Tree : **Weak; Messy**

Musa acuminata - Edible Banana : **Messy**

Musa zebrina - Red Banana : **Messy**

Myrica cerifera - Wax Myrtle : **Invasive**

Myrica pusilla - Dwarf Wax Myrtle : **Invasive**

Parkinsonia aculeata - Jerusalem Thorn; Palo Verde : **Weak**

Parthenocissus quinquefolia - Virginia Creeper : **Invasive; Weedy**

Peltophorum dubium - Copperpod : **Weak**

Peltophorum pterocarpum - Yellow Poinciana; Copperpod : **Weak**

Persea americana - Avocado; Alligator Pear : **Weak; Messy**

Phyllanthus acidus - Otaheite Gooseberry; Star Gooseberry : **Weedy**

Phyllostachys aurea - Golden Bamboo : **Invasive**

Phyllostachys aureosulcata - Yellow-groove Bamboo : **Invasive**

Phyllostachys bambusioides - Giant Timber Bamboo : **Invasive**

Phyllostachys nigra - Black Bamboo : **Invasive**

Phyllostachys viridis - Yellow Running Bamboo : **Invasive**

Physostegia virginiana - False Dragonhead; Obedient Plant : **Invasive**

Pilea microphylla - Artillery Plant : **Weedy**

Pistacia chinensis - Chinese Pistache : **Messy**

Pistia stratiotes - Water Lettuce : **Invasive**

Pithecellobium dulce - Manila Tamarind : **Weedy; Weak**

Pouteria sapota - Mammee Sapote : **Messy**

Prunus angustifolia - Chickasaw Plum : **Invasive**

Pseudosasa japonica - Arrow Bamboo; Metake Bamboo : **Invasive**

Psidium guajava - Guava : **Weedy; Messy**

Psidium littorale - Cattley Guava; Strawberry Guava : **Messy**

Psilotum nudum - Whisk Fern : **Weedy**

Quisqualis indica - Rangoon Creeper : **Invasive**

Rhus copallina - Winged Sumac; Shining Sumac : **Invasive**

Ruellia brittoniana - Mexican Bluebell : **Weedy**

Ruellia makoyana - Monkey Plant : **Weedy**

Salix babylonica - Weeping Willow : **Weak**

Sansevieria cylindrica - Spear Sansevieria : **Invasive**

Sansevieria trifasciata - Snake Plant : **Invasive**

Sansevieria zeylanica - Ceylon Bowstring Hemp : **Invasive**

Sapium sebiferum - Chinese Tallowtree : **Messy; Weedy**

Sesbania punicea - Daubentonia; False Poinciana; Purple Rattleb : **Weedy**

Shibataea kumasaca - Bamboo : **Invasive**

Solidago spp. - Goldenrods : **Weedy**

Spathodea campanulata - African Tulip Tree : **Messy**

Strelitzia nicolai - White Bird Of Paradise : **Messy**

Syagrus romanzoffiana - Queen Palm; Cocos Plumosa : **Messy**

Syngonium podophyllum - Syngonium : **Invasive**

Syzygium cumini - Jambolan Plum; Java Plum : **Messy**

Terminalia muelleri - Mueller's Terminalia : **Messy**

Tetrapanax papyriferus - Rice-paper Plant : **Invasive**

Thespesia populnea - Seaside Mahoe : **Weedy**

Thunbergia fragrans - Sweet Clock Vine : **Weedy**

Thunbergia grandiflora - Bengal Clock Vine; Sky Vine : **Invasive**

Wedelia trilobata - Wedelia : **Invasive**

Wisteria sinensis - Chinese Wisteria : **Weedy**

Zebrina pendula - Wandering Jew : **Invasive**

Notes